FOREWORD

In the past progress in medicine has come largely through new ideas as to the causes of disease and the evolution of sound principles of treatment based on such concepts. But despite all the progress that medicine has made in principles and practice, sickness still prevails and trumpets its challenge anew to each and every generation of physicians.

With progress has come complexity. Modern medicine is exceedingly complex, as are the human beings with whom it has to deal. Each stage of life has its own particular hazards, and man in each must adhere to the way of health if he is to survive the normal span. Man's ego is complex. Psychosomatic medicine represents the summation of environmental (including sociological) influences. When these factors all operate in harmony, health results; when they are in conflict, disease makes its appearance. Solomon, reputed the wisest of men, taught that "as a man thinketh in his heart, so is he." The role of mental and emotional factors in disease was recognized early by Paracelsus and by Van Helmont, but it is only within the last three decades that a body of information has been assembled on the basis of which this recognition can be practically applied in diagnosis.

Bacon formulated and taught the principles of inductive science. Descartes divided the world into mind and matter but unfortunately insisted that the two things were wholly unrelated. The psychosomatic approach in medicine represents the merging or confluence of the biological and the psychical branches of science. Both are intimately concerned in the etiology and manifestations of disease and in the prevention and cure of disease.

We must avoid the concept that any disease is wholly physical or wholly mental. Rather all disease is both physical and mental and an efficient approach to its control must give correct weight to both factors. At various times the weight of the different factors will vary.

In this time of stress, mental factors may be of much greater significance than they are ordinarily.

The psychosomatic approach is new only in the sense that it attempts to substitute a scientific basis for things sensed intuitively by the physician, especially the old-fashioned practitioner: things vaguely seen as "through a veil darkly." Though young in years, it introduces new understanding as to the cause and nature of some of the oldest diseases known to man.

As the result of the teaching of psychosomatic medicine, we, as physicians, are led to examine more closely the psychical side of some of our patients with certain diseases, to determine the role played in each particular instance by the mental and emotional factors of each patient concerned, whether or not the existing disorder represents functional visceral expressions of a disturbed mind or ego. This information can come only from the patient himself and calls for the development of a special history pertinent in this regard. It necessitates the use of special techniques and a new methodology. In many instances, the key to the cure of the illness is the physician's insight into the life problems of the patient.

Dr. Flanders Dunbar brings to the profession the results of twelve years of research and clinical investigation in this field. Her work was carried on in an environment which may be regarded as almost ideal, that is, in the psychiatric and medical divisions of Columbia University, New York.

At the present time this nation is at war, engaged in a savage, ruthless, gigantic struggle for survival; millions of young men are being called to arms; families and homes are being disrupted; emotional and mental distresses abound; men and women are breaking physically and mentally in alarming numbers. Statistics reveal the undue prevalence of certain psychosomatic disorders at this time, many of them engendered by the unusual war stresses and strains to which our people are now being subjected.

Those who read this work will better understand the origin and nature of many of the disorders and diseases they now encounter and will deal more intelligently with the problems of war psychiatry which now confront them. Investigation of psychosomatic problems has progressed so greatly that it seems justifiable to demand the inclusion of instruction in this field in the curricula of all the medical colleges of the country. Psychosomatic medicine is especially important now, during war, and will become increasingly so later in dealing with post-war problems.

LEONARD G. ROWNTREE

Washington, D. C.

PREFACE

Psychosomatic medicine, though in practice as old as the art of medicine itself, is new as a scientific discipline. Its frontiers are being so rapidly expanded by research, and its concepts and theoretical background are subject to so much further definition, that it is impossible to present in this field a textbook of the traditional type, such as we know in anatomy or physiology. Nevertheless there is an insistent and rapidly growing demand for instruction in the subject, together with a need for information so presented as to be useful for the general practitioner. The present volume represents an endeavor to meet this need in a way that will not be inconsistent with the stage of scientific development which has been attained.

It will be recognized, for instance, that fundamental to all practice, as well as to research, is the taking of an adequate case history. If psychosomatic principles are to be applied, the type of information required and the techniques best adapted to eliciting it, differ markedly from those used in conjunction with the routine medical or psychiatric history.

The chapters on the several syndromes studied, with the accompanying case histories, will be useful to those treating these specific diseases as well as to those whose interest is in the research which underlies the conclusions reached. Since the illness syndromes chosen for detailed discussion here account for the major part of labor wastage, as well as for the major part of present day morbidity and mortality, this material suggests applications in the field of industrial medicine. Chapters on the more general or theoretical aspects of the subject (Chapters IX, X, and XI) need not be read by those whose interest is only practical. Yet in pioneer territory, a record of the processes involved in exploration will lead to a broader understanding than the familiar textbook list of definitions and instruction usually adequate for subjects of which knowledge is more nearly complete. This volume then may be considered a textbook in embryo.

FLANDERS DUNBAR

New York, N. Y.

ACKNOWLEDGMENTS

The research material included in this volume was prepared with the co-operation of the Departments of Medicine, Surgery, and Psychiatry at Columbia University—Presbyterian Hospital Medical Center. Dr. Walter W. Palmer, Bard Professor of Medicine, and Dr. Nolan D. C. Lewis, Professor of Psychiatry, have read this manuscript in detail and have contributed many valuable suggestions, in addition to their constant help while the work was under way. I wish to express appreciation also to Dr. William Darrach, Dean Emeritus and Professor of Clinical Surgery, for time given at regular staff conferences in discussing and helping to integrate our observations concerning patients seen on his ward. Special gratitude is due the Josiah Macy Jr. Foundation, which contributed materially during the years 1934–1938 toward making this work possible in its present scope. Particular mention should be made of Dr. Ludwig Kast, whose vision eleven years ago did much to hearten the author for the sometimes tedious investigation of which this volume is the outcome; and to Dr. Frank Fremont-Smith whose unceasing critical interest since 1936 has contributed much to this presentation.

Assistants in the Department of Psychiatry in Medicine collaborated in the initial preparation of much of this case material: Doctors Theodore P. Wolfe, Janet McK. Rioch, Edward S. Tauber, and A. Louise Brush. Dr. Brush (1937–1943) assisted also in reviewing current literature and in preparing the follow-up material. Dr. Sigfried Berthelsdorf assisted in the follow-up review for a period of six months. The statistical evaluation of the clinical material here presented was done by Francis F. Dunbar in consultation with other statisticians. Dr. Hilde Bruch did some preliminary Rorschach studies in 1938 but aside from a few scattered reports, full credit for the Rorschach material is due Miss Camilla Kemple. Her more recent studies have contributed to the personality profiles, especially that for the fracture group. In addition, these studies throw considerable light on some more fundamental concepts. I want to express appreciation to Miss Kemple for her reading of the whole manuscript.

F. D.

CONTENTS

PSYCHOSOMATIC
DIAGNOSIS

INTRODUCTION

Psychosomatic medicine is that part of medicine which is concerned with an appraisal o both the emotional and the physical mechanisms involved in the disease processes of th individual patient with particular emphasis on the influence that these two factors exerf on each other and on the individual as a whole.—OSLER, The Principles and Practice of Medicine.
Psychic and somatic phenomena take place in the same biological system and are probably two aspects of the same process.—Psychosomatic Medicine, Vol. I, No. I.

PSYCHOSOMATIC DIAGNOSIS—PROBLEM AREA

The student of medicine today, whether he be undergraduate or practicing physician, finds himself entering a terrain quite different from that with which his forebears were familiar. The maps supplied by his teachers and his predecessors are likely to prove uncertain guides. Of course every generation is confronted with new problems, but it is of the utmost importance for each generation to clarify what is known and unknown, to learn where further investigation is vital, and where pitfalls and blind alleys lie.

The most baffling and critical of our present problems have become so because of the achievements of medicine itself. Students leaving medical school with a knowledge of the latest methods for control of epidemics and treatment of certain specific illnesses are often unaware of the fact that those illnesses concerning which their knowledge is most exact will bulk very small in their later medical careers. Medicine has so nearly conquered these scourges as to make them less common than others about which much less is understood. The statistician or the public health officer knows that the illnesses which accounted for our major mortality fifty years ago are no longer among the first ten causes of mortality and morbidity. Among those were such diseases as typhoid and scarlet fever, concerning which the physician now has some secure knowledge; replacing them at the head of the list are cardiovascular disease, arthritis, and other illnesses about which little is known.

1

Having to a large extent conquered the acute infections and learned to prevent epidemics, we are left with diseases of unknown cause as accounting for the majority of illnesses in this country. In addition, these particular illnesses take their greatest toll in middle and later life. This fact is of particular significance since America is rapidly becoming populated by people of advancing years.

In 1850 there were in the population of this country six times as many children under 5 years as adults 65 and over, while at the present time these two groups are almost equal, and it is predicted that by 1950 they will be equal. In 1850 there were about 50 per cent more children under 5 than there were adults in the 45 to 64 age group, in 1940 there were more than twice as many adults in the 45 to 64 age group as children under 5. In 1850 more than half the population was under 20, in 1940 only about one-third of the population was under 20, and it is predicted that by 1980 three-quarters of the total population will be 20 years or older.

This change has been brought about by the application of medical knowledge, but in the meantime what Dr. Boas has called the Unseen Plague—Chronic Disease, has been increasing by leaps and bounds and is taking its toll in terms of disability as well as mortality (Dublin [136]). An important illustration is hypertensive cardiovascular disease. "According to the statistics of the Metropolitan Life Insurance Company,[134] every other individual in the United States past the age of 50 years dies of cardiovascular-renal disease. From other sources [170] we have evidence that probably half of these deaths are due to essential hypertension, that is, that almost one-quarter of all people past the age of 50 years die of the effects of hypertension on one or another of the vital organs. Thus essential hypertension becomes the greatest problem of middle adult life, not even excepting cancer" [226] (Weiss [414]). And yet this important illness is one in which the causative agents are essentially unknown. But one thing we do know is that in this illness the emotional factors play an important and often determining role.

Anyone inclined to give little heed to such statements as these because of a feeling that it is the young rather than the old who deserve medical protection, should consult the recent National Health Survey [286] which has shown that nearly half of our sufferers from chronic disease are under 45 years of age, and 70 per cent of them under 55. As a matter of fact only 15 per cent of all persons with chronic disease are over 65 years of age.[44] Furthermore, other surveys have shown that the very illnesses which take their major toll in terms of death, disability and invalidism in the older age groups are as prominent in proportion to total illness in younger age groups, for example, cardiovascular disease and accidents.

Hence, in spite of the great achievements of our predecessors in medicine, Dublin [186] predicts that *the total volume of illness will increase in the next decades.* This is partly because the major causes of mortality and disability are no longer illnesses etiologically understood, and partly because the increasing age of the population increases the frequency of these particularly baffling illnesses. To this must be added the fact that they have a tendency to become chronic. *The illnesses, then, with which the physician is least well prepared to cope are the illnesses he will meet with greatest frequency in his practice.*

Chronic illness has never before constituted the problem that it constitutes today, whether considered in purely medical or even in socio-economic terms. And the problem is increasing. The fact that since the turn of the century the average life expectancy for the white male has increased by twelve and a half years, and for the white female by fourteen years (an increase of close to 30 per cent), speaks for itself. It is estimated that by 1950, 30 per cent of our population will fall into the age group 40 to 60, in contrast to the previous 20 per cent (Perrott and Holland; [330] Metropolitan Life Insurance Company [285]). Already more than half of our patient-hospital days are devoted to the care of the chronically ill. Such patients require one half the annual services of physicians and almost three fourths of the annual bedside nursing days (Perrott and Holland [330]). It is estimated that even now one out of five persons in the United States has some chronic disease, and that about two thirds of these are disabled for twelve months or more (Boas [44]).

Just before World War II, a prominent British medical officer discussing the question "Is our nation becoming more or less healthy?" emphasized one more aspect of our problem. He found evidence of a marked increase "in chronic and recurring neurotic illnesses, as well as in many examples of organic sickness labelled by such terms as anaemia, rheumatism, gastritis, peptic ulcer, bronchitis, etc. (psychosomatic illnesses) . . ." (Halliday [218]).

In an article, Halliday [217] noted that the major increase in neurotic and psychosomatic illness is in the younger age group, whereas one might expect the contrary since this group has been better nourished and suffered less economic hardship than any other age group in the community. In conclusion he said: "The question, 'Is the nation becoming less healthy?' can no longer be answered with a vigorous and self-satisfied negative."

These changes in the nature of the illnesses with which we must cope, together with the rapid increase of chronic illness, are responsible at least in part for the present demand for the psychosomatic approach in medicine. It is responsible also for the fact that so many practicing physicians find themselves ill-equipped to cope with the problems confronting them.

Heretofore too many patients have served only to furnish valuable pathological material for those of us who follow Virchow or Ehrlich. But our patients and the public at large are not satisfied with a concentration of medical interest on pathology and autopsy. They ask: "Is all this illness necessary?" They become impatient, visit religious and mystical healers, quacks and charlatans, seeking a relief we do not give them. The treatment they receive is likely to be inadequate and when the physician is called in to pick up the pieces, it is usually too late. On the other hand, many such patients make dramatic recoveries or gain considerable relief from these non-medical practitioners. This is a phenomenon which demands scientific study on the part of the medical profession.

Another challenging fact is that many patients, discharged from our leading hospitals or by qualified physicians as having no demonstrable organic disease, still remain sick and return later with recognizable organic illness, often the very illness which their earlier symptoms suggested. And sometimes, having become persuaded that their physicians will not take their symptoms seriously, they find relief or come to grief through the ministrations of non-medical healers.

It is tempting to say that we will restrict our attention to the conditions we understand, or hope to be able to understand by further research carried out in accord with old principles and methodology. But if we do this we find ourselves caring for a rapidly diminishing percentage of the sick population. Perhaps this is as it should be, but the public and some leaders in medicine think otherwise. As a result the medical literature of the last twenty years has dealt more and more with this increasing majority of the sick in our country whom we have not learned how to cure. The question arises: *Are basic concepts, methodology and techniques* of an entirely different type demanded? [152]

BASIC CONCEPTS

For such reasons as those just given we undertook to investigate the rapidly increasing literature of what is coming to be called *psychosomatic medicine*. We found first, contributions on the subject of functional illness, illnesses of unknown etiology, and borderline problems between the specialties. We then found literature calling attention to emotion as an *x*, or unknown quantity, playing a greater or lesser role in all illness, and accounting for many failures in dealing even with those diseases about which most is known. This *x* factor has been shown sometimes to vitiate results obtained by the most accurate laboratory procedures and diagnostic methods.

At the time this study was undertaken there was no major division in the "Quarterly Cumulative Index Medicus" devoted to this problem, and yet there were few headings under which relevant articles were not found. Today the student can find much of this literature—although not all of it—in the index under the heading "physical-mental relationships." *

The most striking development revealed in this literature is the gradual molding of medical thinking by the organismal theory elaborated especially during the last twenty-five years in the biological and medical sciences. Ritter [354] expresses this as follows:

The organism in its totality is as essential to the explanation of its elements as its elements are to an explanation of the organism. . . . No natural object which in its nature is more distinctly synthetic than analytic can be understood by knowledge-processes which are more analytic than synthetic.

This theory which emphasizes an equilibrium within the organism and of the organism in its environment is becoming increasingly useful in facilitating the relating to each other of the medical specialties and the application of facts discovered in them. It has given rise to

* For our review of this literature see Dunbar. [149]

the term *psychosomatic medicine* in accordance with which psychic and somatic represent two angles of observation from which the organismal unit should be studied, two pictures which then should be superimposed or viewed stereoscopically.*

The effect of this point of view on our definitions of health and disease is indicated in the following statements from a neuro-anatomist and a clinician, respectively:

Studies of the embryonic behavior from its beginning lead "inevitably to the conception that the organism is primarily a unit (not an aggregate) and that normality requires that all parts be approximately subject to the organism as a whole, or conversely, that the organism as a whole retain its power of activating the behavior of its parts." [88]

There is no such thing as a purely psychic illness or a purely physical one, but only a living event taking place in a living organism which is itself alive only by virtue of the fact that in it psychic and somatic are united in a unity.[308]

The following statements from a leading psychiatrist, on the one hand, and from a leading internist, on the other, seem to indicate a new emphasis in the thinking of some of our clinicians:

The question "Physical *or* psychic?" therefore, is in most cases wrongly put and should be replaced by the question: "*To what extent physical* and *to what extent psychic?*" [40]

We can no longer separate either nervous or organic, or functional or organic. If we think in terms of disturbed function the only adequate concept is that changes take place which are reversible and irreversible in a series terminating in the gross anatomical.[34, 271]

Of course this organismal concept changes our focus both from that of anatomical pathology and from that of the functionalists who, in searching for the origin of a given illness, assume that they must choose between physiogenesis and psychogenesis. In order to understand disease processes we must give up the "either/or" type of thinking and shift our emphasis to "both/and."

If there is no such thing as purely psychic illness or purely physical illness, the question arises how then are we to study illness? Our methods are directed to one or the other, and our students and practitioners of medicine have been brought up to think of themselves

---

* For further discussion of this concept see page 647.

as being specially trained to deal with one or the other almost exclusively.

Returning again to the literature of the last two decades we find multiple examples of the confusion created by this aspect of the trend toward specialization in medical training. Some investigators have been impressed by the emotional disturbances created by physiological dysfunction and organic damage and have tended to look at the whole problem of psychopathology as "some sort of neurotic superstructure." * There is, of course, some truth in this point of view. An injection of adrenalin may give rise to a subjective feeling of anxiety, but there is the additional fact that all patients do not have the same response to adrenalin, or to the same amount of adrenalin. There may be a constitutional factor here, and there is definite evidence of a personality factor. That is, a patient who is already suffering from an anxiety state will react much more strongly to a small amount of

---

* Dunbar [149] (pp. 59 ff.). This is manifest in contributions with such titles as: "The origin of neuroses and psychoses in chronic gastric disturbances" (Alt, 1892); and "Gynecological lesions found in suicidal mania and gynecological prophylaxis against suicide in women" (Bossi, 1911). Bossi's book "Gynecological Prophylaxis in Insanity" which appeared in 1912 was widely discussed even considerably later.

In a leading textbook of gynecology as late as four decades ago appears the statement: "It is pre-eminently diseases of the uterus and its adnexae which lead to the most pronounced and frequent symptoms of hysteria (Küstner, Lehrbuch der Gynäkologie, p. 112)." In 1901 Freund described chronic atrophic parametritis as a new and certain cause of hysteria. Walthard in his Frankfurt clinic is known as the first European gynecologist to insist on isolating patients with psychogenic disturbances from those with essentially organic disturbances, and to insist that the former be treated psychotherapeutically.

In other words, not more than two or three decades ago suicide and all manner of neuroses were held by many leading physicians to be *caused* by diseases of stomach and uterus, even by such minor disturbances as erosion of the cervix or gastritis. They were to be corrected or cured by correct local therapeutic management of these organs. (The attempt was even made to cure certain of them by castration.) It is interesting that the majority of articles of this nature relate to the fields of gynecology and gastro-intestinal disease, fields in which today even the specialists concerned are most ready to recognize factors (Dunbar,[149] pp. 330 ff.; fn. 1, p. 1–5B).

Commenting on this tendency Crookshank [104] writes: "It always seems to me odd in the extreme that doctors who, when students, suffered from frequency of micturition before a viva voce examination, or who, when in France, had actual experience of the bowel looseness that occurred before action, should persistently refuse to seek a psychical correlative—not to say an etiological factor—when confronted with a case of functional enuresis or mucous colitis. I often wonder that some hard-boiled and orthodox clinician does not describe emotional weeping as a 'new disease,' calling it paroxysmal lachrymation, and suggesting treatment by belladonna, astringent local applications, avoidance of sexual excess, tea, tobacco and alcohol, and a salt-free diet with restriction of fluid intake; proceeding, in the event of failure, to early removal of the tear-glands. This sounds of course ludicrous. But a good deal of contemporary medicine and surgery seems to me, to be on much the same level."

adrenalin (other factors such as organ weakness being equal) than a patient not suffering from anxiety, and the degree of consciousness of the anxiety plays a role also.[270]

A characteristic statement from a member of this group is as follows: "I have now had some twenty-seven years of experience with the Freudian method of analysis; I have used it as a method of diagnosis and treatment; but I have never been willing to give up my status as a scientific physician for that of an applied psychologist. I have not been able to dissociate the brain and nervous system from a very intimate relation with the rest of the body. . . ."[293]

The organismal biologist would comment: "Why should you try?"

Others, erring in the opposite direction, when they have discovered that many types of illness, ranging from some cardiovascular disorders, hyperthyroidism, and other glandular dysfunctions to broken bones, are essentially the result of emotional or character anomalies, find it difficult to do justice to the somatic component of the disease in question.* And finally, those who have come to realize the fallacy in the "either/or" type of thinking, in the opposition of physiogenesis to psychogenesis, speak in terms of a continuous interplay between emotion and physiology. But even this concept is not adequate to the biologists' conception of the organism † in terms of which manifestations in both spheres are expressions of one fundamental factor: a disequilibrium of the organism within itself and in its environment.

Finally, the word *emotion* occurs frequently in the literature of

---

* C. A. McKendree, for example, writes:[295] "Frequently organic systemic disease is masked by hysterical or other neurotic manifestations, as in a patient who, through excessive irritability, selfishness, by frequently insulting members of her family and by devitalizing forty nurses and twelve to fifteen doctors, was found to have carcinoma that had invaded practically every bone of her body. And previous to having had x-ray assistance, the clinical picture resembled a border-line psychosis very closely." McKendree goes on to point out that such mistakes in diagnosis have led clinicians to make extensive and thorough examinations of all neurotic cases. On the other hand, he states, it is due to such examinations that pathological local disturbances are discovered, which then very often are misinterpreted as having etiological significance in the production of neurotic symptoms. Physicians who talk in this way are well on the way to becoming Christian Scientists.

† "Wenn ein Mensch erkrankt, so ist ja nur für den Spezialisten—den Spezialist im schlechten Sinn!—*ein* Organ, ein Organsystem ergriffen; es ist eine reine Laxheit, eine verführerische und verwirrende Abkürzung im Sprachgebrauch, wenn wir von 'einer Pneumonie,' 'einem Karzinom' usw. sprechen. In Wirklichkeit *ist mehr oder weniger der ganze Mensch erkrankt*; philosophisch gesprochen: das Ganze kann nicht heil sein, wenn einer seiner Teile geschädigt ist; biologisch gesehen: der Stoffwechsel das ganze Organ-, Drüsen- und Nervensystem stellt sich um, wenn irgendwo ein Trauma, eine Infektion vorliegt." [239]

diverse specialties relative to psychosomatic medicine but it is rarely defined. The neuro-anatomist may call it a function of the hypothalamus, and the psychologist may call it a connecting link between somatic and psychic functioning, or between what Coghill has called a factor representing the organism as a whole and the diverse functioning of the parts. It is obvious then that even if we accept the organismal theory, considerable work remains to be done in making it a useful concept capable of application to the practical problems confronting the clinician today.

SUGGESTIONS FROM PHYSIOLOGY AND PSYCHOLOGY

Perhaps the most important new data revealed by our initial and subsequent reviews of the literature have come from two disciplines once widely separated from each other, physiology and psychology. This has come partially as an outgrowth of the change in basic concepts just outlined, and partially as a result of independent developments within physiology and psychology. A brief and highly condensed outline of this data from the point of view of clues offered concerning the connection between the physiological and the psychological may serve to clarify further our choice of method for this study.

*We know now that bodily changes may be brought about by mental stimuli, by emotion, just as effectively as by bacteria and toxins, and that physiological changes accompanying emotion may disturb the function of any organ in the body.**

Following Pavlov and Cannon, physiologists in the last two decades especially, have clarified the physiological changes accompanying such emotional responses as fear, rage, sexual excitement, and the confusion resulting from inability to make a satisfactory decision. These are, in the main, changes in tension of smooth and striated muscles, changes in secretion and in circulation including respiration. (There are also more complicated responses such as changes in blood sugar, clotting time, and so on, involving or brought about through sympathetic, parasympathetic, and endocrine systems. One of the most interesting approaches to this problem is study of chemical and elec-

---

* Further treatment of this material may be found in Dunbar [149] and in a forthcoming study; "Hospital and Community." For a discussion of mechanisms *of*, See Chapter VIII of this volume.

trical changes taking place between cells and their environment, the body fluids.) These changes have the following general characteristics in common: *first*, they all serve in some way to prepare the organism for action usually in terms of battle or flight; *second*, they may exert an influence on every organ system of the body to the extent even of temporary alteration of function; * *third*, if they are not discharged in action they tend to persist or to be followed by other changes, such for example as disturbed endocrine balance with effects on the vaso-motor and other systems following prolonged hyperstimulation of adrenals or thyroid, or dilatation of the esophagus following pro-longed cardiospasm, and later changes resulting from inadequate nu-trition; and *fourth*, any state of chronic disturbance of function tends to become crystallized in structural change. Simple examples are the muscular atrophy resulting from chronic contraction of the limbs as in catatonia, cardiac hypertrophy following prolonged hyper-tension, and hemorrhoids resulting from chronic constipation. Changes which have not become so crystallized we think of as functional and reversible, but after the structural change has occurred they are likely to be irreversible. Finally, of course, such changes all have their sub-jective component, that is, palpitation, rapid breathing, pallor or flush-ing, accompanying changes in blood distribution, and so on, which are the picture of anxiety.

It should be noted furthermore, that these are just the changes produced the most readily by hypnotic suggestion, but that they can be produced best, and sometimes only by suggesting the appropriate emotion, not the change itself. For example, the suggestion made to the patient when he is under hypnosis that he vomit, is relatively ineffective unless one suggests a situation involving feelings of disgust, such as to make him feel like vomiting. The same is true of the sug-gestion that a patient develop a tachycardia. To obtain the desired result one must suggest a situation of fear so that the patient will develop tachycardia—one of the somatic manifestations of fear. There is evidence that merely by hypnotic suggestion it is possible to alter

* An added point of some interest here is Parker's [322] description of animal reflexes as of at least three types, purely nervous, neurohumeral, and humoroneural. Illustrating the latter type in the respiratory organization of the higher vertebrates, he gives the following descrip-tion: "Here the humoral afferent arm is represented by the stream of lymph and blood carrying carbon dioxide or other exciting metabolite from the animal's tissues to the respiratory center in its medulla oblongata. The nervous afferent arm in this reflex is the motor nerve connec-tions between the medulla and the respiratory muscles."

the functioning of any organ system, even to produce changes in temperature, blood chemistry, cell count, agglutination reactions, urinary output, or to produce or "cure" lesions such as herpes or warts (Dunbar, [149] pp. 69 ff.).

Investigations, then, have shown that if any such physiological disturbance persists over a long period of time it is likely to result in structural change. This may come about in one of two ways: (a) in direct sequence, as just illustrated; and (b) through facilitating injury by other means. Alkan [20] gives the example: "If there happens to be a source of infectious material above a long-lasting circular spasm, which otherwise, because unhindered in its passage, produces no clinical symptoms, the following may result: The infected fluid is dammed up under increasing pressure, thus bringing about a febrile, purulent inflammation which may lead to perforation, thrombosis, etc. (e.g., infection in gall bladder obstruction)."

These responses enter as units into the more complex lesions in which emotion has been found to play an etiological role, such for example as gastro-intestinal ulcer. Cushing discovered that even mechanical irritation of the hypothalamus, which had been called the "emotional center," might influence the secretion of gastric juice, the motility of the stomach, and its blood supply, thereby in some cases leading to ulcer in the gastro-intestinal tract. It is noteworthy that here again we have as units disturbances in tonus, secretion, and circulation. It may be that other factors must be added for ulcer to develop. The student interested is referred to the extensive literature in this field. But for our present purpose it is sufficient to note that an organ of which the fluid medium is disturbed, and of which perhaps also the blood supply and so nutrition is disturbed, is thereby rendered more susceptible to injury by any additional noxious agent that may be present. This may be brought about whether the subcortical irritation be mechanical or the product of short-circuited psychic impulses.[307] We are learning more and more the importance of thinking of illness as produced by a particular constellation of factors rather than by one single factor. Even in the field of epidemiology we know now that exposure to a pathogenic organism is not sufficient to bring about illness in all persons. The organism itself must be in a certain state in order to be susceptible to the bacteria in question. But this latter factor is of even greater importance in more complicated illnesses such as hypertensive cardiovascular disease, or ulcer of the gastro-intestinal tract.

These facts have a relevance for those who are unable to give up the satisfaction of telling a patient that his illness is imaginary. Such a statement implies that it is something that the patient himself can control or that it is something harmless. As a matter of fact neither of these two inferences is true. Imagination in the broader sense acts as suggestion; it is about the same as autosuggestion. If a patient "imagines" long enough that he has this or that symptom physiological changes will come about, and the sequence of events described in the foregoing will be set under way. Obviously then, such an "imaginary illness" is not harmless and of course we all know that it may be just as incapacitating as a so-called real illness, or even become what is generally known as a real illness. That it is not something the patient can control is explained in the following pages.

A behavior response, if it becomes chronic and fixed, may cause permanent trouble when no expression or adequate solution of the problem it presents has been found. Even animal experimentation has confirmed this. Liddell's neurotic sheep is perhaps a good example. In his laboratory the following observations were made on animals which had been adjusted to laboratory conditions and trained in accordance with the conditioned reflex techniques (Anderson and Liddell; [23] Anderson, Parmenter, and Liddell; [25] Karn [261]). It was found that if such an animal listens to a metronome and is fed when the metronome has a rate of 120, but at the rate of 50 is given no food, this animal readily learns to distinguish between the two and opens the food box only when the metronome has the proper rate. If then the rate of the slower metronome is increased to 80 or 100, so that it becomes difficult or impossible to distinguish between the two rates, many animals develop a constant state of tension. At the same time the heart rate increases (it is often even doubled), the heart may beat irregularly, miss beats or develop extra systoles, and the animals show similar disturbances in other bodily functions. The interesting thing is that after the animals have been subjected to the strain of attempting to make this discrimination they can no longer distinguish between even a very slow and a very fast metronome. They become worried; minor disturbances in the barnyard which never disturbed them before become problems; they cease to get along well with other sheep or pigs and they are unable to relax at night. If then, such animals are turned out to pasture and left alone with the others for a year or more the heart often quiets down, but as soon as they are brought back to the laboratory in which this difficult problem was presented to them, the first sound of the metronome or sometimes even the laboratory itself, produces trembling, palpitation, and all the other physical disturbances they had experienced before.[23] If you did not know, you would jump to the conclusion that they had been badly frightened there.

One might wonder why the sheep was so disturbed by all this, why it did not simply open the food box whenever the metronome sounded, knowing it would find food sooner or later. It is interesting that if a sheep is left free in the pasture and taught a maze with the finding of more food as a goal, it does not develop a neurosis. When the problem becomes too difficult for it, it simply lies down or grazes, showing no further interest. What makes the sheep susceptible to development of the neurotic type of behavior described when frustrated in its expectation or unable to distinguish metronome rates, seems to be the fact that it has already given up a good many degrees of freedom in its submission to the laboratory situation.* This seems to have a bearing on neurotic types of behavior developed by human beings who have given up a good many degrees of freedom by submission to cultural patterns (Frank; [187] Fremont-Smith; [190] and *also* the work of the Liddell laboratory).

Anderson and Liddell [23] observed, furthermore, that thyroidectomized sheep when confronted by predicaments in the laboratory suf-

---

* "It is reasonable to imagine that locomotion, or more generally spontaneous neuromuscular activity, provides an escape from situations to which adequate adjustment is difficult. . . . A difficult problem faced implies increased nervous tension (increased cerebral excitation or inhibition, according to Pavlov's theory), but the neuromuscular mechanism provides an outlet through which this tension may be lowered by the performance of random muscular movements. According to this point of view, the most striking feature of the conditioned reflex method is that through training spontaneous activity is suppressed, with the consequence that the animal can be forced to attempt difficult adjustments such as reacting to stimuli presented according to a rigid schedule and discriminating between closely similar rates of ticking of a metronome." . . . When this adjustment is too difficult a nervous breakdown ensues, and the neuromuscular outlet which has been closed through previous training now opens "because of actual damage to the nervous system to prevent any further rise of tension (excitation or inhibition in Pavlov's sense). The nervous movements of the leg, and in a more exaggerated form of the neurosis, the tremors observed in the rest intervals between stimulations are to be regarded as the protective operation of the neuromuscular system to prevent the nerve cells of the higher centers from being subjected to further strain.

"The comparison between the maze method and the conditioned reflex method suggests a new field of research on behavior in which the role of free or spontaneous activity versus restricted activity is the main object of investigation" (Anderson and Liddell [28]).

ficient to induce experimental neuroses in normal sheep, behaved in quite a different way. After they had been brought to the preliminary phase of the neurosis, continued training, which in the usual neurotic sheep would aggravate the symptoms, led to a complete subsidence of the developing neurosis and the athyroid animals achieved a steady level of performance.

These authors suggest that such observations will "give a useful orientation to investigators wishing to place the problems of psychiatry on a simple experimental basis." In any case, there is sufficient evidence from the study of human subjects for the following statements.

Inadequate expression or solution of emotion or emotional conflict is particularly likely to occur when the emotion is not a response to what appears to be real, an external situation or danger. The physiological changes brought about by the response to an imagined attack may be identical with those brought about by a real attack except that they are potentially more dangerous somatically because less likely to be appropriately expressed in action.*

Psychological-physiological responses are more or less appropriate to situations in the outer world, and in different cases are more or less adequately carried to conclusion. In the case of fear aroused by a scene of shooting there is possibility of adequate somatic expression in a number of ways, as for example running to cover, which may be the most appropriate thing to do under the circumstances. The somatic accompaniments of the emotion, such as the change in blood distribution, the increased red blood corpuscles, adrenalin and extra sugar, all of which are preparing the body for crisis in terms of battle or flight, are utilized in action. But for the man upset by a crash in the stock market, those somatic changes are not likely to be useful because the action for which they are preparing is not likely to take place. *If action is inappropriate to the actual situation, or inadequate to solution of the confronting problem, the emotion with its physiological accompaniments is likely to be inadequately discharged and so disturb the equilibrium of the organism concerned.*†

* As Sherrington [379] pointed out, the greatest release of instinctual tension is in action, and the least in thought, speech falling in between.

† This statement may be considered an oversimplification since there are numerous special cases. The individual's grasp of the reality situation may be inadequate, but this point will be discussed later in further detail.

If then, an emotion or an impulse cannot be expressed because of some limitation provided by the environment or the patient's own inhibitions or misconceptions, a conflict is set up and the emotion or the conflict itself tends to be excluded from consciousness. *Conflicts excluded from consciousness create a permanent tension which may occasion persistent or recurrent disturbances of organic functions.* (Freud,[196] pp. 63–66; Fromm.[197])

There are some connecting links lacking but we may say in general that the development of consciousness and an increasingly complex adjustment to the outer world, including both physical and social environments, have tended to come about simultaneously. The most complex adjustments seem normally to take place through consciousness or more specifically the system which has been called the conscious ego. Our voluntary innervations aim to satisfy the biological needs of survival and reproduction just as do our involuntary ones by means of appropriate activity, but if passage through normal channels is blocked some other channel of expression is substituted which may or may not be adequate to discharge the emotion in terms of both physiological and psychological components. By way of the short circuit this may bring about all the physiological changes which can be brought about by any other known type of subcortical irritation.

If then, the personality is unable to cope with the problem, if any marked degree of unpleasantness or conflict is involved, the whole process is likely to be excluded from consciousness and thus to create a sort of short circuit into subcortical mechanisms. The innervations no longer go through the cerebrum, that is, the problem is not registered in consciousness. Familiar examples are laughing or weeping or states of tension "for no reason at all," or exaggerated out of proportion to the stimulus apparently provoking them. Such reactions as these may continue for long periods of time unless the reason for them is brought into consciousness so that more adequate adjustment to the situation responsible for them can be accomplished. Sometimes such behavior is of the nature of neurotic overreaction and sometimes it appears to be completely irrational, for example, a childish reaction to something that could be dealt with in more adult terms, or a reaction displaced from the original situation to another situation associated with it calling for a different response. Sometimes the mechanism involved resembles that of the conditioned reflex, but usually it is much more complex. On the subject of the expression of emotional conflict in physiological spheres Alexander [10] has written as follows:

Normally the individual who laughs or weeps is able to some degree, at least, to define the psychological reason that impelled him to laugh or to weep. This is not the case with patients who are suffering from a stomach neurosis. Such a patient is not able to describe those emotions which are responsible for his stomach symptoms; he is not even aware of the psychic origin of his symptoms; he will deny it and try to find some somatic basis for his ailment, and in so doing is, in most cases, supported by his physician. The psychogenic disturbance is an unusual or, one should say, an incomplete expression of a psychic tension. It does not give full relief to the causative emotional tension in the same way as laughing or weeping does. The symptom not being able to relieve the psychic tension in the same way as normal psychomotor reflexes do, a permanent tension is sustained which is the cause of the chronic dysfunction.

Whereas conscious fears are aggravating factors, there is evidence that the fears and conflicts which have been excluded from consciousness are of the greatest significance to general medicine, that is. those most likely to be etiological in illness. Grinker [212] has supplied the following formulation:

In anxiety . . . the danger is not real, it is unknown, internal, and results from an increase in instinctual tension demanding expression. As Freud points out, it is a conditioned signal within the ego, conscious within the personality as a warning of impending danger. There are specific unpleasurable feelings, efferent discharges and their perception. The result may not be fight or flight, as to a real danger, but a paralysis of certain higher ego functions. Anxiety is then the first sign of an autonomic influence on the cortex or ego, which has been learned by previous testing to indicate danger for the organism. It is a feeling which accompanies autonomic forces sufficiently strong to overcome cortical inhibition and force the cortex into activity, movement resulting in an attempt at solving the situation which has evoked the internal tension. Psychological fight or flight or compromises are attempted. Often successful solutions are not possible and the cortex or ego "gives up," allowing regressive and infantile modes of exteriorization of emotional expression, for the sake of avoiding more prolonged or greater emotional feelings. They result in visceral expression or organ dysfunctions, which we term organ neuroses, that constitute the first step toward organic disease. (See also Chapter II of this volume.)

In spite of the hints from the physiologists and psychologists which existed when we began our work we found that most of the medical literature of the last three or four decades was unconvincing and unsatisfactory because even where the best psychological methods had been used, adequate physiological observations were lacking, and vice versa. It seemed, then, that in terms of our present knowledge, the necessary procedure would be the simultaneous application of the best methods developed by physiology and psychology. It was clear that little more could be learned from case studies closing with the refrain: "After everything else had been tried with no success, this patient was cured by psychotherapy." The need seemed to be instead for painstaking descriptions of the techniques by which they were cured. What was required was knowledge of the mechanisms revealed in both psychological and physiological spheres, by which reversible changes on the one hand become irreversible, leading to gross anatomical changes, or on the other hand lead back to health and normality. The whole question of psychodynamic mechanisms, however, is a complicated one and for the general physician more readily understood in terms of clinical experience, hence this matter is discussed further on the basis of the data supplied by our research in the concluding chapters of this volume.

Choice of Method

At the time when the conflict between functionalists and organicists in medicine was at its height, one of our leading physiologists, Walter B. Cannon, made a suggestion which is only beginning to come to the attention of physicians and scientists who have been struggling with the problem just described. He said:

"An escape from the insistent demands of the pathologists for morphological evidence of disease, and also from the vagueness and mysticism of the psychological healers, can be found . . . in an understanding of the physiological processes which accompany profound emotional experience."

This, of course, is in effect a modern formulation of the old aphorism, *nemo physiologus nisi psychologus*. The import of this statement should be clear from the foregoing summary of our knowledge concerning physiological and psychological mechanisms, although some of the data just given in highly condensed form were not available at the time Cannon made this statement and indeed some of it not until our own study was nearly completed.

PERIOD OF PRELIMINARY STUDY

After a survey of existing opportunities for a study of this nature, we selected as material for our research patients admitted to a general hospital suffering from one or more of the following illnesses: cardiovascular disease, diabetes, fracture, gastro-intestinal disease, and allergy.

It will be noted that these are all among the major causes of death and disability, or both, in the age period 15 to 55, and hence constitute a majority of hospital admissions and of patients seen in private practice. Cardiovascular disease has the highest disability rate of any illness in the age period 20 to 64, and in the age period 15 to 24 is exceeded only by nervous and mental disease, diseases of the puerperal state, orthopedic conditions, and accidents.

According to the National Health Survey [286] 7,500,000 persons are disabled by cardiovascular diseases on any given day, and another 500,000 by other diseases of the circulatory system.* Furthermore, nearly another 7,000,000 are disabled by rheumatism, a large part of which is rheumatoid arthritis.† These illnesses account for loss of more than 250,000,000 days annually.‡

Of the 1,500,000 invalids in the United States, well on to 12 per cent are invalids because of cardiovascular disease (exclusive of rheumatic fever and rheumatoid arthritis). No illness ranks higher as a cause of invalidism except nervous and mental disease, which is responsible for 18 per cent of all invalids. But in terms of days lost from work cardiovascular disease accounts for 20 per cent, and nervous and mental disease for only 17 per cent.

In studying these patients we became increasingly aware of our lack of adequate methods and techniques, even though we were assured that each patient in the general hospital where this study was carried out, was being treated in accordance with the best practice known to clinical medicine at present, and was under study in terms of the best diagnostic precedures, including physiological and laboratory observations.

* Including aneurysm except heart, gangrene, low blood pressure, and other diseases of arteries or veins, excluding diseases of the lymphatic system.

† According to this table rheumatism includes arthritis, gout, neuritis, neuralgia, lumbago, etc.

‡ Rheumatism 97,200,000; heart disease 95,200,000; and arteriosclerosis and high blood pressure 56,900,000.

During four years, as a member of the regular medical staff, the author personally turned attention more and more to the patients that seemed to present "medical psychiatric problems." In some instances these patients were admitted to the hospital and treated in accordance with the usual routine, and in other instances they were referred to the psychiatric clinic. In neither instance were the results entirely satisfactory. We then arranged for psychiatric diagnosis and treatment of patients who simultaneously were undergoing medical treatment in some cases during the period of the patient's stay in the hospital. The results were more satisfactory. Gradually it became clear that most errors in diagnosis, as well as in the treatment program, had a basis in the medical history itself, so that a first problem became a procedure for what we have called a "psychosomatic history." Next came the working out of techniques for more accurate observation of the psychic component in the illness.

After four years, feeling better equipped to study the chosen problem and having accumulated a good deal of apparently significant material, the author had become increasingly interested in the following question: If all illness has a psychic aspect, were we not all perhaps getting a distorted picture from focusing attention on individual cases that were more or less obviously psychiatric medical problems? This question is particularly important in view of the further question: Is there any personality factor that is to any degree specific for one type of physiological disorder as compared to another? We had a clinical impression that in the five groups of patients studied we were actually dealing not only with five different illnesses, but also with five different types of people.

We then paused to review again the literature relative to emotional specificity, only to find that such investigations as have avoided the distortions arising from a study of selected cases have gone to the other extreme in employing *dragnet methods* on a large scale, making all possible records and tests without rationale and hence with considerable waste in time and funds, through lack of ability to evaluate findings. Findings arrived at on this basis cannot be adequately evaluated because what we need to study is *disturbance of the total equilibrium* of the organism, a factor which cannot be arrived at by way of adding up of measurements of discrete and partial functions.[72] These dragnet procedures are inadequate both because they are not built around any reasonable concept, and because it is impossible to measure both position and rate of change simultaneously.[149] Todd's[408] study of the stomachs of a group of college freshmen illustrates this point in one aspect. A freshman's stomach under the fluoroscope seems not to be identical with the freshman's stomach not submitted to any type of study. We decided therefore to combine a general survey in terms of orientation and procedures, appropriate to the psychosomatic approach, with an intensive study of individuals, in which the most adequate observations of the psychological and physiological component were combined (page 831).

STUDY OF SERIAL ADMISSIONS

It was at this point that with the co-operation of the Department of Medicine of Presbyterian Hospital, and with additional co-operation from the Departments of Surgery and of Psychiatry, we obtained assistance from the Josiah Macy, Jr. Foundation to make possible the study of all patients admitted to the hospital with the illnesses above specified, in our selected-age-group. We have records for some 1600 patients which include observations in both physiological and psychological terms concerning both the physical and the psychic component in these different disease processes. More recently we added to this study Rorschach examination of a new group of serial admissions, and re-examination of patients from the first series in connection with their follow-up visits. These patients have been followed from one to twelve years.

The serial study itself was carried out over a period of more than five years, and completed nearly five years ago. The following chapters are devoted to a description of it and our resulting conclusions. In another volume not yet completed under the title "Hospital and Community" we discuss the possible implications of this study in terms of further research, the everyday practice of the clinician, and programs for more adequate medical care.

Chapter I

THE PSYCHOSOMATIC HISTORY

Don't devote all your energy to the study of medicine; from time to time study a patient comprehensively and not merely according to existing medical curricula and horizons, —THOMAS M. RIVERS. "Introductory Remarks," *Mental Hygiene, Publication No. 9. 1939.*

The research and clinical work on which this volume is based has occupied twelve years. In the interim the psychosomatic approach to medicine which it embodies has made a rapid, and in the latter part of the period, a dramatic advance. Even since the drafting of the introduction, four developments have taken place which indicate the growing interest in psychosomatic concepts. First in significance, the latest (14th) edition of Osler's "Principles and Practice of Medicine" has just appeared with a first section devoted to psychosomatic medicine and functional diseases of the nervous system instead of the traditional chapter on infectious diseases. Earlier, in January 1939, occurred the initiation of the journal *Psychosomatic Medicine, Experimental and Clinical Studies.* This journal is unique in that within the range of the author's knowledge it is the only medical periodical with a board of editors composed of heads of departments of the usually separated specialties such as internal medicine, pediatrics, psychoanalysis, psychiatry and neurology, animal physiology, all of whom pass judgment on the same articles. Third, there was inaugurated, December 18, 1942, a society for research in psychosomatic problems which provides a common meeting ground for representatives of the diverse scientific fields interested, who, heretofore, have been able to meet only in separate sections of their several societies or in specially arranged conferences. Fourth, came the publication, just as this book is going to press, of the first textbook of psychosomatic medicine, by Edward Weiss and O. Spurgeon English.[415]

Except, however, for my own article "Psychosomatic History and Techniques of Examination" (1939), and quotations from it in the new textbook by Weiss and English, there has been in all this increasing volume of literature in the field no thoroughgoing discussion for the general physician of techniques of history-taking from the psychosomatic point of view.* And all clinicians know that medical treatment begins with the patient's history.

I. The Routine Medical History and Psychosomatic Problems

Most errors in diagnosis and treatment have a background in the medical history. In the course of our early work on medical wards it became clear that many of these resulted from the fact that both the focus of the history, and the method of history-taking, precluded any adequate evaluation of psychic as related to somatic aspects of illness, even in terms of a general therapeutic program.

INADEQUACIES FREQUENTLY FOUND IN THE MEDICAL HISTORY

We studied the routine medical history as taken by ourselves and others, in terms of the psychosomatic picture presented: where was information lacking and what were the distortions? It appeared that some of the more important omissions if borne in mind were usually readily avoided or corrected.† Simple examples are the following.

(1) The age and cause of death of parents was pretty routinely noted down, yet there was rarely indication of the year of death, or the age of the patient at the time of the parent's death, including the patient's reaction to it, a fact which often gives important clues (Case No. HP 1, page 40).

(2) Where the patient was born, and whether or not the parents were in this country was pretty routinely noted, but almost never whether or not the patient was still in contact with them, whether or not he nursed one or the other of them during the terminal illness, and whether or not he was exposed to illness in the sense of witnessing

---

* See also Deutsch.[122] This article is written from the point of view of the psychiatrist and trained examiner.

† Some of these were outlined in our research report presented in May, 1936 in St. Louis.[152]

Of course sometimes information is known to the physician which he fails to write down in the chart but his omission to note it down is misleading to the consultant and may even interfere with his own evaluation of it.

dramatic attacks in others. Yet notation of close associations with a parent, brother, sister, or friend suffering from an illness with dramatic symptomatology, if it occurs during the early years (and even under some circumstances, later) is often as important as the notation of exposure to tuberculosis (Case No. HP 3, page 107).

In the course of calling such points to the attention of colleagues and of answering questions they raised, a major difficulty revolved around the question, "Well, how do you know what to ask? What is a psychiatric history?" And then would come comments: "But in the 80 pages of history outline that we learned to use in psychiatry, your questions aren't asked either." Gradually it became apparent that the usual psychiatric history as well as the usual medical history belonged to the "either or" phase of medical practice: that is, Is the illness physiogenic or psychogenic? Has this patient organic damage? If not, the practice was likely to be to tell him there was nothing wrong or to refer him to the psychiatrist. Such histories were essentially inadequate for the ready evaluation of the predominance of the psychic and somatic components in illness as well as of relationship between them. (See case, page 45.)

We attempted to work out and have been using for the last five years in our routine study of hospital admissions, a history to which (with the significance given at the outset) we have applied the adjective "psychosomatic." This history, supplemented by a few relatively simple techniques of examination, differs fundamentally from the usual psychiatric, medical, or social history. It includes information that is usually omitted, overlooked, or given in distorted form in such histories. But, more important, it is differently obtained and supplemented.

The development of this psychosomatic history took place at a time when I was serving primarily as a member of the medical department, seeing patients before they were admitted to the ward, while on the ward, after their discharge from the ward, and later on following some of them through treatment in the psychiatric as well as the medical follow-up clinics: *Hence the first part of this chapter will be devoted to the psychosomatic history as it might (probably should) be taken as a basis for diagnosis and treatment by physician, internist, or surgeon who sees a patient for the first time.* Although this history differs from that used in the study of serial admissions (because in this study most patients had already had "a medical work-up" before they were seen by a member of our research staff), some brief discussion of it may shed light on the reasons for choice of our final history form and certainly will indicate the way in which the form itself evolved.

The first clues as to the essentials of a psychosomatic history came from study of the questions that members of the staff were likely to ask by way of supplementing those required in the form which was routine for the medical history. The majority of these were found to fall under the heading *Personal History,* which normally includes place of birth and time in this country, civil status, work status, number of children and habits; and *Family History.* Some of them fell under the heading *Previous Health and Illnesses and Present Illness.*

The next clues came from patients who were difficult diagnostic problems. A comparative study was made of the medical histories, diagnostic psychiatric histories, and subsequent more intensive study. The divergencies were so profound that the original picture was sometimes completely altered, and with it the whole medical therapeutic program, sometimes the medical diagnosis itself. These alterations in the medical therapeutic program included in their range frequent obviation of surgical intervention * and seemed in some instances to have obviated impending fatality.†

* For example: Case No. RHD 21. A married German-Jewish woman, aged 45, was admitted to the ward with a history of dyspnea, precordial pain, and bloody, frothy sputum immediately before admission. After a delivery nineteen years previously, she had been told she had heart trouble and she had been increasingly invalided by frequent periods of rest in bed, limitation of activity, and more or less continuous digitalis medication. In the hospital with rest in bed and digitalis, she improved rapidly; there was a decrease in pulse deficit by the third day. She was discharged three weeks later, the diagnosis being inactive rheumatic heart disease, cardiac insufficiency, mitral stenosis and insufficiency, aortic insufficiency, chronic auricular fibrillation, and chronic cholecystitis.

Four weeks later in spite of continued digitalization she was readmitted, having become dyspneic and orthopneic, and again brought up pink sputum. There was fibrillation, the heart rate was 120, the blood pressure 150/80. *Thyroidectomy* was considered although her basal metabolic rate returned rapidly to normal after a few days' rest in bed. (The readings were +21, +9, +7.) *Cholecystectomy* was considered also. Because we had found an important psychic element in this woman's illness which we were convinced bore a relationship to the attacks of pulmonary edema these operations were postponed.

This patient was seen by Dr. Wolfe in the hospital and in the clinic after discharge on an average of every one or two weeks for a period of six months. She has had no more attacks of pulmonary edema, feels much better generally, is capable of considerable exercise without experiencing decompensation (walking 40–50 blocks on a stretch), and of doing her own housework. She has been followed for nearly four years.

† Familiar as we are with this possibility, the point is of much more general and critical importance than is usually recognized so that further routine studies would seem to be called for (for example, Bennett and Semrad [32]).

The divergencies between these histories can be grouped roughly as omissions and distortions essentially dependent on bias or lack of time, interest, or training in the physician himself, and omissions and distortions having their origin primarily in the patient, and requiring some skill on the part of the physician to avoid.

Omissions and Distortions Essentially Dependent on the Physician. In addition to the instances noted at the outset, two more minor points may be mentioned.

(1) Statistics, even on the hereditary side, were often confused by lack of care in determining whether it was father, or stepfather, mother or stepmother, and so forth, to whom these notations applied.

(2) Although civil status was usually noted, changes in civil status often were not noted in the interval note on subsequent admissions. This applied often to the year of marriage or of second and subsequent marriages.

Such omissions may be rather simply rectified even though the list be considerably expanded. At first, under the limitations of a heavy hospital and clinic load this seemed not to be the case, but experience proved that careful attention to such details not only did not require more time but actually saved time in the end, both through clarification of the picture, and through the effect on the attitude of the patient himself.

The following errors and distortions, on the other hand, result essentially from the tendency to *read in* when attention is directed to the patient's emotional life. It happens not infrequently that if a patient appears nervous and excitable on the ward or tends to create problems for the nurse, a note appears in the chart: "This patient is reacting like a spoiled child," or "has always been a spoiled child."

A case in point is that of a diabetic patient, 29 years old, who had a marked tendency to go into shock (Case No. D 29). Her physician took this attitude toward her, justifying it partly by the fact that she was an only child; and the social worker, possibly impressed or confused by his attitude, added to her note the following:

Patient is of Spanish parentage, and has quite an accent although she is American born. She particularly dreaded the cold, and as a child was not very strong. *For this reason she has been coddled a good part of her life.*

The facts, not revealed prior to the psychiatric contact, are the following:

The patient's life, as long as she could remember, had been lived under the shadow of her father's statement that she (that is, her birth) had driven her mother crazy. This mother was cared for in the home until the patient was 8 years old, at which time the mother attempted to poison her and took poison herself. The patient had run to the nurse and both patient and mother had had their stomachs pumped out and recovered. Because of a feeling of shame the father still wished to keep the mother in the house and the patient began to have convulsions. The doctor then insisted that the mother be sent to a hospital for the care of mental illness where she was at the time this patient was seen. The patient continued to have convulsions whenever she went to see her mother, until the doctor forbade further visits. The first time the patient saw her mother again (about twelve years later) was shortly before the discovery of the diabetes. In the meantime, the guardian appointed to take her mother's place treated her so unkindly that she had run away from home and supported herself in night clubs, working gradually up through office work and sales jobs until she had become a buyer in a hotel gift shop when she was married. She was married five years before admission and had continued to work because her husband could not earn enough to support both of them.*

This is scarcely the picture of a temperamental Spanish girl who had been coddled most of her life.†

An example of a different type, also of frequent occurrence, is the following: When the patient is quiet, obedient, and conscientious about carrying out the physician's instructions, the deduction is sometimes made that the patient "is well adjusted to his illness"; he is spoken of as a model invalid and encouraged to think of himself in those terms. As a matter of fact such patients are often inadequately adjusted to their illnesses. The physician's misimpression comes because the patient is discharging his inner conflicts by a sort of somatic short circuit (page 15) and the symptoms thereby created appear to the physician to be part of the unavoidable in the disease picture. A case in point is the following:

Case No. RFD 122. A cardiac patient, aged 35. The history of illness began with chorea at the age of 10 and continued through thirteen hospitalizations for cardiac breaks. The medical note refers to this patient as "in

* For manner in which this information was obtained see page 48.

† Incidentally, this attitude on the part of the doctors and nurses recalled her very unpleasant early experiences, subjecting her to additional emotional strain. It is interesting that the striking tendency to go into shock was influenced by a relatively superficial psychotherapy.

view of the extent of cardiac damage, amazingly untroubled by her condition, co-operative, free from nervousness and worry." The superficial psychiatric contact revealed the fact that this patient had felt useless and inferior all her life because she was an orphan, because of her sex, and for other reasons. Her reactions had been colored by her relation to an older brother who bullied her, whose visits to her still filled her with terror. Incidentally, the first onset of illness, chorea at 10, she herself ascribes to a fright he gave her. She cut herself off from all association with men. The only place she felt safe was in the hospital, and she therefore rather enjoyed the breaks which gave her an excuse to seek the protection of its walls. She stated that she had no dreams, but nonetheless she woke up frequently during the night in a panic and her chart showed marked spiky increases in pulse rate. It showed also a rise in the pulse rate between one and two o'clock daily. Rounds on her ward take place at two o'clock and it was learned then, although she had mentioned the fact to no one previously, that she had a deep-seated apprehension in connection with the ward rounds. She considered this terror quite unreasonable; but she could not help imagining each time that "all those doctors were going to do something terrible" to her.*

This again is scarcely the picture of a placid, non-neurotic woman, well adjusted to her illness. Psychotherapy had never been recommended for this patient during the twenty-five years of medical care, yet even superficial psychiatric contact produced a change in her condition, and had this been thought of ten or fifteen years previously it might have altered the whole course of her illness as well as of her life.

Omissions and Distortions Having Their Origin Primarily in the Patient. These divergencies, falling in the category of distortions and misrepresentations by the patient, seemed usually to be conscious as well as unconscious on the part of the patient as they appeared in the medical history, and essentially unconscious on the part of the patient as they appeared in the preliminary psychiatric examination. This difference appeared to result in part from the simple fact that it is only too easy for the physician to give the impression of being too much in a hurry, or for some other reason unprepared to listen to heavily charged emotional material. Not infrequently patients stated in the first medical interview that a parent was dead when the parent was actually an emotional problem in one way or another, whether

* For the manner in which this information was obtained see page 48.

because institutionalized, criminal, or merely wished out of the picture for some less serious reason. Patients themselves often ascribed such misrepresentations to their feelings about the physician taking the history.

Case No. HP 1. A patient was referred to the psychiatric service because she was un-co-operative. (Full history, page 40.)

According to the medical chart the patient's father died at the age of 95 in an accident, and her mother at the age of 65 of apoplexy. *Incidentally, this gave her a cardiac heredity which actually she did not have.* The patient confessed that this information was made up because she did not like being asked personal questions. Her father and mother were both living, but she "preferred not to discuss them." "Of course I don't mind telling you but no other doctor has ever given me time to say my say. And I would not like to give them a wrong impression so I decided it was best to avoid the question. . . .

This of course confuses statistical and sometimes even clinical impressions because when patients state that a living parent is dead they usually invent as the cause of death the illness of which they themselves are the most afraid, or from which they believe themselves to be suffering or are actually suffering. In our material we found this particular error in somewhat more than 5 per cent of the cases.

Stewart [395] stated that "he thinks of a physician as an attorney who is collecting evidence and examining a witness. He must not take what is given him but must hunt for what he needs, sifting the essential story out of a mass of fiction and extraneous fact." This point of view is essentially accurate but is open to two objections: first, in this process the focus of the examiner is all important, and there has been a tendency to collect evidence relative to physical symptoms without adequate attention to psychic symptoms, except from the point of view of circumventing them. And second, too little is said about the physician-patient relationship which in itself may be the determining factor in the information obtained. (See Koelsche. [273])

NEED OF A DIFFERENT FOCUS

Important discrepancies between the medical and the preliminary psychiatric histories are, of course, essentially avoidable,* whereas

* That is in case material like ours from which psychotics and persons of low mentality have been excluded.

most of those between the preliminary psychiatric histories and the deeper psychiatric investigations are unavoidable, because, as unconscious factors make their appearance, certain distortions in the patient's conscious idea of things become clear and are gradually corrected.

The problem of course is that of determining when deeper investigation is indispensable for accuracy of diagnosis as well as for therapy. Although general principles had been suggested in the literature, there was little written of practical help in their application, with the exception of the psychoanalytic technique,* which was too time-consuming to be feasible except with an occasional patient. It is not primarily content or sequence of events that stands in relation to disease processes but rather mechanisms by means of which the patient has attempted to handle his problem; and it is not concrete worries, but unconscious conflicts that lead to somatic disorders. In terms of our knowledge of physiological processes accompanying emotions, satisfactory approximation to the true pictures can be obtained only with investigation that is sufficiently detailed, or treatment sufficiently intensive to reveal unconscious contents.

The need therefore was to determine to what extent indications could be obtained from the routine medical history or from the superficial psychiatric examination as to the probable nature, or at least direction, of many of the corrections to be expected as the data furnished by the unconscious content comes to light (see Case No. HP 3, page 107).† It was concluded that many clues could be obtained from the briefer examination, but only if changes were made in the usual evaluation of data and in techniques of obtaining it.

II. THE PSYCHOSOMATIC HISTORY

FOCUS

As already noted, most of the patients included in this study were seen by a member of the research group only after a preliminary medical work-up had been completed. This statement applies to all those included in the second period of the study, that is the serial-

* For further discussion see page 117.
† For further discussion see page 86 ff.

admission groups. With these patients, then, the first problem
was review of the medical history (the first procedure to which the
patient was subjected on or before admission to the general hospital):
What picture of the patient did it present? To what degree was this
a psychosomatic picture? Through what lens had it been taken?
It often seemed that the photographic mechanism was of the old-
fashioned make, set like the old Brownie camera for bright and
cloudy but giving inadequate detail when these were intermingled or
borderline, that is, when the disease picture was not clear-cut.

Of course the attention of both patient and physician is likely to
be focused on somatic abnormalities in the hypothetically normal
human being. (When this was the case important information was
particularly often lacking.) Where these were not found, or could
not be understood in terms of reaction of tissue to injury, information was sometimes obtained concerning potentially traumatic elements in economic or social situations if a social worker was available.
But the social history usually contained defects similar to those
described in the medical history, because attention was focused on
symptoms and environmental difficulties, rather than on the patient
himself and the factors in his psychosomatic make-up which rendered him particularly susceptible to injury by them.

How then could one evaluate the relevance to the present illness
of the various injuries and stresses to which the patient had been
exposed? Obviously, it would help were one able to answer the
question: "Under what circumstances do normal physiological responses to emotional situations become pathogenic?" As previously
indicated, this is likely to happen when the emotional response itself
has become chronic and fixed, and this in turn is likely to happen
when no adequate expression of the emotion or solution of the
conflict has been found, and this in its turn is particularly likely to
happen when the emotion is not a response to a real present situation
or danger. Hence the psychosomatic history must give information
on this point (page 14).

If this statement is to be given a positive meaning capable of
application in the examination of each patient, it is clear that the
necessary information must include an outline of the patient's difficulties and conflicts, especially the conflict that has become chronic
or most strongly repressed, whatever the diverse ways in which it is
expressed; and an outline of the patient's behavior patterns: the

ways he has found to deal with his difficulties or to defend himself against his anxiety.*

For example, some patients on receiving bad news dash to the ball field or to a movie, or to work, and others under the same stimulus call in all the neighbors or make a round of visits to their friends to tell them what has happened, while a third group go off by themselves and think it all over. With due regard to the constitutional factor, the physiological accompaniments of the emotion aroused will be different in each case. In terms of Sherrington's formula, the first group will discharge considerable tension in action; the talking of the second group provides somewhat less outlet, and the counter-reactions roused by the response of the audience to the story may be such as to create new tensions, with the accompanying physiological component of rage if the response is not satisfactory; the third group, in the absence of active discharge of emotion, suffers the greatest likelihood of disturbances of autonomic equilibrium involving one or more organ systems.

The focal problems then are the relationship to symptom formation, on the one hand, of character (Fenichel,[177] Reich,[344] Kardiner.[260]) *(quite apart from traumatic and economic handicaps), and, on the other, of somatic make-up (including constitution, physiological types, etc.).*[189] They constitute the focus of the psychosomatic history. Without such a focus it seemed impossible to avoid or correct such distortions as occur in medical, social, and psychiatric histories. These distortions themselves can, of course, be understood in terms of the characteristic focus of each type of history. Even in the patients who have been studied from all three points of view, however, one is likely to get the impression after reading the three histories that the patient himself has in some way fallen in between. An adequate psychosomatic picture is not given in any or all of them.

---

* "Speech, since it provides some degree of externalization of energy, may be regarded as standing between musculo-skeletal behavior (i.e., action) and thought, and is also a manifestation of partial motor inhibition. The degree of availability of these modes of cortical expression to the instinctual levels is in direct proportion to the degree of motor inhibition, because of diminishing external risk, yet the degree of relief of instinctual tension depends on the degree of sheer motor component in the expression. Thus action gives greatest relief, thought or fantasy the least. But instinctual action carries with it the gravest external threat and thought the least grave. Speech stands midway between them with regard to both considerations, and is thus a singularly happy medium of expression. The symbols, the fantasies, with which the patient occupies himself represent a constant effort to translate the physiological energies of instinct into a form adequate for corticospinal expression, or at least into the dissipation of pure thought" (Sherrington [379]).

The focus of a history determines its content. Yet in what has been termed psychosomatic history there seem to be few questions that must be asked beyond those that belong in good medical and social histories (especially if the personal data section is expanded so that it really gives personal data and not just civic status, exercise, and addiction to tea, coffee, and alcohol). But a different organization of material is of great assistance in its evaluation.

The first aim was the delineation of the personality as a whole: heredity, constitution and physical status, reaction patterns physiological and psychological. It was found helpful as part of the medical history to obtain pictures taken from several different angles, that is, *pictures of the patient's habitual manner of reacting in the various spheres in which life demands adjustment,* and then to superimpose them (e.g., Case No. HP 1, page 40). This is merely an extension of the principle essential to the psychosomatic approach, of obtaining a stereoscopic picture of disease. These seven appeared to be of fundamental importance: the patient's reactions (early and present) to himself, his body as well as his personality; to his family, to his work; to his social environment (including his economic status, friends, church, hobbies, and the like); to sex; to his present illness; and the degree of his insight concerning these reactions.

Next, from a study and superposition of these pictures, and with attention to some specific points (listed below), a record was obtained of the patient's preparation for illness (Case No. HP 1, page 42). By this is meant that a patient who has been repeatedly injured by conflicts with the environment that aroused strong emotion and accompanying physiological disturbances is rendered more susceptible to illness, just as is the patient who has repeated attacks of influenza or bronchitis or habitual sleepless nights. Furthermore, patients whose frequent pattern of response to emotional shock is, for example, swallowing their tears and accumulating steam under pressure, that is, accumulating anger which they are afraid to express, are more susceptible to illness than patients who are under no such pressure and have no such tensions. This holds true whether the immediate cause of the illness be a bacterial infection, to which the patient has been made more susceptible because of sleepless nights and lowered resistance, or whether it be a new emotional shock.* Hence, in the psychosomatic history particular attention was paid to the following points:

SPHERES OF ADJUSTMENT AND INJURIES FROM THE ENVIRONMENT

(1) Note was made of any important conflicts in the spheres just listed in which our present-day culture demands adjustment. In some cases this was done in terms of a review of the medical history already taken, especially in connection with the "personal history," "family history," and "previous health and illnesses" divisions of the medical history, somewhat as follows:

(a) After place of birth and residence were noted, questions might be asked about present living conditions as compared with earlier ones, thus usually eliciting facts as to *social and economic adjustment*.

(b) After *marital status* was noted, and in connection with the question as to health of partner and number of children, it was found that a question as to whether or not the children were wanted and why, elicited a great deal of information concerning the patient's *sexual adjustment*. In the case of the unmarried woman this information was more readily elicited in connection with the menstrual history by such simple questions as: "Was the patient prepared for the first menstrual period or did it take her by surprise?" "Was it a shock?" and so on to which patients respond variously: "It was the greatest fright of my life, mother never told us anything," or "Mother never told us but I learned about it from dirty stories at school. I think such things are disgraceful," and so on. Women, as we all know, respond readily and gratefully to any interest in the difficulties of pregnancy and childbirth. Often they will mention incidentally that they "didn't want to have the child anyway" or else that they very much did want to have one. This aspect is important also in the case of the man with children, who, too, has gone through emotional experiences in connection with his wife's pregnancy. After a few such sympathetic questions have been

* Emerson [166] said: "The bacteriologist also recently has helped, for he no longer teaches that bacillus typhosus, for illustration, is the 'cause' of typhoid fever. It certainly is the only known specific cause, nevertheless the chain of etiology of typhoid fever is made up of other links also, and among them some which he had named 'immunity,' 'resistance,' 'susceptibility,' etc., and these, he knows, the affective psychical states of the patients can easily modify."

asked, if adequate information has not been given spontaneously, one can raise the question of more children: wanted, unwanted, why, what has been done to prevent, and so on. Such information is important not only in connection with certain obvious neuroses but particularly in certain types of cardiovascular disease where the sexual life is of fundamental importance. Often the causative sequence leading to an accident or setting up of an accident habit may be obtained through such channels. (See cases, Dunbar, Wolfe, and Rioch.[152])

(c) *Occupation*. After inquiring as to the patient's present occupation, it is relatively easy through simple questions to elicit his work history, attitude toward the job, and so on, thus getting a very clear picture of *his vocational adjustment*.

(d) Some information as to *family adjustment*, early and present, may have been elicited in the foregoing, but it seemed most readily elicited in connection with questions as to the cause of death of parents, brothers and sisters, with their ages at the time of death in relation to the patient's age, and the patient's exposure to them during illness and his attitude toward them.

A long-persisting conflict in one or more of these spheres may undermine general resistance and integrity in such a way as to render the organism more susceptible to injury from whatever source. In some cases it may even develop in the organism a tendency to provoke such injury, as, for example, through unnecessary exposure or purposeful accidents.

(2) It seemed especially useful to note pseudo-hereditary as opposed to hereditary factors, that is, exposure to any given disease as experienced by parent, relative, or friend.* (See case, page 112.)

(3) Special note was made of both the patient's general physical status and his reactions to (including his ideas about) *his body* and his *personality*. Evidence was often found in his account of his previous illnesses and of his successes and failures as well as in his general behavior and dreams.

(4) In connection with the previous *health and illness history* and the *history of the present illness*, it seemed important to pay special attention to *chronological correlation* of the periods of major stress and strain in the patient's life with the time of appearance of particu-

---

* For discussion of this subject see Dunbar *et al.*[152] and for illustrative case histories, Dunbar [145] and *Columbia University Text-Book of Psychiatry*.[99]

lar conflicts or symptoms, and with specific events such as exposure to illness in a patient. Such exposure, for example, during the first five years of life is quite different in its effect from exposure during the latency period, adolescence, or adult life, and must be evaluated in terms of the patient's general personality structure and development.* It is a common experience that a patient in whose illness the emotional factor is important will give a different chronology prior to examination and afterward, or at some later date, and often omits important points which he will suddenly remember. or fill in on subsequent interviews.

DEFENSES AND REACTIONS TO STRESS

The etiological significance of emotional stresses can be discovered only after a picture of the fundamental personality structure has been obtained. But it is important to study *shifts in the patient's life from psychic to somatic manifestations and vice versa.* There are cases reported of psychotic patients whose minds seem suddenly to clear when they are dangerously ill, only to return to their previous condition as the physical illness improves.† And it is common experience to find a perfectly cheerful, normal-appearing patient with heart disease or asthma, who gradually manifests more and more symptoms of neurosis as the somatic disorder is alleviated. Many have had patients who were jittery and neurotic and suddenly became "like their old selves," and even showed great courage and bravery as soon as they discovered something "was really wrong" with them— that an operation was necessary, or a special diet, or something of the kind, only to become neurotic again when "cured" (e.g., Jelliffe [251].) Incidentally, it has been thought that no psychological test known today will pick out patients who have or are predisposed toward the accident or illness habit.[312] (Chapter XI. Section IV.) This can be done only through an analysis of the patient's character.

Symptoms were studied in terms of their possible functions as defenses against certain conflicts, and expression of them, together with the tensions created in the patient. It was said long ago: "Re-

---

* To Adolf Meyer we owe much for his early stressing of these facts.

† See Leo Stone's [397] report of a case with coronary occlusion, for clinical material relative to the inverse relationship of psychic and somatic symptomatology. See also Cannon [73] and Sherrington [379]; also Culpin [105]: Report, Third, of the Miners' Nystagmus Committee [351]; Wilson.[418]

member that many symptoms are part of nature's defensive mechanisms."

Finally, the degree of the patient's insight concerning his past and present behavior as well as his reactions to his illness were noted, and the possible falsifications, amnesias, and scotomata checked.

As just noted, if such a patient were asked what he did and what happened to him on the day that he became ill, especially immediately prior to the onset of illness, it happened frequently that in answering he contradicted his previous statements about the time of onset of the illness or presence or absence of traumatic occurrences, or suddenly remembered an important experience that he had completely forgotten.

A further device which was often helpful is the following: When it was obvious that the patient's symptoms might be a reaction to fear or rage he was asked to describe the physical appearance of someone who is angry or afraid. In these cases the patient often described other symptoms very accurately but omitted the particular symptom that he himself had.* The following case illustrates this point (other examples are Cases No. C 54, C 42, C 293, C 234, F 117):

Case No. ASC 156. A woman, aged 31, married and with three children, was admitted to the hospital with pain over the precordium radiating to the back of the neck and left arm, with attacks of palpitation and dyspnea on exertion, of three months' duration, and much worse during the last three weeks. Her diagnosis was hypertension of three months' duration and anginal syndrome.

CHRONOLOGY

Events in Life Situation	Patient's Response
Seven years ago when the patient was eight months pregnant, her mother-in-law died of heart failure after giving birth to a child. Just before this the patient had been visiting a friend whose mother was having pains in her arm, particularly her left arm.	The patient had a nervous breakdown with sticking in her throat, precordial pain, dyspnea and palpitation, and fear of dying and leaving her own children, including the one still unborn. She told no one about her cardiac symptoms.

* Acknowledgement should be made here to Dr. Frank Fremont-Smith [140] who reported to me several cases which illustrated dramatically the value of this procedure.

Events in Life Situation

The doctor, who had been there before, had chided the family for not recognizing that the mother in the family had heart disease. He said: "I can't understand that you couldn't realize that your mother had heart disease. Don't you know that all pains in the arms are not just due to rheumatism?" The patient reported "I said at the time 'Thank God I haven't got pains in my arms,' and then five months later I developed pains in the arms." She went on to say that she knew a lot of people who had slight enlargements of the heart, and yet "they run up and down stairs, and visit, and so forth, without any ill effects." Therefore she had deduced her own heart must be much worse.

Five months later the patient's father died of a heart attack when she was not with him, "for which I shall never forgive myself or my brothers and sisters who didn't notify me in time."

Six years ago the patient's mother, who had been ill for a year with what was thought to be a tumor, died suddenly of "heart failure."

Two years ago: "I'll never forget two years ago my daughter developed the grippe out of a blue sky. The doctor examined her, turned around to me and said, 'Do you know that your daughter has an irregularity of the heart?'" The patient went on to say that she was

Patient's Response

The patient developed pains in the arms.

The patient's cardiovascular symptoms still continued and her menstruation became irregular. She told no one about the former but did tell her husband about the latter.

Increase of cardiac pain and exhaustion. Fear of hearing the telephone ring, and dreams of being waked up by the telephone (the way she was notified of her father's death).

Events in Life Situation	*Patient's Response*
sure that the child's irregularity of the heart was due to the fact that she, the patient, when her own child was only a year old, had "dragged" her about too much, and had injured her heart that way. The patient went on to say that nobody knows about this, but that she brooded for months and months over the fact that she had damaged her daughter's heart. Since that time she had had her daughter in the hospital here, and her heart had been found to be perfectly normal. But at any rate, the patient explained, "I was just frantic."	
Three months before admission, according to patient's statement, nothing particular happened.	The symptoms became so severe that the patient had to tell her husband about them, which she felt had affected his health. There followed increasing fatigue, loss of ability to concentrate, pain in the lumbosacral region, in addition to the patient's previous symptoms.
Three weeks before admission, a girl friend of her 7-year-old daughter's told the latter that she thought her mother would die because she was always so quiet, and never did anything. That night the patient's daughter cried during her sleep and kept calling "Mummy, Mummy!" Since that time the patient has been worse.	Increased fear, palpitation, and shortness of breath.

The relaxation technique to be described later (page 86) was used with this patient and she was asked in several days to tell her story again, beginning about three months ago. She described her general situation with her husband as noted above, stating that she was becoming more and more afraid that something would happen to her and that she would leave her husband

and children high and dry as happened in the case of her mother-in-law and her father. Then she sat up, looking frightened, and said, "That's the first time I saw a doctor. As soon as he came into the room I got hysterical and shrieked: 'I have heart trouble and high blood pressure.' That was why I had to tell my husband about having had a bad heart all those years." It was called to her attention that she had omitted this incident when she first gave her history. She said: "Sure enough I did. I don't know why. I guess I was scared." She was asked to define fear and said that it consists of being upset, nervous, tense; she said that sometimes a person screams out, and the face is all distorted. She forgot to mention breathlessness and palpitation or throbbing of the heart. As soon as that was pointed out to her, she said it was funny she had omitted that, and then spontaneously said: "Maybe that is my main trouble, fear," and in addition she said "I never get palpitation when I go upstairs, or do any exercise." Her blood pressure registered 175/90 before this interview and 120/80 at its close.

EVALUATION IN TERMS OF FACTORS PREDISPOSING TO ILLNESS

In brief, then, the material was arranged to show the major stresses and strains in the patient's life in correlation with his illness history and to give a picture of his patterns of reacting (physiologically and psychologically) to environmental pressures. This we have termed *his preparation for illness,* determined through evaluation of any indications of constitutional or physiological impairment, and also any indications of psychological impairment by way of specific emotional sensitivities or unfortunate (or potentially pathogenic) patterns of reacting to the everyday difficulties of life. An illustration here is what was long ago termed the "spasmogenic aptitude" (Dunbar,[149] p. 219; Gallavardin;[198] Houston[241]); that is, the tendency to respond by some sort of general spasm of smooth or striated muscle or both to any kind of pressure from the environment. This tendency may predispose to infection or chronic dysfunction of the systems particularly involved.

Care was taken to guard against, or correct, so far as possible any distortions that might result from the patient's amnesia or anxieties, or the physician's lack of skill or attempt to read in. In many cases important clues were obtained through a history such as that described; in some cases no adequate clues were obtained in this way and additional techniques were necessary. In order to illustrate this point two cases are given of which the first falls in the former category, and the second in the latter.

Case No. HP 1. A spinster, aged 50, came to the psychiatric clinic April 27, 1934, after nearly two years' treatment on the medical service. She was referred on the basis of the following material elicited by the author in the course of a review of the medical history taken on admission. She was suffering for serious cardiac disease (chronic valvular defect, mitral stenosis, and insufficiency; chronic auricular fibrillation, cause unknown). Her major symptoms were attacks of sleeplessness, dyspnea, and palpitation (auricular fibrillation), somewhat difficultly controllable by digitalis. (The patient's first hospitalization was June 6 to August 29, 1932, symptoms having begun in April of that year; the second, September 23 to December 17, 1934; and the third January 29 to April 27, 1935.) The patient was referred to the psychiatric service because she was un-co-operative.

Personal data. The patient was a spinster, aged 50 years when she came for treatment. She had never really found herself vocationally. She was interested in art but had lost a series of jobs, and objected to the work outlined by the Charity Organization Society. She lived alone in a room in a cheap boarding house on the "lower West side."

Family history. According to the original medical history the patient's father died at the age of 95 in an accident. The mother died at 65 years of heart disease and apoplexy. (Note: the patient stated that both bits of information were untrue. The father and mother are both living. She did "not care to say where." She is "ashamed of them." It is further interesting that the clinical clerk's note on the first admission was as follows: "The patient is co-operative and intelligent, but wilfully unable to recall details. Probably because of feelings of resentment toward the world." This statement was proved true by subsequent psychiatric contacts.) The uncle had gout and the mother rheumatic arthritis. There were no other important illnesses in direct or collateral lines. The patient's forbears on both sides were early colonial settlers. The father was a merchant marine captain seldom at home. "All the family and their relatives were neurotic" according to the patient's statement. The family came of strict New England stock but because of dissension within never adjusted harmoniously to any community. Such friends as they had they alienated by spreading stories about each other.

Personal history. The patient was born in New England in 1884, her mother's only pregnancy, and an unwanted child. Delivery was instrumental. She was sent to a convent school, "because Mother wanted to get rid of me," at the age of seven years, although she and her family were Protestant. Her main interests were mathematics and science. "At first it was a relief to get away from Mother. But the Sisters were strict and stupid and often beat me, too." The patient had a nervous breakdown just as she was coming up for her college degree and so failed to receive it, although she states that she never "thought degrees meant much anyway." After college she spent four years in a Chicago Art school and became a designer. In 1913 her parents separated, her mother going to Pittsburgh where the patient went "to stay two weeks to get her mother settled." She lived the next fourteen years there, neither living with her mother nor seeing her. She sold flowers, taught one year in a business college, designed clothes, did mechanical drawing, and taught arithmetic. All of a sudden she "got sick of it" and came to New York in April, 1927. She lived with a girl friend who decided to go on Broadway, but the patient was so much shocked by this girl's behavior that they parted company. In 1928 the patient worked in a fashion studio coloring the designs. She lost the job because of conflict with authority. She then did "free lance work." In 1929 she got a job in a hotel doing upholstery. She lost this job in April 1932, and entered the hospital one and a half months later, with the diagnosis noted above. Other important elements in her history will be covered in relation to her treatment.

(Attitude toward self—physical status.) The patient states that she has always been tough and able to do what she wants. Aside from a nervous breakdown * in college twenty years before, the patient had no illnesses † until the present one of which the onset was similar; "I suddenly had the feeling my body wouldn't obey me any more and I hated it because it made me so much trouble."

Personality. The patient was above average intelligence and her judgment was good when it was not too definitely biased emotionally. She was a big bony spinster, aggressive, sharp tongued, and sharp faced, always dressed in black. She disliked colors because she had nothing to be joyful about. She had become convinced that she owed the world nothing, but that it owed her a lot. She insulted and estranged most people with whom she came in contact. She was sure her mother was responsible for her illness.

Physical examination. Findings were unimportant except for the cardiac condition.

From this history it seemed likely that the psychic component in the patient's illness was of importance, and bore a relationship to her illness. This relationship was clarified in the course of six subsequent interviews (this patient was not accepted for treatment because her

---

* When the patient's father married "the other woman."

† Except for periods of fatigue, sense of depression with difficulty in breathing and a tendency to palpitation.

illness was so far advanced and her emotional reactions so violent),
and may be summarized as follows:

Preparation for illness and its course—Physiological. No definite physiological preparation for illness was discovered, either hereditary or acquired,
unless the mother's rheumatism can be so considered. The patient was not
at all sure that her mother actually suffered from this. Her own cardiac
diagnosis is with the notation "cause unknown."

Preparation for illness and its course—Psychological. The psychological
preparation for illness was definite. The patient was unwanted, neglected and
cruelly treated from infancy to the age of 18 years. Other factors will be
brought out subsequently. In discussion (first visit to psychiatric clinic
May 11, 1934) of the onset of her illness after the loss of her job in April
1932, she said: "I had the same feeling I had during the breakdown at college, my body wouldn't obey me any more." Associating along this line, the
patient suddenly "talked freely for the first time in my life," expressing a
great deal of resentment toward her parents, especially her mother, and confessed to having lied in giving her history previously, because "her parents
ought to be dead."

"The first thing I ever heard my mother say was when I was wheeled in
a baby carriage into the room where she was fighting with my father, and
she screamed out: 'Take that brat away. I hate it! I hate it!' " The patient
insisted that she was always nagged by everybody and that she had tried to
love her mother and her mother was not worth it. Her mother had made her
father's life miserable by having hysterical attacks so he finally had had to
leave her. The patient had wanted to go with her father to keep house for
him, but he had become interested in another woman. The patient had not
seen her father for ten years although she occasionally heard about him indirectly.

Following this conference the patient found herself able to work and
sleep, for the first time since her discharge from the hospital, fifteen months
previously. However, she developed hives. She woke up in the middle of the
night feeling that she was burning up. She "hated her body for causing her
so much trouble." But she suddenly hated people very much less. She reported
a dream in which she saw her mother in hell burning in a fiery furnace and
she herself was throwing in coal. "I saw her skin come up into blisters." This
patient was not seen again until August 8. She came in with sore throat and
pain in ankles and wrists, having nearly had another breakdown. According
to her statement this was preceded by the discovery that a man who had been
a father to her, and her only friend since her separation from her parents, had
gone off with another woman "just like father."

The patient had been seen on this occasion at her own urgent request, it having been decided during the first interview after discharge that owing to her age and the seriousness of her organic condition as well as the deep-lying neurosis that she should not be accepted for clinic treatment.

She was not seen again until two months later (physician having been on vacation from the hospital) when she said: "Life is just a progressive disgust with oneself and being born. It's too awful to go on living when your body can't mind you. I am getting more and more like Mother. She used to get breathless and faint, and now I am doing the same thing. I get so mad at living I'd like to die. I can't tell you how I resent being born. The end of October is my mother's birthday. I am always sick in the fall—September, October, and November—because I think of Mother and of being born. She might have spared me that."

Attacks were precipitated during interviews when the patient discussed her mother, particularly her fear of becoming like her. She complained constantly of her fear of becoming like her mother. She particularly hated herself for her attacks of dyspnea because her mother during her hysterical episodes would turn blue with rage, hold her breath, sometimes to the point of becoming unconscious. A related theme was her feeling of having been smothered at home and her personality crushed, in relation to which she reported "fantasies of being whirled through space so that she couldn't catch her breath at all" and her constant wish that she had never drawn her first breath.

This information was taken in conjunction with the fact that attacks were precipitated during interviews discussing her mother, particularly her association between the psychic and physiological components in her illness and that the former (like the latter, as already shown in the medical examination) was of considerable magnitude. There was the additional fact that her attacks were colored by her memory of her mother's hysterical attacks. Further confirmation was given by this patient's subsequent history.

Although the patient became more co-operative after discussion of these things it soon became obvious that her resentment was so deep-lying that psychotherapy of a deep nature was contraindicated because of the strain it would be likely to impose on an already seriously damaged heart. Even the general discussion had been a serious strain on her heart. For this and other reasons it was decided that she should see a psychiatrist only when she felt it essential to do so. (A technical problem became moderation of her outbursts of rage because these in themselves, quite apart from psychotherapy, regularly resulted in an exacerbation of her condition.) In a subsequent interview she said: "I get so mad at living I'd like to die. I can't tell you how I resent being born." *General experience indicates that had psychotherapy been initiated before her heart had been so severely damaged much might have been done to relieve cardiac strain, diminish invalidism, and retard the progress of her disease. In judging whether or not psychotherapy is justified, and also in determining whether psychotherapy should be superficial or radical, it is important to evaluate both the degree of damage present and the severity of the vegetative response to discussion of emotional situations.*

The patient became interested in a sick girl (who had had an illegal abortion). She both nursed and took general care of her. She said: "It was funny, I could go up and down stairs when I was waiting on her without getting out of breath at all. I showed her what a mother ought to be." Then the girl got well and the patient collapsed within a few days and was admitted as an emergency to the ward. She talked a good deal about how she could get even with her parents. Five weeks later she was admitted to the hospital in another period of decompensation and succeeded in dying on her own birthday (page 45).

The following abstract from the medical discharge note is of interest:

Three years ago this patient was admitted for the first time with congestive failure and auricular fibrillation. Second admission, two months ago, again with congestive failure. The patient was discharged five weeks ago, ambulatory. A few days after discharge she began to have signs of increasing decompensation and she returned with orthopnea and massive edema.

Examination at this time revealed orthopnea without cyanosis and pitting edema of sacrum and ankle. The head was negative. The thyroid showed nodular enlargement. The lungs showed congestion at the bases. The heart was enlarged to left and right; the rhythm irregular; there was a loud blowing apical systolic murmur. Abdominal examination showed the liver down 7 cm.; and examination of the extremities, massive edema. The temperature was 100° F.; pulse 100; respiration 22; and blood pressure 130/90.

Laboratory findings were: Hemoglobin 110; red blood count 5,930,000; white blood count 17,200; polys. 80; sedimentation rate 5; urine, albumin 3 plus; stool negative; blood culture sterile; gall bladder series normal; electrocardiogram, auricular fibrillation, right preponderance. Film of the chest showed pleural fluid at both sides.

During the first ten weeks in the hospital the patient showed no improvement despite large doses of digitalis. She had a fever sometimes as high as 103° F. which we thought might have been due to rheumatic activity. She was finally put in an oxygen tent, and the immediate improvement was amazing. The temperature dropped to normal; the heart rate slowed and the edema began to disappear. The subjective improvement was also striking.

At this point we contemplated total thyroidectomy. However, we decided to do a thoracentesis preparatory to operation. Following this procedure she had a pneumothorax. The oxygen concentration in the test was increased and she improved for a couple of days and then died suddenly.

If the course be compared with the history, that is, if the somatic and psychic pictures be superimposed, it becomes particularly significant: that the patient "improved for a couple of days but then died suddenly" for no obvious reason, but she died on the day on which she had stated that she wished to die, the day on which she had been subjected to the "indignity of birth."

Abstract of the final diagnosis was: Inactive rheumatic heart disease; chronic auricular fibrillation; mitral stenosis and insufficiency; cardiac insufficiency; left pneumothorax, traumatic.

PSYCHOSOMATIC PICTURE, INADEQUATE IN SPITE OF REVIEW,
REORGANIZATION, AND RE-EVALUATION OF THE
ROUTINE MEDICAL HISTORY

The following history, in which the relationship of psychic and somatic factors is not clear although taken in the same way as in the preceding history, will be given as organized:

Case No. CA 318. The second admission of an 18-year-old colored girl, who complained of a rapid heart rate for the past twenty-four hours.

Physical status (early). The patient was admitted September 27, 1935, because of exceedingly rapid heart rate and shortness of breath for the preceding week. She was treated with digitalis, and was soon able to be up the pulse rate having returned to normal. She was discharged on October 4, 1935, since it was considered that she had paroxysmal auricular tachycardia without underlying pathology.

Physical status (present). After leaving the hospital the patient had several short attacks. The present attack started on the day before admission. She gives the impression of being mildly annoyed at this rapid beating of her heart, as if it were an annoyance she would gladly get rid of, but which does not seem to occasion her any marked anxiety at present. At least, she does not give evidence of being anxious. She has never been sick before, except for a few colds with fever.

Family adjustment (early). The patient is the third of eight siblings, two older sisters are in this country. The patient was born in the Virgin Islands, where her father and mother and four younger sisters and brothers remain.

The father is now 62 years old and disabled by rheumatism. The patient has not seen him for five years. One sister, who was three years older than the patient, died there of pneumonia two years ago. Of the four younger children the eldest is a brother, and there are three sisters, the youngest of whom is 3 years old. (The patient thinks that there is one 3 years old.) In the home setting the father was extremely strict, and often hit the children if they did not do what he wanted. "We had to go straight and come straight. We went to church three times on Sundays, and had to come straight home. Father didn't believe in our going out, but they say that he's changed since my sister died."

Family adjustment (present). The patient gets along well with one of the sisters in this country. She came here at the age of 15, and was glad to get away from the severity of the father's upbringing although she stated that it never really bothered her—he had his reasons.

Vocational adjustment. The patient came to the United States because she thought that she could earn more money, and send it back to her family. She had done very hard housework, involving scrubbing floors, washing windows, and heavy washing and ironing. She held that job for about one year, and wonders why she stayed so long. Her second job had to do with the care of an apartment and two small children, where she was kept busy all day. She says that she would rather do some other kind of work than housework. Her employers have been very strict, keeping after her constantly. She feels that it has been too hard for her, and in view of her present illness, she considers doing something in a factory "with her hands, sitting down."

Social adjustment (early). The patient has had very little social life. She had no friends at home, and was never allowed to have boy friends.

Social adjustment (present). Her work has kept her confined during the evening, as her employer went out every night. She used to go out occasionally, but since she could not go every time the boy wanted her to, "he left me flat."

Sexual adjustment. Further details with regard to the patient's sexual life were not obtained during the first interview.

Personality and insight. The patient is an agreeable, mild appearing, and attractive girl who insists constantly that she "doesn't want to give any trouble." She says "other people holler at the nurses, but I wouldn't do that sort of thing. I would never talk back." Although there are evidences in her history of a difficult early family situation she insists that these things never bothered her. She learned from her father never to get angry and she never has been angry. This is a great help to her in connection with her job where her employer is strict and checks up on her activities. Even the problem created by the working conditions which make it impossible for her to see her friends, or to be with boys, she says does not really bother her. After all she is "only nineteen and there will be time later on." This patient was a model patient on the ward and no emotional problem was felt to be present.

From this history it would seem:

(1) That this patient had been well adjusted in the spheres in which her life situation demanded adjustment; that although she might possibly have been given common sense advice or help regarding changing her job or going out more frequently, there was nothing on the surface to indicate that the psychic component had any very important relationship to her illness. The social worker's note confirmed this impression: "This patient is a pleasant, rather placid looking girl who has a certain maturity beyond her years. She seems to have few interests outside her job, but is anxious to continue living here. She thinks there is nothing for her to do at her home in the Virgin Islands, that there is no work available there, and is happy in having made the change."

(2) There was no history of exposure to illness of the type from which the patient was suffering except for her father's rheumatism, but this seemed to have made no very great impression on her, possibly as it developed after the last time that she saw him.

(3) There was not a long history of previous illnesses.

(4) The present illness showed no close correlation with any specific event in her life.

(5) There was only a slight suggestion that the symptoms might have been serving to provide the patient with an excuse to change her job, but this point was something about which she had thought in common sense terms anyway.

(6) The most striking thing in this patient's history was her lack of insight concerning her own feelings and her failure to blame her illness on overwork or any kind of personal difficulties. Her apparently good adjustment was on the basis of "never being angry, taking what comes, and making the best of it, being pleasant and agreeable." (For further observations concerning this patient see page 52.)

On the basis of these histories it is clear that even if the physician, through careful drawing out, is successful in obtaining an impression of the patient's preparation for illness in terms of undermining by important conflicts in the necessary spheres of adjustment, physical, family, social (economic), sexual, vocational, in addition to the usual information concerning heredity and exposure to attacks of specific illnesses in parents or friends, this is not sufficient. As has been noted, it is not conscious worries most directly related to somatic symptomatology that are the most likely to find expression by way of the somatic short circuit, but conflicts of which the patient himself is not conscious.

Hence, even if the history is adequate in its focus and scope, the necessary information frequently *cannot be obtained by the usual questionnaire method* supplemented by the routine forms of medical and psychiatric observation. In such situations clues may be obtained concerning difficulties about which the patient cannot tell the physician, somewhat as one may obtain clues by abdominal palpation concerning functioning, of which the patient himself is unaware.

III. Manner of Obtaining History—Spontaneous Statements and Their Evaluation in Diagnosis and Prognosis

It seemed necessary in order to obviate or correct the distortions introduced by the questionnaire type of history to give systematic attention to a procedure and type of observation familiar to most physicians, but not given sufficient attention by them usually because they are unaware of its importance. As all physicians realize, the patient does not know what is or is not important to tell the doctor, and often has not observed or has forgotten points of fundamental diagnostic importance.* Relative to the psychic component in illness, the patient is likely to have, in addition, conscious or unconscious reasons for wanting to omit or forget certain things; or, on the other hand, to give the answer that he thinks the physician hopes for, or that he thinks will make him stand well in the physician's eyes. Hence the fewer the direct questions and the more spontaneous the patient's story, the better, both from the point of view of content and from the point of view of the opportunity to observe the patient's habitual patterns of reaction.

---

* Not least among the problems here is the fact, as Manley Hudson said, that emotions are attached to words (specific sensations and events), not to ideas.

EVALUATION OF ATTITUDE AND INCONSISTENCIES

An effort was made, then, to encourage the patient to talk casually about his illness, himself, his family, his work, his friends, and amusements, before any definite questions were asked. (For further discussion see Chassell,[80] Menninger.[302]) Special attention was devoted to the subjects concerning which he was the least voluble, but also occasionally those concerning which he was disarmingly glib. Where the patient did not respond well to this approach such conversation was encouraged in the course of the usual medical history. This procedure in itself supplied clues of great diagnostic importance (see case histories, Chapters X and XI).

When the patient made statements which in some way contradicted the information given in previous histories, or his own earlier statements, his attention was called to this by way of determining whether the physician or the patient's amnesias were responsible or whether the misstatements resulted from an unwillingness to give the information originally asked because of its painful associations, as for example in the Case No. HP 1 (page 40). It is to be remembered that Sherrington wrote, "Pain is the psychical adjunct of a protective reflex." In other words, an attempt was made to ascertain, on the one hand, whether such contradictions or omissions had their *origin primarily in physician or patient;* and, on the other hand, their significance in terms of the patient's illness. It is obvious for example from the case of the spinster with cardiac damage (No. HP 1) that her misstatements concerning her parents should have been corrected at the time of her first admission to the hospital, or better by the physicians who saw her when her symptoms first developed, before so much organic damage had taken place that little therapeutic use could be made of the material.

The patient's "will to get well" and its reverse was studied. This is revealed in his attitude toward the hospital, toward his present and past illness and toward invalidism; in his reaction to the psychological changes present, the effects of the illness on his life, and the importance of "secondary illness gain," such as compensation. The absence of the will to get well was of course an important factor in patient No. HP 1, both in influencing the decision as to whether or not psychotherapy was indicated in connection with her medical treatment, and in determining the outcome of the illness.

SYMPTOMS WITH A "PURPOSE" AND HYDRA-HEADED ILLNESS

Patients who were most recalcitrant to treatment and who had paradoxical reactions to drugs were often those whose symptoms served a somewhat concrete purpose. To Mr. Healy, M.P. (1885), is ascribed the statement that Lord Hartington and Mr. Gladstone had "diplomatic colds" when they pleaded indisposition as an excuse for not giving addresses at public meetings where they had been announced as speakers (both gentlemen were said to be much better on the day after the meetings).

Some symptoms are readily understood in some such terms as these. Unless they are so understood the patient is sometimes harmed rather than helped by their removal. Jelliffe [251] reviews a number of such cases under the suggestive title "What price healing?," and sev- eral illustrations of shifting symptoms will be given here. Every physician has had experience with the patient who, as soon as one pain or spastic disorder is removed, returns with another and then another; or with the patient who has had almost every removable organ removed, and then demands one laparotomy after another for the removal of adhesions (Dunbar,[149] Chapter XVI). Unless such patients are relieved of their need for symptoms, the best care in the world for each symptom as it presents itself cannot stay them or divert them from their path of illness and invalidism, and may actu- ally hasten them along their way toward complete incapacitation. Their illness like the hydra is a single entity, but such treatment of its somatic manifestations is no more effective than cutting off one hydra-head after another.

It is important to note, however, that the significance of the ap- parent concrete purpose of the symptoms can be evaluated only in terms of the total personality structure. This point is well illustrated by a case (No. S 1) of a girl with severe generalized urticaria.[406]

This skin lesion developed shortly after the patient had taken aspirin, and was therefore thought to be related to this drug. After all other possible somatic factors had been excluded, it failed to clear up with the usual therapy including adrenalin and calcium. There was no allergic history, and physical examination including all the usual skin tests was negative. After the lesion had persisted for three weeks a psychiatric consultation was requested.

It developed that the patient, who had been very strictly brought up, was carrying on a clandestine affair with a man who beat her. On the day she had taken the aspirin he had visited her in an apartment to which she had just moved where she was known to other tenants. The rooms had very thin walls. The man, after having intercourse with her, had whipped her, beginning in his customary playful manner of wrestling and dragging her around by the wrists. She said: "He hit me harder than ever before. I decided I just couldn't put up with it any more. I was sure the people in the house could hear the sounds of the belt. I was awfully upset and told him he could never do this again. He is so funny though; he won't stop till he sees welts on my body. He always says he loves to see the welts. I get humiliated by this and yet he has threatened to leave me unless he can beat me. Besides, I like him and he is so nice in other ways." She then added: "He hasn't beaten me since because of this awful urticaria. I am all covered with welts anyway. He likes to see them. And I haven't had to give him up."

Now it is obvious that the urticaria well served the purpose of enabling this patient to avoid beatings and at the same time to keep her lover. The urticaria cleared up as soon as this became clear to her, that is, after the first interview with the psychiatrist, which had lasted about an hour. She, and the medical staff, were so much surprised by this outcome, however, that she insisted on taking large doses of aspirin, "Just to see what would happen." The urticaria failed to reappear. This, of course, from the point of view of the skin specialist is a perfect and convincing result: the somatic symptoms with which she came had been relieved. The psychiatrist, however, having discovered the extreme passive masochistic personality structure of this girl realized that her illness had not been cured with the removal of the skin lesion. She was clearly the type of patient who, under pressure, would readily develop fresh symptoms. The hydra had been only partially decapitated—not cured. One can scarcely stress this point sufficiently, and only long experience with the medical histories of such patients will convince hospital and community of the preventive significance of psychotherapy, that is, treatment that really goes to the root of the illness and so obviates the development of further symptoms.[152, 153]

EVIDENCE FROM DREAMS

We found that the evidence given by dreams as to the presence or absence of anxiety was useful when evaluated in relation to the degree of anxiety manifested. Other divergencies between dream material and the patient's statements, such for example, as marked hostility in the dreams of patients who state they are never angry, were noted.[153] This technique was used in the case of patient No. CA 318 whose history has already been given (page 47) and may be summarized here as follows:

A pleasant, placid-looking, unmarried girl, aged 19, with paroxysmal tachycardia, dyspnea, and on the second admission some signs of congestive heart failure, was admitted to the medical ward twice in quick succession. No reason was found to account for this condition, but a psychiatric problem was not suspected. In the course of routine investigation we discovered that the father was strict, often beating his children; requiring them to go to church three times on Sunday, and never allowing them to go out after 3 P.M.: "We had to go straight and come straight."

This patient, after coming to this country, went to work for a woman whose attitudes and principles were strikingly the same as the father's. The patient spoke of all this gently with apparent great understanding, insisting that it never upset her because she had been used to it all her life. In the hospital she was very co-operative, saying that she did not want to give any trouble. She began to have what she called "funny dreams" of knocking over the vase of flowers by her bedside, of hurling things and smashing them. When it was suggested later that she might have some pent-up feelings of anger and resentment she became amused at the idea, then said with sudden vehemence: "If I ever let it out I wouldn't know who to begin on." She gave vent to her anger at some length, abusing her employer, the attending physician, with whom she had been on the best possible terms, and so on. After this her heart quieted down. She said: "I never knew before that I could be that kind of person. Perhaps that was what was wrong with me."

Case No. CAP 6. A 40-year-old divorced woman, with palpitation and attacks of dyspnea, spoke very kindly of her mother to whom she was devoted, but in her dreams the mother was a threatening figure and the onset of her illness was ushered in by a dream of her mother as a huge black bear about to crush her. The patient woke from this dream being sure that something was going to happen to her, but it was not until her treatment was somewhat advanced that she realized consciously the feelings of fear and hostility she had kept pent-up. As she became able to face this fact there was a marked improvement in her dizziness and palpitation (this of course does not mean that her cure was as easy as that but simply that this factor was ascertained to have a direct relationship to her symptoms).

EVALUATION OF PSYCHOSOMATIC REACTION PATTERNS

Action Versus Thought and Fantasy. One factor in the type of somatic disorder developed seems to be the degree to which the patient tends to express his conflicts in action, on the one hand; or in thinking, philosophizing, and creating fantasies, on the other. In either case, of course, the prominent pattern may be an attempt to meet the situation, to escape from it, or an oscillation between the two.

In another connection attention has been called to the prominence of the acting-out tendency in patients who are accident-prone.[153] These patients tend to escape from their emotional conflicts into action, or to express their aggression in impulsive behavior resulting in injury sometimes to others and usually to themselves. Fear and resentment are pent up and conflicts are managed psychosomatically in different ways by patients with cardiovascular disease.

Sherrington's [879] analysis of the mind as essentially subserving an inhibitory function in relation to behavior is of interest in this connection because it means something to the general physician as an introduction to the additional comments the psychiatrist would make concerning the psychodynamics involved. Sherrington notes that the greatest relief of instinctual tension is provided by action, the least by fantasy and thought, whereas speech stands half way between. If tension is expressed directly in action, the action is likely to be ill considered and to create situations injurious to the patient (page 197). If, on the other hand, action is inhibited or entered upon only after considerable thought and the suppression of emotion, the development of particular types of psychic or somatic symptomatology or both is favored.

Degree and Type of the Patient's Muscle Tension. The degree and type of the patient's muscle tension, his postural attitude, voice, gestures, and particularly their variations in relation to specific material under discussion were found to be revealing, although considerable experience is required to enable the physician to evaluate these traits correctly. They bear a definite relation to a tendency to action, on the one hand, and to fantasy, on the other. As Freud, Reich, and some others have pointed out, the musculature represents a sort of characterological armor; hence it should be of special interest to all students of psychosomatic problems. Muscle tension is a real psychosomatic borderline, a borderline between instinct and outer world, restraining aggressive action toward the latter and binding vegetative energy. Attention has been called elsewhere to the welling up of emotion that often comes when a patient is asked to relax.[140, 425]

All patients are not tense in the same way. Some patients who are tense show this in an appearance of stiffness, jerky movements, or a high strident voice; whereas others give no obvious evidence of tension so that one is surprised to discover in the course of physical examination how tense they really are. The former are usually called jumpy, nervous, hysterical, while the latter often escape notice entirely from this point of view. Among the former are those who tend to act out their conflicts in one way or another, and get considerable satisfaction from the attention paid to their symptoms. Sometimes they actually get themselves injured and sometimes they merely get sympathy for being such highly strung individuals. In general patients with certain symptom neuroses, allergies, and those who tend to have accidents, belong to this group. In some disorders localized spasms are prominent.

Patients with hypertension, gastro-intestinal disease, or some other smooth muscle spasm, on the other hand, are likely to have a generalized tension which often escapes notice because of their appearance of quiet control. Patients in this group, furthermore, tend to give great attention to correct external behavior, and unless there is a marked accompanying symptom neurosis they usually dislike too much attention to their symptoms, and tend to go on in spite of them. They are likely to deny that they are nervous. This seems to be in part because these patients are universally afraid of their aggressive impulses. As already noted they are outstanding for the degree of their repressed or pent-up hostility. Hence they are usually considerate of others and are loath to arouse criticism of any kind so that they try to conceal their tenseness itself. The question arises as to whether the necessity of subjecting to special control the manifestations even of their tension, which itself is serving the purpose of keeping aggressive thoughts and actions in repression, may not have something to do with the development of smooth muscle spasm. The tension seems to be driven inward to involve also the vascular or gastro-intestinal systems. In any case, as patients are relieved psychotherapeutically of their symptoms we often see the process taking place in a reverse direction.

Patients with hypertension, for example, as they lose their symptoms, are likely to show an increased nervousness and jerkiness, and often say, "I don't know what makes me feel so funny. I don't know what I might do." These patients may become quarrelsome, show a tendency to get into fights or to have accidents, but in the end they show a poise and general ease involving a change in their breathing also, which is so striking that they themselves or their friends are likely to comment on it, usually in some such words as "why, you look years younger." [140, 425]

The nature of patients' tension is quite as significant for the somatic disorder as is quantitative predominance of specific trends and their expression through symbolically appropriate somatic channels.

The Symptom Pattern.   Special note was made of the degree and nature of *organization of the patient's symptoms*, psychic on the one hand, and somatic on the other, as a basis for judging the relationship between them. With reference to *somatic symptomatology*:

(a) Does the history show a long series of previous illnesses in which disturbances in muscle tonus and secretion or circulation are prominent, such as colitis, hypertension, muscle spasm, gall bladder disease and so on? (Page 11.)

(b) Are the disturbances of secretion or muscle tension out of proportion to the other symptomatology, or the obvious somatic factor in a case?

(c) Are several systems involved simultaneously; for example, does the hypertensive patient suffer, as is so frequently the case, from chronic constipation also, and from general increased muscle tonus?

There is evidence that with such symptomatology one may suspect an emotional etiology, that is, discharge of emotional conflicts by way of the somatic short circuit rather than, or in addition to, a local response of tissue to injury.

The evaluation of *psychic symptomatology* is a matter for the psychiatric consultant. It seemed important, however, for the physician taking the medical history for any given patient, to obtain an impression of the prominence of fantasy and of action in relation to his conflict; that is:

Does the patient give evidence of anxiety or active fantasy?

Does he report elaborate dreams, nightmares, compulsions, phobias?

Is he relatively inarticulate, casual, and reticent about his personal problems, appearing to be a "man of action rather than of thought?"

It should be noted that this superficial clinical impression is often incorrect, as recent Rorschach checking of the material makes clear (page 673). *The psychic factor may be of equal importance to the illness in any of these cases,* a fact which is readily overlooked. It is given different somatic expression, however, in the one as compared with the other. For example:

On the basis of our material then, it appeared that at least one factor in the personality which predisposes to accident is this tendency to solve the conflict between repressive authoritarian pressures and individual spontaneity by striving for satisfactions and security outside of the authoritarian hierarchy. By focusing their values on immediate concrete experience and by avoiding any marked submission or domination in vocational and social roles, they usually managed to minimize or avoid serious conflicts with authority. When thwarted, deprived, or subjected to some strain such as unemployment or a mother-in-law living in the family, patients who developed "accident proneness" had the tendency to *do something* either to modify the situation or to get away from it instead of just keeping their anger bottled up and boiling inside. As children, if they had been angry with their parents or felt neglected, they had run away from home or arranged an elaborate revenge, or they had found some way to get at all costs (including lying and stealing and later occasionally even killing) the thing of which they had been deprived, or at least a substitute for it. They had the habit of escaping from emotional conflict into action. Patients with coronary disease, on the other hand, under similar circumstances would sulk or become ultra gentle and considerate, turning to philosophy or trying to repay injury with kindness, and develop sensitive consciences.

In this tendency of fracture patients lies the basis for the further observation that these patients are relatively inarticulate, characterized by action rather than thought and brooding, which probably has a bearing on the fact that there seem to be few full-fledged psychoneurotics among them, and many eccentric characters. Furthermore, unlike asthma and hay-fever patients, whom they resemble in the tendency to act out, they report few dreams. Many of them show a marked inability to bear severe pain and the men particularly are likely to make the following statement: "You see, doctor, my nerve is in action—driving a car and taking risks. But when I have to stay still in one place I haven't any nerve at all." Sherrington's analysis of the mind as essentially subserving an inhibitory function in relation to behavior is of interest in this connection. This formula which is so suggestive for the clinician is useful but needs further definition and refinement (page 673ff.).

IV. COMMENT ON PROCEDURE WITH CASE ILLUSTRATIONS

The type of history to be presented can be obtained, after a little practice, in from fifteen minutes to two hours. It can be obtained in conjunction with the usual medical history with little or no additional time expenditure. With the psychiatric consultation, as in our research, it seemed best obtained in the spirit of conversation plus rechecking of certain material in medical history. This latter was found to be especially useful if the patient was reticent. An example of such a conversational interview follows (Case No. C 363, see below).

In connection with the recording of the interview it should be noted that although major points were written down at the time, the remainder was filled in from memory immediately afterward. This was the procedure of choice with most members of the research group, but occasionally as a basis for analysis a full record was made during the interview. The interview to follow is of the latter type, and I think it will be clear that the remarks of both patient and physician were somewhat less spontaneous and that the casualness of the patient was to a considerable degree interfered with by this procedure.

PRELIMINARY CONVERSATIONAL INTERVIEW *

Case No. H 363. A married woman, 32 years old, was admitted to the hospital for the first time with hypertension of nine years' duration. She complained of attacks of headaches, dizziness, nausea, vomiting, and sleeplessness. She was of linear build with dark hair.

The patient was seen on the ward and because she was ambulatory she was asked to walk with the physician to the psychiatric office just off the ward. She leaned on the physician's shoulder, grabbed the physician and said she was up and about now but planned to see if it would bring on an attack, because when she was in bed, resting, she did not have any attacks and perhaps the walk down would start one. She hoped so because she wanted the doctors to see what the trouble was.

Her face showed lines on each side of the mouth, and as she talked she

* Interview by A. Louise Brush.

continually kicked her knee back and forth. She had a somewhat marked generalized tension. She held her hands together and at times chewed her fingers.

First Interview Lasting About One Hour

DOCTOR: We wanted to be sure we have a clear picture of what led up to your illness. In the first place we would like to know something about your past health, your childhood illnesses and illnesses later on.

PATIENT: When I was a young lady I was not ill at all. I had a slight case of measles as a child and then every winter had bronchitis. As far as I can remember that is all the illness I had. I was a thin child, a poor eater too, I know that. (Stops talking.)

DOCTOR: How was that?

PATIENT: I don't know. My mother always had trouble making me eat. I never used to like butter, it made me sick. I had a violent distaste for it. (She stops.)

DOCTOR: Any unpleasant associations with it?

PATIENT: Mother tried to give it to me. She would sneak it to me under some cream cheese or something but I would always detect it and stop eating it. (Stops talking.)

DOCTOR: Did any other food make you sick?

PATIENT: Only when I smell food and I get my spells, I can't eat, I vomit. (Stops talking.)

DOCTOR: How about coffee and tea?

PATIENT: I like coffee. Since I know my condition I have cut down on it.

DOCTOR: What did you use to take?

PATIENT: Only two cups, now I have cut down on that. I was surprised when they gave it to me here. They told me to keep away from it as much as possible.

DOCTOR: Tea?

PATIENT: We don't have tea.

DOCTOR: Smoking?

PATIENT: No, I never smoke. I never ran around. I am not that type. (Stops talking.)

DOCTOR: What did you do?

PATIENT: I used to work as a girl, took care of my mother, took care of my family and was mother to them when my mother passed away. (Slows down and stops.)

DOCTOR: Had your hands full?

PATIENT: Yes, that was quite a job. 'Til my Dad married again. (Stops talking.)

DOCTOR: How old were you when your mother died?

PATIENT: I was 13. Mother always had a headache. I never knew that she had blood pressure. I didn't know that was the matter with her. Except that she had symptoms. I can tell it is like mine. She got up in the morning with a severe headache. I am very much like her. We never give in to anything. One day she got paralyzed on one side. She didn't try to lift her right arm—she couldn't have—but lifted her left arm. She was only 39 years old. From all the symptoms she seems to have had what I have. (Stops talking.)

DOCTOR: Of course, the treatment is different now.

PATIENT: No, I am not worried about myself, if that is what you mean. (She moves her foot back and forth rather tensely as she talks at this time.) She was too far gone, just waited until she got that stroke and then— (Patient stops talking again and there are tears in her eyes.)

DOCTOR: When did your trouble start?

PATIENT: Right after she died. I had headaches and overworked but I guess it really started after I was married.

DOCTOR: How about your father?

PATIENT: My father is all right. He is 61. He is pretty well. I hope I feel like that when I am 60, youthful and spry. He takes care of my kiddies better than anyone else can do it. He was very good to us children all the time. (Stops talking.)

DOCTOR: What about your brothers and sisters?

PATIENT: I have two. One died when very young. He got a cold coming over on the boat. I have a brother and two sisters beside myself. We were four.

DOCTOR: How old?

PATIENT: My brother is 36.

DOCTOR: What is he doing?

PATIENT: He still works in the millinery line when there is any work. It is seasonal. Positions are somewhat that way with everything now. (Patient stops.)

DOCTOR: What about your sisters?

PATIENT: One seems perfectly all right. One is very sensitive to a lot of things. She is the weaker of the two—allergic. Has hay fever. I am not allergic to anything. I don't catch cold either.

DOCTOR: How old are they?

PATIENT: I am 32. I am trying to figure out how old they are. One is 22 and one is 28. I am not really sure of their ages.

DOCTOR: What do they do?

PATIENT: Office work.

DOCTOR: Are they married?

PATIENT: No.

(*Note:* Following the same technique, negative responses were obtained concerning serious illnesses in the patient or her family: diabetes, broken bones, injuries, operations, rheumatism, other heart trouble, etc.)

DOCTOR: Are there any other sicknesses that you think of that anyone has had?

PATIENT: My sister has hay fever. My brother since he was a young man generally has a little nervous tick in his eye and in his shoulder. I have been after him for a year to do something about it but he won't. He says I am the one to do that. That is the way they are.

DOCTOR: Does that worry you?

PATIENT: Well in a way. He says, "Worry about yourself." You see I had charge of them. Quite a lot of responsibility after my mother died. When I had gained a little weight (I was about 100 and went up to 120 lbs.) I didn't mind it. Maybe it was because I was pregnant. I don't know what had to do with it at that time. (Stops talking.)

DOCTOR: How about your stepmother?

PATIENT: I think I was about 17 at the time father married. (Stops talking.)

DOCTOR: Less responsibility?

PATIENT: The only reason my dad did marry was because of responsibility. These things never bothered the boys. Maybe I did have too much responsibility. I made my sisters finish high school, but I didn't.

DOCTOR: Like your stepmother?

PATIENT: (Expresses uncertainty more in her movements than in her voice.) In a way. (Sounds doubtful.) She was nice to me in later years. As good as she could be I guess. (Stops talking.)

DOCTOR: After you have been head of the house. . . . I suppose . . . ?

PATIENT: (Picks up unfinished question.) *I had to step out.* There were plenty of little nuisances. Since I have been married she has been very nice. She took care of me in bed for eight weeks. Makes you wonder—maybe you are to blame.

DOCTOR: What was your mother like?

PATIENT: A very nice woman—nice looking. *I didn't do her justice.* (Laughs.) She helped my dad in the store and everything. You see four years before she passed away they had an epidemic of influenza and she was weak. Had severe headaches all the time. I always thought the flu left her with some weakness, 1918, I nursed her, but I didn't get it. You know about it. I stopped school and was home two months. They sent my work in and I passed everything for school. I was very ambitious—only 11 years old then. (She stops.)

DOCTOR: You must have been pretty smart.

PATIENT: Maybe, I don't know—(Tears which have been threatening begin to trickle out of patient's eyes.)

DOCTOR: How old were you when you started school?

PATIENT: The regular age—about 6, I started. *I was never left back, I skipped.* (Stops talking.)

DOCTOR: What did you want to do?

PATIENT: *Teach. My children are very bright.* (The tears continue.)

DOCTOR: What makes you feel bad?

PATIENT: I always feel bad when I think about my mother.

DOCTOR: Why?

PATIENT: I was always very close to her. She treated me as a pal. We used to go out together. (Patient cries more.) I try not to think of it. I try to keep it back.

DOCTOR: It might be better if you let it out.

PATIENT: Since I have been married I have kept busy. I sometimes think of her when I take care of the children. *I dreamed of her quite a little after she died.*

DOCTOR: What sort of dreams?

PATIENT: I dreamed a year later that she was alive. That she came and talked to me and said, "you called for me and I came." She looked well generally but sometimes she was in a wheel chair. I was pleased that at least she was in a wheel chair and we had her still with us.

DOCTOR: It must have been a very big shock.

PATIENT: She was a very devoted mother.

DOCTOR: Any other dreams? About your mother?

PATIENT: No.

DOCTOR: Any other kinds of dreams?

PATIENT: When I was sick I dreamed—terrible dreams. Dreams about my husband. That he had committed a crime. He was about to be executed.

I pleaded with the judge that he was a good husband and a father. *I just felt my heart pounding in the dream.* I pleaded with the court. There was *just one minute left to go.* They were taking him out of the cell. I had given them such a good plea that they took him out after all and let him off. That was the only dream I had when I was sick.

DOCTOR: Did you wake up after that?

PATIENT: Yes.

DOCTOR: How did you feel?

PATIENT: I had a headache and my heart was racing.

DOCTOR: Did you feel better or worse?

PATIENT: Yes, I was feeling worse. Quite a few years ago I dreamt something that wasn't true. My husband had a little car. I wouldn't want this (dream) to ever come true. This one did. He told me he was going to sell the car. I told him that I dreamt that the man took the car and wouldn't give him the money and that he had to have a fight with him. He was using the car to go to New York and they did have a real fight about it. He said I had good judgment. He abides by my decision. We get along. When I was married we had to live with my *mother-in-law* for three years. *Now you will get all the dirt.* I was a very quiet girl. I became pregnant while I was there. I never let on to my husband. *I kept everything in.* I used their family doctor. He said my pressure was going up. I said I was fine. I felt fine. I wanted to know what was the matter. This doctor said to me—"Must you live with your mother-in-law?" He said, "Oh, if you could only get a room for yourself. I know your mother-in-law and she is very neurotic." He said "I would like to speak to your husband." I said, "Oh, no." I didn't want him to think I was complaining to the doctor. Finally he did or my husband guessed it and we got out. We had quite a time trying to get out of there. She wanted to hang on to her son. She is more of a selfish type of person, has a habit to interfering with her children. She was very strong willed and she didn't listen. Her own daughters know what type of girl I was. *I made her go out and I'd stay in.* She appreciated that. My little girl was about 2 and my mother-in-law wouldn't look out for her and I took her with my sister-in-law to buy a dress. When I came back I found my husband sitting there all blown up. "Why did you have to take the baby down town?" She had gotten him all excited. My sister said, "I never realized until today that you have a real mother-in-law." *She used to steam up all of her children one against the other*—just that type. (Patient gave one or two more details which were not written down as she was talking so fast.) *She is a very sick woman—has heart trouble.* That is why I didn't tell you—she is not in our family. Otherwise, I haven't been upset by any other factor.

Of course, I had a baby when I shouldn't have—the last one. Every doctor said I shouldn't have. When I found I was in that condition the doctor said I should have it done away with, but my pressure was a little lower—160. He spoke to another doctor and he said to watch the kidneys and if they were all right and I wanted to go through with it maybe it would bring it down since it went up with the first pregnancy. I was O.K. until the seventh month when it went up to 200 and he drove me home—was afraid to have me walk. I felt all right. I was put to bed. He came in every morning and watched me carefully, until the eighth month when I got a *facial paralysis*. He assured me it wasn't the blood pressure but a cold. They rushed me to the hospital and they terminated that pregnancy. I remember the doctor talking at the foot of my bed and saying that I didn't have to have a convulsion. I didn't but they were all ready for it with clamps and everything. The facial stayed with me for three months. I don't feel quite right yet on that side when I laugh. I had the baby—the baby is fine. So cute and sweet. It would have been a shame if she hadn't been here. Of course I had a trying time bringing her up. (Tells of being tired and so on after leaving the hospital.)

DOCTOR: How many children have you all together?

PATIENT: Two. I had a very bad time with that one. They did everything to bring on labor. They had to take me down and put me to sleep. When I got up I couldn't even talk. My dad sat in the room and the nurse was there. I was very weak. Then they gave me an injection. (Tells of getting the injection in the hip, that her husband was there and that she could hardly answer him. The nurses came in and out asking if she had any pain.) They had it from the doctor that I didn't like to bother anybody but I really didn't have any pain. Finally when I did have a pain they rushed me down.

DOCTOR: What did you think?

PATIENT: I didn't think I would pull through.

DOCTOR: Do you remember any more?

PATIENT: The only thing I remember is that before the baby came I got shivers—all tingles. My whole body was trembling. I was gasping and felt as though my heart was going out. They gave me oxygen and I felt better. I was watched very carefully. Even though I was not a private patient. I had a room by myself until I rebelled. For ten days. I wasn't concerned about the new baby but about the old one all the time. I went in a room with other girls, and they asked me about my baby. I said it was in the incubator. I hadn't seen it. They asked me how I knew it was there. I asked the doctor and he said yes it was all right. It shows you don't care about them until you take care of them yourself. Later on when I was able to walk he took me down to see the baby. (Stops talking.)

(Patient says she had quite a time taking care of the baby when she got home as she felt weak.)

DOCTOR: Why did you become pregnant?

PATIENT: It was only an accident. My husband used something, but we weren't as careful as we should have been.

DOCTOR: Does that work out all right now?

PATIENT: (Hesitates) I guess so. He makes sure that everything is all right.

DOCTOR: There is something you can use.

PATIENT: I'd be afraid that wouldn't be enough.

DOCTOR: Does that interfere with your happiness?

PATIENT: No. I am pretty sure he is careful. With the last baby we may have been a little careless. Didn't blow the things up or anything. All that does make a difference. I went through the second pregnancy willingly. If I had said I didn't want to they would have done away with it. (Stops talking.)

DOCTOR: Are you tired?

PATIENT: No. He wants me to get tired. I'd rather have my spell here than at home.

DOCTOR: What is this spell?

PATIENT: I start in with headaches and work around the house for about two days. If I eat anything it is very bad. I throw it up. Bile and so on. I sometimes vomit until I can't stop and then I have to get an injection.

DOCTOR: What brings on the spell?

PATIENT: They come on all different times. They asked me if it was my menstruation—I don't think so.

DOCTOR: Have you any idea?

PATIENT: I am always tired. This year I have been taking it very easy and still they come. The same doctor has been taking care of me. He insisted that I go to the hospital. He has always been able to bring my pressure down by tablets. This time he couldn't.

DOCTOR: What did you think?

PATIENT: I *don't worry about myself*. If that's what you mean. I could lie in bed and get over it.

DOCTOR: How often did they come?

PATIENT: Pretty often. All this year there have been quite a few. The first few years I would go a few months without.

DOCTOR: How often?

PATIENT: These last have been every few weeks. I can tell you.

DOCTOR: How many?

PATIENT: Quite a few. One and then in a couple of days another. I kept feeling nauseous. I stayed in bed and then I went to the hospital. I felt uncomfortable at home about asking for the bed pan, so I got up to go to the bathroom.

DOCTOR: Why?

PATIENT: I didn't like to trouble people. One day I felt very weak and I had to. I don't like to ask when I can get up. One day I jumped out of bed to throw up—the doctor was there and scolded me. I had thrown up three times. I am very careful of what I eat. I eat more now I am here. I never eat heavy. Mostly dairy products. I mentioned that to the doctor. There were days I didn't eat because of my nervousness. I lost a lot of weight before I came in.

DOCTOR: How was your weight?

PATIENT: The last few years I wasn't very heavy—112 to 116. When I came here I was 108. I don't think it is much of a low weight. Still I couldn't take much of a low weight. My face is thin. My husband said last night that I looked much better.

DOCTOR: You stayed in school until about how old?

PATIENT: I was very ambitious. I took care of the house and I went to night school, but I couldn't continue. I was in the second term of high school. I took care of the home.

(There was a telephone interruption in the office and the interview stopped for a moment.)

PATIENT: So then—then Father got married, and that relieved me of my duties. That is why he got married. I started going out with girl friends. Once in a while I had a date. I made hats. He took me into his place.

DOCTOR: Did you like it?

PATIENT: I did. They thought I was experienced I did so well. I lately made my daughter a little suit from a pattern and they thought I bought it, it was so good. (Stops.)

DOCTOR: What else did you do? Then?

PATIENT: Oh yes, later on Dad opened a store. I used to sell. It was very pleasant nice work. Kept it for about a year or two. The main business in selling hats is Saturday night and he sold it because that had me tied down too much. Thought I wasn't keeping up with my friends. I was so conscientious I wouldn't want to leave the place. I was doing the same thing until I married.

DOCTOR:　How did you marry?

PATIENT:　I met his sister at a mountain resort. I was going back and forth there three years, until he started to take me out. I must have looked extra nice that time. I kept going with him for nine months and we were married.

(Physician told the patient that we would like to see her again to check her history further. She said she would be glad. Physician explained to her that sometimes in a very careful checking of history we find some things which might help us about her illness and she said she hoped so and smiled. Patient thanked physician and went with the nurse for an x-ray.)

Second Interview

DOCTOR:　Well, how has everything been since the last time?

PATIENT:　I have been as happy as I could be. I don't worry about anything.

DOCTOR:　Well, why would you worry? What *would* you worry about?

PATIENT:　Children, they are contented. They weren't happy when they weren't together but now they are together and they are contented.

DOCTOR:　Is there anything else?

PATIENT:　I could worry about the bills. My husband said not to so I *left that out of my mind* as long as they are taken care of.

DOCTOR:　Anything else?

PATIENT:　Financial things—I have always lived with a limit. It has been a bit of a worry. Now there is a depression you know—*everyone has been in that situation.*

DOCTOR:　Yes.

PATIENT:　He has tried to do all he could—he lost a good job.

DOCTOR:　I'd like to know what things you enjoy.

PATIENT:　I like the movies, reading and the radio. Now that I am walking around I can't concentrate on reading. When I was in bed I read two books. I asked for something light and they gave me a book on love. Towards the end of it, it was very free. I read passages of it to the other one. My companions were very low when I came in but now they are better. I don't know whether I did it for them or whether it is because they are feeling better from their sickness. I have a good many friends. I do that often— cheer them up. *I like to do things for people.*

DOCTOR: Enjoy it?

PATIENT: Yes.

DOCTOR: What kind of friends?

PATIENT: Mostly women. Mostly friends of my own age.

DOCTOR: What else do you like?

PATIENT: Belong to a Pythian sisterhood. Quite a few of the people have written me. Send me cards and so on. I enjoy their meetings when I am well.

DOCTOR: Any more things you like?

PATIENT: Let me see. I know how to knit. I used to make things for the children. Now I sew and make over dresses for them.

DOCTOR: How would you like to spend a day in which you could do anything you wanted to?

PATIENT: I would like to take a walk—take a book or paper along and read.

DOCTOR: What did you like when you were a little kid?

PATIENT: Well, I remember something I didn't tell you before. I was a very sensitive kid. I would cry. My father was very soft spoken, and yet I would cry if he said anything. I was a bed-wetter. Mother took me to a lady doctor. I was so ashamed of it. I remember I was very sensitive. You couldn't talk to me. I could cry at any little thing. I learned to control myself as I went on. I stopped the crying—I stopped the bed-wetting.

DOCTOR: How?

PATIENT: *I don't know how I controlled it.*

DOCTOR: Do you cry now?

PATIENT: No. When I was home for the last eight weeks and sick for the last of it I cried. The doctor came in and saw me, and when he saw me crying he said I must have been very sick indeed to cry.

DOCTOR: Do you feel better?

PATIENT: Well, he gave me an injection and I had nausea and headache and vomiting. I used to put an ice bag on my head to try to get rid of it. (Starts crying.) The doctor was looking at me and was trying to ask me why I didn't get an attack. (Few more tears.) I can't have an attack. (More tears.) Now I am all unnerved from walking around trying to get one. *I can't control myself, but I can't be accommodating here and turn on an attack.* I don't want to be in bed forever. I'd like to get over it.

DOCTOR: What bothers you about it?

PATIENT: Well, I would like to get out and be with my children. I'd like to get out and not be uncomfortable from headache. I went to a lady doctor too about my menstrual periods. They hadn't started yet and I was very thin.

DOCTOR: When did they start?

PATIENT: Fourteen and a half.

DOCTOR: Had you stopped bed-wetting then?

PATIENT: I can't remember. Yes, I do—I was having my periods right after my mother passed away. I was wetting my bed at that time—at 15—I was much ashamed.

DOCTOR: The periods started before your mother died?

PATIENT: Yes and then stopped and then started again.

DOCTOR: Did you know about them ahead?

PATIENT: Yes, I knew. I wasn't alarmed about it but I had no pain.

DOCTOR: How has it been since?

PATIENT: No discomfort. I am all broken out and I feel tired and shaky.

DOCTOR: Shaky, how?

PATIENT: All inside. My legs feel stiff.

DOCTOR: Anything else you notice?

PATIENT: When?

DOCTOR: Here, or any time?

PATIENT: Nothing except I never feel quite right—I always have that dull feeling. My husband used to ask if I was all right and I would say "yes" and *drag around like that*. I would take a few days to rest and then be up and going again. (Speaks about bed-wetting.)

DOCTOR: Did you ever suck your thumb or bite your nails?

PATIENT: No, I never bit my nails. My oldest daughter bites her nails. I never bite my nails. But I do remember my mother saying I was *always a cry-baby since I was born*. She attributed it to the fact that she cried so much when she was pregnant. She had just lost a baby. After me I had a sister who was healthy, and after that *she had one she didn't want. She is the one who has hay fever.*

DOCTOR: Anything else like that?

PATIENT: I like things. I like to read.

DOCTOR: What makes you feel the best?

PATIENT: I used to like to relax after the children were asleep. Would put the radio on with the music soft and sometimes we would go out to the movies.

DOCTOR: What sort of thing makes you the most angry—or what is there you don't like in contrast to what you do like?

PATIENT: I never find things bother me much. I can stand everything. For example, *I am not easily angered with people.* The things they do and say.

DOCTOR: You used to be?

PATIENT: I couldn't tell you. As I say I used to be annoyed with my mother-in-law. I thought living with her made me sick.

DOCTOR: Do you see much of her now?

PATIENT: No, my husband brought her up to see me. He is annoyed with her. I sometimes *get annoyed because he talks out to her,* but never to me.

DOCTOR: Have any more ideas about these things?

PATIENT: I was trying to think. *That seemed to be my greatest annoyance when I was first married.* Whether I was run down or what—I don't know. At the end of the year I told my husband I thought we only had to be there a year. *The family took advantage of my husband.* He worked in a store for his father and we only got room and board. I used to be *very independent, and earn my room and board and everything.* When I came there I had enough clothes for two years. (Talks so fast that physician could not get down the wording. Tells of getting an inexpensive house and fixing it up and friends coming to visit them and how everybody enjoyed it.) *I still kept getting sick while I was alone.* I was happier but I still kept getting sick. (She kicks leg back and forth as she says this.) My husband felt happier there—he told me. She even made a scene while we were moving out.

DOCTOR: How?

PATIENT: Said I was taking her son away from her and cried. I said we were only moving. I said, "We will come to see you but if you carry on this way we will not be able to." He was the oldest son. She has lost all her children. She drives them away. Both of her daughters couldn't stay with her. A daughter can speak out but a daughter-in-law has to keep quiet. Since I have gone from there I don't see why I continue being sick. I am happy. I have two lovely children. If I felt well I'd forget about it. I start getting these headaches. I just dread them. (More tears.) I don't feel like getting up but I make myself move around.

DOCTOR: Of all the things that your husband does—what are the things that would bother you most?

PATIENT: He is very considerate. *He is a good son to his mother.* She has irritated him so much that he just has to tell her to quiet down. She keeps telling my little girl, "I am going to see your mother—don't you want to kiss me for her?" She dramatized everything. It has always been just that way. You have to listen to her when she tells you about her illnesses. When I lived way from her I felt worse. *I developed a steel armor.* It didn't bother me. I would discount it.

DOCTOR: What is your religion?

PATIENT: Jewish.

DOCTOR: Is your husband the same?

PATIENT: Yes.

DOCTOR: Are you very religious?

PATIENT: No. Neither of us or our family.

DOCTOR: Do you get any comfort out of religion?

PATIENT: *I don't go for religion. I do good anyway.*

DOCTOR: Have you ever had a headache in relation to your intercourse?

PATIENT: I used to sometimes get sick a couple of days later. My husband asked the doctor if he should keep away from me. The doctor said it was all right in moderation. When I was quite sick at home we slept together one night. Later he asked the doctor. He didn't tell me.

DOCTOR: What do you feel about it?

PATIENT: I didn't feel it would harm me. I felt rested. I went to sleep. I have been sick these eight weeks. *I didn't know whether to blame him. I was getting better until then.* He went to the doctor and asked him did he spoil anything.

DOCTOR: Do you get complete satisfaction most of the time or some of the time?

PATIENT: In the early years I didn't care—I had no temptation, yes or no. In later years I seemed to like it much better. I guess you grow used to everything.

DOCTOR: Do you know what I mean by complete satisfaction?

PATIENT: Yes. You feel relaxed and go to sleep. In the early years I never wanted him to bother me. I just pleased him and then went to sleep.

DOCTOR: What did you plan to do as a young girl?

PATIENT: I planned I would get married some day and look forward to my own home. I did think I would like to teach.

DOCTOR: Did you have other boy friends before your husband?

PATIENT: I went out with others but it never meant anything. I was not particularly fond of them.

DOCTOR: Did you ever have a headache stop by itself?

PATIENT: Every morning I have a headache and it seems to stop by itself.

DOCTOR: Any idea of what does it?

PATIENT: I used to get up and walk around and it would stop. I used to feel I couldn't get up but then I would. *I'd force myself* to get up the pain in my head was so severe. The only time I stayed in bed was when it was worse. (Speaks rapidly of baking and working hard and looking right when she went to the store. Said just before she was sick, people in the bake shop remarked how white and sick she looked. She felt a pressure under her heart and started throwing up when she went home after that.)

DOCTOR: Did throwing up relieve it?

PATIENT: No. It relieved the pressure sensation. (She points over her stomach.) But not the head.

DOCTOR: Were you angry?

PATIENT: Yes at the children—if they started things that aren't right I'd scold them. When the older girl was younger I had a scare with her. The older girl fell down the steps in a kiddy car. They couldn't see how I had the courage to run down after her. She was 7 months. Then she was scalded at 20 months. She moved so fast she pulled her chair over, upset the pot on the stove and it went over. She was standing in hot water. We had to rip her pants off. She was a mess. The doctor got a cradle and took care of her at home. She was sick enough to be a hospital case.

DOCTOR: How is she now?

PATIENT: Fine, there are no marks.

DOCTOR: Was there anything else?

PATIENT: Both her ears had to be cut. She was quite a trial when she was young.

DOCTOR: Who is in the house now with you?

PATIENT: My stepmother, father, aunt, and two sisters.

DOCTOR: How long have they been there?

PATIENT: For two years. It is quite comfortable. Father and sisters are devoted to me, and she is married. (Referring to the stepmother.) I can't complain about her but—(cries and shows more tension in her hands and legs as she talks about the stepmother.)

DOCTOR: Did you ever talk these things over with a doctor before?

PATIENT: No, they haven't asked me.

DOCTOR: Living with your stepmother was rather difficult.

PATIENT: Yes, they tell me to rest. I don't like to rest. I like to be in action. I always like to be free—to make a fuss for people. Especially when they visit me. I get scolded when I do. I have never had a good sleep these nine years because of my children. I have the little one to attend to. I couldn't take a nap in the day time. I just attribute all these things to the built-up factor—one on top of the other. I try to analyze myself.

DOCTOR: Have you talked things over with your husband?

PATIENT: I tell him things. He takes it and doesn't come back. Sometimes I say to him "Why don't you come back?" (Cries.)

DOCTOR: You might feel better if you cried more.

PATIENT: I often feel like it but I try to control it. I think perhaps I suspected it would help. I sometimes feel better after I do but I don't like to make a nuisance of myself.

(*Note:* On the way back to the ward the patient asked if she *might go to the bathroom.* She said she really wanted to go before she started with the interview. Physician asked her why she did not say anything about it and she said she did not want to. Grabbed physician's arm and thanked her. She said she knew everyone was trying to help her. The patient appeared more tense and showed more facial display, cried more, through this interview than during the first interview. Also she showed more emotion in discussing the fact that *she could not bring on these attacks to please the doctor and did not want to make a nuisance of herself in general.*)

COMMENT

The reader, on reviewing this long conversation, will see that Dr. Brush obtained in this way information concerning the patient's adjustment to her family, work, economic and social status, sex, as well as concerning her adjustment to herself. It is clear that this patient's major difficulties were her adjustment to her early and present family situations, and crises in this sphere bore a definite relationship to exacerbations of her illness. It is clear also that there were possible hereditary and clear-cut psychological factors in this patient's preparation for illness. Her major techniques of handling her difficulties stood out in the frequency with which she used the phrases: "I am never angry," "I never fly into a temper like my mother-in-law," "I never let on to my husband," "I kept everything in," "I developed a steel armor," "I have always had good control, *but I can't seem to control my sickness.*" In other words this patient's life situation was such as to rouse her anger and aggression day after day, but she never found any satisfactory way of expressing this in either action or speech. It did come out, however, in her dreams. (See page 53, relative to development of internal tensions under these circumstances.) As a matter of fact, she bent all her efforts to attempting to endure and to please. She was disturbed even by the fact that she could not bring on an attack to please the doctors, and sat through a long interview enduring the discomfort of very much needing to go to the toilet because she did not want to inconvenience Dr. Brush by interrupting.

REVIEW OF THE MEDICAL HISTORY

What we learned in this preliminary conversational interview * may be clarified through comparison of it with the long and carefully taken medical history. In addition to the routine laboratory work-up the patient was subjected to the following tests: electrocardiograph, cystoscopy with careful urological examination, x-ray of the skull, and spinal tap. The urologist felt that the pyelograph findings indicated no reason for operative intervention. Incidentally, the patient was referred to a neurologist. Had he advised an operation to lower her blood pressure it would have been done. The time necessary for this and the after-treatment would have involved a good deal of expense. The *physical examination* was essentially negative except for slight enlargement of the left ventricle, marked precordial thrust, and local vasospastic narrowing of the retinal vessels. The *impression* was idiopathic hypertension.

The final note on the medical chart was as follows:

"Therefore, in a summary, this was a very young hypertensive, with hypertensive familial background, who showed retinal changes with minimal cardiac damage, no evidence of renal damage and severe headaches out of proportion to her disease, but unexplained in this work-up."

INFORMATION LACKING

Although considerable attention was given to this patient, the following information did not come out in the medical history, and furthermore, that history contains several misstatements and misimpressions which were corrected automatically in the conversational interview; that is, as soon as the patient was off her guard and started to talk freely. As a matter of fact, the reader has probably gained the impression from the foregoing pages that the patient spoke easily, almost to the point of being loquacious, whereas the impression of the medical historian had been that she was rather reticent. Attention may be called to the following points:

* This is one of the few that was written down verbatim while the interview was in progress.

I. *According to the Medical History:*

(a) "There was no strain after the patient's marriage," whereas the strains in relation to her marriage form part of the outstanding subject matter of the foregoing conversation; and it is interesting that the medical history closes with the remark that the patient's "statements are reliable," and her "attitude co-operative."

(b) There is no mention of living with the mother-in-law, the conflict of personalities there, just before and during her pregnancy, which led the patient to say in the foregoing interview: "Now I will give you all the dirt."

(c) *Onset of attacks* is described in relation to bodily symptoms such as nausea, weakness and headaches, in terms of the past few months, but there is no mention of the early precursors of these attacks, nor of the emotional situations in relation to which they occurred.

(d) *Onset of illness* in the medical description * is focused entirely on increases of blood pressure and gradual increase of headaches, nausea, vomiting, with each pregnancy, but the patient described the onset of the illness as associated with emotional upsets, related to her mother's death, her father's remarriage, her own marriage which involved living with her mother-in-law, and later her stepmother and father who came to live with her. These upsets prior to her first pregnancy and during it, because of her mother-in-law, are omitted in the medical history. In the psychosomatic interview, however, she stressed the fact that she kept her emotions to herself but also that the mother-in-law "used to steam the children up one against the

---

* The note in the medical chart relative to the present illness read as follows: Eight years ago in the fifth month of this patient's first pregnancy she was discovered to have hypertension of 150 and albuminuria. But she continued the pregnancy. Several months postpartum she developed severe vertical headaches with nausea and vomiting. Her systolic blood pressure was 160 but it returned to normal after two weeks in bed. During that year she had a sudden attack of suprapubic pain and frequently passed some gravel. There have been no symptoms of stones since. Thereafter the patient suffered further attacks of increasing severity which confined her to her bed with headaches, nausea and vomiting. Four years ago there was a second pregnancy with accompanying edema of ankles and feet. In the seventh month her systolic blood pressure was 200. During the eighth month she had suddenly developed Bell's palsy on the right side with eventual recovery. The pregnancy terminated in the eighth month with a live baby. Thereafter, the patient suffered further attacks of headaches, nausea and vomiting, confining her to her bed. During the past eight weeks she has had palpitation, "two pillow" orthopnea, dyspnea on mild exertion, no pain or edema, varying nocturia with frequency. There have been no central nervous symptoms, bilateral headaches; no eye symptoms and no nose bleeds. Digitalis and luminal failed to give relief. Her blood pressure was: right arm 250/155; left arm, 260/160; left leg, 265/165.

other," that the mother-in-law had heart trouble and was a very sick woman so she tried to be nice to her, and so on. She showed the relationship of heart activity to dreams, saying that she dreamed of her husband having committed a crime and being in court, and she woke up with her heart trembling, that she had developed a very strict armor, that she always wanted to cry a lot and tried to control it, that she is very ambitious and never let herself go, that she was a sensitive child, a born cry-baby, likes to do things for others, does not go in for religion but does good anyway, that she works hard and fast, worries about bills, although she tries to put them out of her mind. She has been depressed, never sleeps well. She always says "yes" to her husband, and drags around not feeling well. At first she said she was not easily angered and then she contradicted herself saying that she was angry when her husband talked to her mother-in-law. She said finally that she did not like to make a nuisance of herself in the hospital and she had worked very hard walking around trying to bring on these attacks as she had been instructed.

Chronological Summary of Relevant Material as Developed in the Conversational Interview

Events in Life Situation	*Patient's Response*
Age 1–11. The patient was her mother's pal, very ambitious and bright in school.	A constant battle with her mother over eating, especially butter. She was also much ashamed over bed-wetting which continued to the age of 15. The patient doesn't know how she *learned to control it* after her mother died.
Nineteen years ago (when the patient was 13) her mother died (at the age of 39) from stroke and high blood pressure, having been ailing for a long time because of severe headaches.	The patient became a mother to the rest of the family and started to have headaches herself. Soon she gave up school. She continued for a while in night school, but gradually gave up her ambition to be a teacher because she had too much to do. She insisted that her younger brother and sisters all finish high school. It was at this time that she gave up bed-wetting; and her

Events in Life Situation	Patient's Response
	periods, which had stopped at the time of her mother's death, returned regularly again after about a year.
Fifteen years ago the patient's father remarried.	The patient resented the fact that she was no longer the head of the house, but went to help her father in his store.
Nine years ago the patient married and went to live with her mother-in-law.	Her headaches became increasingly severe and she began to have attacks of nausea and vomiting following encounters with her mother-in-law. In spite of this she insisted to the doctor that she was fine, and when he suggested their moving away from the mother-in-law, she refused to let him tell her husband because she didn't want him to think she had complained to the doctor.
Eight years ago first pregnancy.	
Four years ago the second pregnancy, an unwanted child as was the patient's mother's last child, the neurotic sister with allergy.	Termination of the pregnancy at eight months. Bell's palsy, which she was sure was a paralysis due to high blood pressure like that of her mother before her death. Marked increase in all symptoms.
Two years ago the patient's stepmother, father, aunt, and two sisters came to live with her. Her youngest child pulled over the kettle on the stove and scalded herself.	Increasingly rapid alternation between anger, which the patient kept to herself, and severe attacks of nausea, headaches and vomiting which sent her to bed.

II. In the careful *physical examination* it was noted that reflexes were slightly hyperactive but the patient's extreme generalized tension was not mentioned.

III. A *progress note* ten days after admission reads as follows: "The patient has gone through a gamut of exercises, labors, etc., to induce a typical episode of cephalagia, all to no avail. In despair she called me to take her blood pressure so that she could rest her over-weary body."

In view of the above material it is obvious that her attacks were not likely to be brought on by exercising in the hospital away from the stress and strain to which they were dynamically related, that is in the home where she had constantly to push herself to do things, and to keep her emotions to herself. As a matter of fact, these exercises probably served as an outlet for the patient's emotions and so probably decreased the likelihood of an attack, rather than helping to bring it on.

IV. The *social service note* contained no specific additional information relative to the emotional component of the patient's illness, but it did include the following important comments: "While talking she cried constantly but told us that 'this was nothing' since 'she was always affected this way.' " The patient is very nervous and immature, and "evidently finding a great deal of satisfaction out of her illness. . . . It would seem that there are many other factors which would clarify our picture of the situation."

Although it is true that there are other factors in the situation which need to be studied, it is obvious from the foregoing that the patient is not finding a great deal of satisfaction out of her illness, and is not crying for no reason.

This patient was sent back to an environmental situation which for her was as pathogenic as a crowded east-side tenement of the old type would be for a patient with tuberculosis, and nothing was done either to change her environment, or what would have been much more important, to enable her to cope with her problems. Incidentally, recent work on the study of the autonomic nervous system has indicated that changes in heart rate, blood pressure, and other bodily symptoms occur in relation to emotional stresses and strains in sensitive or reactive types of individuals. (For further discussion of this point see Chapter VIII.)

REVIEW OF THE PSYCHOSOMATIC INTERVIEW

Perhaps at the outset the point should be stressed again that an adequate psychosomatic history or interview is impossible if the questionnaire method is followed. Both patient and doctor are too likely to be satisfied with "yes" or "no" answers, omitting the essential emotional components. The initial misimpressions obtained by some of our assistants were largely due to the fact that the interview

was not sufficiently spontaneous from the point of view of both patient and doctor. This is a major reason for some of the discrepancies
between our clinical profiles as originally outlined and the impressions gained of these same patients through more intensive therapeutic
study and projective test procedures.

The interview just quoted is fairly typical of the physician who
is beginning to deal with psychosomatic problems on the basis of a
good medical internship and several years of orthodox psychiatric
experience. While it supplies a good deal more information than the
medical history, it is, however, an unsatisfactory example of the psychosomatic approach.

One major defect, as noted earlier, is the interference with spontaneity by the physician's attempt to make a verbatim report of the
interview. Such an attempt always interferes with the contact between patient and physician. Observing the physician busily writing,
the patient feels a change in his relationship to the physician from
that of friend to that of a caterpillar on a pin. Almost invariably
patients resist having their emotional expressions recorded. Conversation is necessarily slowed down and the doctor's awareness is
dulled. Both the phrasing of a question and the tone of voice make
a great difference. For example, the physician's question in the
preceding interview: "Why *would* you worry?" might imply to the
patient that he is silly to worry. Whereas what was really meant was
"What kind of things might you worry about?" And even in this
form the question tends to force the patient to find rational reasons
for worries instead of eliciting a spontaneous expression of the patient's uneasiness and doubts.

Physicians interested in the psychosomatic approach are often
disturbed by the idea of spontaneous conversation and are uncertain
about where to draw the line between allowing the patient free rein
and interjecting a guiding question or comment. While no absolute
rules can be laid down as to where to draw the line, the patient's
emotional focus and tension is one of the best guides. The interview
given might have been more immediately productive and less prolonged had the physician taken better advantage of the opportunities
for such observations.

In some types of patients, a projective technique such as the Rorschach test is of inestimable value. It penetrates beneath the defenses

to deeper levels of emotional conflict and reaction patterns. This material may be a long time in appearing and only uncertainly perceived through interviews. The Rorschach diagnosis not only offers a check upon clinical impressions but is frequently essential for an evaluation of the clinical material.

In connection with the interview just given, by way of illustration, the following positive points should be noted:

(1) The questions asked were as little suggestive as possible, being limited in general to "How was that?" "How about your father?" "Why?" "What did you feel?" "What do you think," and the like.

(2) Questions were such as to draw the patient out without indicating bias on the part of the physician, as for example at the beginning of the second interview (in terms of the previous discussion, aim good but technique poor):

PATIENT: I have been as happy as I could be. I don't worry about anything.

DOCTOR: Well, why would you worry? (a question just partially retrieved by next question) What *would* you worry about?

PATIENT: Children, they are contented. They weren't happy when they weren't together but now they are together and they are contented.

DOCTOR: Is there anything else?

PATIENT: I could worry about the bill. My husband said not to so I *left that out of my mind* as long as they are taken care of.

DOCTOR: Anything else?

PATIENT: Financial things—I have always lived with a limit. It has been a bit of a worry.

(3) When the patient appeared emotional, questions indicating a sympathetic interest were asked, except in cases where it seemed easier for the patient to have her attention diverted for the moment. For example:

PATIENT: No, I never smoke. I never ran around. I am not that type. (Stops talking.)

DOCTOR: What did you do?

PATIENT: I used to work as a girl, took care of my mother, took care of my family and was mother to them when my mother passed away. (Slows down and stops.)

DOCTOR: Had your hands full?

PATIENT: Yes, that was quite a job. 'Til my dad married again. (Stops talking.)

DOCTOR: How old were you when your mother died?

PATIENT: I was 13. Mother always had a headache. I never knew that she had blood pressure. I didn't know that was the matter with her. Except that she had symptoms. I can tell it is like mine. She got up in the morning with a severe headache. I am very much like her. We never give in to anything. One day she got paralyzed on one side. She didn't try to lift her right arm —she couldn't have—but lifted her left arm. She was only 39 years old. From all the symptoms she seems to have had what I have. (Stops talking.)

DOCTOR: What was your mother like?

PATIENT: A very nice woman—nice looking. I didn't do her justice. (Patient laughs.) She helped my dad in the store and everything. You see four years before she passed away they had an epidemic of influenza and she was weak. Had severe headaches all the time. I always thought the flu left her with some weakness, 1918, I nursed her, but I didn't get it. You know about it. I stopped school and was home two months. They sent my work in and I passed everything for school. I was very ambitious—only 11 years old then. (She stops.)

DOCTOR: You must have been pretty smart.

(4) Questions on subjects concerning which the patient was reticent were asked simply, and instead of being stressed, were returned to later in a different context if further information was needed. The patient says she had quite a time taking care of the baby when she got home as she felt weak.

DOCTOR: Why did you become pregnant?

PATIENT: It was only an accident. My husband used something, but we weren't careful as we should have been.

DOCTOR: Does that work out all right now?

PATIENT: (Hesitates) I guess so. He makes sure that everything is all right.

DOCTOR: There is something that you can use.

PATIENT: I'd be afraid that wouldn't be enough.

DOCTOR: Does that interfere with your happiness?

PATIENT: No. I am pretty sure he is careful. With the last baby we may have been a little careless. Didn't blow the things up or anything. All that does make a difference. I went through the second pregacy willingly. If I had said I didn't want to they would have done away with it. (Stops talking.)

Students and young physicians, for example, are often at a loss as to how to obtain information concerning the sexual adjustment of a patient, particularly a woman patient. They upset patients seriously by the questions they ask. Now, one can perhaps say to a psychotic patient, "When did you start masturbating?" without obtaining too disturbing a response although in many such cases caution is necessary also. But such a question can arouse great antagonism and destroy an otherwise co-operative attitude in a patient on the medical service, who considers herself normal and is so considered by the attending physicians and nurses. We all of us have had patients who have been disturbed by similar questions, bluntly asked by physicians not trained in psychiatry, who have decided to "pick up a little psychiatry" by reading.* If, however, as already noted, in the course of routine medical questions, when one comes to the menstrual history, onset and so on, one says conversationally: "And did you expect it to happen? Was it what you thought it would be like?" (using of course the patient's expression, if the patient happens to have supplied one), one often obtains the whole history of the patient's relationship to her mother, school friends, boy friends, and sexual development in general, with no emotional reaction on the part of the patient beyond one of relief and possibly the statement: "Why, doctor, I don't know why I told you all this. It must have been on my mind but nobody asked me about it" (which means "let me talk about it"). Theodore P. Wolfe [425] has called attention to this same situation in both male and female patients suffering from anxiety neurosis, who themselves had reached the conviction that something was wrong with their sexual life. They rather scorned their physicians for not having thought of it, but none the less wandered from doctor to doctor being treated for all possible maladies and even subjected to operations.

It should be noted also that these points relative to method, although they may seem very elementary, are often, perhaps because of

---

* Fortunately most students now receive more adequate training in these things in medical schools. But it would seem still to be a better rule not to ask questions that are suitable only in the form of more elaborate psychotherapeutic procedure, or to give interpretations based on them. As a matter of fact most necessary information can be obtained without use of elaborate psychiatric or psychoanalytic terms or concepts, and common sense comments are always more effective than intrepretations involving such words as "castration fear," "incest fear," etc. (For further discussion see page 114.)

their very obviousness, inadequately stressed in psychiatric teaching of medical students. Incidentally, the questions chosen for detailed illustration were chosen not because, as many laymen and some physicians used to think, the sexual life in terms of sexual activity is of primary importance in connection with organic illness, but because it is in this field that physicians are most likely to traumatize patients, to aggravate symptoms and to create difficulties for the consulting specialist. Physicians aware of psychosomatic mechanisms but insufficiently trained to evaluate psychosexual history can usually avoid this. (See Chapter XI, page 681.)

The road to understanding of psychosomatic syndromes complicated by or leading to organic damage, in contradistinction to somatic disturbances occurring on a purely hysterical basis, was opened up only after psychoanalysis had added to the libido theory (with what was popularly called its emphasis on sex) ego or character analysis, with its focus on the patient as a whole in relation to his environment. Patients in a general hospital, whose illnesses are complicated by emotional factors, suffer in the main from neurotic characters, not symptom neuroses in the classic sense.

SUMMARY OF DIAGNOSTIC POINTS OBTAINED FROM THE HISTORY

By means of such a history as that described there was obtained:

(1) A picture of the patient's life in which his major environmental stresses are outlined, together with his psychological and physiological reaction to them.

(2) A picture of the patient's characteristic reaction patterns in terms of the environmental and emotional situations to which he has adjusted with ease or with difficulty, again in relation to illness history.

(3) The topics that he tends to avoid and misrepresent, and the topics that are accompanied by an increase or decrease in his skeletal or vegetative response, and temporary increase or relief of his symptoms. The type of defense used by the patient in connection with such subjects may bear a relationship to his symptoms in indicating whether he is more likely to try to keep them to himself, to seek relief in talking about them, or to seek relief in action, as for example fidgeting, walking up and down the room, or smoking a cigarette (page 200).

Also, special attention was paid to the times at which the patient was hesitant, cried, laughed, evaded, became tense, or showed increase or decrease of symptoms.

This information was sometimes sufficient to enable one to determine the presence of fear, anxiety, or conflict and its significance in terms of the energy economy of the total personality, including the degree of awareness of emotional problems and the characteristic defenses against them. In patient No. HP 1 this was the case. In patients No. CA 318 and No. DP 2 this was not the case. Through study of cases like the latter some special techniques of examination were worked out, which are useful and often necessary in addition to the psychosomatic history to complete a psychosomatic diagnosis.

As a basis for prognosis and therapy as well as for research purposes these techniques proved to be important in all cases because they helped to establish the relationship of the fear, anxiety, or conflict present to the symptom from which the patient was suffering. For the establishment of this point the intensity of the symptomatology considered in its physiological aspects is irrelevant, but its type and its significance to the patient may give clues. Although one may suspect the presence of a prominent psychic factor when the somatic symptomatology is out of proportion to the degree of somatic damage present, the psychic factor was often found to be just as important when this was not the case.

Such clues must be supplemented by more specific observations and examination, but they are of great importance and may be completely invalidated by injudicious questioning in the course of history taking. Incidentally, it is essential to the success of initial therapy (as well as of research) that the examination be conducted with a minimum of disturbance of ordinary hospital regime and in general without attracting too much attention from the patient himself, both of which factors must be considered in the manner of history taking.

V. SUMMARY OF PSYCHOSOMATIC HISTORY

Method:

Casual conversation, utilizing free association (Deutsch [122]) and careful questioning, comparison of the patient's statements with those recorded in medical and social histories, or on different occasions, supplemented by observation of his shifting tensions and exacerbations of his illness in relation to the material given, and of his reactions to the physician.

Content:

1. The patient's reactions early and present to
   (a) Himself, his body as well as his personality
   (b) Family
   (c) Work
   (d) Social environment, including his economic status, friends, church, hobbies
   (e) Sex (auto, homo, hetero-overt, latent)
   (f) Present illness.

2. His preparation for illness by
   (a) Important conflicts in any of the necessary spheres of adjustment
   (b) Constitution, physique, previous illnesses, and reactions to them
   (c) Hereditary and pseudo-hereditary factors including illness of relatives and friends, and age at which patient was exposed to them
   (d) Chronological correlation of periods of stress and strain, traumatic events, time of appearance of conflicts and symptoms
   (e) Symptoms as defenses against conflicts and expressions of them, and of the tension they create.

3. Material relative to his insight, amnesias, scotomata, and the operation of unconscious factors.

Diagnostic Points:

1. Origin of falsifications, contradictions, and omissions in patient or physician.

2. Patient's will to get well as revealed in
   (a) Attitude toward the hospital, toward his present and past illnesses, toward invalidism
   (b) Reaction to physiological changes, effects of the illness on his life, the idea of compensation
   (c) The specific purpose served by the symptom
   (d) Patient's ability in terms of his total personality structure to handle the conflict expressed in the symptom.

3. Dreams and other indications as to unconscious and manifest anxiety and conflict, especially divergencies between dream material and the patient's statements.

4. Patient's muscle tension, degree, type, and localization.

5. Organization of the patient's symptoms, psychic and somatic.

Special Techniques of Examination (Chapter II):

1. Patient's response to relaxation and to enlightment concerning his tensions.

2. Patient's response to the calling of his attention to specific material in relation to which attacks occur during interviews.

3. Reactions of the patient to the physician.

4. Clues from free-association.

5. Special tests.

(*Note:* The psychiatric history and examination more than any other requires experience for the development of firmness of touch and security of interpretation.)

Chapter II

SPECIAL TECHNIQUES OF EXAMINATION TO SUPPLEMENT THE PSYCHOSOMATIC HISTORY

But in science we must bethink ourselves of the method not less than of the results. Of the latter you will take as much as you can. The method is even more valuable than the results, for it had produced them all, and will reproduce countless others in the future.—ANATOLE FRANCE.

The psychosomatic history just outlined, although important and helpful, was often inadequate to give a basic psychosomatic picture. This point was illustrated in the preceding chapter. The inadequacies were particularly marked in the case of patients in whom the emotional factors most closely related to their somatic symptoms were deeply repressed, or appeared in consciousness in a much distorted form. We asked ourselves the question: What further clues could be obtained without intensive examination and without taking recourse to the techniques of depth psychology? We developed some additional aids to making a diagnosis and prognosis. These can be used to supplement the psychosomatic history with little additional expenditure of time before undertaking intensive investigation. We found them extremely helpful also in ascertaining the advisability of such investigations, as well as in connection with later more detailed examination and therapy. Incidentally, these may be used by the psychiatric consultant or even by the patient's physician, before the psychiatrist is called in. In most cases these aids, added to the type of history just outlined, are sufficient to give a basic psychosomatic picture.

I. RELAXATION

Advantage can be taken of the relationship that exists between *muscle tension* and the *keeping of important emotional material in repression.* Patients often become particularly tense when a question arouses emotions associated with unconscious conflicts.[189, 140] Watching the patient's shifting tensions, therefore, gives important clues.

Muscle tension is a general defense against expression of vegetative energies. Except for some psychotics there are few uncommunicative patients who do not become communicative if their attention is centered on learning to relax and they become able to do so.* Many patients who have been unaware of their tension, when they relax are overcome by a welling up of emotion which takes them entirely by surprise.

In some patients it is desirable to make use of this principle as a technique in conjunction with the first interview (as well as in subsequent examinations). For example:

Case No. DP. 2.† The patient was an Austrian-Jewish seamstress, 43 years old, who had been treated for diabetes for seven years. Consultation had been requested because of difficulty with her diet and failure to lose weight. The question was whether this patient was subnormal mentally, or for some other reason so un-co-operative that continuation of her treatment was not feasible. In addition to her diabetes, she suffered from pain around the heart; "shivers" and pain in the left shoulder and arm (which had been considered diabetic neuritis); numbness of tongue, the left hand, and both legs; attacks of dizziness and headaches.

The patient came into the examining room with an appearance of reluctance and veiled defiance, having been given the impression by the referring physician that this interview was a sort of punishment for her bad behavior; hence the form of the first question.

DOCTOR: Good morning Mrs. ———. Your treatment for the last seven years hasn't seemed to help you very much, has it?

PATIENT: No, Doctor. I know my doctors have done their best for me, but I guess I'm just a hopeless case. I seem to go from bad to worse.

DOCTOR: What bothers you most?

(Patient enumerates symptoms, ending, "The neuritis is worst.")

DOCTOR: Do these feelings interfere with your everyday life?

* For a discussion of techniques from the physiological side see Schultz [372]; from the point of view of experimental psychology see Jacobson [249]; from the point of view of the medical psychologist see Freud [194], Reich [345], Ferenczi [179].

† Patient of the author.

PATIENT: I hate to go around ailing and complaining all the time, but I can do my work around the house and my sewing.

DOCTOR: Is everything all right at home, or do some things bother you?

PATIENT: No, nothing worries me. I have a good son and two good daughters.

DOCTOR: Your husband?

PATIENT: He's all right. Only the trouble everybody has, being mostly out of work. But I don't complain.

DOCTOR: Does it mean more work for you?

PATIENT: Yes, but I've always liked sewing. It's just world conditions.

(*Note:* One should be cautious in asking a patient if anything worries him, but it may be said in general that the patient who categorically denies such a possibility is likely to be under considerable stress, either consciously or unconsciously. The two following statements indicate some degree of defensiveness.)

DOCTOR: Do you sleep well?

PATIENT: Yes.

DOCTOR: Never wake up in the night or have dreams or nightmares?

PATIENT: No, I've always been a good sleeper.

(*Note:* At this point the physician gained the impression that this patient was unlikely to become very communicative if this procedure were followed. She had become superficially pleasant, frank and co-operative, but extremely stiff and inhibited, therefore the relaxation technique was applied as follows)

DOCTOR: You seem to be pretty stiff.

PATIENT: It gets worse and worse. Maybe it's from getting old.

DOCTOR: How about the neuritis? Do you have it now?

PATIENT: Most of the time, but I guess I'll get used to it.

DOCTOR: Suppose you lie here (examining table) and let me find out a little more about your stiffness. (Patient complies and doctor attempts to check reflexes but has difficulty in bending the patient's arm or leg.) You are about as stiff as a marionette, but even marionettes have joints somewhere. Couldn't you relax your arm enough so it would bend at the elbow?

PATIENT: It hurts too much.

DOCTOR: How about the other arm, or one of your legs?

PATIENT: Doctor, please don't. I don't mean not to co-operate. They think I don't co-operate but they don't understand how much it hurts me.

DOCTOR: Well, then suppose you just let it rest on my hand and see if you can't make it limp. It really will help the pain if you do. (Patient's arm rests in doctor's hand, stiff, with clenched fist.) Nobody can relax with a clenched fist. It looks as if you wanted to hit somebody.

PATIENT: (With some emotion) Why, doctor, I would never do anything like that! (Unclenches fist but arm remains stiff.)

DOCTOR: I guess I should have called you a wooden soldier instead of a marionette. (Patient was mildly amused, so the physician attempted to distract her attention by casual conversation about puppet shows, whether her son played with wooden soldiers, encouraging her at the same time to relax. In the midst of this she suddenly stiffened up.)

PATIENT: I wish you wouldn't talk about soldiers.

DOCTOR: Why?

PATIENT: I don't know. I wish you wouldn't keep me lying here.

DOCTOR: All right, let's talk about anything you really enjoy; movies? books? (Conversation along these lines—with the patient still lying on the table—was more successful, and the patient began to relax apparently without being completely aware of the fact. In the midst of this conversation she suddenly sat up on the examining table, became flushed, showed signs of extreme anxiety and burst out crying.)

PATIENT: Doctor, you don't know what you are doing to me. I don't know what's coming over me. I feel awful. I feel as though something awful were going to happen. I don't know what I might do.

DOCTOR: What is it?

PATIENT: Oh, I don't know, I don't know. Something terrible. I'm so frightened.

DOCTOR: Nothing will happen to you. But if you'd feel better just lie down again and you can be as stiff as you like.

PATIENT: (Lying down) You must think I'm silly. But you see I feel safer when I'm stiff. My aggravations don't bother me so much. That's why I go to sleep stiff like that, only when I wake up in the morning sometimes I'm so stiff I can hardly get out of bed. But if I weren't stiff I couldn't even go to sleep. (Note how the patient's admission of aggravation slipped out in spite of her previous denial of worries.)

DOCTOR: What about the aggravation?

PATIENT: Oh, doctor I guess I should have told you, but I don't like to talk about my children. You see I always wanted to be a teacher like my brother, and I couldn't. because I got married and had to work. My son was such a bright boy I thought he would do it and—well—it makes me ashamed but he's not getting good marks in school. I'm afraid he'll fail.

DOCTOR: Well, no wonder you feel upset. Is that why you have to get stiff at night, so you won't think about it?

PATIENT: Well, I guess so. I always used to dream about him. He always used to be nice in my dreams and now he isn't. (Note the patient's previous denial of dreams.)

DOCTOR: How is he now?

PATIENT: I don't know. I couldn't bear to remember what I dream. (Patient again shows signs of agitation.)

DOCTOR: What about your daughters?

PATIENT: Well, that's bad too. One of them is going to marry a man that's weak and irresponsible like my husband. I don't know what's gotten into her. She used to be so sensible. But now I talk, and talk, and I scold her. It's gone on for years and I can't change her mind. And then mother is always around complaining. She has just imaginary pains. I have real ones but I don't complain. I think it's really her fault that I married my husband. He's a good man but he's weak. I should have taught school. All my life I dreamed of being at school and learning all sorts of wonderful things. Then I would wake up and find that I knew nothing at all. It used to make me cry. I wanted to kill myself sometimes. (Note the patient's initial statement that she had a good son, two good daughters, and a good husband.)

DOCTOR: When did you first begin to feel so upset about it?

PATIENT: I guess it was right after my father was killed in the war. When I was 23. (Note the patient's annoyance with the physician for mentioning soldiers.)

DOCTOR: Tell me about it.

(To conserve space the substance of her story as she then told it with little further questioning is given briefly as follows:

She was the oldest child in a family of eight, of whom five were boys and three girls. All of them were living and essentially well at the time of examination, except for the oldest brother, two years the patient's junior, who is nervous. The patient is greatly devoted to this brother because he reminds her of her father; at the same time, she envies him because he has accomplished what has always been her highest aim in life, that of becoming a school teacher, and because having a neurosis he is able to afford to go to a "real psychiatrist" instead of going to a clinic. Her parents were healthy except that her father suffered from migraine and her mother suffers from "neuritis" of twenty-five years' duration. Her grandparents, both paternal and maternal, were all very healthy and good-natured and died of old age, with the exception of the maternal grandmother who although always healthy died of pneumonia just before the patient was born.

The patient had trouble with the women of her family, having been named after the maternal grandmother, Rose, a name she dislikes; having been bossed by her paternal grandmother who insisted that girls should not go to school but should help in the home and should go to church; and having been exploited by her mother who "loved her least of all" the children and worked her very hard.

In spite of these difficulties the patient completed elementary education and then, after keeping house for her parents for six years without being allowed to study, she came to this country with the idea of continuing her education and becoming a teacher. In making this decision her only conflict was in the matter of leaving her father, whose favorite she was. But she became engaged to a cousin in this country who helped her out by paying her fare. Soon after her arrival, however, the engagement was broken, allegedly because she could not speak the language. By one of those unfortunate coincidences in life this insult occurred just prior to the time of her father's death, and was aggravated by the cousin's engagement to her younger sister. The patient shut herself in the bathroom and turned on the gas. She was greatly annoyed because she was discovered "in time," feeling that there was nothing in the world for her.

But instead of making another suicidal attempt she developed the pain described at the outset and married a fruit-stand clerk, as she said, in order "to prove to herself and the world that she could get a husband if she wanted to." This meant, of course, giving up her ambition to continue her education and become a school teacher, but her dreams continued to concern themselves with finding herself *very intelligent*. It is interesting that she was still having such dreams at the age of 43 when she came for psychiatric consultation.

The patient insists that she is happy with her husband (although she dislikes intercourse) but she wishes that he were more intelligent like her brother, and would get regular work so that she would not have to work so hard. She has three children, two girls and a younger boy, whom she is trying to develop into the kind of a man "a son of hers ought to be," namely, kind and devoted like her father, and brilliant and a school teacher like her brother. In response to this attitude on her part, the boy has a habit of failing examinations. This is *one of her major aggravations* as noted at the outset and the boy started this practice just prior to the onset of her diabetes. A *second major aggravation* is her feeling that her husband has failed her.

DOCTOR: I don't wonder you feel annoyed about a lot of things. Aren't you ever annoyed with your husband too? (Although leading questions are usually avoided, this was asked because the patient had already admitted her annoyance with her husband, and it seemed important to draw her out and to relieve her guilt relative to this subject.)

PATIENT: Well, I often think if he were a real man he would try harder to get a job when he sees how numb my arm gets from sewing. My day is never done, and he, even when he has work, comes home and settles down just to have me make him comfortable. He forgets about everybody else.

DOCTOR: Maybe you did want to hit somebody, when I said you had your fist clenched awhile ago?

PATIENT: I guess I do. But I keep it in. I would rather kill myself than do a thing like that.

DOCTOR: Maybe it's keeping it in that makes you so stiff. You see your stiffness seems to have started long before the diabetes.

PATIENT: You're smart yourself, doctor. I knew it wasn't the diabetes that made me stiff. But when the doctors called it diabetic neuritis I thought it wasn't my place to contradict them.

DOCTOR: Have you never been free from the stiffness in all these years?

PATIENT: Yes, it was better after my son was born. I thought he'd be a real man like my father and my brother—do all the things I couldn't do. But then when I found he wasn't very bright it got much worse. Then I got the diabetes.

DOCTOR: Is it all your troubles that make it hard for you to follow your diet?

PATIENT: Well, doctor, I'll tell you. I know the doctors mean well by me and do the best they know, but I know it's not the diet that makes the sugar. Just to be sure, one day I ate all the things I wanted to, potatoes, and candy and ice cream, and then I went to the drug store for a test, and there was only the faintest trace of sugar. Another day I had a lot of aggravations, so many aggravations that they made me feel as if I must have sugar, although I had been following my diet very carefully, and I went to the drug store and the sugar was 4-plus. So I just decided I wouldn't bother with the diet. But of course I couldn't tell the doctors because they couldn't understand. (The patient was anxious incidentally, that this information not be given them, because, as she said) They are very nice to me and I like to come to see them once in a while just to chat.

DOCTOR: Why didn't you tell your doctors these things long ago?

PATIENT: Well, they didn't ask me. If they had I might not have told them. I don't want to talk about my troubles like my mother. Anyway I'm ashamed. I wouldn't have told you either if you hadn't made me relax. It was such an awful feeling. As if I couldn't keep it all in any more. And then you spoke about soldiers (that's the way my father was killed) and my son playing soldiers when he was little and I was so proud of him. And me being mad. It was as if you were killing me, or I would kill somebody. (Patient cries.)

(*Note* that in this statement the patient, with no suggestion from her physician, has indicated her awareness of the role of muscular tension in keeping "things in.")

DOCTOR: Are you sorry?

PATIENT: I ought to be very mad at you, but I guess I feel much better.

DOCTOR: You're much less stiff. How about the pain?

PATIENT: (Appearing surprised) It isn't there any more. I feel as if I could walk better. Perhaps you were really right about its making me stiff.

DOCTOR: We'll talk about that again. Would you like to?

PATIENT: Any time you say. My only pleasure these days is when I can talk to smart people.

Review of this interview, which lasted only about an hour, will show that a fairly clear picture has been obtained of the patient's social, vocational, and family (early and present) adjustment, including her physiological and psychological behavior. Her sexual adjustment did not come up naturally and discussion of it was postponed until the next interview. Important clues were obtained also relative to the role played by her conscious as well as her unconscious conflicts in relation to her symptoms. For example, the emotional upset and the beginning of her symptoms followed the news of her father's death, her broken engagement, her precipitate marriage to a man she did not respect and the accompanying relinquishment of her ambition to teach. The relief of the stiffness followed the birth of her son. Its recurrence in a severer form, followed by the diabetes, came when her son began to disappoint her.

Indications were given also of the role played by her feelings toward the physician, of which more will be said later. Since the present context includes only history-taking, diagnosis, and prognosis, further details will not be given except for the following note. The various numbnesses, shivering sensations and cardiac pain cleared up with relatively superficial psychotherapy (twelve interviews, five months). She began to lose weight, the polyuria disappeared and the diabetes began to improve together with a decrease in her blood sugar.

This is noteworthy in view of the late period at which this patient came to treatment and the further fact that she must remain in an unsatisfactory life situation (and thwarted so far as her life-long ambition of becoming a school teacher is concerned), and must learn to give up her desire to make up for it by realizing her ambition in her son. Such patients should of course be followed.

In our study no uniform technique specifically directed toward production of relaxation was used. Each physician used the technique he preferred and often varied this in terms of the individual patient. In the main the procedure was to concentrate the patient's interest on his physical tensions, noting the relative ease or difficulty with which he was able to eliminate them voluntarily, and then to suggest that he remain as relaxed as possible while "we go on talking." Special note was made of the type and regularity of his breathing also.[*] The physician was then able to make observations on these points, and the patient was prepared to have his attention recalled to this matter at appropriate moments. [†]

This principle has an application even to the technique of preliminary history-taking and physical examination. Many inconsistencies and amnesias are corrected if the history given prior to physical examination is checked after physical examination. Physicians in general hospitals have commented on the fact that relatively uncommunicative patients often become communicative after the physical examination. Of course, relaxation is not the only factor to be considered here (page 87), but asking the patient to relax is in many cases a useful device in taking or checking a history and in attempting to evaluate psychic and somatic factors in illness.

II. EMOTIONAL SETTING OF ATTACKS

Another way in which attention to relaxation may help is in making somewhat clearer the *relationship between emotional material and attacks of symptoms or pain.* For example, a patient with hypertension and an anginal syndrome who was asked to relax during a discussion of her family relationships, showed a tendency to become

---

[*] In an occasional instance use was made of the usual apparatus for determination of basal metabolic rate in order to make clearer to the patient variations in his breathing. Deutsch [121] and Alexander and Saul [16] in particular have reported observations along this line. (*See also* French and Alexander.[193])

[†] Wilhelm Reich has developed these principles in combination with psychoanalysis to a high degree, and created a "new therapeutic technique" which he terms vegetotherapy. Theodore P. Wolfe, has given special attention to this matter.

tense and in several instances to develop an anginal attack whenever discussing a particular aspect of her relationship to both her father and husband. Observations of such reactions proved useful not only to the physician but also to the patient who was thus made aware that a relationship existed between emotions and symptoms. The physician might say, for example, after marked changes in tensions or attacks had occurred several times: "Do you happen to remember what you were talking about each time you got tense?" or "each time you got an attack?" There is a danger connected with this procedure, however, if one is not sufficiently aware of the nature and intensity of the patient's conflicts. (See Case No. HP 3, page 107; and Case No. HP 1, page 40.) Dreams associated with attacks are useful in the same way (page 52).

These two techniques have been developed in the present study, but they are, of course, only an outgrowth of the psychosomatic approach. Felix Deutsch,[121] for example, as early as 1926, speaking of the technique of free association in the psychoanalytic procedure, made the following stimulating observation. It is possible to observe the somatic and the psychic components more nearly simultaneously if we ask the patient to give not only all his associations, but also all the accompanying somatic sensations. One soon finds to one's surprise that somatic sensations, which otherwise go quite unnoticed, slide in between associations, precede, or accompany them. One finds that these seemingly irrelevant somatic manifestations are full of meaning, and an inherent part of the existing psychic situation. If one is awake to these manifestations, one finds that scarcely anything happens in the body which is not understandable in terms of the psychic picture. One finds that the patient is speaking a double language, a somatic and a verbal one. To one experienced in interpreting it, the somatic language is as intelligible as is deaf-and-dumb language for the initiated. These somatic phenomena are outposts of the preconscious, the first signs of a content which is seen to become conscious and expressible in speech.

We observed, from this point of view, not only attacks occurring during interviews, but also the patient's whole life history, including not only onset and previous attacks of the illness in question, but also the complete illness history. This is particularly valuable as a check on the chronology established by the psychosomatic history when somatic symptoms and life situations have been arranged in parallel columns (page 99). Inconsistencies are often corrected and amnesias relieved. Most important of all, if the emotional setting of previous attacks and illnesses be compared with the emotional setting of attacks during interviews, clues are often obtained as to which factors have been more or less coincidental and which more dynamically related to the syndrome under observation.

Examples are:

Case No. RHDP 4. (Full history is given on page 137). A girl, 23 years old, with rheumatic heart disease, came to the clinic frequently, suffering from extreme dyspnea and palpitation and occasionally symptoms suggestive of beginning decompensation. She thought these were brought on by her dislike of the clinic. When she was studied by this method it appeared that the dyspnea and palpitation came on during an interview only when she was discussing the general subject of pregnancy or fear about her husband. Only then did she remember the emotional setting of her earliest attacks and the further fact that these attacks, apparently brought on by visiting the clinic, occurred only when she happened to go up in the elevator with a pregnant woman. When her fears and fantasies along these lines were clarified these attacks disappeared.

Case No. F. 25. A woman, 43 years old, had been in a taxi accident and after her recovery continued to have attacks highly incapacitating in their nature, including headache, palpitation, nausea, which the physician in charge ascribed to a general vasomotor instability and menopause, together with a desire to obtain the maximum compensation possible. These attacks came on during interviews in connection with one very specific topic,—a topic that had been uppermost in her mind at the time of the accident, which however, bore no specific relationship to the accident. When this problem was worked out with her the symptoms disappeared (and this was before the compensation question had been settled) and furthermore a subsequent taxi accident, in which she was frightened but uninjured, failed to bring them back.

III. Use of the Physician-Patient Relationship

If the reader will refer again to the preliminary interview given for Case No. DP 2 he will note that the patient's shift from lack of co-operation to a willingness to co-operate was considerably influenced by her reaction to the physician: "I like to talk to smart people." Furthermore, the physician in question was a woman and was known to teach medical students—hence a teacher, which she herself had always wished to be. If it be remembered that her son's lack of capacity to measure up to her ideal for him in this respect was an important factor in her illness and lack of co-operation, it is easy to appreciate the role played by the physician-patient relationship in her changed response. It is true that one of the physicians who had treated her previously for her diabetes was a woman, but as the patient herself said: "She was too busy to be interested in me, and she tried to take care of me like a mother (note patient's hatred for her mother) instead of talking to me like an equal as you do."

This is a very simple illustration, but such observations direct our attention to the extreme importance of the physician's knowledge of his own personality in general and in terms of its impact on the patient. If the physician is aware of the reactions usually produced in a patient by contact with him, he is in a better position to judge unexpected reactions and may learn much through study of them. Thus his personality itself may become an instrument useful in diagnosis as well as therapy.

When a patient reacts in an exaggerated or unexpected way, this may be because the physician has reminded him of some other individual or some experience of emotional importance in his life. The extent to which the patient's reaction is usual, unusual, rational or irrational, gives invaluable clues to the patient's past history and his personality. Transference has been called the sum total of the irrational elements in the patient's attitude toward any other individual (especially the physician)—a sort of mirror image of all his community relationships. Every physician is aware of the importance of objectivity, but it requires training to be objective concerning one's own personality, that is, concerning the *patient's reaction to oneself or one's reactions to the patient*. Yet experience indicates these factors objectively evaluated are of both diagnostic and therapeutic significance.[426] (For further discussion see Dunbar.[189]) But for them to become so, special observation and training beyond that of the ordinary experience with bedside manner is essential. This was acquired by all our associates in this study and is discussed further in subsequent sections of this chapter.

IV. FREE-ASSOCIATION

There has been much vague discussion and application of free-association as a technique useful to the physician in examination of nervous patients, especially with a view to relieving amnesias and bringing to light repressed material. The scientific discussions of the subject have come from psychoanalysts, for the most part as an element in the psychoanalytic procedure (page 117).

Obviously the set-up of our general hospitals is such as to provide a favorable background for general medical and surgical, rather than for psychoanalytic procedures. Free-association as part of the psychoanalytic process was not a part of our research routine, although an occasional patient for whom psychoanalysis seemed to be indicated was treated later by this method.

But a psychiatric consultation in a general hospital is very much like the preliminary interview in psychoanalytic practice. It is often possible to supplement this by daily interviews over a period of one or two weeks, thus carrying out a procedure more or less equivalent to a trial analysis. In this way the psychoanalytically trained psychiatrist can have some confidence in his diagnostic judgment and his recommendation as to therapy.

We were impressed with the quick response of most general medical patients to relatively superficial psychotherapy — though for an occasional patient psychoanalysis was indicated. The first part of this statement applies especially to patients whose major symptomatology was in the somatic rather than in the psychic sphere.

An interesting by-product of our study was the establishment of a better basis on which to determine the severity of the psychic component in the illness, so that a sharper distinction could be made between patients with a good and those with a poor prognosis by means of brief psychotherapy.*

Free-association was used, however, to a greater or lesser extent in conjunction with all the techniques described, more or less after the pattern of the "associative anamnesis" described by Deutsch.[122] For

---

* It is highly desirable that patients whose illness is complicated by a psychic component, for which intensive psychotherapy is the only procedure that is likely to be successful, be recognized and the situation explained to the attending physician. If some more superficial psychotherapeutic technique or no treatment at all is then decided on, the situation will be clear at the outset and our psychiatric clinics will be saved, in part, the reputation of being places where patients come back year after year, showing little or no improvement. A major problem for psychiatrists today is created by the fact that patients come to them too late. And because the situation is not made clear to the general physician, the impression has been that the best psychiatry can offer is a crutch for the hopeless. As a matter of fact there is no better way to see psychiatric patients early than to see them in a general hospital (Billings [36]).

example, a patient who showed a strong emotional reaction to one or another of his physicians might be asked of whom the physician reminded him. In this way he was frequently assisted in the recall of an experience with father, mother, brother, teacher, which shed light on the early onset of his illness. Or a patient who had a strong objection to being confined to bed, or a more than average enjoyment of it, might be asked what other life experience this recalled. In one instance the answer might be: punishment by father for a misdemeanor, a diet of bread and water, followed by running away from home, and a determination never again in all his life to allow himself to be put into a position where anyone could tell him what to do. Or the answer might be: "The only time mother ever paid attention to me or bothered about my troubles was when I was in bed. It was the only time I ever felt equal to my brothers and sisters." Answers such as these often provided an entering wedge into a discussion of the major maladjustments, disappointments, and traumatic experiences, sometimes leading also to a discussion of early illness in connection with such thwarting experiences.

The following case excerpt (Case No. RFO 145) may help to make these general statements more concrete. A married woman, aged 50, had had a thorough medical, neurological and endocrinological work-up to ascertain the basis for her increasing "arthritis." All these examinations were negative. For the preceding ten years she had been troubled by stiffness in both legs, then in her back and arms, which was rapidly interfering with her ability to walk. She said this trouble started after a series of gland injections during her menopause.

The chronology of her life history was as follows:

Events in Life Situation	*Patient's Response*
The patient was *born* a year after the death of her older sister at the age of 3 from diphtheria. For the death of this sister the patient's mother blamed her husband, the patient's father, who was a physician and refused to take the sister's illness seriously, thinking it was just croup or a cold "until it was too late."	The patient's earliest memories are of her mother's exaggerated concern over every minor illness including the croup, and numerous fights between her mother and father as to whether she would die like her sister because her father was not giving her adequate attention. As a child she had constant nightmares of "war in the distance." Furthermore, the

Events in Life Situation   *Patient's Response*

date of the patient's birth coincided
almost exactly with the date of her
sister's death, and on such anniversaries the daily lectures that she received from her mother concerning
her inferiority to the sister that died,
"who was a little angel," were repeated with ceremonial solemnity.

An Irish nurse who took care of
the patient during these early years
regaled her with stories of ghosts of
little children who had been killed
by their parents' neglect, coming
back on important anniversaries to
haunt and torment the wicked parents.

The patient began to have nightmares of being smothered to death as
her sister had been, or hallucinatory
experiences in which she saw this
"angelic" sister reproving her for
her bad behavior.

The patient's only sibling was a
half-brother, fifteen years her senior,
the issue of her mother's first marriage, in whom the mother was obviously more interested than she was in
the patient. But there were constant
conflicts between her father and
mother relative to this brother, who
was required by the (step) father to
become a physician like himself, so
that the brother could take over the
sanatorium (for treatment of rheu-
matics and arthritis) of which the
(step) father was head. The brother
was sensitive and literarily inclined,
and took the position that even
should he become a physician (as he
actually did) he would want to have
a city practice and not merely run a
sanatorium where people came to
die.

The patient was not good in athletics and was constantly taunted by
her father and her playmates about
being as clumsy as her father's patients.

Shortly after overhearing one of
these family conflicts, the patient

The patient became increasingly
clumsy at athletics, continued to

Events in Life Situation	*Patient's Response*
then *aged 4 or 5*, was playing with a little boy in the village, the son of the undertaker who took care of the final rites for patients in her father's sanatorium. The little boy said: "Do you know what father does to people that die?" The patient replied: "He closes their eyes and gives them a funeral." The little boy said: "You ought to know better than that. After they die they get stiffer than they were before so no one can bend their arms and legs without breaking them, then he takes away all their blood and injects them with something to make them look more natural, then he stuffs things into their mouths and down their throats so they can't breathe, and puts color on their faces so they look alive. I sometimes think they are alive and get buried that way." Shortly after this the patient saw a young woman of about 30, just after the undertaker had left, looking more alive and beautiful than the patient had ever seen her.	have attacks of croup, and nightmares of being buried alive.
At the age of 7 the patient was sent to school, entering a class of children most of whom had had at least one year's schooling. Her teacher, a man, was very rough over minor misdemeanors, holding up to her another girl in the class "who was a perfect angel."	The patient ran to her mother for protection and was disillusioned because her mother could not protect her from her teachers as she had protected her from her father and his tempers. The patient appealed to her father, who was stern with her, but helped her with her lessons, telling her at the same time that she must never dance or go to the movies because "those things made you sick."

Events in Life Situation

Age 17. The patient went away to college.

Age 18. "I had just about made up my mind to give up college and go home, although I had never felt so well as in that year, when father died, and brother took charge of the sanatorium to take care of mother. I went back to college and for the first time had a lot of admirers. The one I liked best frightened me because his idea of women was like my father's, and I didn't want to be a martyr. Then I became engaged to one of them, very gentle—some people called him a sissy—like my brother."

Age 19. The patient married her fiancé and was immediately disillusioned by discovering that, like her brother, he loved his mother more than anyone in the world, and that he was not very adequate in his profession. He held her up to the stand-

Patient's Response

She had felt that she must get away from home and have a chance to lead her own life, but she felt guilty because her father was then ill and disappointed in her brother (then an interne in a New York hospital), who refused to come home and help his father with the sanatorium. "At least I should have stayed at home. I should have stayed at home because of my mother too. She was always the martyr, doing just what father told her to, and needed me to help. I was angry with her for being like that and believing that women are only the servants of men, and I was ashamed of being angry."

"I kept on having a good time and felt like myself, although I kept asking myself what right did I have to be having such a good time when brother and mother were so miserable."

The patient accepted her husband's ideal of her and devoted herself to making a success of New York social life and running a home that both his mother and her mother could admire. She was constantly aggrieved because he refused to live

Events in Life Situation

ard of "being an angel like his mother" and took recourse to drinking and gambling whenever things went wrong.

Age 21. The patient took her mother and sister-in-law, who was then pregnant, to the theatre to see "Get Rich Quick."

Age 26. The patient gave birth to her first child.

The husband was disturbed by the additional responsibility of a child and blamed the patient for insisting on it. Her mother came to live with her.

Age 23 to 35. The patient's husband became a business success.

Age 35. "We had another child— this time he wanted it."

Age 37. "We went for our first real vacation in Florida. Everything was happy and we both *felt successful*. We had to come home early because my husband got a bad throat infection, a streptococcus. He died three days after we got back, when we had just moved into a new house we had bought."

Patient's Response

up to his responsibilities and was afraid to have a child.

The patient suddenly felt all eyes were focused on her instead of on the stage, questioning whether or not she was a failure. She felt she had to have a child. She felt smothered, as if the walls were closing in on her so there was no way out, and wondered if she would die.

During her pregnancy she had been disturbed by attacks of palpitation and stiffness, feeling smothered, clumsy, and as if she couldn't walk.

"I felt more and more a martyr like my mother, and let her take care of my daughter so I could devote myself to my husband. I was living a part on the stage of life, and since then I have never been able to go to the theatre without feeling smothered and stiff."

"I had made him a success and felt happy."

"I had palpitations again during pregnancy, and the doctor was surprised that I didn't die."

"During those three days I didn't know what was happening. The Irish maid kept seeing burglars at the window. She would run upstairs and tell me that the eyes she saw, or a black cat, meant bad luck and somebody was going to die."

Events in Life Situation	*Patient's Response*
Age 37–40. "My husband's best friend took me into his house which was close to ours, and he and his wife did everything for me."	"Before long I knew I was in love with him. He was a little frightening like my father. His wife was a baby and in love with a woman who came to the house every day and had more authority over his children than his wife had. I told him we couldn't go on keeping everything secret, that he must tell his wife that he wanted to marry me."
The man she loved finally yielded to her demands, but his wife said that although she knew he didn't love her, she liked her life as it was and if he suggested divorce she would ruin his business reputation. The man became frightened and told the patient that they must continue their affair *sub rosa*. (They had not had intercourse.)	The patient was disillusioned at this lack of courage, "broke it off" and moved to a different part of the country.
Age 40 to 50. The patient's elder daughter resented this move, saying that she was now the man of the family in her father's place (quoting a statement made by the patient's best female friend) and became completely unmanageable. The patient's best friend died of "menopausal complications."	The patient saw the man she loved in a final attempt to find a solution; she yielded in a vain hope that this would bring him to marry her. Immediately after the intercourse, the patient developed menopausal symptoms, "a smothering cold and stiffness. I felt as if life were ended for me."
The patient was treated by "endocrine injections" which did no good.	"I felt as if I were dead, and *all this were being done for me afterwards.*"

Note: This patient's history, taken in accordance with the psychosomatic history outline, given previously, revealed almost none of the details just given: She had had a completely happy childhood, she had had "a perfect husband," "two perfect children," and "everything one could wish in life." She had never in her "life been stiff before." It was only when she was questioned as to her associations with injections that she remembered the conflicts between father and brother about the sanatorium, the conversation with the undertaker's son, and the feelings of being stiff and smothered at the theatre. She said: "Well my blood was gone (*v.s.*). I felt that life was ended and when they started to inject me I was sure I was just a corpse the way he said. It all happened—the death of my friend from menopause, and my own sickness in January, on the anniversary of my sister's death."

It is important to note here only that *even such medical treatment as may be indicated may have associations in the mind of the patient which may render it more harmful than helpful.* When the injections stopped the patient improved slightly, only to have a more crippling attack when her daughter married the wrong man. "I felt I was becoming more and more dead."

V. SPECIAL TESTS

INTELLIGENCE TEST

The revised Stanford-Binet was used only occasionally as a means of checking our clinical impression. It was employed in the main for the purpose of excluding patients from study because, as set forth in Chapter III, we decided to limit our research material from the point of view of serial admissions to patients with normal intelligence.

RORSCHACH TEST

The Rorschach test was used in certain cases as an additional check on our impressions obtained from the psychosomatic history and the special techniques of examination described in this chapter. Its most specific aid at the beginning was in helping us to determine patients to be excluded from study because of actual or potential psychosis (Chapter III). Because this test was applied only in certain cases, and by way of check rather than as a routine measure, it will not be described here.* Our limited experience with it, however, convinced us that it has a real value if rightly used, not only to detect psychoses but also in study of the psychic component in the illness of "normal" patients. (See Case No. 34 FA, page 230.) The major handicap to its routine employment is of course the tremendous amount of time, training, and experience required for its adequate interpretation.

* Those interested may wish to consult Klopfer [272] and Rorschach. [361]

Like all highly geared tools it may be a detriment rather than an asset in unskilled hands. Z. Piotrowki, in a personal communication summarizes the field of usefulness of this test as follows:

As far as diagnosis is concerned the Rorschach method can be fruitfully used in determining whether or not the patient has a psychoneurosis, a functional psychosis or is suffering from a cerebral organic disorder which is affecting his personality. Thus the Rorschach can be an aid in discovering or in eliminating these mental disorders which might complicate the disease picture in cases suffering from a somatic illness (other than organic disorders of the central nervous system).

It seems that the Rorschach method could also be developed into an instrument of measurement. It might be possible to measure approximately although validly the degree to which the somatic disorder has disturbed the patient's personality, more precisely, the degree to which the somatic illness has widened the discrepancy between the actual and the potential functioning of the patient's mental capacities.

Our review of the literature indicates that to date no one has adequately studied the possible usefulness of the Rorschach test in outlining the typology of psychosomatic illness (Chapter XI).

At the conclusion of the study which has been used as a basis for this book it was decided that the potentialities of the Rorschach test in psychosomatic research should be investigated.* Up to the present time it has been possible to test only a small percentage of the 1500 patients covered in the original study. But the results are extremely suggestive, when taken in conjunction with a combined Rorschach and clinical study of a 1942 series of patients (about 100) admitted for the illnesses discussed in this book.

First, in a blind test covering not only fracture patients but others with organic syndromes, the expert correctly grouped the patients suffering from each type of illness though without attaching the diagnosis to the several groups.

Second, one group isolated was that which was accident-prone. The Rorschach expert picked out characteristic traits which proved to be corroborative of the points brought out in the personality profile.

---

* A continuation of the research with application of the Rorschach test was made possible by a special anonymous grant.

Miss Kemple's recent Rorschach study of these patients, however, accomplished not only this but also a clarification of three fairly clear-cut subgroups in the total fracture series (Chapter IV). It is interesting that the Rorschach study did not result in the discovery of major subgroups in the other syndromes studied. This fact supported our initial impression that there is greater homogeneity among sufferers from these other syndromes than among fracture patients.

VI. APPLICATION OF THESE TECHNIQUES—CASE ILLUS-
TRATIONS SHOWING SOURCES OF ERROR AND THEIR
THERAPEUTIC IMPLICATIONS

Having developed these techniques, and experimented with their applicability to our case material, we attempted to review the possible pitfalls in working with them. Those relating specifically to an evaluation of our own research methods are summarized in Chapter III. Those of greatest importance to the patient himself in terms of his therapeutic program and treatment are mentioned here. Incidentally, helpful as these aids are diagnostically, their effects in terms of therapy or the reverse are sufficiently deep-reaching so that the utmost care and skill are required in their use. This was of importance in training our assistants.

Case Illustration. The tremendous therapeutic importance of history-taking itself, as well as of some of these techniques, can be shown best perhaps in terms of an actual case whose symptoms were relieved by brief psychotherapy of which the history-taking constituted an integral part. In so doing it will be possible to illustrate both the dangers that make it important to stress psychiatric training of the physician who is to use some of these techniques, and the application we made of the procedures outlined.

Case No. HP 3.* A married woman, 39 years old, had suffered twenty years of invalidism as a result of gastro-intestinal and cardiovascular syndromes, including hypertension. Her symptomatology was relieved in ten periods of psychotherapy and she has remained symptom-free through eight years of follow-up. Her blood pressure is still normal.

* Case reported in somewhat different form in Dunbar [144] (pp. 556–558); and Dunbar [145] (pp. 1101–1102).

Chronology

Events in Life Situation	Patient's Response
At the *age of 11* the patient came to this country from Russia.	
At the age of 12 the patient had to help support her sick mother and father.	She felt resentment toward her older sister, who might have carried the responsibility and allowed the patient to realize her ambition to finish high school and go to college.
Age 12–16. The patient worked up in a business office from filing clerk to private secretary and went to night school at the same time. She then fell in love and her parents forebade her to marry.	The patient felt increased resentment toward her parents and her older sister; and there followed a struggle with the man on the subject of marriage; i.e., she was not sure she loved him anyway.
Age 21. She made a final decision to marry the man although she still was not sure she loved him.	She felt guilty about her disobedience to her parents, although she was of age, and had decided to continue her job and go on supporting them as before.
Age 21–22. The patient was disillusioned with her husband and shocked over the sexual relationship, for which she was totally unprepared. Father underwent an operation for carcinoma of the stomach.	She developed *severe attacks of nausea and vomiting* which necessitated giving up the job.
The patient consulted a general physician who assured her that her indigestion would be cured by a pregnancy.	Pregnancy, nine months of which she spent in bed, vomiting steadily, losing weight and "nearly died" when the baby was born.
Difficult labor and instrumental delivery of a daughter.	According to the statement of the attending physician she had *high blood pressure*.
Age 22–25. At the age of six weeks this daughter was operated on for pyloric spasm and was somewhat sickly thereafter. The patient's husband became interested in other women.	The patient was unable to recover from her delivery and continued to have attacks of nausea and vomiting. At the age of 23 she had an appendectomy and shortly thereafter an abortion.

Events in Life Situation

Age 25–37. The patient's husband showed little interest in working and there were many financial reverses which reached a peak in 1929 when the patient was 36 years old. Her husband continued his interest in other women.

Age 37. The patient's father died of gastric carcinoma. The patient had been estranged from her father since the time of her marriage. Her mother, who was suffering from hypertension and angina pectoris, came to live with her.

Age 38½. After one and a half years of treatment in the medical clinic which had resulted in no improvement, the patient was emaciated and depressed. Her mother died of "angina pectoris."

Patient's Response

The patient remained in bed for most of these years suffering from attacks of nausea, vomiting, and abdominal pain not related to meals. She became a member of an Ethical Culture Society and a Christian Scientist. She studied Theosophy and Yogi.

The patient came to the hospital complaining of anorexia, nausea between meals and burning pain in the epigastrium not related to meals. She complained also of attacks of palpitation and frequent lumps in her throat. Physical examination and all laboratory tests were negative. It was decided that she had gastric neurosis, but teeth and tonsils were investigated for possible foci of infection, and she was put on an ulcer diet. Then what looked like a chronic salpingitis was discovered and treated in the gynecological clinic. The patient failed to improve under medical treatment, lost 15 lbs. weight, had frequent attacks which kept her in bed for days or weeks at a time, with nausea, vomiting and severe pain.

Subsequent to her mother's death, nearly a year before her visit to the department of psychiatry, she had been unable to sleep, was awakened by nightmares in which she saw her father and mother jumping out of their graves.

Her physicians suspected a hysterical element which they tried to handle on the "talking out" basis,

Events in Life Situation   *Patient's Response*

but she failed to improve. At the end of two years of treatment we have the following note on the chart: "Pelvic symptoms negligible; patient complains of weakness, dizziness, trembling, nausea, palpitation, tenderness and pain over the eyes, and vague pains all over the body associated with numbness. Now carries a cane regularly because of fear of falling. Refer to psychiatry as soon as possible."

The patient was first seen in the department of psychiatry on the following day (two years after her initial visit to the medical department) and in addition to the gastrointestinal story, the patient complained particularly of pains in her arms and legs. She complained also of attacks of anginal pain and said that a private physician had told her that her blood pressure was over 200. She was dizzy, could not focus her eyes, staggered in walking, and complained of pain in her ears. Blood pressure recorded at this time was 190/100 and heart rate 130.

It became clear that her inability to focus her eyes, dizziness, etc., was the result of a sedative habit. She had been getting from the clinic chloral hydrate and bromide regularly and, in addition, from her friend the corner druggist, triple bromide tablets and from a distant cousin of the family, luminal; all of which she had been taking regularly three or more times a day.

She said of the period when she was torn between her parents and her suitor: "If only there had been someone to advise me. I was nearly crazy. I used to cry myself to sleep every night and wake up with nightmares feeling sure I was going to marry the wrong man, and yet I somehow couldn't help it." The patient was completely unprepared for the marriage relationship, and her early adjustment was further complicated by the fact that she felt guilty for having disobeyed and deserted her parents. Her husband, who was far below her socially, made it difficult for her to entertain her friends, made fun of her aspirations and intellectual interests, and after a few difficult months began to go with other women. She complained that he was not better than her father in that he could not earn enough money to support her. Since the abortion sixteen years previously there had been either the avoidance of the sexual relationship or the practice of coitus interruptus. She had refused contraception advice because she hated the relationship anyway, and was afraid it would give her husband more excuse for insisting.

Summary of Psychosomatic Examination and Treatment

Obviously this is a patient for whom one would have favored intensive psychotherapy. Because of the limitations imposed by clinic conditions she was seen only ten times during a period of two months. The central problem handled was that of her rage and repressed aggressive tendencies, these being brought into conscious relationship with her symptoms. This having been accomplished, she spontaneously sought advice as to sexual hygiene.

This patient was seen subsequently on three follow-up visits at intervals of two, four, and six months. She has remained completely symptom-free for more than nine years and her blood pressure has registered in the neighborhood of 130/87 on each of these visits.

The patient's relationship to her husband has changed completely. She stopped attacking and blaming him, she accepted the fact that she was intellectually superior to him, and began to help him with his work. As a result even though all this happened during the period of the 1929 economic depression, he went rapidly ahead in business, and the circumstances of the family improved so that she was able to send her daughter to college. The patient accepts the fact that her marriage may have been a mistake, and says that if she had had in her teens the opportunity of psychiatric help she probably would have married a different man. But she is going to look at things as they are.

In this case history we have a gastro-intestinal picture suggestive of ulcer, and typical anginal attacks of incapacitating severity, together with cardiac arrhythmia, tachycardia and an actually increased blood pressure. There was an increasingly acute symptomatology which did not yield to medical treatment, but disappeared rapidly when attention was directed to the underlying emotional disturbance. It is possible that this patient, like many others, might have been saved eighteen years of invalidism had the meaning of her disease picture been understood earlier in its psychic and somatic components. Of course at present we can say only that the symptomatology has been interrupted. But it is important to note that there had been no symptom-free periods during the eighteen years of her illness preceding her psychiatric treatment, and she has been followed for nine years since.

Considering this patient's story in terms of *predisposing* factors to her illness, we find on the physiological side a possible hereditary factor in cardiac disease on the part of the patient's mother. On the other hand, assumption of a hereditary factor often blinds the physician to psychic factors which are of far greater clinical importance. In this patient at least, a large part of what might be called a hereditary factor proved to be "pseudo-hereditary," resting on a psychic basis, involving imitation and identification. Before her initial visit to the medical clinic her father, from whom she had been estranged since her marriage, had died of cancer of the stomach. (His first stomach operation had coincided with her marriage, in which she had both disobeyed and refused to support him, following which her own gastro-intestinal complaints began.) After his death she went to care for her mother, who was suffering from angina pectoris and high blood pressure, from which she died six months before the patient's first visit to the psychiatric clinic. The patient's attacks of dyspnea and palpitation had begun when she went to nurse her mother, and the anginal syndrome, together with nightmares and sleeplessness, commenced after her mother's death, concerning which she felt unaccountably guilty.

These symptoms, furthermore, had a definite meaning to the patient which became clear in the course of treatment. She complained that her mother was always nervous and sickly and her father could never earn enough money. She had felt herself overpowered, crushed by the personality of the older sister who took the place of the weak and sickly mother, forcing her to give up school and go to work to help support the sick parents. This situation was a determining factor, both in her unfortunate marriage against her parents' wishes at the end of six years struggle with them, and in her subsequent illness.

The fact that this patient has remained well for nine years, there having been no symptom-free periods in her eighteen years of invalidism, is the more interesting in that her external situation has not changed very much. Although, as previously pointed out, the patient's attitude toward her husband changed, and during the first year following the treatment she helped him so much with his work that he went rapidly ahead in business, four years ago he again suffered serious financial reverses and entered into a new love affair. The patient has reacted to these things on a common sense basis rather than by symptom formation and has succeeded in staying well without further treatment, although the external situation is again more difficult. The fact that the blood pressure continues at a normal level means that she is to some degree protected against the *secondary or organic changes* which probably would have developed had her blood pressure persisted at a level of 200/100.

The *first period* of psychiatric treatment, as so often happens in such cases, was entirely occupied by an attempt to resolve the patient's resentment at having been sent to see a psychiatrist. She had seen some twenty doctors in her life and been to all big clinics. She had tried Christian Science, Ethical Culture and Yogi and they had all failed her. Now her doctors were sending her to psychiatry, which meant that they were no longer taking her seriously and had given up her case; they had decided that her pains were all imaginary. The patient walked up and down the room alternately weeping and shouting, her hair in disarray. After letting her express her feelings, the physician stated emphatic agreement with her where agreement was possible, e.g., that if her doctors thought her pain was imaginary they were wrong; pain on an emotional basis is just as real as pain on a physical basis, for example, your heart beats faster when you are frightened or excited just as it may when you have a fever, and both are equally real, etc. This provided an excellent opening for suggesting that she lie down for a little physical check-up. In connection with this her extreme muscular tension was pointed out to her and she was asked to relax. In this interview she was asked practically no questions, but she gained the impression that whatever else was wrong, learning something about relaxation might help her.

It is not necessary to comment on the importance of taking the patient's pain (in this case anginal syndrome and gastro-intestinal symptoms) seriously, whatever its origin. *Physiological functioning may be as seriously disturbed by fear as by bacteria or toxins.*

The *second period* (beginning with checking-up on the patient's ability to relax, and asking her to try to relax as much as possible during the interview), was occupied entirely with the taking of the patient's history. Because this patient presented an unusually satisfactory entering wedge into her deeper problems in the form of stereotyped nightmares, almost all of her history was taken by way of association to these. Of course no searching questions were asked. The nightmares consisted in vivid pictures of her parents jumping up and down in their graves. She would waken in an anginal attack. It was necessary to comment only that she must have a deep emotional relationship to her parents, in order to have her pour forth the story of her life, of their illnesses, of her guilt and resentment. Incidentally, the illnesses had not been recorded in the medical history, although the father had had his first operation for gastro-intestinal cancer at the time of onset of her gastro-intestinal symptoms, and her mother had died of angina pectoris at the time of onset of the patient's anginal syndrome. This had made a particularly deep impression, because the patient had been estranged from her parents through her marriage against their wishes. The relationship to her mother had been restored only after the father's death when it was necessary for the patient to care for her during her terminal illness.

In the course of relating these things, the patient, on several occasions, had put her hand over her heart, become cyanotic, and developed a severe anginal attack. It should be noted that no interpretative comment was made on this material. This fact is important because during a discussion of this patient with a group of third-year students a question arose as to the significance of the stereotyped nightmares; should they be disregarded or could they be made useful in any way? A student immediately spoke up: "Why, of course, the first thing you do would be to tell her that the nightmares showed she had incest wishes and that's what made her sick." Incidentally, it should be noted that so far as the medical curriculum was concerned these students were innocent of Freud. They had just entered their third year, beginning with the medical, not the psychiatric clerkship. The moral here, and a moral might well be pointed out, is that such ideas are likely to be put into the heads of patients by physicians who have tried to make up for their lack of psychiatric training by reading some popular books on psychoanalysis and using the impressions so derived in conjunction with their general medical or neurological experience. From what happened in the two succeeding therapeutic periods it should be clear that had some well-meaning physician enlightened our patient in this way the results might have been for him unexpected and for her disastrous rather than therapeutic.

In the *third period*, continuing by way of association with the nightmares, which also continued, further history was taken and it was pointed out to the patient both on this occasion and on the preceding one that pain, cyanosis, tachycardia, and dyspnea had occurred in relation to certain specific material: She had said, "I felt crushed by the family. I was overpowered by my sister and resented not having the strength of mind to leave them and set out on my own. At night I used to feel a heavy weight on top of me. Father was so weak and useless. Mother was worse. I was frightened of her, and yet I needed to be taken care of."

At the beginning of the *fourth period*, the patient said, "The nightmares changed: I woke up in the night having an attack. This time I saw lightning over my parents' graves and their faces peering out. I felt murderous, as if I could kill them, and I felt all day that if I picked up a knife I might kill. I have never felt that way before in my life. I didn't know I could be like that. It's terrible. I wanted to smother them in their graves."

At this point it was necessary to hold the patient back a little in her associations (discussing her repressed aggression, fear and guilt), because of the tendency to act out which came with the welling up of the emotional material related to her symptoms. Skill is necessary in order to keep this tendency in check and protect the patient from these impulses. The popular impression among laymen and medical men as well, that catharsis always does good is far from a universal truth. This patient might even have killed her husband under the stress of the emotions released, especially if she had been subjected to the trauma of being told that she had incest wishes. Some patients have damaged themselves and others with this type of assistance from well-meaning physicians.

In the *fifth period*, the patient said: For the first time in my life that I can remember, I have been able to talk with my husband and sit quietly and not fidget. I feel confident of my world. I am relaxed but something funny happened. I tried to talk about business and did not lose my temper. But afterwards I had an attack and fainted.

Here we see clearly a vegetative syndrome, or what has been called a more or less generalized response of the vegetative nervous system affecting diverse organs, released as the muscle tension and much of the emotional tension was relaxed. And even such vegetative release is not always without danger, especially in patients with actual organic damage.

By the time of the *sixth period* (a week later) the stereotyped nightmares had stopped and also the anginal attacks and gastro-intestinal symptoms. She had a vague dream of curly things, and considerable fear. She said: "Those thoughts about my sad state made my heart go. Sometimes I feel as though I might get asthmatic."

Here we have another symptom which we know to be related to the conflict between acting out and repressing.[144, 145]

In the *seventh period* the patient spontaneously brought up her practical problem for discussion along common sense lines. She said, "whether or not my marriage eighteen years ago was a mistake, two courses are open to me; divorce and supporting myself and my daughter; or to see what I çan do toward working out a satisfactory relationship with my husband. I have realized that all along, but I was too sick to *think* about it."

This illustrates the function of the illness in keeping emotions away from consciousness, and accordingly their blocking of thought.

As we all know, few patients need to be given advice as to what to do when once they are emotionally free to *think* about their problems. We often give patients too little credit in this respect, perhaps because of some idea that we must be all-wise. The "all-wise counsellor" often carries his patient along a different road from the road to health. To the extent to which the road is the road to health, such physicians do literally carry or drag their patients along it, and a really healthy adult prefers his own two feet to his parents' shoulders.

The remaining three periods with the patient were devoted to a working-through of the matter. Incidentally, this did not involve elaborate interpretation. (This patient has remained symptom-free to the present moment without so far as I know ever having heard of an oedipus complex.) Her history is given in earlier reports.[150]

VII. The Role Played by Psychoanalytic Orientation in the Application of These Techniques

GENERAL

In the course of this chapter, especially under the heading of free-association, reference was made to psychoanalysis. The place of psychoanalysis among diagnostic and therapeutic techniques is still a matter of question, controversy, and misunderstanding, not only for laymen and for physicians in the other medical specialties, but even for psychiatrists themselves. Hence a brief and somewhat elementary picture of this discipline within the framework of modern medicine may be useful as an introduction to our orientation in this field from the point of view of the study to be described.

An important change in the attitude of physicians is coming about because of an increasing appreciation of the exigency of further research concerning the psychic component in many of those illnesses which at present confront medicine with its most baffling problems. Even the question of possible approaches to the psychosomatic problem has found medicine at a loss and embarrassed by an awareness of difficulties for the overcoming of which science seemed to offer no proper tools. Recent research has indicated that psychoanalysis has a unique contribution here.

Psychiatrists have to admit that when psychiatric aid has been sought by physicians from the ranks of general medicine, the psychiatrist of the past has had little to offer, except in the case of patients suffering from severe mental illness or from a psychoneurosis with outspoken symptomatology. General physicians have found their own common sense and experience more satisfactory than the psychiatrist's when it came to dealing with emotional aspects of somatic disorders. Yet at the same time they are increasingly aware of the need of more specific knowledge.

It is important to remember that psychiatry is relatively new as a medical specialty; that it operates in a field left uncharted by the medicine and the medical sciences of the last one hundred years; that it has been forced to grow up more or less like Topsy to meet an urgent demand. Anatomy, physiology, clinical medicine, epidemiology, and even microscopic analysis had all passed into what has been called the "modern stage" before Pinel in 1793 removed the chains from the sufferers at the Bicêtre in Paris and insisted that he was dealing with sick patients, not criminals and sinners possessed by devils. Cellular pathology, anesthesia, antiseptic surgery, bacteriology, were all well developed before there was such a thing as descriptive psychiatry or psychiatric diagnosis, even to the extent of distinction between the feeble-minded, epileptic, general paretic, or any psychiatric methodology. It was just one hundred years after Pinel's remarkable reform that Freud with Breuer issued his preliminary paper on the "psychic mechanism of hysterical phenomena." (The first lumbar puncture was done three years previously.) It was slightly later, that is only some forty years ago, that Freud gave up the practice of hypnotic catharsis and laid the foundation for the psychoanalytic method.

Medicine took a great step forward with Virchow and the development of pathology, again with Pasteur and bacteriology, and Ehrlich and immunology. Today the physician who is *au courant* speaks of the chemical basis of medical practice, or the physiological basis of medical practice, and reads books and articles bearing such titles. But success in medical practice rests on an understanding of its basis not merely in chemistry or .physiology but in psychophysiology. Yet what tool has medicine had for the observation of such sequences that can in any way be compared with chemical analysis and the techniques developed by physiology? Until thirty or forty years ago medicine had no hope of such a tool. This lack (added to the danger of intermingling sequences which at the present stage of our knowledge must be kept distinct) accounts in large part for the fact that the physician interested in psychosomatic medicine so often finds himself dealing with what seems to be a vicious circle. The problem eludes his grasp like the surface of a well-oiled sphere.

A terrain to us inaccessible or only clumsily accessible, however, is conquered with agility by the mountain goat aided by a relatively simple equipment consisting of a sharp edge to the hoofs supplemented by rubber-like pads, an equipment which is strikingly similar to that needed by anyone who would gain access to the heights and depths of the human personality. In other words, physicians, including psychiatrists, not only have lacked an instrument by means of which to gain a foothold on the hard surface presented by the psychosomatic unity, but also and perhaps to make up for this lack, have been inclined to be too aggressive. They have had recourse to a rapid fire of questions, quizzing patients about the secrets of their lives and souls, against which, as already shown, patients cannot but defend themselves by conscious lies and unconscious censorship, no matter how co-operative they may desire to be. It is a law of nature that the inner citadel of the personality is not taken by storm, or if so taken is destroyed thereby. The psychiatrist then must progress by other means. His technique must be incisive, he needs a sharp-edged tool, but if he is to hold his ground he must have something like the rubber pads of the mountain goat to enable him to wait quietly, maintaining his equilibrium no matter what crags and chasms in the human being he has partly seen. This is perhaps the essence of the psychoanalytic technique and, combined with its microscopic quality, the reason that up to the present it is our instrument of greatest precision in diagnosis and control of psychic processes as well as of their somatic manifestations. It is of course important that adequate attention be given to these manifestations in terms of general medical care also, but this alone is very often self-defeating [138, 427] as is shown by some of the cases cited.

It should be clear from the foregoing that valuable as psychoanalysis is as a therapeutic technique, it is even more valuable to the psychiatrist in the general hospital, who thereby acquires training in the maintenance of equilibrium as well as in the application and interpretation of the techniques just described. This equilibrium is a prerequisite, for objective scientific study must be as nearly as possible automatic, or at least without effort such as to interfere with concentration and keenness of observation. The physician's equipment should be such as to offer the best protection we know against making false steps and jumping to hasty conclusions because confused by reverberations within himself as human being or as scientist.

While any physician may apply the techniques described in this chapter, they are most readily employed by one with psychoanalytic training. A physician with such training has had already more practice in the use of free-association and the interpretation of the significant material that is yielded by the patient in this manner.

Analysis of the libido elements as explained in Freud's earlier work will of course not be possible in interviews of this kind, though knowledge of this subject may offer illuminating suggestions. Libido analysis concentrates on the instinctual drives such as love or aggression, their thwarting in early life, and the nature of the basic conflicts which lie deeply hidden in the unconscious; only long-continued and thorough treatment can uncover these conflicts. But experience in analysis of the character or ego as developed in the more recent practice of psychoanalysis will often enable the examiner to recognize quickly the character traits of the patient and to classify his emotional type, thus focusing the attention on areas where trouble is to be expected, and on his habits of dealing with difficult situations.

Character analysis does not focus on probing to the depths of the unconscious and the instinctual life as in analysis of the libido, but rather on the manner in which the patient's defenses against his conflicts have found expression in his habits of feeling, thought and action, and have warped or colored his personality (Kardiner [260]).

The psychoanalytically trained physician is alert for signs pointing to crucial conflicts and defenses against them in the significant omissions made by the patient. He is prepared to recognize defense mechanisms of almost infinite variety, not only in physical symptoms observed in attacks induced by particular parts of the examination, but, for example, in over-reactions in speech, rationalizations, slips of the tongue, and many variations of facial expression, posture or muscle tonus. He is accustomed to the physician-patient relationship in the psychoanalytic sense of "transference," and is experienced in utilizing this relationship to elicit relevant information and in preventing it either from blocking * the patient or obscuring an objective view on his own part.

It is against this background that I decided that psychoanalytic training should be added to general medical and psychiatric training as a basic part of the fundamental preparation for this study of psychosomatic problems. Subsequent associates and assistants have all had good general medical and psychiatric experience. Those who had had psychoanalytic training in addition were much more successful in their ward and research work than those who had not had

* As in the case of the woman physician who was unable to get the co-operation of patient No. DP 2 because she was too motherly in her attitude toward a patient who hated her mother and motherhood as well. This attitude might have been very helpful to a patient of a different make-up and experience.

it, and all of them either during or after their research service in connection with this study have reached the same conclusion.

SUMMARY IN TERMS OF SPECIFIC POINTS

Any physician's success in using these techniques will depend to a considerable degree on his undergraduate and graduate training in psychiatry, as well as on his human understanding and the length and breadth of his clinical experience. Here, as in abdominal palpation, much experience is required for development of the right touch and the ability to learn from it.

We have been seriously hampered by the lack of adequate means of estimating the psychic component of many of the most important illnesses with which we have had to deal. The usual psychiatric examination is inadequate, as just indicated, and also clumsy and time-consuming. It is as unsuitable for routine office use as were many procedures for blood analysis when first discovered. Now some of the more fundamental of these can be carried out quickly with a few drops of blood and with sufficient accuracy to serve as a guide. This is the more important in view of the additional responsibility with which we are confronted as medicine is called upon to deal with social problems such as health insurance. It is interesting, for example, that the panel physician in England is already being urged to equip himself with at least rudimentary psychiatric knowledge.

The material given as *additional diagnostic aids* the general physician can use only partially, and probably for his purposes these points should be observed merely as *additional clues*. The difficulties in the way of his adequate evaluation of a psychosomatic history are as follows:

(1) The most valuable information is that given by the patient spontaneously, and the general physician often has neither the time nor the skill to obtain such information. He can, however, give special attention to what happens to be given, bearing in mind the importance of avoiding the type of comment that would lead the patient to suspect that he takes any particular attitude toward what is said, other than that of the interested listener.

(2) Spontaneous statements, associations, dreams, and gestures have a significance to the psychiatrist in terms of the patient's personality structure, repressed conflicts, and all that lies below the level of consciousness, which they can never have to the general physician, just as is the case with neurologi-

cal signs of cerebral injury, only the most obvious of which the general physician has either the training or the constant experience to recognize or evaluate.

(3) The general physician (whether he be member of a general hospital staff, family physician, or attached to some social group such as an insurance company or factory), is usually associated with discipline and is somewhat in the position of a judge from whom the patient awaits the sentence; operation or no operation, confinement to bed, or discharge. This in itself puts the patient more on his guard than he is with the psychiatric consultant.

(4) Of all our diagnostic and therapeutic resources there is none more important in the psychosomatic field than the *transference situation*, and for its adequate understanding and use psychiatric training is essential. Many points suggested could be incorporated in the general medical history, and it is hoped that in the course of time this will be done. Even these, however, may need to be evaluated by the psychiatrist (who is psychoanalytically trained) and supplemented by such additional examination as only he can give.

An important practical example here is the following: All patients, when ill, regress in some degree to infantile attitudes, placing the physician in the position of parent or nurse, from whom the utmost of care is demanded, but whom, on the other hand, it is very amusing to trick or annoy.

Such behavior on the part of the patient is revealing. Its correct handling is of great therapeutic importance. It has been a determining factor in the skill of physicians from ancient times and has usually been referred to under the heading of "bedside manner." Today we recognize it as an integral part of the physician-patient relationship, and recognize the importance of scientific control of it. Scientific control of it, however, is possible only by those who have had the best training at present available (psychoanalysis) in the handling of transference phenomena. It has been said that psychiatry is the oldest of the medical arts, and the youngest of the medical sciences. The scientific evaluation of the physician-patient relationship has been a determining factor in opening the way for psychiatry to develop also as a science.

VIII. Conclusions

To anyone inexperienced in this field, these two chapters on psychosomatic history and technique of examination are likely to be disappointing. He will wish that the complete list of questions asked had been set down. It should be noted that no such list can be given, that what is and is not asked depends on what the patient has contributed spontaneously and on the total physician-patient situation.

Incidentally, even if such a list were given, it would not be used in the same way by every physician. A very elementary illustration at this point is the following: One of our young assistants asked the question in connection with the patient's illness: "Has anything been worrying you?" Attention has already been called to the fact that this question usually should not be asked (page 78). The patient, as usually happens, said flatly, "No." The physician, however, retrieved himself by saying: "Well, *why would* anything worry you? You have two lovely children, your husband has a job . . ." In the course of this enumeration the patient interrupted, saying, "Yes, doctor, all you say is true but you don't understand; my husband loves his mother more than he does me and insists upon having her live with us and upsets the children so I'll never be able to bring them up. . . !" A medical student who had read this interview asked his patient the same question: "Has anything been worrying you?" The patient said, "No." The medical student than said: "Well, *why would* anything worry you anyway?" The patient responded: "That's right, doctor, why would it, nothing does." Considerable time was required to make clear to the student why use of the same words with merely a different emphasis and context elicited a less satisfactory response from the patient. And of course such factors as these enter into history-taking in many salient ways.

Information relative to the patient's difficulties and his characteristic ways of dealing with them must be obtained with technical accuracy in sufficient detail to make possible the evaluations indicated under diagnostic points. One learns history-taking by taking histories and evaluating them. The psychiatric history and examination more than any other approaches in quality the surgical operation which cannot be learned merely from a description of procedure.

Nevertheless, our associates, although, like ourselves, at a loss at the beginning, in spite of their previous training in medicine and psychiatry, learned to use these methods very quickly. For the reader, this chapter and the preceding one will have their major usefulness as description of the techniques by way of which we studied the clinical material to be described in the remainder of the volume. It is hoped that they will provide a basis for evaluation of the criteria (page 163) on which our conclusions are based, together with the conclusions themselves.

Chapter III

REVIEW OF GENERAL HOSPITAL ADMISSIONS

When pestilence falls on the people there is a story to tell. The story of the people who do not fall sick has never been told. Perhaps it is the most important part of epidemiology.— GEDDES SMITH, *Plague on Us.*

I. MATERIAL AND PROCEDURE

The background for our choice of problem area and material has been given in the Introduction to this volume. Our general approach, techniques and methods have been described in Chapters I and II. This chapter will be devoted to a statistical review of serial admissions to Presbyterian Hospital of patients suffering from cardiovascular disease, diabetes, or fracture. This review will be restricted to patients in these three groups admitted over a four-year, and in two instances a five-year period. Patients suffering from gastrointestinal disease, skin disease, and allergy, as well as individuals from the three disease groups mentioned who were studied during the first four years of this study, are not included in this statistical picture. They will be discussed, however, in the special chapters to follow.*

As was indicated in the Introduction, the illnesses here discussed are responsible for the majority of mortality and disability today, and are both the most frequently encountered and the most puzzling to the general practitioner. (See Tables I and II.) Better methods of dealing with them, furthermore, would lift a tremendous financial burden from the community.

---

* Material relating to asthma and hay fever has already been published.[150] Subsequent publications will relate to gastro-intestinal and skin disease.

TABLE I[1]

RANK OF SPECIFIED CHRONIC DISEASES ACCORDING TO FOUR INDICES

CHRONIC DISEASE	RANK ACCORDING TO			
	Estimated No. of Days Lost, 1937 (Health Survey)	Estimated No. of Invalids, 1937 (Health Survey)	Estimated No. of Cases, 1937 (Health Survey)	Estimated No. of Deaths, 1937 (Census Bureau)
Nervous and mental diseases....	1	1	10‡	7
Rheumatism..................	2	2	1	14
Heart diseases................	3	3	2	1
Arteriosclerosis and high blood pressure...................	4	5	3	3
Tuberculosis (all forms)........	5†	4	15	5
Cancer and other tumors.......	6	9	13	2
Nephritis and other kidney diseases......................	7	7	9	4
Diseases of female organs.......	8	10	14	15
Hay fever and asthma..........	9	8	4	19
Diseases of gallbladder and liver	10	12	17	8
Diabetes mellitus.............	11	·6	16	6
Ulcers of stomach and duodenum	12	14	20	10
Hernia......................	13	13	5	12
Chronic diseases of the skin.....	14	16	22	*
Anemia......................	15	15	23	16
Diseases of bladder and urethra .	16	18	21	17
Chronic bronchitis.............	17	17	8	18
Chronic appendicitis...........	18	28	24	*
Goiter and other thyroid diseases	19	20	11	13
Other diseases of the circulatory system......................	20	19	18	11
Sinusitis.....................	21	24	12	20
Varicose veins.................	22	21	7	21, 22
Chronic tonsillitis and other throat affections.............	23	23	19	*
Hemorrhoids..................	24	25	6	21, 22
Chronic pleurisy..............	25	27	27	*
Chronic diseases of the eye.....	26	11	25	*
Chronic diseases of the ear......	27	26	26	*
Diseases of the prostate and male genitourinary organs.........	28	22	28	9

* Excluded from ranking because death rates include both acute and chronic conditions.

† If the estimate for this disease were complete, it would probably rank fourth.

‡ If the estimate for these diseases were complete, this group would probably rank seventh.

[1] Reprinted with permission from Boas, Ernst P., The Unseen Plague—Chronic Disease, pp. 12.

TABLE II [1]

ESTIMATED PREVALENCE OF SPECIFIED CHRONIC DISEASES IN THE
UNITED STATES AND ESTIMATED NUMBER OF THOSE INVALIDED
BY THESE DISEASES

DISEASE	TOTAL NUMBER OF CASES IN U. S.	TOTAL NUMBER OF INVALIDS IN U. S.
Rheumatism.............................	6,850,000	147,600
Heart diseases...........................	3,700,000	144,200
Arteriosclerosis and high blood pressure.......	3,700,000	60,900
Hay fever and asthma......................	3,450,000	29,200
Hernia..................................	2,100,000	16,000
Hemorrhoids.............................	2,000,000	2,900
Varicose veins...........................	1,750,000	6,200
Chronic bronchitis........................	1,700,000	9,200
Nephritis and other kidney disease............	1,550,000	31,000
Nervous and mental diseases.................	1,450,000	269,300
Goiters.................................	1,200,000	8,300
Cancer and other tumors....................	930,000	28,100
Diseases of female organs...................	720,000	18,500
Tuberculosis—all forms.....................	680,000	77,900
Diabetes Mellitus.........................	660,000	34,300
Diseases of gall bladder and liver............	640,000	16,100
Ulcers of stomach and duodenum.............	330,000	16,000
Diseases of bladder and urethra..............	270,000	8,900

[1] Reprinted with permission from Boas, Ernst P., The Unseen Plague—Chronic Disease,
pp. 13.

SELECTION OF MATERIAL

Our selection of material was for the purpose of providing contrast groups, since control groups were out of the question. Aside from their importance in public health terms (see Chapter I) these particular groups of patients were chosen for the following reasons:

(1) In the interest of perspective, there seems to be a real advantage in routine study of total admission groups rather than of special cases that are referred because an important emotional element has impressed the internist or surgeon.

(2) By way of eliminating some obvious variables, this study was limited to patients in the four decades 15 to 55. (Such a study of patients under 15 is, of course, of supreme importance but demands somewhat different techniques; whereas with patients over 55 the picture becomes confused or at least complicated by senescence, and the number of patients in whom the

malignant process, once reversible, has become essentially irreversible, increases rapidly.)

(3) From the point of view of contrast the three groups of patients selected seem particularly suitable. An actual control group in the strict sense of the word was, of course, practically out of the question. (Incidentally, the general medical man inclines to regard fracture patients as the most "nearly normal" of any group of patients in the hospital, that is, except where compensation is a factor and there he becomes puzzled about a syndrome which he has semi-humorously labeled "compensitis.")

(4) These groups present contrasts not only with one another but also with the groups in which what Alexander has called the vector factor is more prominent, such, for example, as groups with gastro-intestinal or genito-urinary disturbances, where the physiological function is clear cut and lends itself readily to the expression of dynamic tendencies in such categories as incorporation, elimination, and retention.

(5) From a psychosomatic point of view there is probably no more fundamental detriment to the organism's equilibrium, together with its capacity to make adjustments (that is to maintain homeostasis), than the degree of anxiety, and in the diabetic and cardiovascular groups anxiety is a prominent factor. In their somatic and psychic conditioning and in expression of the anxiety these two groups appear to present a contrast with the fracture group. Subjectively, that is from the patient's point of view, there is a significant contrast in that in the diabetic and cardiovascular group the danger as well as the handicap is more diffuse and threatens from within, whereas in the fracture group the danger as well as the damage produced is concrete and seems to have come from the outside.

(6) Practically, it is advantageous that for diabetic and cardiac patients we have some of the most satisfactory objective measures yet available as part of hospital routine, i.e., blood chemistry, pulse and blood pressure curves, electrocardiograms (and frequently sedimentation time and basal metabolic rate) which facilitate comparison and contrast on the physiological side. Moreover in relation to the theory and mechanisms of psychosomatic interchange, these two disease processes are of interest for the prominence in them of "autonomic functions," and especially because changes in the fluid medium of the cells, standing in close relation to metabolism and circulation, represent the organism's conditioning by its inner environment at a point where a dualistic concept of psychic and somatic is difficult.

It soon became obvious that certain patients in these admission groups had to be excluded from detailed study for the reasons indicated in Table III (page 132).

GENERAL PROCEDURE

The method of history-taking used in the present study was essentially that just described (outline, page 84), except that the medical history and work-up was done usually by the internes and regular attending staff of the hospital. Every patient in the groups selected was seen by a member of our research group. The histories were taken independently by five different physicians, usually only one or two seeing each patient. All patients admitted to the hospital in a condition such as to make them suitable for study (page 132) were given from one to six interviews of about one hour each, for the purpose of obtaining a preliminary impression of the personality and of the nature and importance of the emotional component in the illness. In some instances this was done by way of checking the medical history, in some instances on a conversational basis, beginning in some such informal way as how they like the hospital, or the book they happen to be reading. With most patients it was possible in this way to obtain a good psychosomatic history, together with additional material obtained by way of the special techniques described in the preceding pages.

Cases in which a definite impression could not be obtained in this time, as well as cases which seemed particularly suitable for psychotherapy, were worked with intensively when feasible, that is, daily while they were on the ward and two to five times a week in the clinic after discharge, careful simultaneous record being kept of changes in physiological function.* After termination of treatment they were followed at intervals of six months to a year depending on the case.† Unfortunately, in view of the limitation of staff time, intensive investigation and treatment was not possible in all cases in which it was indicated.

In each case studied the superficial survey afforded information supplementary to medical case history and to the charted record of present illness and course, together with basis for review of the total therapeutic program. Among the points in the *first category*, of which

---

* See page 86 ff. The exact time of each psychiatric interview was noted, determinations being made before and after.

† In the interest of early detection of danger signals pointing to relapse in patients where the treatment could not be carried to completion (page 689) and for the purpose of checking our own results.

note is made, are the following: hereditary and pseudo-hereditary factors (including heart disease or diabetes as the case may be, and nervousness in the heredity; and exposure to heart disease, diabetes, fracture, or nervousness in family or friends); previous medical history including the patient's reactions to his illnesses; specific emotional factors (periods of stress and strain in the patient's life; major spheres of conflict, e.g., family—early and present—social, vocational, sexual, etc.); preparation for the illness; omissions and distortions in the medical history and their evaluation. As belonging to the *second category,* note is made of: anxiety, manifest and otherwise (dreams); major syndromes (for interpretations see page 594 ff.); nature of organization of symptoms; psychiatric diagnosis; the patient's reaction to his present illness compared with his reaction to past illnesses (reaction to the physiological changes; attitude toward illness and toward hospital, acceptance of invalidism, will to get well, and so on; effect of illness on the patient's life; "compensitis," etc.). *Finally,* the attempt was made to answer the questions: Would the patient be benefited or would the therapeutic program be changed significantly by psychotherapy; was the emotional factor important in the development of the illness although not readily subject to treatment now; was the emotional factor primarily a reaction to the disease itself? This initial impression was checked by deeper investigation and where feasible by brief or intensive psychotherapy.*

Our records concerning these patients show in summary the medical course in the hospital side by side with all the psychiatric contacts. Occasionally we asked for additional medical records such as more frequent blood pressure reporting, electrocardiograms, and so on, if our study seemed to warrant this.

CHANGES IN PROCEDURE

Minor changes were made at the end of the first two years. These are mentioned for their bearing on the statistical tables. They are as follows:

(1) Inclusion of all fracture patients (exclusive of those with fracture of the skull)., instead of merely those remaining two weeks or more on the ward.

---

* This material is not obtained by the usual questionnaire method, it being important to have it as spontaneous as possible (Chapter II).

(2) Limitation of the age group of 15 to 50 instead of 15 to 55. For this the primary reasons were the following:

(a) Of the 55 cardiac patients over 50 years of age admitted during the first two years, 39, or 71 per cent, had to be excluded from detailed study. In other words, with these patients the suitability for psychiatric investigation was decreased by more than a third in the age group 50 to 55 as compared to the age group 15 to 50, and the suitability for psychotherapy was decreased even more. There is no such striking difference in fracture and diabetic patients in this age period. Hence it seemed that our groups would be more comparable if this period were excluded.

(b) After obtaining a rough general picture of our material, intensive study of as large a proportion of the group as possible became more important, and this was facilitated by reduction in the size of the group.

(c) There is much greater complication of the problem by mental and environmental as well as physical factors in the half decade following the age of 50 than in that preceding it.

(3) Exclusion of all colored patients for the reason that the majority of Negroes who were available for study were relatively inarticulate, and poor observers of themselves. Since there had been no fundamental differences in our findings in the Negroes as compared to the white groups it seemed that the disproportionate amount of time required for the Negroes was not justified in view of limited staff time.

(4) As this project developed it split up into increasingly limited concrete studies involving the elimination or the cross-checking of variables: for example, patients combining hypertension and fracture, and so on; and more detailed records of physiological changes such as the circulatory reflex, continuous blood pressure, pulse and respiration, and so on.

Nevertheless, our picture for the two years 1936–1938 is in closer accord* with the picture for the years 1934–1936 than might be expected in view of the fact that one of our major problems in the beginning was the working out of an adequate method of psychosomatic examination. The present analysis is based on material of about 1200 cases.†

* The correspondence occurred not only in spite of the four changes in material noted, but in spite of changes of assistants. It may be the result of chance, although that seems unlikely.

† Tables III, IV A, IV B, and V are limited to the patients in the three groups studied during all four years, and do not include the additional contrast groups which are described later.

II. Statistical Picture

GENERAL

As will be seen from Table III, an average of 50 per cent of all the patients in these groups of serial admissions was found to be unsuitable for study for such reasons as (a) death shortly after ad-

Table III[1]

PATIENTS IN THE TOTAL ADMISSION GROUPS EXCLUDED FROM DETAILED INVESTIGATION

Reason for Exclusion	Cardiovascular Disease		Diabetes		Fractures		Total
	1934 to 1936	1936 to 1938	1934 to 1936	1936 to 1938	1934 to 1936	1936 to 1938	
	Out of 456	Out of 292	Out of 85	Out of 63	Out of 64	Out of 168	1128
I. On the basis of illness or defect: d							
(a) Death shortly after admission............-	91	23	5	2	0	0	121
(b) Other primary complicating disease...........	73	91	13	7	2	15	201
(c) Psychosis..............	4	2	0	0	0	2	8
(d) Low mentality.........	8	9	0	1	1	6	25
II. On the basis of feasibility:							
(a) Referral elsewhere for chronic or terminal care	25	9	4	0	2	0	40
(b) For some reason not to be readmitted...........	9	0	2	0	0	1	12
(c) Transferred to the private service, referred to local physicians, or otherwise impossible to follow.................	34	32	13	8	10	39	136
(d) Language difficulties....	9	7	0	1	0	3	20
Totals..............	253	173	37	19	15	66	563
Percentage of the total admissions both years excluded .	(57.0)		(38.0)		(35.0)		(50.0)

[1] Reprinted with permission from the *American Journal of Psychiatry*.

TABLE IVa [1]

THE PSYCHIC FACTOR FROM THE POINT OF VIEW OF THE
THERAPEUTIC PROGRAM

NUMBER OF PATIENTS	CARDIOVASCULAR DISEASE		DIABETES		FRACTURES		TOTAL No.	
	1934 to 1936	1936 to 1938	1934 to 1936	1936 to 1938	1934 to 1936	1936 to 1938	1934 to 1936	1936 to 1938
I. Admitted*..........	456	292	85	63	64	168	605	523
II. Suitable for detailed study..............	203	119	48	44	49	102	300	265
In whom the psychic factor was:								
(a) Inadequately determined.......	42	17	8	12	17	23	67	52
(b) Too much complicated somatically or too deeplying for more than palliative treatment.	55	9	12	6	5	2	72	17
(c) Such as to indicate psychotherapy	106	93	28	26	27	77	161	196

* The smaller figures for 1936–1938 result from: (a) The decrease of age from 15 to 55 to 15 to 50; and (b) Omission of, all colored patients.

The increase in the fracture patients for the period results from the elimination of the arbitrary requirement in the first period that they stay two weeks or more on the ward.

[1] Reprinted with permission from the *American Journal of Psychiatry.*

mission; (b) other primary complicating disease; (c) psychosis; (d) low mentality; or because referral elsewhere made adequate study impossible. It is of some interest that of the patients with cardiovascular disease, slightly more than half were excluded; of the patients with diabetes slightly more than a third; and of the patients with fractures about 38 per cent.

Our statistical impression of the role of the psychiatric factor in this general hospital material, as studied routinely over a period of four years (Tables IV A and B, and V), is as follows:

(1) The psychic factor was found to play an important role during the period of hospitalization in the illness of more than 38 per cent

TABLE IVʙ [1]

THE PSYCHIC FACTOR FROM THE POINT OF VIEW OF THE
THERAPEUTIC PROGRAM

NUMBER OF PATIENTS	CARDIOVASCULAR DISEASE 1934–1938		DIABETES 1934–1938		FRACTURES 1934–1938		TOTAL
	No.	Per Cent	No.	Per Cent	No.	Per Cent	
I. Admitted............	748		148		232		1128
II. Suitable for detailed study..............	322	43.0	92	62.0	151	65.0	565
In whom the psychic factor was:							
(a) Inadequately determined.........	59	18.0	20	22.0	40	26.0	119
(b) Too much complicated somatically or too deeplying for more than palliative treatment .	64	20.0	18	19.0	7	5.0	89
(c) Such as to indicate psychotherapy .	199	62.0	54	59.0	104	69.0	357

[1] Reprinted with permission from the *American Journal of Psychiatry.*

(1934–1936, 38.9 per cent; 1936–1938, 38.5 per cent) of the total admissions. It probably plays such a role in a greater proportion in view of the fact that half of the patients admitted had to be excluded from adequate investigation because the illness at the time of admission was too far advanced (or the situation otherwise too unfavorable) to permit the establishing of this fact.† In many patients with cardiovascular disease who died shortly after admission, for example, there was evidence from earlier records that important psychic factors existed.

(2) The psychic factor played an important role in the illness in 79 per cent (1934–1936, 79 per cent; 1936–1938, 80 per cent) of patients admitted to the hospital *during a stage of illness such that*

† Exclusion from detailed study for such reasons as death shortly after admission, psychosis, and so on (Table III).

TABLE V [1]

COMPARISON OF TWO TWO–YEAR PERIODS

	First Two Years	Second Two Years	Four Year Period
	Per Cent	Per Cent	Per Cent
I. Of the patients admitted:			
The psychic factor was found of significance in	39.0	41.0	40.0
Study was impossible of	50.0	49.0	50.0
II. Of the patients suitable for study the psychic factor was:			
Of significance in	79.0	80.0	79.0
Inadequately determined in	21.0	20.0	21.0
III. Of the total patients adequately studied the psychic factor was:			
Too much complicated somatically or too-deeplying for more than palliative treatment in	32.0	8.0	20.0
Such as to warrant psychotherapy in	68.0	92.0	80.0

[1] Reprinted with permission from the *American Journal of Psychiatry.*

psychiatric investigation was possible. The remaining 21 per cent were divided about equally between those in whom the picture was confused and those in whom brief examination revealed no important psychic element in the illness.

(3) The psychic factor was of therapeutic significance in 80 per cent of the patients of whom adequate examination was made. In part of the remaining 20 per cent psychotherapy would have been warranted had there been any way of making this possible on an intensive basis.

The following points should be noted relative to the statements summarized in Table V.

I. The figure for the percentage of the total number of patients admitted in whom the psychic factor was ascertained to be important for the illness in the second period is in surprising accord with that for the first. A factor in the slight increase is that patients with cardiovascular disease in the age group 50 to 55 were not seen and, as Table I shows, this markedly reduced the percentage excluded.

Note: The decrease in those who died shortly after admission or were sent elsewhere for chronic or terminal care is significant. The decrease in the total number excluded would have been more marked had it not been partially cancelled by the inclusion of all fracture patients (many of whom are quickly discharged to their family physicians), so producing an increase of exclusions under this heading.

II. The figure giving the number of patients suitable for study in whom the psychic factor was inadequately determined is likewise in surprising accord for the two periods. Because of the relatively greater difficulty in studying the psychic factor in fracture patients (page 194), the greater number of fracture patients in the total group (they constituted about 16 per cent in the first two years, and about 38 per cent of the total group in the second two years) would be expected to result in an increase instead of a decrease in the number inadequately determined. As a matter of fact, however, in the first two-year period the psychic factor was inadequately determined in 35 per cent of fracture patients suitable for study; and in the second period in 23 per cent of them, hence again we have two factors tending to cancel each other. (This difference may be in part a matter of increasing skill, but is probably largely the result of seeing a higher percentage of patients with relatively minor accidents and first accidents in whom the psychic factors leading to the accident were less deeply repressed, therefore more readily ascertained.)

III. The only important differences between the figures of 1936–1938 and those for 1934–1936 are an increase in the number of patients warranting therapy and a decrease in the number of patients in whom the psychic factor was thought to be too deep-lying for treatment. Both of these probably indicate an increase in our skill as a result of longer experience. Another factor of importance, however (although it does not account for the total difference), was the exclusion of patients in the age period 50 to 55 among whom in the cardiovascular group the feasibility and value of psychotherapy is markedly less than in the earlier age period.

The third change in our procedure, exclusion of colored patients, probably had little effect (except under II), because their distribution in group III (Table V) as studied in the first years did not differ importantly from the general distribution.*

IV. Follow-up studies of about half of these patients over a period of from one to twelve years have provided a useful check on our first impressions.

* Inclusion of all excluded (except morons or psychotics) does not change the percentage in these tables.

III. Observations Relative to Specific Syndromes— Character and Symptom Formation

GENERAL

The general criteria on which we based our decision as to whether or not the emotional factor played a role in the illness are discussed in section IV of this chapter. We may note here that the 80 per cent of patients in whom this appeared to be the case were divided into the following groups:

1. Those in whom the psychic component was primarily a reaction to the illness itself—less than 5 per cent.

2. Those in whom it was a complicating factor affecting the course of illness and response to treatment—75 per cent.

3. (A subdivision of 2.) About 50 per cent in whom it was of *demonstrable* etiological significance in the development of illness.

Relative to *demonstrable* we may note:

(a) So adjudged by different observers;

(b) So appearing in the chronology of the emotional setting of early attacks as well as of attacks precipitated during interviews;

(c) Appropriateness of physiological symptomatology (in terms of our knowledge of physiology) to the conflicts and defenses diagnosed;

(d) Improvement with therapeutic attention to the specific behavior pattern alone without reference to modification of the external situation or the patient's total personality adjustment;

(e) Disappearance of the syndrome with such therapy;

(f) A follow-up period indicative of the patient's ability to stay well in spite of subsequent similar injury by the environment, *whether through* exposure to infection or to such difficulties as mother-in-law or loss of job.*

The following case is typical for the patients judged in terms of the points just given.

Case No. RHDP 4. A married woman, aged 28, came to the medical clinic in the spring of 1931 complaining of palpitation, shortness of breath, and fainting spells, which were so incapacitating that she could scarcely walk two blocks and was unable to do her housework. The diagnosis was severe

* For illustration, see case No. HP 3, page 107.

cardiac damage (*specifically, cardiac hypertrophy, mitral stenosis and insufficiency, aortic insufficiency, with probable stenosis and chronic myocarditis*).

In the patient's personal history the points that stood out were timidity and extreme devotion to her father. She had left school voluntarily in order to work in his store. When the patient was 15 years old, an uncle died of heart trouble, and a brother died one month later of "heart failure" following an appendectomy. Fifteen months later her father died in her arms of angina pectoris. The next week she became engaged to a man ten years her senior who had been a life-long friend. She was married two years later, and her married life was happy until 1930 when her husband began to stay out late at night and his attitude toward her seemed to change. At this time also she heard of her brother's unfaithfulness to her sister-in-law. This came as a great shock to the patient and increased her worry about her own husband. At the same time a break occurred between a life-long friend and this girl's husband.

In 1931 the patient began to suffer from dyspnea and palpitation, following which she would "shake for hours," as had happened in her first such attack when her father died. On one occasion, sitting at home alone waiting for her husband who had promised to return at 2 A.M., an attack of palpitation occurred and she felt as though the walls of the room were closing in on her. She felt as though she were being crushed. She dressed and ran to her mother's house which was a few blocks away and fainted. There her husband found her when he came home at 5 o'clock in the morning. During the next two months the patient lost 16 lbs. (her weight having been constant at 130 lbs. until then). The dyspnea and palpitation increased and she failed to improve on a strict medical regime.

Now, thinking in terms of this patient's *preparation for illness*, we have the following facts. On the *physiological side*, there is a possible hereditary and constitutional predisposition toward disease of the cardiovascular system. Furthermore, the patient had growing pains following a tonsillectomy, which may have been the only symptoms of an actual rheumatic involvement present when she first came for treatment. In view of the patient's close association with her father in his attacks, a "pseudo-hereditary" factor is to be considered also; that is, what we may call, in brief, the effect of exposure to him in his attacks. Incidentally, studies indicate that in cardiac patients with cardiac heredity the symptoms are more incapacitating in patients who have been exposed to their parents' or relatives' heart attacks than in patients with no such exposure.

As was revealed during the course of the treatment, this patient had been prepared psychologically also for some type of illness although time does not permit my giving this in any detail. There were both psychic and physiological reasons for the centering of her attention on her heart, or to use Connor's [100] phrase, "the centering of the patient's fluid anxieties on the heart."

In discussing her symptoms, the patient revealed the fact that the attacks of palpitation and dyspnea and the sense of being smothered occurred only when she was waiting for her husband to come home, or when she saw a pregnant woman; not with physical exertion *unless* in combination with one of these two factors. (She had several such attacks, when she saw pregnant women in the clinic elevator.)

The patient's resentment against her mother and the fear of loss of her mother's affection were discussed. She recalled the fact that her first cardiac attacks were associated with her father's death, and the fact that she had immediately replaced her father by her one life-long boy friend (now her husband) who had been "both father and mother" to her, and that now she was about to lose him. She felt he couldn't really leave her when she was so sick.

Treatment and course. After ten periods of psychiatric treatment, the patient became symptom-free and remained so for two years without medication and with no definite restriction of diet or activity.

Late in 1933 she came back to the clinic saying that she had decided she would like to have a child and wanted to know whether it would be safe for her. She said: "It's funny, I want one now when we have less money than we had before, and then I thought we couldn't have one because of lack of money."

She was examined in the cardiac and gynecological clinics where she was told that she could go ahead with a pregnancy if she desired to take the risk, and if she were willing to spend the last two or three months in bed as might be necessary because of her cardiac condition. When she became pregnant the fear of seeing pregnant women returned and there were some mild attacks of dyspnea, none of these symptoms being of the previous intensity. She was seen once a week for six weeks and has remained symptom-free ever since, in spite of the pregnancy which, from a purely physiological point of view, might have been expected to increase her symptoms.

The patient was active (doing her own work) and free of dyspnea and palpitation throughout her pregnancy, and the spontaneous term delivery of a normal boy was without complications. This is the more significant in that her husband's attitude toward her did not change. She herself, however, had become much less dependent on him, and incidentally no longer runs to her mother at the slightest provocation.

This history indicates, among other things, that it is possible to change the patient's attitude toward an unpleasant situation even where the situation itself cannot be changed. The bringing about of such a change in the patient of course has distinct advantage over the attitude which says: "Well anyone would be worried, or would be nervous, living in such a situation. We will see that she gets enough sedative to keep her quiet."

This case then illustrates what we mean by an important emotional factor in the illness. It shows also that the degree to which "perfectly normal" worries which react disastrously, or produce symptoms in the physical sphere, can be definitely decreased with careful handling of the underlying emotional problem, and that when an actual organic lesion is present, such handling may profoundly alter the course of the illness and the degree of incapacitation. The personality profiles worked out on the basis of our routine study of the different disease groups which will be discussed in the following chapters, were of great assistance in judging the type of therapeutic program to be followed in each case. Furthermore, in many cases where the diagnosis was doubtful at the time of admission it was possible to predict on the basis of these profiles the probable course of disease with a considerable degree of accuracy, as is indicated by follow-up of these patients.

Relative to the personality characteristics selected as significant for each syndrome studied, we may note that patients in each of the disease groups have fundamental similarities in the constellation: somatic make-up, focal conflict or sphere of major conflict, behavior patterns for dealing with conflicts and difficulties ("action syndrome," Kardiner [266]) and character defenses. Each group differs in these respects from each other group, although no factor is definitive. Differences in this constellation seemed to be important because:

(1) They were present in a high percentage of patients in each group in contrast with patients in other groups.

(2) They could be shown to bear a close relation to the symptoms in question, often understandable in terms of physical changes accompanying emotion.

(3) Psychotherapeutic attention to them even without correction of the fundamental personality difficulty produced changes in the symptoms, first exacerbation when the material was brought up, and second relief as the material was worked through.

(4) Follow-up of patients with symptoms suggestive of certain of these illnesses and the related psychic problems has shown in some cases that the

illness suggested by the symptoms had actually developed. An example is the following:

Case No. GIP 5. A patient with symptoms suggestive of gastric ulcer, although repeated gastro-intestinal series were negative, was studied over a year and a half by the medical service, which then decided that she was a psychiatric problem exclusively. She was transferred to the psychiatric service. The patient actually was under serious emotional stress because she was unmarried, living alone with a Puritanical mother, and carrying on an affair with a married man. With the discussion of this difficulty her symptoms disappeared.

Because it was necessary for the patient to carry on a job which interfered with clinic attendance she was discharged with the advice that should she have any recurrence she return to the psychiatric clinic, and that even if there were no recurrence she have a medical check-up at least once a year. A note was made in the chart: "This patient should be followed in Medicine. Although the immediate emotional problem has been relieved and with it her symptoms, she has the specific reaction pattern to any type of stress and strain which is characteristic of the ulcer patient."

This patient returned to the psychiatric clinic when her physician was on vacation and was treated by a neurologist for three years with sedatives. While still under this treatment she wrote the physician who had seen her in Psychiatry, saying: "Last week I was so sick I called in a doctor from the neighborhood and he said I was having hemorrhages from an ulcer in my stomach. If this is what you were treating me for six years ago why didn't you tell me?" The patient was asked later to return to the clinic. The story of her gastric ulcer was checked and confirmed. She had been hospitalized and had had to be transfused. Incidentally, the hemorrhage had occurred immediately following her lover's decision to divorce his wife (her friend) and marry her, to which the patient had responded by giving him up completely.

Of course our conclusions based on intensive study or psychoanalysis of individual cases can be evaluated only by colleagues who are trained in the use of these techniques. But others may have some impression of these conclusions since they were in all cases complementary to the material obtained on superficial study and a purely statistical check-up for which no training beyond an understanding of statistical methods is required.

Such histories and findings (be it noted parenthetically) are of course not conclusive and at present we must be content with describing and recording without making deductions concerning emotional etiology. Our assurance is increasing, however, as we find that our impressions from psychosomatic histories, including physical examination and study of course-of-illness in physiological and psychological terms in large groups of patients, are borne out and at the same time clarified and made more specific with intensive treatment or psychoanalysis of individuals in each group, as well as by an objective study of each group such as could be made by any statistician with no medical or psychiatric training, who had access to the charts.

SPECIFIC SYNDROMES

Personality Characteristics

The material relative to the specific personality picture which we associate with each syndrome studied is to be found in the succeeding chapters. In this context it is probably useful to note only that this was much more specific than any of us anticipated at the outset, and in the course of the study assumed a validity far beyond our expectation. The different disease groups did show marked differences in family and environmental history, especially sphere of conflict, taken in conjunction with habitual ways of dealing with difficulties (including action, speech, and fantasy); that is, in preparation for illness, as well as in response to treatment, including reaction to illness and to the physician, and the type of treatment required.

Statistics

Having found these striking differences in personality and character which were far beyond our expectation, it occurred to us to see whether these groups of patients differed from each other also in terms that could be checked by any statistician having access to the records, e.g., education, income, occupation, illness history. Charts I to IX give a picture of our conclusions relative to this point.

Incidentally, we became convinced that the sample on which we are basing our statistics was what is called in the parlance of the statistician "an adequate sample," because the pictures given were not importantly changed by:

(a) Leaving out the age group 15 to 21, except relative to a few obvious points.

(b) Tabulating either males or females alone.

(c) Basing figures on the total 1600 patients studied (in terms of information on their charts) rather than just figures on the serial admissions studied intensively (100 more or less in each group), concerning whom we had full information.

It should be noted relative to *sex distribution* (Table VI) four (half) of the groups studied showed an almost equal distribution between males and females; namely, patients with diabetes, 48 per cent males, 52 per cent females (a slightly higher percentage of males than would be found in the general population); patients with fracture, 53 per cent males, 47 per cent females (a lower percentage of males than would be found in this group for the general population); patients with hypertensive cardiovascular disease, 39 per cent males, 61 per cent females (a somewhat lower percentage of males than would be found in the general population, which is actually about half and half); patients with an anginal syndrome, 59 per cent males, 41 per cent females. The remaining four groups, which are fairly accurate in terms of the general population are as follows: patients with cornary disease, 86 per cent (five-sixths) males, 14 per cent (one-sixth) females. (It should be noted here that although this is accurate in terms of the latest statistics available for the general population, the percentage of *females* with coronary disease is rapidly increasing.[229]) Patients with cardiac arrhythmia on no demonstrable organic basis, 31 per cent (one-fourth) males, 69 per cent (three-fourths) females. (Relative to this figure it should be noted that the percentage among *males* is increasing.) Patients with rheumatic heart disease, 36 per cent males, 64 per cent females; and patients with rheumatic fever or rheumatoid arthritis, about 34 per cent males, and 66 per cent females. (This is in accord with the general public health statistics [227, 228, 231, 232, 233, 234, 235].) In terms of the total number of patients included in these charts the number of males and females is approximately equal.

Relative to *age distribution* (Table VI) it should be noted that the patients with fracture were distributed almost equally in the three age groups 15 to 24, 25 to 34, 35 to 54. Patients with rheumatic heart disease and patients with diabetes ranked second from the point of view of equality of age distribution in the three age periods, although about 40 per cent in each group was in the age period 35

TABLE VI

AGE AND SEX DISTRIBUTION

PATIENTS WITH	SEX		AGE		
	Per Cent Males	Per Cent Females	15–24	25–34	35–54
Fracture...............................	53.3	46.7	34.6	31.8	33.6
Hypertensive cardiovascular disease.............	38.8	61.2	12.2	14.3	73.5
Coronary occlusion.........................	86.4	13.6	0	4.5	95.5
Anginal syndrome..........................	58.8	41.2	17.6	52.9	29.5
Rheumatic fever and rheumatoid arthritis.......	34.3	65.7	41.7	31.5	26.8
Rheumatic heart disease.....................	36.0	64.0	28.0	28.0	44.0
Cardiac arrhythmia.........................	31.3	68.7	25.0	62.0	13.0
Diabetes.................................	48.1	51.9	31.5	27.8	40.7

to 54. Each of the other groups had their characteristic decades. For patients with hypertensive cardiovascular disease and coronary disease this was 35 to 54; for patients with anginal syndrome and cardiac arrhythmia 25 to 34; and for patients with rheumatic fever or rheumatoid arthritis 15 to 24.

These statistics for age distribution show clearly that although we are dealing with illnesses which rank among the first ten in terms of disability and incapacity, and illnesses which have been called the major afflictions of the older age groups in the population, these illnesses nonetheless have a major incidence in the younger age groups where the human organism is supposed to be at its best.

The illnesses studied in this volume account for 45 per cent of the invalids in this country and nearly 85 per cent of all the days lost from work by reason of illness.[44]

The age distribution of the general population is as follows: about one-eleventh in the age group 15 to 20 (note for obvious reasons this group is omitted from the following charts); about one-third in the age group 21 to 34; about one-sixth in the age group 35 to 44; and nearly one-sixth in the age-group 45 to 55. Hence the age groups covered in this study may be considered representative of a little more than two-thirds of the total population.[393]

Education. In charting educational records for the patients covered in this study it was necessary to use as a base line figures representing the educational grouping of the upper 60 per cent of the total population over the age of 21. Had we based our comparisons on the figures for the total population the records of our patients would have shown a positive deviation in practically all cases. The base line for all groups studied lumped together, however, falls very close to the base line selected, representing the upper 60 per cent of the population. Hence we have one more indication that our series represents an adequate sample of the upper three-fifths of the population. The figures for each group represented by this base line are as follows:

I. Grammar school:
   Not completed.......................... 14.12
   Completed.............................. 31.13

II. High school:
   Not completed.......................... 31.65
   Completed.............................. 11.42

III. College:
   Not completed.......................... 6.8
   Completed.............................. 4.88

Chart I, educational records, shows clearly that although a certain selective factor is brought in by the fact that we are dealing with a metropolitan hospital drawing from a specified income group, the

TABLE VII

EDUCATIONS: DEVIATIONS FROM UPPER 60 PER CENT OF TOTAL POPULATION

	Incomplete Grammar	Grammar	Incomplete High School	High School	Incomplete College	College and Graduate
Fracture........................	10.91	− 26.47	25.92	− 5.08	11.47	− 1.43
Hypertensive....................	58.99	11.43	− 9.73	− 28.55	− 40.00	− 58.19
Coronary.......................	− 45.53	60.92	− 63.53	68.39	− 43.38	57.58
Anginal........................	− 3.47	31.42	− 56.94	59.19	− 33.09	86.94
Cardiac arrythmia..............	− 46.00	− 1.00	− 75.00	25.00	336.00	77.00
Rheumatic fever and rheumatoid arthritis	20.00	− 9.00	− 34.00	25.00	114.00	33.00
Rheumatic heart disease without joint pain.....................	80.00	− 12.00	− 16.00	8.00	− 14.00	
Diabetes.......................	− 6.00	− 70.00	25.00	16.00	57.00	166.00
Base line: upper 60 % total population						

educational averages for all the syndromes studied stick closer to the base line of the general population than does that for any single group studied. They are significantly closer than the educational

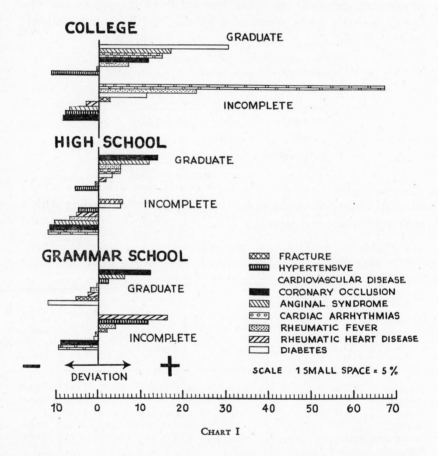

EDUCATION

MALES FEMALES 21-55
BASE–UPPER 60 % OF GENERAL POPULATION

Chart I

average for any group, with the possible exception of the patients with fracture and the patients with rheumatic fever and rheumatoid arthritis.

In terms of educational average the only two groups that are below the average for the upper 60 per cent of the total population are the patients with hypertensive cardiovascular disease and the patients with rheumatic fever and rheumatoid arthritis. If our own average is taken as a base, the patients with rheumatic heart disease fall below, and patients with fractures fall practically on, this base line.

The question may arise as to why we are interested in this statistical material. First, it is one further bit of evidence that the series reported represents an adequate sample for the disease group studied. Second, it shows that each disease group studied has its particular educational pattern in terms of (a) general educational level, and (b) tendency to complete or not to complete the educational units undertaken.

Chart II represents the educational patterns for groups with anginal syndrome, coronary occlusion, and fractures. It will be seen first, that the educational patterns for patients with anginal syndrome and coronary disease are very similar; the only important difference is that fewer patients with anginal syndrome terminated their academic education at the end of grammar school or high school, and more were college graduates or better. Both patients with anginal syndrome and patients with coronary disease, however, differed from the group of patients with fracture in the tendency to complete the educational unit undertaken. As compared with the general population a much higher percentage of these patients ended their academic education with graduation from grammar school, high school or college, and a much lower percentage than that of the general population terminated their academic education in the middle of one of these three educational units. With the group of patients with fracture the situation is just the reverse; a higher percentage terminated their academic education in the middle of one of these three educational units, and a much lower percentage than that for the general population terminated their academic education with the completion of an educational unit.*

As will be seen from Charts I and III, this does not mean that patients with fracture have a lower educational average than patients with cardiovascular disease: patients with hypertensive cardiovascu-

---

* The only exception to this statement is the incomplete college group. This minus deviation is probably to be explained in terms of the tendency of these patients not to go to college, plus other factors, which in view of limitation of space cannot be discussed here.

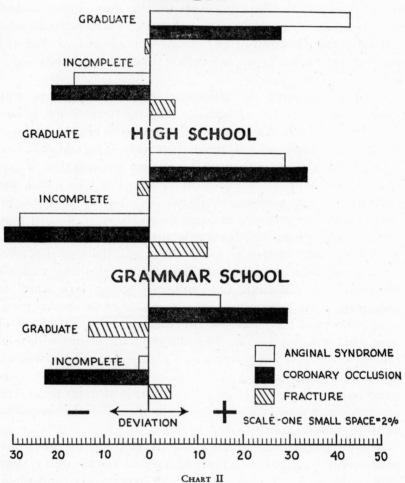

EDUCATION
MALES- FEMALES 21-55
BASE—UPPER 60% OF GENERAL POPULATION

CHART II

lar disease as well as other groups studied fell much below them, although in our series patients with coronary occlusion and with the

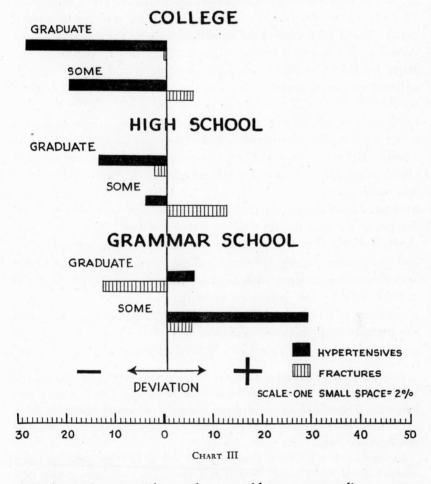

EDUCATION
MALES- FEMALES 21- 55
BASE – UPPER 60% OF GENERAL POPULATION

CHART III

anginal syndrome without demonstrable coronary disease were markedly above them.

What is the bearing of these charts on the problems we are discussing? What is their significance for psychosomatic medicine? They interested us for the following reasons in terms of our personality studies of patients with fracture and patients with coronary disease.

First, both groups were in conflict with authority and in both cases the onset of illness coincided with circumstances which made this conflict acute.

Second, these two groups of patients had completely different ways of dealing with authority. The former attempted to avoid submission to authority or to minimize its importance by striving for independence and by focussing on immediate values. They were less concerned with vocational success than with day-to-day pleasures. The latter tended to identify with authority figures and strived for vocational success in order to become themselves the authority. They would stick to one job, usually their first job, for many years, working long hours without vacations. These characteristic tendencies were borne out even by the history of marriage and divorce and size of family. Although about the same percentage of each group married, the average size of family for the patients with coronary occlusion was much greater than that for the general population, whereas the average size of family in the group of patients with fracture fell far below the average for the general population. The educational charts indicate that this personality tendency toward self-discipline and persistence among coronary patients and toward impulsive * activity among patients with fracture started early in life and was characteristic of the groups in question: the fracture patients had a tendency to leave school in the middle of an educational unit, and the patients with coronary occlusion only after they had completed an educational unit. Typical case history excerpts are the following:

Fracture patient: "I had always planned to study engineering. During my third year in high school I discovered that to do this I had to have two languages. This sort of discouraged me. It didn't seem worth bothering about at the time. So I left high school and joined the Navy. And so, ever since I've just done odd jobs."

Coronary patient: "When I was twelve I ran away from home because I couldn't stand being bossed by father. I got a job as an errand boy in a butcher shop and finished high school at night. I worked up in the business until I was a clerk, a manager, and finally I was the boss of the business. I

* See page 195 for discussion of this term.

worked fourteen to eighteen hours a day and never took a vacation. But things went well and now I own a chain of butcher shops in the city."

In the fracture case the accident occurred while the patient who had been out of work for some months was looking for a job. "I was walking across the street with my hat pulled down over my eyes, thinking if I got turned down once more I could never go home and face my wife. I might as well sleep on a park bench."

In the patient with coronary occlusion the onset of illness followed the acceptance of a partner in business "because it had become too much for one man to manage. But it always rankled because I wasn't my own boss any more. My heart was heavy and I began to have pains."

Such case illustrations are interesting in themselves but assume diagnostic significance when heard over and over again from patients suffering from given syndromes. Exposure to such repetition makes it easier to evaluate outstanding differences between the disease groups. (For further material see Chapters V to X.)

If an index is worked out giving equal value to educational average and tendency to complete educational units (subtracting the percentage failing to complete units) the ranking is as follows: patients with anginal syndrome, coronary disease, cardiac arrhythmia on no demonstrable organic basis. Patients with fracture and diabetes are close to the base line, and those with rheumatic fever or rheumatoid arthritis, hypertensive cardiovascular disease, and rheumatic heart disease below it. There are no groups consistently below the base line in all three rankings, but the fracture group is consistently on the base line in terms of all three rankings, and the following groups are consistently above: patients with anginal syndrome and patients with coronary disease. Patients with cardiac arrhythmia are above in terms of two of them, and patients with diabetes have a slightly better rating than the fracture group in all three rankings, hence in terms of such an index our lowest education groups are the patients with hypertensive cardiovascular disease, rheumatic heart disease, and acute rheumatic fever or rheumatoid arthritis. Although age of onset of illness might well play a role in many patients in the two latter groups, this is not the case with patients with hypertensive cardiovascular disease.

Income. Relative to Charts IV and V it is interesting to see that the two groups whose education is lowest, patients with rheumatic heart disease or hypertensive cardiovascular disease, include nearly double the number of patients on relief found in any other group (in spite of the fact that the major incidence of at least the latter

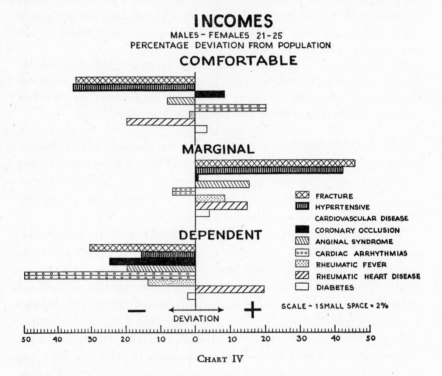

INCOMES
MALES – FEMALES 21–25
PERCENTAGE DEVIATION FROM POPULATION

COMFORTABLE

MARGINAL

FRACTURE
HYPERTENSIVE
CARDIOVASCULAR DISEASE
CORONARY OCCLUSION
ANGINAL SYNDROME
CARDIAC ARRHYTHMIAS
RHEUMATIC FEVER
RHEUMATIC HEART DISEASE
DIABETES

DEPENDENT

SCALE – 1 SMALL SPACE = 2%

DEVIATION

50 40 30 20 10 0 10 20 30 40 50

Chart IV

is well beyond the age in which academic education in concluded). It is interesting also that their average income is the lowest of any group studied.

The group for whom the major incidence of illness is in the decade 15 to 24 (of whom only the latter half are included in the charts), namely, patients with acute rheumatic fever and rheumatoid arthritis, as well as two groups having a relatively high incidence in this period, patients with fracture (35 per cent), and patients with diabetes (31.5 per cent), for all of whom the illness might have been expected to interfere with education and income average, have relatively high incomes. Patients with cardiac arrhythmia on no demonstrable organic basis, patients with anginal syndrome or coronary occlusion, represent the highest income groups, as well as the highest educational groups. It should be noted that these last three syndromes have their major incidence after academic education is normally concluded, but sufficiently early to interfere with income.

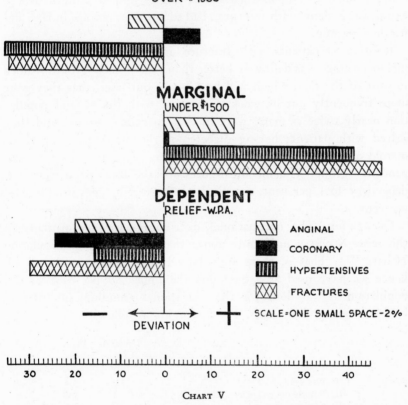

INCOMES
MALES-FEMALES 21-55
BASE - GENERAL POPULATION

COMFORTABLE
OVER $1500

MARGINAL
UNDER $1500

DEPENDENT
RELIEF-W.P.A.

ANGINAL

CORONARY

HYPERTENSIVES

FRACTURES

DEVIATION   SCALE=ONE SMALL SPACE-2%

30   20   10   0   10   20   30   40

CHART V

In so far as was possible income was charted in terms of income at the time of onset of illness. For the group of patients with coronary occlusion, however, this is misleading for two reasons: (1) in 27 per cent of the cases in our series the onset of the coronary disease was preceded by a period of hypertension which had already resulted in financial reverses or been preceded by them; and (2) since a financial reverse was usually the precipitating factor in the illness many of them had sunk from the classification "comfortable" to that of "dependent" in the year prior to onset. In spite of these facts, however, it will be noted that patients with coronary disease are the only patients in our series among whom there was a higher percentage in the "comfortable" group than would be expected in the general population. It is significant also that the percentage in the "marginal" group is small as compared with other groups studied. And no group, except the patients with fractures, had so low a percentage in the "dependent" group.

Relative to patients with fracture, it may be noted that their income average was definitely better than that of most groups studied in spite of the fact, which will be brought out later, that they were more frequently out of work. Compared with the general population nearly twice as many were in the "marginal" group, and they shared with patients having diabetes or rheumatic fever or rheumatoid arthritis the record for the lowest percentage in the "dependent" group. The income figures for the total population are, dependent 15.1 per cent, marginal 41.7 per cent, comfortable 43.2 per cent.

Occupation. The occupational distribution for the patients in this series is pretty uniformly above that of the general population (Chart VI). That is, there are relatively few patients in class VI, hence we have used as a base line the upper 60 per cent of the population as was done for the educational grouping, in order to bring out group differences. The figures are as follows:

Class	General Population	Upper 60 Per Cent
I I. Professional	3.2	5.4
III. Proprietors, managers, officials	1.1	2.0
II. Clerks, salesmen, stenographers	6.7	11.2
V. Skilled workers	5.4	9.0
V. Unskilled workers	22.8	38.0
VI. Retired persons, invalids, housewives	60.7	34.4

The professional grouping in Chart VI is more affected than the other groupings by the selective factor in ward admissions. Many professional patients were cared for on the semiprivate rating, but of course this applies to a certain extent to classification II also.

With reference to class II, four of the disease categories studied showed a marked positive deviation. Patients with cardiac arrhythmias

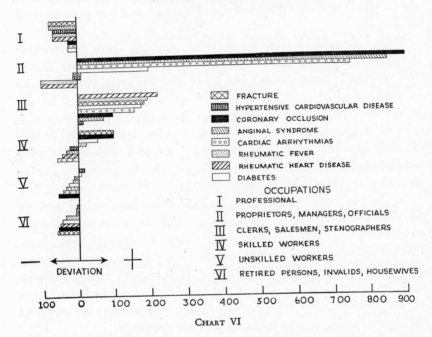

OCCUPATIONS
MALES – FEMALES 21-55
PERCENTAGE DEVIATIONS FROM UPPER 60% OF INCOME
GROUPS IN TOTAL POPULATION

FRACTURE
HYPERTENSIVE CARDIOVASCULAR DISEASE
CORONARY OCCLUSION
ANGINAL SYNDROME
CARDIAC ARRHYTHMIAS
RHEUMATIC FEVER
RHEUMATIC HEART DISEASE
DIABETES

OCCUPATIONS
I   PROFESSIONAL
II PROPRIETORS, MANAGERS, OFFICIALS
III CLERKS, SALESMEN, STENOGRAPHERS
IV SKILLED WORKERS
V   UNSKILLED WORKERS
VI RETIRED PERSONS, INVALIDS, HOUSEWIVES

DEVIATION

100   0   100   200   300   400   500   600   700   800   900

CHART VI

and with anginal syndrome were in the lead. Patients with coronary disease and diabetes came next. This occupational record is consistent with the educational and income records for these groups of patients. It is interesting that patients with fracture and hypertensive cardio-vascular disease fell on the base line with respect to this occupational grouping.

With reference to class III, clerks, salesmen, stenographers, we find again a positive deviation for all groups studied, but the patients with hypertensive cardiovascular disease have the lowest percentage in this category, and patients with rheumatic heart disease the highest.

With reference to class IV, skilled workers, it is significant that these patients with fracture, diabetes, and coronary disease show a marked positive deviation, and those with cardiac arrhythmia, rheumatic heart disease, and anginal syndrome a marked negative deviation. One reason for this striking negative deviation is that such patients as had started out in category IV had at the time of admission risen to executive positions, such for example as contractor, chief of the technical staff of a laboratory, and the like, and hence are charted in class II.

With reference to class V, unskilled workers, there is a positive deviation among patients with hypertensive cardiovascular disease and rheumatic heart disease; and a negative deviation for the group of patients with fracture, although from the point of view of exposure to injury in this group the opposite might have been expected.

With reference to class VI, retired persons, invalids, housewives, the only group showing a positive deviation is that with hypertensive cardiovascular disease, and the groups with the greatest negative deviation are those with fractures and those with coronary occlusion.

In the two lowest classes then (unskilled workers, retired persons, invalids and housewives), the major positive deviation is among patients with hypertensive cardiovascular disease, although this illness, in view of its late onset, should interfere less with occupational rating. The major negative deviation is among patients with coronary disease and those with fracture (where both because of the early incidence of the accident habit, and because of the susceptibility of unskilled laborers to accident, one might expect the opposite).

Previous Illness Record. The ratings of these patients in terms of education, income, and occupation are consistent, although they leave much to be explained. Chart VII giving previous illness history provided some clues, but the most important information is to be found in the chapters to follow.

It will be noted that in terms of operations and major illness prior to the present illness the patients with fracture have the best record. They present a health record far above that for the average population. The patients with coronary disease, anginal syndrome, and cardiac arrhythmia with no demonstrable organic damage give an operative and illness history indicative of health far below that of the average population although their educational, occupational and income rating remain at the top. This material will be discussed in later chapters. For clarification of questions left unanswered in this chart, other charts in the series should be consulted.

PREVIOUS ILLNESS INCIDENCE

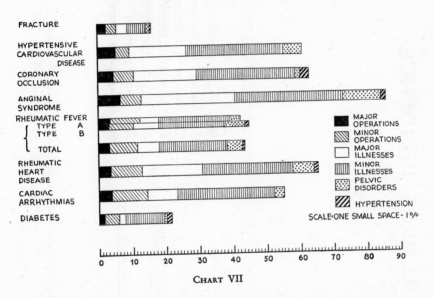

CHART VII

As will be seen from Chart VII, each disease group has its own pattern for previous illness. The reason for the division of the rheumatic fever group into type A and type B is explained in Chapter VI.

Chart VIII offers a basis for correction of these pictures from the point of view of sex distribution within each group. It will be seen that for all groups the previous health record was worse for the females than for the males.

Chart IX offers a basis for correction in terms of the age distribution of each group studied. It is noteworthy that the accident group maintains its good previous health record even in the decades 35 to 54, just as the groups of patients with anginal syndrome and cardiac arrhythmia show their characteristically poor health record even in the decade 25 to 34.

Chart X, giving the percentage of patients in each group having one, two, or three or more accidents, shows that 79 per cent of the

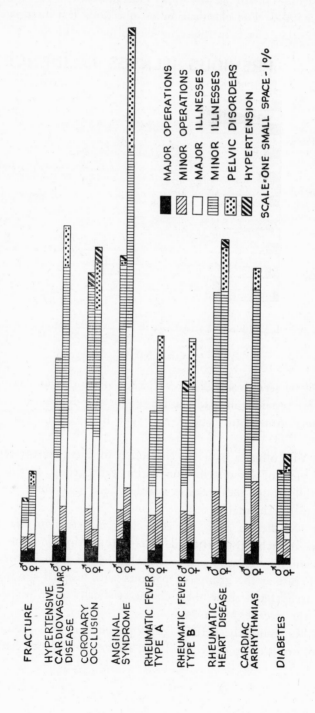

PREVIOUS ILLNESS INCIDENCE
SEPARATED BY SEX

MAJOR OPERATIONS
MINOR OPERATIONS
MAJOR ILLNESSES
MINOR ILLNESSES
PELVIC DISORDERS
HYPERTENSION
SCALE=ONE SMALL SPACE = 1%

FRACTURE
HYPERTENSIVE CARDIOVASCULAR DISEASE
CORONARY OCCLUSION
ANGINAL SYNDROME
RHEUMATIC FEVER TYPE A
RHEUMATIC FEVER TYPE B
RHEUMATIC HEART DISEASE
CARDIAC ARRHYTHMIAS
DIABETES

CHART VIII

PREVIOUS ILLNESS INCIDENCE
BY AGE GROUPS (MALE)

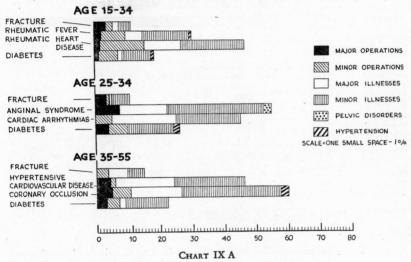

AGE 15-34

FRACTURE
RHEUMATIC FEVER
RHEUMATIC HEART
DISEASE
DIABETES

■ MAJOR OPERATIONS

▨ MINOR OPERATIONS

☐ MAJOR ILLNESSES

▥ MINOR ILLNESSES

▦ PELVIC DISORDERS

▨ HYPERTENSION

SCALE=ONE SMALL SPACE=1%

AGE 25-34

FRACTURE
ANGINAL SYNDROME
CARDIAC ARRHYTHMIAS
DIABETES

AGE 35-55

FRACTURE
HYPERTENSIVE
CARDIOVASCULAR DISEASE
CORONARY OCCLUSION
DIABETES

0   10   20   30   40   50   60   70   80

CHART IX A

PREVIOUS ILLNESS INCIDENCE
BY AGE GROUPS (FEMALES)

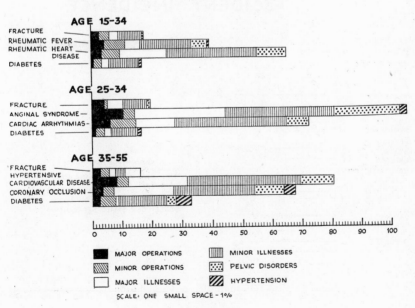

AGE 15-34

FRACTURE
RHEUMATIC FEVER
RHEUMATIC HEART
DISEASE
DIABETES

AGE 25-34

FRACTURE
ANGINAL SYNDROME
CARDIAC ARRHYTHMIAS
DIABETES

AGE 35-55

FRACTURE
HYPERTENSIVE
CARDIOVASCULAR DISEASE
CORONARY OCCLUSION
DIABETES

0   10   20   30   40   50   60   70   80   90   100

■ MAJOR OPERATIONS   ▥ MINOR ILLNESSES

▨ MINOR OPERATIONS   ▦ PELVIC DISORDERS

☐ MAJOR ILLNESSES   ▨ HYPERTENSION

SCALE: ONE SMALL SPACE - 1%

CHART IX B

ACCIDENT INCIDENCE
INCLUDING PATIENTS HAVING MORE THAN ONE SYNDROME

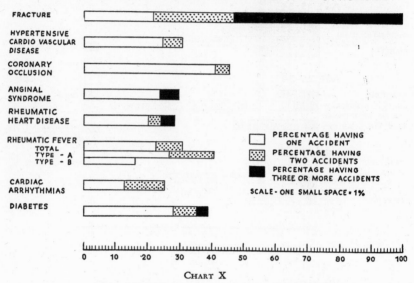

CHART X

ACCIDENT INCIDENCE

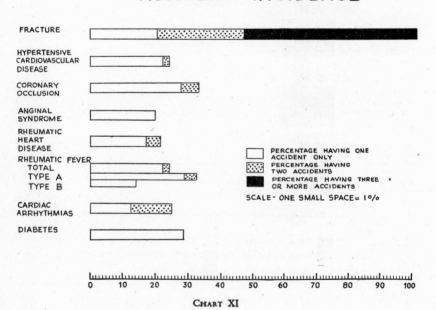

CHART XI

patients with fracture had two or more injuries, whereas in no other group studied were there more than 11 per cent with two or more injuries. Aside from the patients with fracture, in only three of the other groups studied were there any patients with three or more accidents, and there were ten times as many patients with three or more accidents in the group of patients with fracture as in the most accident-prone of the other groups studied. The reader is referred to Chapter X for further discussion of this matter, and to Chart XI (page 160) from which patients suffering from more than one syndrome have been omitted from all groups. When this is done we find twenty-one times as many patients in the fracture group reporting two or more accidents as the average for all the other groups studied.

The accident history constitutes only a fraction of 1 per cent of the total illness history for the other groups studied, whereas it constitutes nearly two-thirds of the illness history for the group of patients with fracture. This matter is discussed more fully in Chapters IV and IX and the type of accidents represented by these figures is given in Charts XV and XVI C (page 552 and page 555).

Finally, reference to Table VIII will show that these groups differ

TABLE VIII

MARRIAGES—CHILDREN

	Per Cent of Marriages— No Children	Per Cent of Marriages— One Child	Average Number of Children Per Marriage	Per Cent Married, 21 Years and Over		
				Males	Females	Both
Fractures..................	45.9	19.7	1.15	70.7	76.2	73.5
Hypertensive cardiovascular disease..................	23.5	29.4	1.79	61.1	79.3	72.3
Coronary occlusion.........	19.0	23.8	1.9	94.7	100.	95.5
Anginal syndrome...........	16.7	33.3	1.5	77.8	71.4	75.0
Rheumatic fever............	22.0	40.0	1.6	45.8	74.5	65.3
Rheumatic heart disease.....	33.3	41.7	1.17	60.	64.3	63.2
Cardiac arrhythmia.........	37.5	25.0	1.25	60.	55.6	57.1
Diabetes..................	32.1	14.3	2.	40.	83.3	63.6
White urban population..... 15 years and over			1.6	60.7	58.7	

from one another and from the general population in percentage of marriages, and size of family. The group with coronary occlusion, for example, leads all the others by about 33 1/3 per cent in percentage married, and is rivaled only by patients with diabetes in size of family. The accident group, although third in percentage of marriages, stands at the bottom of the list in number of children per marriage. The group with cardiac arrhythmia, on the other hand, ranks lowest in percentage married and third from the bottom in number of children per marriage. There is thus no relationship between degree of physical incapacitation and size of family. The significance of these and other differences will be discussed in the succeeding chapters.

SUMMARY

This material was inserted here simply to indicate that these disease groups do differ from each other in ways that can be determined objectively. These differences seem to be independent of age and sex distribution since:

(1) In the three groups with the best educational ratings we have, among the patients with *coronary disease,* a preponderance of males and a late age incidence; in the patients with *anginal syndrome* an equal division between males and females and an early age incidence; in the patients with *cardiac arrhythmia* with no demonstrable organic damage a preponderance of females but also a relatively early age incidence.

(2) The two groups with the worst educational ratings were the patients with *hypertensive cardiovascular disease,* among whom there was a nearly equal distribution of males and females, but late age incidence; and patients with *rheumatic heart disease* among whom there was a preponderance of females but a relatively early age incidence.

(3) In the other three groups, patients with *fracture, diabetes,* and *rheumatic fever* and *rheumatoid arthritis,* together with early age incidence we have in one case a preponderance of males and in the other cases a preponderance of females, but in all cases a relatively high rating for education, income, and occupation.

(4) The illness records, although characteristic for each group of patients studied, do not seem on first sight to be consistent with

education, income, and occupation records. This matter is discussed
in subsequent chapters. The only points to be noted here are, first,
that each group of patients has its characteristic illness history; and
second, that the group of patients with fracture has a previous accident history many times that of any other group studied as well as
a general health record that is much better than that of any other
group studied.

These differences, although they may seem unimportant, confirm
the impressions obtained from the psychosomatic histories and assist
in defining the personality profiles. *The personality profile is a constellation and should not be read as a statistical table in which each
point is evaluated separately.* This concept is discussed in Chapter IX.

IV. CRITERIA

The foregoing tables show that the differences between disease
groups given in section III are based on tables such as are used by
any statistician. About 80 per cent of the patients in each disease
group studied conform to the profiles. The divergent 20 per cent
suffer from more than one important illness syndrome or have
changed their illness pattern from time to time. In brief, 80 per cent
of the patients studied fit the profile and the other 20 per cent diverge
somewhat because of other complications which will be discussed
later. Apparently any person may have one to one-half of the traits
suggested in any profile and may or may not be sick. (See Chapters
IX and X.)

Soule [392] made a statement that may be useful by way of orientation: "The mark of a mature science is that it has found it possible to
mobilize all its resources about the same purpose. Research is used
to test hypothesis; hypotheses are developed to guide research. Both
result in a kind of knowledge reliable enough so that man can use it
for practical ends."

Shryock in "The Development of Modern Medicine" [381] had said
earlier: "Apparently every science, whether we begin with dynamics
in the sixteenth century or end with sociology in the twentieth, goes
through certain phases which might in a loose sense be termed stages
of development. . . . The first stage reveals a minimum of observation and a maximum of theoretical synthesis; the second, an early
attempt at objectivity and measurement, characterized by pioneer

enthusiasms; the third reveals a partial reversion to speculative synthesis (with its inevitable 'schools' and controversies) and a partial lapse of quantitative procedures—due to difficulties encountered in carrying out the quantitative program; the fourth level witnesses a revival of the quantitative procedure, this time upon a firmer factual basis and with a technique so improved as to make possible a final victory for modern methodology."

We have hoped that our study might correspond with this fourth level of development. Our basic hypotheses were those explained in Chapter XI—the dynamic law of the conservation of emotional energy and the interplay between psychic (emotional disturbance) and physical symptoms. These hypotheses having determined the field of our study and the nature of our techniques, our method was from that point purely inductive. We attempted a maximum of observation with no preconceived ideas as to what we might find, allowing any further theoretical formulations to arise from our results.

In pursuing this plan of observation we employed every practicable safeguard against bias in the outcome. Certain defects in the scientific method were inseparable from the nature of the study, but these we have recognized and attempted to check or make allowances for, as far as possible. The safeguards, together with corresponding defects and necessary allowances, are briefly described in the following paragraphs.

1. *Use of Investigators.* The patients reviewed here were studied by five different people with different backgrounds, training, and prejudices. Each worked independently of the others in his interviews and reports on cases. Yet there were no important differences in the conclusions reached by the several members of our group.

It may be considered a defect that all the investigators were psychiatrists and that the same conclusions could not be confirmed by observers without specialized equipment. The conclusions may be regarded, in this particular, as embodying a large "subjective" element. Yet most of the same observations may be made and the conclusions confirmed by any physician once he has been given the necessary clues. And it must be remembered that just as with the work of the specialized medical diagnostician, observations of this kind were in large measure confirmed by the subsequent progress of the cases and the results of therapy. Furthermore, many of the observations, which consisted of statistics regarding life history, and were complementary to the definitely psychiatric observations, could be checked by any qualified layman (section II, pp. 132–137).

2. *Choice of Cases.* The cases were not selected, but consisted of all those coming to the hospital with the symptoms chosen for investigation, with necessary exclusions, as explained in Table III.

It may be objected that the hospital itself brings in a selective factor, since it serves a specific geographical and income group in a metropolitan area. Corrections may be required for this bias if the conclusions are to be applied to other groups, or generally. Nevertheless it is pertinent that the same selective factor applies to all the disease groups studied, with the possible exception of the accident group, where it may be said that the patients whose accidents were really industrial accidents were probably taken care of by the industrial physicians, and hence were less numerous in proportion. Relative to this point, however, it should be noted that since we are dealing with fractures rather than minor industrial injuries the majority of these cases, even though seen first by the plant physician, were referred to the hospital serving the district.* The extent of this bias can be gauged in part by the following: In 1939, 17 per cent [1] of all accidental deaths were the result of occupational accidents, whereas of the accidents studied in this series 13 per cent were industrial accidents.†

3. *Control.* An element of control was provided by the fact that simultaneous studies were made of several groups with completely different symptomatology. As a matter of fact, the accident group was originally thought of as a control in the sense of a normal group, since in the opinion of the medical staff this group suffered less from emotional difficulty than any other in the hospital. It is one of the discoveries of the study that it did not prove to be so "normal."

Control in the sense of testing a therapeutic method was not in

---

* Furthermore, because of the inevitable duration and cost of such treatment many patients in the slightly higher income groups were admitted to the fracture service but since the procedure is for such cases to be returned as quickly as possible to their own physician for further treatment, the majority of patients in this category could not be followed and were excluded (Table V).

† Unfortunately we have not comparable figures for industrial injuries.

question at this stage of the study, since therapy was only incidentally an aim. Such control could be provided in future, of course, in the usual way of leaving half the patients untreated.

In cases treated it was observed that, the first stages consisted of mild functional conditions such as palpitation, hypertension, gas on the stomach. As emotional reactions recurred, the functional changes became more continuous; the blood pressure repeatedly rose, or there was chronic indigestion. Gradually the heart, or the gastro-intestinal tract, began to show the effect and there were demonstrable pathological changes. *Per contra*, relief from the emotional situation, if provided by the psychiatric treatment, resulted in disappearance of symptoms where no organic damage was present, or improvement of function in already damaged organs.

The stickler for a full measure of scientific control may raise the question: "Granted that the various groups reacted differently to emotional stimuli, how can we know that emotion was really a causative factor when not everyone who goes through emotional stress and strain does develop illness?" Yet the same objections could be made to the germ theory of infectious disease, on the ground that not everyone exposed to scarlet fever develops it. Study of a normal control group may be necessary to develop the mechanisms of immunity, but not always to establish an etiology for those who become sick.*

4. *Choice of Cases in Which the Psychic Factor Was Such as to Indicate Psychotherapy.* From Table IV it will be seen that only those cases were subjected to continued study in which the psychic factor was such as to indicate psychotherapy, a large number being excluded as inadequately determined or unsuitable for more than palliative treatment. This was a necessary condition of the study. It may be asked whether such a division of cases could properly be made without more detailed study than the routine superficial examination. Some of those unsuitable for treatment would necessarily have been so since they died before the preliminary examination could be undertaken (except through study of their charts). Two corrections or checks for the classifications in this table were developed. It was recognized that there would probably always be patients who presented a difficult diagnostic problem. Therefore, first,

* This point is discussed further in Chapter XI.

some 300 out of the 850 selected as suitable for detailed study were chosen at random for more careful observation, treatment on an intensive basis and follow-up, and this more intensive treatment confirmed the original selection. Second, the study in the second two years, though its statistical and other results confirmed those for the first two years in almost every other respect, showed a larger percentage suitable for treatment and a correspondingly smaller percentage inadequately determined. This may be attributed in part to our increased skill in diagnosis; but it also indicated that with such increased skill a larger percentage of patients in the original groups would probably have yielded the same results, if studied. (Further comments on the similarities and differences of the studies for the two periods will be found on page 131.)

5. *Method of Diagnosis.* Care was taken to avoid leading questions or "reading in" (see Chapter II).

As shown in the illustrative conversational interview (pages 57 and 77) no suggestive questions were asked in the initial examinations. The material was obtained from the patient's spontaneous casual statements: hence if one patient in such an interview talks mainly about situations arousing anger and the necessity of keeping his feelings to himself (pages 272 and 400), whereas another patient talks about his care-free life and love for adventure (page 666), we may be justified in assuming that this represents an actual difference between the two patients, at least in so far as his conscious reaction to his life difficulties and to the interview situation are concerned.

The superficial picture thus obtained was checked by contradictions in accord with the outline given in Chapters I and II and these evaluated to determine subgroups.

Further study in combination with treatment directed toward the specific focal conflict and habits of dealing with it that appeared to represent the patient's major problems, combined with follow-up, provided an additional check.

6. *Classifying Behavior Patterns.* Only after the accumulation of a large number of case records of diagnosis and treatments in all the illness groups was an attempt made to identify the behavior patterns characteristic of each group. Then it was found that a given series of traits or types of behavior occurred repeatedly in one group (such as fracture) but were essentially absent from others. Gen-

eralizations as to the type of emotional conflict or character peculiar
to each disease syndrome were based entirely on study of the material
accumulated by observation of the cases.

7. *Summary.* In conclusion, it may be stated that the scientific
validity of this work is of the type associated with systematic quantitative observations by the sampling method, statistically evaluated.
As such, it tends to substantiate the assumptions of the psychosomatic
or organismal view of medical problems in general, and of what we
have called the laws of emotional thermodynamics in particular. It
does not, on the other hand, provide the rigorous scientific proof
which may be obtained only from controlled experiments, though
care was taken to exercise the principle of control as far as possible
in these observatitons. Our quantitative results have to do with the
large percentage of patients with somatic syndromes having significant
emotional components, and with the large percentage of these in
which it was possible to remove somatic symptoms or improve functioning by the application of psychotherapy; that is, by a method of
releasing psychic energy from the symptoms in which it was being
dissipated, and reversing its flow so that it could be employed more
efficiently.

Quantitative observations also occurred in the study, and are recorded—such as observations regarding personality structure associated
with the several syndromes.

V. Review of the Importance of the Accident and Illness Habit

In addition to the discussion in this volume of our problem relative to organic disease, it is probably valuable, since this book will
appear while we are at war, to comment again on the magnitude of
the accident problem. In the armed forces the number of accident
casualties roughly equal the number of disabilities from illness, though
in times of peace the loss from illness is of course the greater. Both
Fleming [290] and Halliday [215, 216] have been interested in the illness
habit.

Accidents kill more males between the ages of 3 and 38 than any
other single cause. They kill nearly three times as many persons of
both sexes between the ages of 10 and 14 as does the next most important cause of death, namely, heart disease. And if we realize that

for every person killed 50 are permanently disabled (this figure varies in different age groups), and about 200 are temporarily disabled, hence in need of medical care, it is obvious that in terms of both prevention and treatment this problem bulks large in the responsibility of the physicians.

Four million workers were killed or seriously injured as a result of accident during the year 1941, according to the latest report by the National Safety Council.[2] If we think of the years of effort involved in building up an army of 4,000,000 men we get some appreciation of the significance of this figure. Furthermore, thinking in terms of industrial warfare, the National Safety Council estimates that these accidents resulted in a loss of 480,000,000 man-days, enough labor to have allowed us to produce during 1941, 20 more battleships, 100 more destroyers, 9000 more bombers, and 40,000 more tanks. This would roughly have doubled our equipment in these instruments of war at our disposal when war was declared on December 8.

Looked at from another point of view, the drain on our supply of men of draft age is startling, amounting to considerably more than a million in the draft age group killed or disabled. The families in this country are daily being deprived of husbands or sons, but the accident rate averages one death or disabling injury for every four families in the country, and it will be a long time before the Army takes such a toll.

Looked at from still another angle, the cost of these accidents as estimated by the National Safety Council, amounts to 4,000,000,000 dollars, and this figure should probably be doubled were all the indirect costs counted also. In terms of these figures one could say that while Secretary Morgenthau and Congress spent months struggling with the problem of raising an additional 8,000,000,000 dollars in taxes, an equal amount of national income could have been raised by coping with the accident problem. In other words their labors could have been spared or made doubly productive.

We have been too ready to assume that this was a problem about which nothing could be done since accidents were obviously the result of "the machine age." But insurance companies have been telling us for years that only 10 to 20 per cent of all accidents can be ascribed solely to mechanical causes. The National Safety Council's recent and more detailed study gives this figure as 17 per cent. If the individual rather than the machine is responsible for 83 per cent of all accidents, this puts the problem squarely up to all those interested in national defense and particularly *up to the doctor.*

This of course does not mean that we should not continue in our effort to improve working conditions which are a hazard, like motor vehicles that are not in perfect running condition. The National Safety Council is waging an admirable campaign which is increasing the efficiency of safety devices and familiarity with them all over the country, and in addition is analyzing the kind of unsafe acts which result in accidents. The former will make it increasingly difficult to have an accident, and the latter is resulting in greater knowledge of how to avoid accidents. Actually the National Safety Council estimates that in these ways it has saved 275,000 lives since the year of its initiation in 1913 in spite of the increased use of dangerous machinery since that time. But this is only a drop in the bucket when compared with the figures given at the outset.

The disturbing facts remain that even among industrial workers only slightly more than one-quarter of their accidents occur on the job, and that the people who have the worst accident record while at work also have the highest record for accidents at home or elsewhere. Falls alone account for more than one-quarter of all accidental deaths, and a very small percentage of these falls occur on the job. Only 1 out of 50 of our compensation cases is the result of occupational disease.

Physicians have hesitated to study the problem of accident-proneness, perhaps because of the difficulties inherent in it—although it is no more baffling than the problem of cardiovascular disease—or perhaps because, like almost everyone else, they have assumed that accidents always happened by accident. But even were we to forget the billions of dollars involved and misery which may visit one out of four families in the country every year, there is an additional fact that compels us to meet the challenge during the national crisis: It has been found that the people who have accidents are also the people who make mistakes, the kind of mistakes that sink a ship, lose a battle or explode a munitions plant.

Since accidents and mistakes which endanger the lives of others go hand in hand, and since our Government is responsible for what happens to men in the Army for twenty-four hours a day instead of merely during the ordinary eight hours of work, the responsibility of the Government is even greater than that of industry. Hence it is even more important that the accident problem be studied in relation to our armed forces. In 1940 the accident death rate in Army personnel was 281 per 100,000 and in Navy and Marine Corps 193, as compared with a rate of 414 for all United States males between the ages of 20 and 44. That is, the Army cut down the average accident rate by only about 30 per cent in spite of its selection of the best physical specimens in the country together with the careful training of them, and in spite of the fact that the figures cover mainly the period in the Army when exposure to danger is least. The Navy and Marine Corps seem to have done twice as good a job in this respect as the Army. But the danger and financial responsibility resulting from accidents in military personnel far outweigh this decrease in frequency.

These studies suggest that the accident-prone person can be spotted rather easily. Actually he can be spotted with less expense than the person with tuberculosis or heart disease, for whom the expense of roentgenograms is often required. Yet the cost of not spotting such persons is relatively greater.

Perhaps an even more important aspect of this problem is the following: "Insurance companies have called attention to the fact that adequate information cannot be obtained from study of major accidents, because there is no such thing as a major accident but only a major injury. Similar accidents may produce minor or major injuries or no injuries at all; it is their potential power to create injury that must be studied if we are to control them:

It has been found that in a unit group of 333 similar accidents 300 result in no injuries, 29 in minor injuries, and one in a major or lost-time case.[236]

We have no analogous figures for the various somatic disorders, such, for example, as gastric ulcer or coronary disease. Whether out of every 330 patients who react to emotional stress with vascular or gastro-intestinal spasm, one develops a major illness and 29 minor illnesses, or whether this figure should be higher or lower remains to be determined. We know enough to realize the great importance of attempting to find out" (Dunbar [149]). In any case, experience indicates that there is not only an accident habit but also an illness habit.

hapter IV

FRACTURES

Studies indicate that from 85 to 90 per cent of accidents are the result not of defects of machinery nor in the gross physical and mental equipment of the sufferer but of something in the personality of the patient.—Heinrich, "The Foundation of a Major Injury," *The Travelers Standard*, January 1929.

I. Nature and Magnitude of the Problem

STATISTICS

Accidents are an important problem for the practicing physician. They are an equally important factor in public health. They rank fourth among all causes of death (third for males) and third on our tables of illness incidence (Collins[95]). They are the major cause of death for the age group 15 to 19, and in the age group 3 to 38 accidents kill more males than any illness.[21]

Seventy-four persons out of every thousand are injured every year. This rate reaches 81 for the age group 15 to 19, and a peak of 86, or nearly one in eleven, for the age group 10 to 14. Accidents have a frequency rate in the age period 25 to 64 that is exceeded only by diseases of the respiratory system; and in the decade 15 to 24 only by diseases of the respiratory system and incapacity resulting from the puerperal state (Collins[93, 94]). They constitute nearly 12 per cent of all disabling illness during this period (Collins[95]).

Accidents cause disability for seven or more consecutive days to 16 people out of every thousand every year, and result in permanent orthopedic impairment for 12.4 persons out of every thousand.[340] It is often assumed that accidents to industrial employees occur almost wholly from dangerous occupations, but in a study by eleven companies it was found that non-industrial injuries among their employees caused disability of eight days or longer for 9.8 per 1000 males and 12.5 per 1000 females per annum.[51] More than one-fifth of all impairments due to accidents are the result of falls and more than twice as many people are injured in this way as are injured in automobile accidents.[340] In terms of non-industrial accidents or home accidents, falls assume an even greater prominence. For example:

Falls caused approximately two-thirds of all the home accident injuries that were treated and hospitalized at Cook County Hospital during 1933 and 1934. This prominence, as pointed out last month, might not hold true if non-hospitalized home accidents were under consideration. It may be, for example, that cuts and scratches occur more frequently in the home than do falls, but they were seldom recorded in this study because they are not often serious enough to result in hospitalization. The average high seriousness of falls reported in this study is indicated by the fact that 78 per cent of them resulted in fractures. Falls caused 198 of the 286 deaths, 19 of the 20 permanent total disabilities, 251 of the 348 permanent partial disabilities, and 2,442 of the 3,948 temporary disabilities.[363]

In a study of a sample representative of the urban population it was found that permanent impairments due to falls alone have a rate per thousand six times that resulting from impairments of wounds of war.[340] * Furthermore present statistics show that:

Off-the-job accident deaths among workers in all industry are approximately half again as great as work-accidents even when consideration is given to the fact that the worker is exposed to work-accidents only one-third of the day, and sleeps about another third. Motor-vehicles account for three-fifths of away-from-work deaths, while falls, drowning, burns and firearms account for the remainder. As steel is one of safest industries, workers in steel mills are safer at work than average.

Safer than at home were 1,200 J & L workmen in Seamless Tube Department where a record was recently established of 28 million man-hours of work without a fatal accident, covering a period of 12 years, 8 months. In the same interval 12 of these men met death by accident outside the mills, 2 of them in their own homes. Many fine safety records have been hung up by J & L workmen eager to have their particular department and mill cited for safety excellence. Records of 500,000 man-hours without lost-time accidents are not uncommon and are boasted of by the men contributing to their achievement.[365]

* See Series published by the Medical Department of the United States Army in the World War of which Number 15, "Statistics," contains data on death and injuries to officers and enlisted men during combat, for instance, Tables 105 and 106. Deaths from disease and accident not during combat are recorded in this Number, Table 48.

Although in the study of accidents outlined in this chapter we limited our observations to patients who had suffered fracture, these patients, of course, had an accident history covering the whole range of causes of accidents. Furthermore, of all non-industrial injuries causing disability of more than eight days fractures comprise 41 per cent for males and 31 per cent for females.[51] *

OTHER STUDIES

A number of studies furnish evidence to the effect that neither dangerous environment nor chance determines the incidence of accidents to nearly so great a degree as is commonly supposed. A number of these studies for instance dealing with industrial accidents show that a very small percentage of the employees suffer a very large proportion of the accidents.† This is true in industries having a high element of danger as well as in those having a low element of danger, and is true of automobile accidents where there is no employer-employee situation, as well as in accidents where there is such a factor.‡ Those employees who have the worst industrial accident records have also the greatest number of accidents at home or on the way to work. It has been found that this is not primarily a matter of slow reaction time or defects in training.§ A recent analysis of 50,000 injuries showed only 8 per cent of them to be related to skill, 3 per cent to being physically unfit, and 1 per cent to being mentally unfit.‖

Marbe[289] in 1926 first called attention to the existence of an accident habit, proving statistically that the probability for having accidents is greater for the person who has had previous accidents.

---

* See also Public Health Reports, No. 2020, 1936.

† Heinrich,[236] and also Farmer and Chambers;[173] Dershimer;[120] and Forster.[183]

‡ Heinrich's report[236] gives less than 0.8 per cent of the employees as responsible for 10 per cent of the accidents. Culpin[105] gives 25 per cent of the employees as responsible for the majority of accidents. Slocombe's unpublished report to the Registry of Motor Vehicles, Boston, in 1932, gives one third of 5000 auto drivers followed for six years as responsible for all the accidents of this group, and 13 per cent of the 5000 as involved in more than half the group's total accidents. Slocombe and Brakeman[388] report that of 2300 men employed in the operation of surface cars, 27 per cent caused 55 per cent of all the accidents. See also Motor Traffic Conditions in the United States.[312]

§ Motor Vehicle Traffic Conditions in the United States;[312] Farmer and Chambers;[173] also Heinrich.[236]

‖ Dunbar.[138]

Alexandra Adler [6] in 1934 published a study of 100 industrial workers whose accident record was from four to thirty-six, with an average ten times the average accident rate for their particular occupation. She was the first to publish any suggestion as to the x factor in the personality to which 80 to 90 per cent of all accidents are now ascribed.

A study of an industrial plant with 6600 employees calls attention to the fact that there is such a thing as an accident habit; * certain individuals stand out as having a tendency to minor accidents which do not result in their staying away from work. They come in with sore fingers and minor cuts and sprains, over a number of years. These injuries obviously do not gain them compensation in the sense of payment or even of getting time off. † Yet it is among these individuals that the majority of major accidents occur. To give one example:

In the dispensary of an industrial plant records "were tabulated to see how often the same workmen were injured. Visits for redressings were disregarded." A 10 per cent sample showed that "625 men had visited the dispensary 2641 times in less than two years. Only 184 of them once, and the rest more often, some twice, some five times, some ten times, some twenty times. The champion had been in thirty-seven times . . ." * 183 men, that is, about 29 per cent of them, had nearly two-thirds of the total number of accidents. They averaged 9.5 accidents each, whereas, the others averaged 2.1 each. The plant had 6600 employees of whom 3600 had had no accidents. Of the remaining 3000 men, 900 had had more than four accidents each in a period of less than two years.

There have been many attempts to ascertain what gives certain personalities the accident habit, and how accident proneness may be detected. A study carried out by the National Research Council of four large companies employing about 1400 commercial drivers with small variation from season to season, reviews this question. "Company A is a public utility, operating a large fleet of trucks and passenger cars, the latter being used chiefly by inspectors, supervisors, foremen, and executives. Collectively, these cars travel between 2,300,-

---

* Although this latter point is doubted by one industrial physician consulted, who says that even a little time off to smoke in the plant's dispensary is much desired.
† Slocombe.[387]

000 and 2,900,000 miles a year. In 1928 this company became seriously concerned about the high cost of its automobile accidents and the unwelcome fact that they were increasing in number every year. It undertook to find the reason, and to see whether it could do anything to reduce the rate." Having worked on the basis of all current theories from weather to reaction time, and from education to punishment of those who had accidents, the conclusion was reached that "the methods which the psychologists thus far have used cannot be made very effective in predicting a driver's performance." This company then shifted those men with the highest accident rates to other jobs in the plant. In less than four years it reduced its number of accidents per year to about one-fifth the original rate, and more than quadrupled the average number of miles between accidents. Moreover, it had held to the new level for three years at the time of publication. More striking than this, however, was the fact that the men shifted to other jobs in the plant began to have personal injuries instead of traffic accidents. "Since that time analysis of the records of more than 2,000 drivers employed by the four companies, showed that their automobile accidents and their personal injuries tend to accumulate side by side." *

On the basis of such studies as these it has been stated that from 88 † to 90 ‡ per cent of all industrial accidents are personal,§ that is, seem to be related to something in the personality of the individual. It may be significant that (although until very recently we had not come across the studies just cited) this figure of about 10 per cent is in accord with our estimate made on the basis of careful case studies of 500 patients with cardiovascular disease and fractures, which showed that 10 per cent of each group had had what seemed to have

---

* Motor Vehicle Traffic Conditions in the United States;[312] also Johnson;[252] and Bingham[88] suggests that by identifying, diagnosing and curing 5 per cent of drivers with bad records, fatalities might be reduced 35 per cent. The *British Medical Journal* published an article entitled "Motor Drivers' Proneness to Accident" from Report Number 84, Industrial Health Research Board. Major observations were that 160 bus drivers, after an intensive course, showed much variation in the numbers of accidents. If the accident prone had been removed, the accident rate for bus drivers would have been decreased by nine per cent in the first year. They comment that a 13 per cent decrease might have been accomplished by use of additional tests.

† Heinrich;[236] and also Menninger.[297, 298] See also Hill;[240] Ackerman and Chidester;[15] Fahrenkamp.[171]

‡ Dershimer.[120]

§ Huddleson.[243]

been accidental accidents; another 10 per cent of the patients with cardiovascular disease had accidents after the pattern characteristic of fracture patients; but only a fraction of 1 per cent of them had had more than one accident, whereas 72 per cent of the fracture group had two or more accidents.

In the words of William Harvey "our first duty is to enquire whether a thing be or be not before asking wherefore it is." Having considerable evidence on the first point, we may proceed to the second. A partial answer to the question as to what in the personality predisposes to accident, may lie in the following observations concerning trends that had a qualitative or quantitative prominence in our study.

At the time this study was undertaken we were unfamiliar with the material just given, and actually little of it was then available in published form. The decision to study serial admissions of patients with fractures was an outgrowth of our preliminary studies as already indicated. We were interested in emotional factors, especially in cardiovascular disease and diabetes. A difficulty presented by most previous studies, including our own, was the lack of material on the basis of which to answer the question: "Are the personality factors found to be operative in a given illness in any way specific for the disease itself? For example, for cardiovascular disease or for diabetes? Would you not find the same traits in the general population?" As already noted, a control group is practically out of the question for such studies as these. There were indications, however, that much could be learned from contrasting one group with another.

Attention has been called to the general impression that the fracture group was the most "normal" of any group of patients under treatment. After all, accidents happen to all of us, and an accident is an accident. Later study of the personalities, the reaction to illness and treatment, revealed marked similarities among the members of each illness group, and equally marked contrasts among the several groups. Incidentally, although this came as a surprise to many of us, the differences are such as to convince us that the fracture patients as a group, do not represent particularly "normal" people.

RECENT REVIEW OF THE ACCIDENT SYNDROME

Although the patients seen on the fracture ward did not turn out to be particularly "normal" people and although we became convinced of the existence of an accident syndrome such as has been described by insurance companies and others, we were impressed with the fact that the accident group seemed in many characteristics to be closer to the base line for the total population than any of the other groups studied (Chapter III, charts).

The preceding statistical material contrasting accident patients with patients suffering from other syndromes represents an attempt to characterize the fracture group as a whole; our clinical study, however, has indicated all along that this group is less homogeneous than any of the other disease groups. Hence it seemed advisable before publishing this material in detail to review it carefully to see whether we might not be dealing with several sub-groups whose outstanding characteristics would tend to cancel each other out. The application of the Rorschach test was of extreme value in this review, and clearly distinguished the sub-groups suspected.

This recent Rorschach study of fracture patients delineates three different types of personalities which are briefly described here in order that the reader may keep them in mind during the following discussion. One group (A) seems to include "constricted" personalities (page 664) and is especially characteristic of the female accident patients. The second group (B) in Rorschach terminology is "introversive" with marked infantile traits. It includes mostly males and the majority of males with a well-established accident habit. The third group (C), Rorschach "extratensive," is also mostly males. It includes a few patients with a well-established accident habit but represents largely persons with a less well-defined accident proneness who have an occasional accident or two under particular stress.

II. Onset of Symptoms

Since an acute onset is of the very nature of fracture there is little to say under this heading except to note by way of contrast with other groups that in only a very few cases was any type of traumatic event or worrying given as the reason for the accident. It should be added, however, that the situations preceding the accident were very similar in most cases.

With these patients supplementary statements concerning the onset were of the following type: A patient would make it clear that he thought he had had an accident as a result of being in a hurry, or carelessness; later he would say that the accident had been more than this.

Case No. F 117. A married man, 31 years old, was admitted to the hospital with fracture of the left tibia and fibula. His first statement was that he had slipped on some ice while hurrying to work.

He said later that he had been out of work for a long time and was looking for a job. He had always disliked job hunting and dreaded it particularly at this time because he had been trying to keep the fact that he was out of work from his wife, whom he feared. If the interview to which he was on his way were to prove a failure, he felt that he would no longer be able to keep his unemployment a secret. "The only good thing about the accident was that it kept me from having to tell my wife that I couldn't get a job." The accident prevented his being turned down again, and having to confess his failure to his wife.

He sustained an injury that kept him out of work for about a year. When seen for follow-up many months later, he said: "If I had not been out of work that accident would never have happened."

Case No. F 123. A Roman Catholic woman, aged 24, married about a year, was standing on the steps of her house on the way to confession, wondering whether she should go back for an umbrella. She was seriously worried about having to confess her use of contraceptives since her marriage. "For no reason I can think of I simply fell down the steps and broke my hip." She added: "But it was a relief not to have to go to confession. I knew Father would either not give me absolution and I would be damned or I would have to have a child—you'd have to go to the hospital with a child too, but that would be worse—they save the child and kill the mother. This way it's only me they're interested in." (Although this was the first accident requiring hospitalization, she gave a history of many minor injuries.)

Several other patients had been out skating or playing games, and at first reported that they fell on the ice or just tripped. Later, they would say that their mothers had told them not to play, or that the accident had occurred at the end of a vacation when they dreaded returning to work or school.

The significance of the case history material relative to onset is discussed in a later section of this chapter.*

* Page 203.

III. Predisposition to Illness—Factors to be Evaluated

ORGAN CONDITIONING—PHYSIOLOGICAL AND PSYCHOLOGICAL

Heredity *—*Actual and Pseudo*

In the chapters to follow heredity is discussed from two points of view: First, heredity in the customary medical use of the word; and second, what we have called pseudo-heredity or exposure to the illness in question, a factor often confused with heredity. Our observations indicate, for example, that cardiovascular disease in an ancestor is likely to have much more effect in predisposing a patient to an illness if the patient has been exposed to the ancestor in question than if there has been no exposure. They indicate, furthermore, that exposure to illness in a close friend may be even more important than exposure to illness in a parent, particularly if such exposure occurs at critical points in emotional development.

In the fracture series studied, slightly more than 40 per cent gave a *history of accident* in the family including the patient's siblings; 46 per cent gave a history of exposure to accident in family or friend. This is more than three times the highest percentage for family history of accident found in any other group studied, and in itself suggests that there may be something in the general make-up of certain individuals predisposing them to accident which may run in families. Whether this is a matter of physiology and constitution or a matter of behavior patterns, or both, is a question that has received little attention in medical circles. Of course occasional comment is made on the structure of the bones themselves from the point of view of the ease with which a given individual may sustain a fracture, but the preceding statements and those to follow refer not merely to fracture but to the tendency to have accidents of all types.

The possible importance of the exposure factor is illustrated in such cases as the following:

Case No. F 45. A policeman, 38 years old, was admitted to the hospital for a broken leg. He was worried because a policeman he knew had slipped on

---

* The figures given relative to heredity here and in the analogous sections of the following chapters are the most unreliable of all the figures given because often the cause of death was unknown. It may be assumed, however, that the error involved would be more or less the same from group to group (see page 543 ff. for discussion of their possible significance). On the other hand the figures given for exposure are obviously more reliable.

some ice a month before, and had broken a leg while on his beat. The patient did the same thing in the same spot.*

Case No. F 83. A married woman, 33 years old, was admitted to the hospital for a fracture of the left tibia and fibula. She reported that at the time of the accident she was walking downstairs crying because her brother two weeks previously had fallen off a scaffold and broken both his legs. Ever since she had felt jittery especially when in situations where there was any possibility of falling.

But, as will be seen later, this is only one aspect of what we have called the exposure factor. Although it happens occasionally that a patient will have an accident of the same type in the same place as one to which he has been exposed, it happens more regularly that some persons exposed to a person with an accident habit develop an accident habit although the accidents may not be parallel in type. In our series accident-proneness was slightly more frequent among patients who had been exposed to relatives or friends who were accident-prone, but was not more frequent among those who had merely been told that Aunt or Uncle so and so whom they had never seen had once had an accident. (See Chapters IX and X for further discussion.)

Also, 38 per cent of these patients gave a *history of cardiac heredity,* but in only the exceptional case was there exposure to relative or friend with cardiovascular disease, and cardiovascular disease was relatively rare in these patients.† It should be noted furthermore, that cardiovascular heredity was no more frequently reported in the groups of patients with rheumatic heart disease or diabetes, than in the group of patients with fracture, although it was somewhat more frequent in the histories of patients with hypertensive cardiovascular disease, coronary disease, anginal syndrome, and rheumatic fever, and exposure to it was a regular occurrence in these groups. In evaluating such material it is important to bear in mind the fact that cardiovascular disease is responsible for nearly half the deaths occurring after the age of 45, so that any person with ancestors living beyond this age, is likely to have cardiac heredity. The limited exposure of accident patients to cardiovascular disease is, therefore, probably influenced by the fact that their parents either died young for other reasons or were completely lost track of by the patients in question.

---

* This patient turned out to be a malingerer. For further information see page 223.
† See Charts VII, VIII, IX, pages 157–159, and the figures in Chapter IX.

Diabetic heredity was reported by 10 per cent of the patients in the fracture group, as compared with 9 per cent of the patients with coronary occlusion, 12 per cent of the patients with anginal syndrome, 19 per cent of the patients with hypertensive cardiovascular disease, 20 per cent of the patients with rheumatic heart disease, and 35 per cent of the patients with diabetes (this includes the patients' own siblings; the figure is 31.5 per cent if the siblings are not included).

Nervousness in the family was reported by only 10 per cent of the patients in this group as compared with 29 per cent of the patients with diabetes, and 77 per cent of the patients with hypertensive cardiovascular disease. (More complete figures and discussion of this material is given in Chapters IX and X.)

Constitution, Age Range, Sex, and Marriage

Build. From the point of view of build, these patients, as far as we are able to determine, did not fall into any definite categories. Some were asthenic, some pyknic, and others of mixed type. A number of men were very small and rather delicately built, especially those in group B. This was true especially of those who showed the most generalized tension and restlessness (e.g., Case No. F 117, page 179, and Case No. F 150, page 242). Characteristic of these was the fact that they had kept themselves excessively busy, taken part in all kinds of athletics and exercise in the attempt to prove themselves strong and "masculine."

Age Range for the fracture patients is given in the following table.

Age Group	Per Cent
15–24	35
25–34	32
35–44	17
45–54	17

These figures are in general agreement with our present statistics for accidents by age groups.

Sex Distribution. Of this group 47 per cent were females. Although according to our public health statistics, death from accident is more than twice as frequent among males as among females, the incidence of accidents shows no such differences between the two sexes. In a study of non-industrial accidents among industrial employees [51] we have under the age of 35, 94 per cent among females,

96 per cent among males; and over the age of 35, 97 per cent among females, 96 per cent among males. In our series there were more females than males over 35 (44 per cent as compared with 25 per cent) but more males than females in the age group under 35.

Marital History. Of the females in this group 64 per cent were married; of the males 51 per cent were married; for the total group 57 per cent were married. Of those patients who were 21 and over, 73.5 per cent were married (71 per cent of the males and 76 per cent of the females); of those 25 and over, 83 per cent were married (81 per cent of the males and 85 per cent of the females). In this group, 46 per cent of the marriages were childless (48 per cent of the males and 44 per cent of the females). Nineteen and seven-tenths per cent of these marriages had one child (21 per cent of the males and 19 per cent of the females). There were 1.15 children per marriage (among the males 1.24 and among the females 1.06). This is the lowest record of children per marriage of any disease group studied, and below the average for the general population.

Previous Health

This series of patients is outstanding among the groups studied for their previous health record. Aside from their accident history, 32 per cent of these patients (21 per cent of the males, and 11 per cent of the females) gave a perfect health history, even to the point of freedom from colds and nervousness.

Their record for *major operations* was lower than that for any other group studied (averaging only one for every four patients) except for patients with diabetes; and if major and minor operations are lumped together (the average was one for every two patients) their record is better than that of the patients with diabetes. Typical operations were appendectomy and hernia repair which comprised nearly half of the total operative history.

Less than one-third of these patients had had any type of *major illness.* Typical major illnesses were pneumonia (which, however, was much less frequent than in any other group studied), tropical diseases (many of these patients had a tendency to wander in foreign parts), and rheumatic fever (Chapter X). Only 5 per cent of these patients had more than one major illness. Allergy, obesity, and poor teeth, which were common findings in the cardiovascular groups, were noticeably lacking among patients with fracture. Allergy was almost completely lacking among the males. Pelvic disorders were also infrequent in this group except for abortions which were unusually frequent (10 per cent with a rate of two and a half per person in this 10 per cent).

The record for *venereal disease* was low (1.9 per cent) as compared with that for the other groups studied, with a slight preponderance among females (1.8 to 2 per cent). This figure would have been lowered by about 25 per cent had Negroes not been included in the first part of the serial study. Most patients with venereal disease had a tendency toward high blood pressure, although at the time that they were studied they were not diagnosed as having hypertensive cardiovascular disease. This point is mentioned because venereal disease was particularly high among patients with hypertensive cardiovascular disease (20.4 per cent).

The only *minor illnesses* at all frequent among these patients were gastro-intestinal upsets.

Reference to public health statistics will show that this is a health record far superior to that of the general population. It should be noted, furthermore (Charts IX A and IX B) that this good health record was maintained throughout life, that is, there is no appreciable difference in the previous health record of patients in the age group 35 to 55 as compared with those in the age group 15 to 34. In accord with our general findings the females had a worse health record than the males, but the difference is not so great as for many of the other groups studied.

In contrast with the excellent health record of the patients with fracture, however, was their history of previous accident resulting in dislocation, fracture, severe burn, or bad cuts requiring several stitches; such a history was given by the majority (79 per cent). This is in striking contrast with patients in the other two groups where such a history was relatively infrequent.

Note Relative to Hypertension Among Accident Patients. Whereas only four of the fracture patients were actually diagnosed as having hypertension (and only six had a diastolic blood pressure of over 90), 11 per cent of all serial admissions and the same per cent of the special series had systolic blood pressures in the upper range of normal, taking this to be above 140/90 for the age group 20 to 50. This point is mentioned because of a study (Bingham [38]) of accident-proneness in motormen and bus drivers in which it is stated that those with blood pressure "higher than normal yet not dangerously high" had two and one-sixth times as many accidents as other men of similar age and experience. In an occasional patient in our series high blood pressure was discovered of which the patient had been unaware. For example, two girls aged 18 had blood pressures of 146/82 and 140/85.* This is above the average for the total population in this age group.

Twenty-five per cent of these patients with slightly higher blood pressure were in the age group 24 to 35; and 75 per cent in the group 35 to 50. Those of the near-hypertensive patients in this group who gave a history of previous accidents differed from the total group reporting previous accidents in that most of them fell in the decades 35 to 55, whereas the majority of the total group fell in earlier age decades. The percentage of them reporting previous accidents was slightly lower than that for the total group, however. (For further data and discussion see Chapter V, section I, and Chart XI, page 160.)

Of the total number of accidents reported by this group of patients, the percentages were as follows:

> 48 per cent were the result of falls †
> 22 per cent were the result of motor vehicles ‡
> 22 per cent were athletic accidents
> 7 per cent were miscellaneous accidents.

For the accident record of the total group see page 554.

Statistics Concerning Previous Injury

General. In spite of their relatively good health record, a very high percentage of patients on the fracture ward revealed what Freud has called the "traumatophilic diathesis." Of course we start with a 100 per cent accident record, and furthermore 79 per cent of

---

* In cases studied from this point of view, single blood pressure readings which appeared on the medical history were not relied on, but the blood pressure readings were checked over a considerable period and the figures given a representative average. Unlike patients in the more obviously neurotic groups, however, this group did not show any considerable variation.

† In only two instances did the fall occur while the patient was on the job.

‡ Two-thirds of these were the result of being knocked down by motor vehicles.

these patients had had two or more accidents, whereas in no other group studied was there a history of two or more accidents in more than 11 per cent (patients with diabetes). Patients with rheumatic fever type A, who turned out to have a tendency toward accident-proneness, had a record of 14 per cent, but if the figure were given for the rheumatic fever group as a whole this figure would be reduced to about 8 per cent. When it comes to three or more accidents the difference is even more striking. Slightly more than half of the group of patients with fracture had three or more accidents, and in only three of the other groups studied *were there any patients with three or more accidents*. These were patients with anginal syndrome, 6 per cent; patients with rheumatic heart disease, 4 per cent; and patients with diabetes, 4 per cent.

For all the groups studied except the fracture group, the accident history is well within the 10 to 20 per cent designated by insurance statistics as "unavoidable accidents." It should be noted, nevertheless, that many of the accidents included in this percentage for other groups were avoidable, as is discussed in the respective chapters. It is noteworthy also that the accident tendency is much greater in patients suffering from more than one syndrome (see Charts X and XI, page 160, and Chapter X).

It is interesting that of the cardiac patients who reported previous injuries, nearly half reported injuries of the following type. Patient No. CD 213 was stabbed while watching a parade. Patient No. RF 337 was standing on a plank which was broken by another man. (The patient, incidentally, did not show the typical fracture personality.) He was on the plank in an elevator shaft. A third person stepped on the plank, unexpectedly; the plank gave way, and the patient fell twenty stories. In spite of having fallen this distance, he was laid up for only a month. Another time he was going down a ladder, and someone let something fall on him from above, which knocked him off. He fell three stories, and fractured his skull. Another patient had his jaw fractured in a fight. The majority of accidents among patients with fracture, on the other hand, resulted from slipping on the ice and falling, stepping in front of a motor car, taking a dare and doing something beyond their strength.*

* Although this patient was a diabetic she had a typical accident pattern: She jumped on the back of a truck, became frightened, fainted and fell off. One patient who, having been told by his boss to use the stairs instead of sliding down the rope to the ground, started on the rope, felt dizzy and sick half way down, lost his grip and fell.

Of course many accidents among the cardiac patients cannot be considered completely innocent; in some cases there was evidence of a tendency to quarrel and to establish feud relationships; and in the case of patient No. RF 337 there was the patient's own statement that if he had been "paying more attention" these two accidents might have been avoided. Nevertheless, accidents of this type, whether innocent or not, were not characteristic of the fracture group. (For further discussion see pages 256, 300, 345, 377, 418, 438, 486, 550.) The fact that as far as could be determined accidents that could possibly have been accidental occurred in considerably less than 10 per cent of the patients in each group may give further weight to the disproportion in the accident record of fracture patients as compared with the other groups studied.

Age distribution among fracture patients with and without previous injury was as follows:

	AGE GROUPS		
	15 to 24	25 to 34	35 to 55*
	PER CENT	PER CENT	PER CENT
Fracture patients:			
A. In total series................	35	32	34
B. Without previous injury......	18	39	43
C. With previous injury.........	41	29	30

Stated another way: Of the 35 per cent in the age group 15 to 24, 87 per cent had had previous injuries; of the 32 per cent in the age group 25 to 34, 68 per cent had had previous injury; and of the 34 per cent in the age group 35 to 55, 66 per cent had had previous injury (see also Chart XII A and Chart XII B, page 548).

It is striking that although one might expect to find more young people who had not suffered previous injury, the situation is exactly reverse. In the age group 15 to 24, 74 per cent of all the patients reported previous injury. Furthermore, more than six times as many of this age group had a history of previous injury as compared with those who gave no such history, which suggests that the "accident habit" is particularly frequent in young people.* In view of the fact

* Incidentally this checks with the figures given by Perrott and Holland [332] of frequency rates of disabling illness per thousand persons, which gives 10.9 under 15 years, 13.1 for the decade 15 to 24, and only 17.2 for the four decades 25 to 64. Furthermore, this observation of ours is confirmed in a study just published by the Medical Research Council of Great Britain.[3]

that accidents are a major cause of death as well as disability for this age period it seems likely that the decrease in percentage of patients in the older age group with a well-established accident habit might be explained by the fact that many of these young people through continuance of their accident habit have succumbed to fatal accidents or become permanently crippled. As to those whose first accident occurred after the age of 35, among whom there is a high percentage of women, several considerations arise which will be discussed in a later section. It may be sufficient to note here that these patients also had histories which coincided with that typical for the accident group as a whole; that is, low previous illness record, low marriage and family records, and so on, except that they seemed to have lived longer before beginning to have accidents involving injury (for discussion of childhood accidents see page 548).

Special Types of Accident. These observations point to the existence of an "accident habit." Studies of patients in our series indicate furthermore, that patients who tend to have accidents fall into distinct groups from the point of view of type of accident or the organ habitually injured.

(1) Some patients are inclined always to injure the *same member*, whether by burning, cutting, or fracturing.

Patient No. F 32 had three injuries to her left arm, and one to her right She had two injuries to the left wrist and finger and then injured her left elbow.

Case No. F 94. Came in with a compound fracture of the left elbow. He had been driving with his elbow out the window, when his car was sideswiped by a truck. At 14 he had accidentally stuck his left index finger into a machine and had part of it cut off. At 8 he had fallen off his bicycle and broken his left wrist. In general he was known as the kind of person who was always getting hurt.

Patient No. F 119 repeated the same injury to the same arm which he had injured under particularly traumatic circumstances previously.

Patient No. F 74, a truck driver, aged 28, separated, injured his left arm (fractured the middle third of the humerus and injured the radial nerve) when he was driving with his left arm on the window sill and was sideswiped by another car. This patient had had four previous accidents to the same arm, the second of which occurred in the same manner. After discharge from the hospital this patient refractured the same arm riding in a bus with his left arm similarly on the window sill.

One may say that coincidence, or an already weakened part may account for some of these accidents, but this does not seem to explain all of them. We have the impression that there is another explanation for some, that is, that there is an inner tendency to injure one part of the body, or to be injured in a certain manner. In the case of patient No. F 74 one could similarly ascribe the series of accidents to an inability to learn from experience. The patient himself said: "I never do what I'm told and I never change my habits." This subject is discussed further in subsequent sections of this chapter.

(2) Still others showed a definite predilection for *accidents of a specific type,* such, for example, as automobile accidents whether as driver or as pedestrian.

Case No. F 149. Came in at the age of 21, with fracture of both bones of both legs, malunion after a Pott's fracture of the leg, and evidence of an old fracture of the right epicondyle. The injury to the legs had come when she was dashing across the street without looking and was struck by a car. When she was 15 she had been running in the sand and had failed to see some glass into which she fell. Ten years previously she had broken her arm while running, tripping over a toy fire engine.

Case No. F 61. A woman, aged 26, had three previous accidents while riding a motorcycle. She came in with a fractured medial malleolus and left tibia, and fractured anterior lip of the left tibia, which occurred in an automobile accident. She had no other accidents.

Case No. F 127. Two of the three accidents which befell this patient were the result of being knocked down by an automobile while crossing under the elevated.

Case No. F 132. A man, aged 38, came in with a fracture of the twelfth dorsal vertebra, which had occurred when he was pushing boards and barrels down a plank on the stairs. A barrel slipped and he slipped also. Eighteen months previously he and another man were rolling a piece of timber and it caught three of his fingers. Eleven years previously he had been standing on the street conversing, when a truck backed into him breaking his right leg. Before that, the exact date being unknown, he had broken his arm while playing football. (Further study of the patient reveals the fact that he had several times had the same type of fall injuring his back, before the fall that brought him to the hospital. And follow-up showed that he was continually falling. Hence he is illustrative also of patients in group four.)

Case No. F 77. A 16-year-old student came in with a fracture of the radius. While playing football, he had bumped into another student and fallen on his elbow. The same accident had occurred to him a few minutes before without his having broken his arm.

Cast No. F 144. Sprained his ankle in the same way twice, playing football before the football game in which he fractured it.

Case No. F 50. A 15-year-old boy had been trying to open the garage door after coming home from skiing, and fell and fractured his hip. Prior to the present accident he had had four serious falls in quick succession, one playing baseball, one playing football, and two skiing. He had also fractured his skull at the age of 8 falling from the handlebars of his brother's bicycle.

Case No. F 141. A man, aged 46, came in with fracture of the shaft of the fibula, received from a ball while he was playing ball with some children. His three previous accidents also had occurred while playing ball.

Case No. F 91. A man, aged 25, came in with a fracture of both bones of the lower third of the left leg. He had fallen through a window while fixing a shade, and been caught by a bar, lacerating the right arm so that he had to have the ulnar nerve repaired. While waiting for a treatment at Presbyterian Hospital for this injury, he, for no reason he could think of, fell off a ledge at 165th Street and Riverside Drive, thus breaking his leg.

(3) Some patients seem to belong to the group previously described by family doctors as "all thumbs," or just careless, or unlucky; their previous accidents showed a *wide variety*.

Case No. F 152. A man, aged 34, was admitted with fracture of the left tibia and fibula. He had simply stepped out of the car and fallen on a muddy road at 1:30 in the morning on his way home from dancing, and a "few beers." Two years previously he had seriously injured his ankle doing a skating stunt. At the age of 12 he had fallen off a tree and caught his leg on a picket fence. He was a carpenter by trade and notorious for bandaged fingers.

(4) Still another group which should be counted among the accident-prone, although this group is not so reported in our statistics, is represented by patients who had had a *previous habit of falling*, or of taking some particular risk when there was no necessity for so doing. These patients are likely to say in relation to the accident: "Why I've done that (e.g., falling down stairs) twenty-five times before and never gotten hurt till now."

Some patients, especially women, had a habit of falling. Examples are patients No. F 90, F 125, F 114, and F 91.

Case No. F 90. This patient had spells of falling down, and even several times fell down a whole stairway before she finally fell down a few steps which resulted in her hospitalization. She said "there must be some reason why I am here on my back instead of on a trip south which is where I planned to be at this time."

This point is of interest in connection with Heinrich's [286] analysis of accidents in which he states that out of every 331 similar accidents, 30 produce minor injuries and 1 a major injury. This information is complemented by that to follow which suggests that careful study might reveal exactly why a given patient is the unlucky one and why in one patient it is falling from a height, while in another it is being hit by a car, and still another it is always trauma to the left hand or arm which causes the injury.

Early Influences and Traumatic Experiences

It should be noted as a basis for contrast with other groups of patients discussed in this volume, that the lives of these patients as first reported by them seemed to be notably free from illness, exposure to sudden death in the family, or any type of traumatic experience or worry. Even their previous accidents they took lightly or ascribed to fate. (This may be in some degree responsible for the fact that their physicians also have tended to regard them as "normal" human beings who are either just unlucky or just clumsy.) Further study showed, however, that in the latter respects the first impression was not actually the correct one.

OUTSTANDING POINTS IN THE PERSONALITY HISTORY

General Adjustment

*Vocation—Education.** As has been pointed out already (Chapter III) our fracture patients had an average educational record, considered in terms of the percentage whose academic education placed them in the grammar school, high school, or college category. They were pretty close to the base line of the groups studied, as well as to that of the upper 60 per cent of the general population. But in terms of the completion of educational units, they differed from the other groups in that they showed a greater tendency to stop before

* It will be remembered that statements under starred headings are based only on patients over 21, in order to make them comparable to national statistics.

graduating from grammar school, high school, or college as the case might be. This tendency was particularly marked in what we have called the B group but was partly reduced as it appears on the chart by the more frequent completion of units in the other two fracture groups.

Income.* The income level of these patients was in general good. Although not many of them were in the comfortable category, fewer were on WPA or Relief than in any other group.

Occupation.* The occupational distribution for these patients corresponded more closely to the occupational distribution of the upper 60 per cent of the population than did that of any other group studied. There were no very marked negative or positive deviations except in group VI. As has been stated already, there were fewer in the category "invalids and housewives" among the fracture patients, although there were not actually fewer housewives. The most considerable positive deviation for the group, however, was in the classification "clerks, salesmen, stenographers."

General Behavior. At first sight the personality histories of these patients seemed to show nothing striking in relation either to their character traits, or to the emotional environment of their accidents, except perhaps that they were usually happy-go-lucky, with few complaints, and often manifested a jerky, restless type of tension.

Social Adjustment. These patients were generally liked socially and showed few outspoken neurotic traits or marked tendency to dominate or submit. They enjoyed groups, were talkative and cheerful. A good many of them had a rough, "don't care" manner. There was little evidence of brooding or philosophizing, but in group B there was considerable eccentricity. They were likely to be good story tellers and enjoyed recounting their adventures. As a rule they were equally liked by members of both sexes.

Sexual Adjustment. Their sexual behavior also was markedly free from overt symptoms of conflict. As compared with the other groups studied, they were divorced or separated with relative ease, and were casual about extramarital affairs. The first impression of the group as a whole was that they took marriage lightly but this impression seems to have been colored by group B, a number of whom were

---

* It will be remembered that statements under starred headings are based only on patients over 21, in order to make them comparable with national statistics.

definitely of the Don Juan type. Unlike patients in some of the other
illness groups, however, they were extremely careful about their
extramarital affairs and managed to avoid both venereal disease and
pregnancies. The 10 per cent of the women in this group having a
high abortion rate were married women, most of whom were Catholic
or married to Catholic husbands, and hence were in difficulty about
contraception.

Attitude Toward Parents and Children. Conspicuous factors in their
relationships with their parents were the frequency with which at
least one parent was described as strict, and, in group B, the irresponsibility toward the parental family, an attitude which carried over to
wife or husband. Also, the fracture group usually exhibited a very ambivalent attitude toward parenthood. For this reason the majority
of them either avoided marriage, or when married avoided having
children. Attention has already been called to the small size of
family characteristic of these patients. A predominant pattern was
the unmarried man or girl who always had to have girl-friends or
boy-friends, as the case might be, in order to be sure that he or she
was successful and well liked, but as soon as the girl-friend or boy-
friend became serious had to call off the affair and start afresh. After
this had gone on for some time the majority of these patients would
marry. The attitude toward children, when they had them, was often
irresponsible and sometimes brutal, especially in group B. A typical
statement is that of

Case No. F 140. A married woman, aged 26: "I have two children who
are very bad. Everyone else says they are not. They do everything I don't
want them to. A lot of people tell me I am cruel because I make them kneel
with their hands on their heads. They mind this and they don't mind being
spanked. They tell such fibs. They make me so nervous I shriek at them so
you can hear it all over."

There were some patients who concentrated on bringing up children "different from the way I was brought up," in order to demonstrate what a good parent should be like. For example, Case No. F 110
spoke of her wish to have a child of her own "so that she could really
know mother love"; her mother had been so unkind. Case No. F 121
was the head of a parents' association and had a major interest in
teaching people to be better parents. In spite of good intentions, how-

ever, many of those that had children had difficulty in being good parents, for example Case No. F 111 said: "I wish I could have a mother, and I would give up one leg. It's hard to think how old some of my friends are and they still have mothers." However, he was rough with the child he had with him, took hold of the child's ears saying that he would pull them off if it did not behave.

Among the percentage of these patients who were without children, for some adventitious reason, such attitudes as the following occur: Case No. F 129 remarked: "I never had any children, I don't know why. We both wanted them." And Case No. F 127 speaking of his wife: "She has a small uterus, and can't have any children, and that is a disappointment." Case No. F 128 was very anxious for children and even thought of adopting one.

Case No. F. 46. A married woman, aged 35, who worked as a railroad clerk, had just returned from a vacation and was due to go to work the next day. She tripped in a break in the pavement. She had always wanted a baby, and had had an abortion in the past because they could not afford it. Being now 35 years old she thought her chances of ever having a child would be very small if she were to work another year but said that perhaps "now that she is laid up she will be able to have a child."

Whatever form the conflict over having children assumes—both among those who disliked the idea of having children or having children were cruel to them, and among those childless patients who spoke of having wanted children—there was usually an association between the conflict over children and the accident tendency, and an association between the conflict and the patient's reaction to his own parents and authority figures generally.

Characteristic Behavior Pattern

In spite of the apparent freedom from conflict in the various spheres of adjustment, certain points gradually began to assume importance in the personality of fracture patients. Their outward casualness about feelings and personal problems proved in many cases to be partly a defensive tendency. They appeared to be striving for a kind of independence or autonomy in relationships with authoritarian figures in contrast with the characteristic dominance or submission in other illness groups. Their casual manner reflected

this effort toward independence and also some sense of guilt stemming from conflicts over their resistance to authority (page 213).
Important in connection with these conflicts is their emphasis upon
immediate values rather than long range goals, their habit of attaching emotions to people and immediate concrete experience rather
than to intellectual values and verbalization. This emphasis represents
a normal stage in the striving for independence but many of these
patients seemed to get arrested at this stage and gave the impression
of infantile behavior which is especially noticeable in group B.
A conspicuous tendency to make up their minds definitely and
quickly is an integral part of their adjustment pattern and reflects
their self-reliance, their resistance to authoritarian strictures, as
well as their emphasis upon immediate values.

Gradually we became impressed by the regularity with which these
patients gave spontaneously in many forms, an impression of impulsive action. Many of them made such a statement as the following: "I always like to keep working, and can't stand to be around
doing nothing." Such a statement as this might be made by any one
of the three fracture types. More characteristic of the constricted A
group are the following: "It wouldn't have happened if I hadn't
been in such a hurry. Mother always told me I'd get hurt sometime if
I didn't stop always being in such a hurry." "When I find a way to
do a thing I always stick to it, but if I don't, I do something anyway
and take a chance." The following statement is more characteristic
of the introversive B group: "Adventure and excitement appeal to
me. I can hold a job if I want to."

It is noteworthy with regard to their constant activity that fracture patients reported with considerable frequency, "walking even
in my sleep." For example: "It seemed as if I just could never stop."
Or, "Mostly I do things on impulse. I like to finish what I'm doing,
but sometimes I like to do something else first, so I jump up and
do it." Or, "I get mad, but I don't say anything. I keep it in and do
something." Or, "I like to do everything in a hurry in order to get
through with it." Or again, "I always used to be on the run, and
my major sport now is horse racing."

This appearance of impulsiveness is, however, somewhat deceptive,
if impulsive is understood to mean spontaneous inconsidered action
dominated by feeling with little rational control (page 672). Actu-

ally, only a minority of these patients were impulsive in this sense. The characteristic decisiveness of fracture patients, their emphasis upon immediate concrete experience rather than long range goals, their energy and activity, combine to give the impression of uncontrolled impetuosity. They even call themselves "impulsive." The quick decisions, the hurried activity, and other "impulsive" appearing behavior is, however, quite consistent with their goals and general adjustment pattern.

Among the introversive fracture patients of group B, this appearance of impulsiveness was particularly marked. Not only were they frequently very active but they showed a conspicuous tendency to wander. Their *work records* were irregular in two senses: First, they were inclined to be interrupted by many periods of being without a job; and second, they were inclined to shift from one kind of job to another and to be willing to try their hand at whatever came along without much planning and without much thought about systematic training for anything in particular. Examples are the following:

Case No. F 102. When asked what he would really like to do, this patient said: "I don't know, I would like to do a lot of things, I never think much about it, it depends on my luck I guess. . . . Come a day, go a day. Life is sweet and short, and everybody is happy."

Case No. F 66. This patient was interested in theatricals, but was given an opportunity to work on a paper, so he stopped school and went into this for a few years. Then he decided to join the Navy. Thereafter, he returned and became a plasterer's apprentice for five years, and finally joined the police force. He does not seem to be particularly enthusiastic about his work but manages on his vacation to go to Florida with his wife and have a good time. He had saved no money and claimed he had little over a dollar in the bank.

The lively imagination, aggressiveness, and limited affective contact with outer reality characteristic of this introversive group result in difficulty with concentration and feelings of frustration which lead to the unstable work records and general picture of irresponsibility.

An expression of the impulse to action and of their concrete interests is the fact that these patients were interested in machinery and liked to see it in operation; they spoke of "driving like mad" to work off tension.*

Case No. F 130. "My father was a railroad man, I was a boiler-maker, a deck-hand and an engineer."

Case No. F 126. After leaving school, this patient worked on automobile repairs, and then, because the mechanical trade was slow, he worked in a butcher shop until he could get back into his chosen line again. Just before his accident he had hoped to get something with Diesel engines. He said: "I'm very active. I feel better when I'm doing something."

Case No. F 128. This patient worked in a woolen mill and then on trains, first as a guard and later as a motor switchman. He said: "I always like to go fast. I guess I got it from sitting watching trains go fast by the house. I could sit for hours watching them." His impulsive behavior was expressed in his coming to this country on the spur of the moment, then he hated it and was rather upset: "That's me, I act first and think afterwards."

Although the activities and interests of these patients do not represent characteristic impulsiveness, many of their accidents do combine the urge to action with an impulsive uncontrolled release of emotion. For example, a patient with a great deal of repressed hostility was having an argument with his mother over a meal she was cooking; a blaze from the stove set fire to a window curtain and the patient, reaching angrily to grab the curtain, thrust his fist through the window pane. He repeated this accident a year later when there was no fire and no apparent provocation.

Neurotic Traits—Early and Present

A history of early neurotic traits or habits of abnormal duration (such as nail-biting, enuresis, truancy from school, tendency to lie and steal) was given by 70 per cent of fracture patients, and only 20 per cent of patients with cardiovascular disease. It is likely that both these figures would have been higher had the parents been interviewed instead of only the patients, but in any case the difference between the two figures must be regarded as significant.[243] (Incidentally, mention should be made of the care with which such statistics as these must be checked. In going over our material I found under the heading "no nail-biting," a female patient who had

---

* This interest is discussed in more detail in the subsequent section (page 202).

said: "Oh, no, I never have bitten my nails and I never would have bitten my nails and I never would think of biting them, *when I do it sends chills down my back.*")

In some cases the neurotic habit stopped, and in others it started again at the time of the fracture. For example, a patient said that he had bitten his nails—always the right middle finger, until he had finally bitten the end of his finger off. Another patient reported that she used to bite the nails of her right hand. She stopped this eight years before her injury. When she was in the hospital, she started again, but this time on the left hand. As she explained, it was because her right hand was tied up, and she *had to have something to do.*

An interesting example of this childhood neurotic picture is a case reported by Dr. Ackerman who became interested in psychosomatic problems as a third year student during his medical clinical clerkship in Presbyterian Hospital:

A 12-year-old girl * with serious social maladjustment, educational retardation, a history of lying, sexual misdemeanors, and a badly scarred left hand and arm, injured in an accident, developed what looked like an accident habit.† When disappointed in not having her way she picked and pulled at the scar on her hand or whined plaintively of the times she had been taunted about it. (Incidentally, she suffers from a persistent enuresis.)

At first it seemed as if her accidents were merely for the purpose of gaining attention. (In spite of excellent motor skill she fell down and skinned her knees, stubbed her toes, cut her fingers, and so on, several times each day. First one, then another part of her body was covered with mercurochrome, but always where it could be prominently seen.) This impression was borne out by the fact that when her teachers and associates failed to express sympathy she would complain of being in great pain. Her doctor pointed out to her that she did not have to hurt herself to be loved, and that pity was not what she really wanted. At first she could not understand this, and her reactions to her doctor, like her reactions to her parents and teachers, were characterized by fear and frequent threats that she would run away.

As she came to trust her physician, the apparently intentional self-injury decreased but she insisted on taking unnecessary risks. Whenever injured as a result of them she directed sullen angry looks at those about her as

* Abstracted from Ackerman and Chidester.[5] Case studied at the Southard School, associated with Menninger Clinic.
† Slocombe.[387]

though accusing them of responsibility for her injury. Gradually it became clear that she was afraid to express her anger in a more positive way by fighting it out, or even by telling her teachers or associates what things hurt or angered her. In other words, the accidents were not merely to get attention, but were an outcome of her intense hidden anger and the fear that kept her from open expression of it.

As she began to understand this, there was a shift from *accidental injuries to her body, to the tendency to arrange situations so as to get her feelings hurt*. For example, she was very sensitive about her father who used to drink and abuse her, and had died a short time previously, yet she was constantly bringing him into her conversations with other children. After she had done this she would burst into tears and run to a teacher saying: "They want to hurt my feelings." When she understood that she "involuntarily" brought this on herself just as had been the case with bodily injuries, her whole personality seemed to change; she was no longer uncommunicative, sullen, and at war with the world. In five months of part time school work she accomplished "more than many children do in two years." When asked why she had not learned before, she replied: "Well, they just hurt my feelings all the time so I just put my head down on my desk and did not pay much attention." Her scores on intelligence tests rose steadily until her score was superior on some of them. She won distinction in athletics.

As already noted, these patients at the time of admission showed fewer overt neurotic symptoms than did the patients in any of the other groups; less than 5 per cent were given any psychiatric diagnosis more serious than "character neurosis." They did, however, give a frequent picture of neurotic repression with considerable anxiety, compulsive traits, depression, infantile trends, and sadism which was usually not overtly expressed. There was a striking absence of perfectionistic tendencies in the sense of conventional virtue and wisdom such as the coronary patients emphasized. An inevitable accompaniment of this fracture picture is a self-destructive tendency, but this does not mean that every accident can be interpreted as an expression of this tendency.

It is interesting to note also that fracture patients seem more likely than the others to boast and take extreme chances, but apart from individual exceptions less likely to be able "to get away with it" when they do so.[152]

An example from our own material of this neurotically determined tendency to take chances is the following:

Case No. F 22. An unmarried man, aged 34, the oldest son who had always been at war with authority, conceited, and much admired by many girls, was working on a high building. The boss had forbidden any of the men to slide down the rope to the ground. "I thought I'd show him; then as I was part way down, that funny fear of falling I sometimes have came over me and I got dizzy and lost my grip." The patient sustained fractures of spine, left tibia, and right calcaneus. Although he was on the danger list for several days and in the hospital for many weeks, his only comment was, "Well, at least I showed I couldn't be bossed."

Addictions and Interests

The characteristic behavior pattern just described for these patients was well reflected in their addictions and interests which of course were studied in terms of their spontaneous statements rather than by direct questioning. Although socially inclined, these patients had little interest in intellectual conversation. When they got together it was to tell stories of their adventures or to play games. Unlike patients with cardiovascular disease most of them did little reading except in relation to health, athletics, and machinery.

Most of these patients indulge in coffee, tea, tobacco, or coca-cola for immediate gratification or to let off steam; coffee and cigarettes were the most frequent. One patient said, for example, "When I get mad I have to go off the floor for a smoke" (to relieve tension). Another who said he drank a great many cups of coffee and tea every day explained, "I guess it's because I like hot things; I like anything that's hot." This point is mentioned in contrast with patients with coronary disease who used coffee and cigarettes for their stimulating effect which enabled them to stay up late and work longer hours. The characteristic reason given by some of the other groups was "just to be sociable." Some of the fracture patients reported drinking ten to twenty-five cups of coffee daily. They usually mentioned this quite spontaneously as an example of their restlessness, and talked about having to "cut down." On the other hand, the history of immoderate use of alcohol was relatively infrequent (as compared with patients with cardiovascular disease). Often these patients were markedly affected by small amounts of alcohol; a characteristic statement is: "I have to keep away from stimulants, they make me crazy because there's too much Irish in me."

Otherwise these patients were inclined to take especially *good care of themselves*, even to the extent of working out and holding to somewhat fadish routines of exercise, sleep, and diet. In some instances the patient himself had explained this as necessary in view of his restlessness and tension.

They were inclined also to be interested in personal appearance, and to fear mutilation. The women were likely to have a particular interest in cosmetics. An interesting example was patient F 61, a girl aged 26, whose major preoccupation was writing for and trying out all the various creams advertised to remove freckles, although her freckles were few and not in the least obvious. It was only the hospital she said which cured her of this preoccupation, because it occurred to her that her numerous and mad motorcycle escapades were much more likely to result in impairment of her beauty than were the freckles. Another example was patient No. F 126 who sustained a rather severe compound fracture, but nonetheless insisted on picking up the pieces of bone that fell out, with the idea that if they were used in the repair, the resulting deformity would be less. Another patient, No. F 153, a girl aged 28, who had had many operations was not happy until she made herself feel that the scars were beautiful, as they represented such skillful work on the part of the surgeon whom she admired. Some, for example, complained repeatedly of what the "foul pus" was doing to their bodies, and how it was eating them away. Interestingly enough, those who did the most complaining and worrying about body care, were also those who expressed the most freely a strong suicidal impulse.

Again and again it comes out that there was an underlying, usually unconscious self-destructive impulse in a great many of the patients. In some of these it seemed to come out in proportion to the degree of conscious self care which they have shown in the past. For example, patient No. F 106 who said she always took good care of herself (diet, exercise) and even stated that she only let herself think healthy thoughts, later came in quite worried because of self-destructive feelings.

These patients were inclined to talk at length about health. A number of them read the health notes in the paper before reading anything else. This point caught our attention in part because, although present to a marked degree in 84 per cent of the fracture patients, it was generally absent in patients with cardiovascular disease, whose tendency was to overdo, to eat inadequately and irregularly, to get up at night and overwork, and to disregard their symptoms when they were sick.

Related to concern of fracture patients over physical vigor and to their general interest in immediate concrete experience is their marked interest in *athletics and machinery*. It is interesting, however, that only 10 per cent of their accidents occurred in connection with athletics or mechanical work. They occurred instead in what the patient called "some silly way," as for example, falling down stairs or stepping off the curb carelessly and falling. The interest in athletics was often compensatory both in the men who felt inferior because of their small size, and in the women who felt inferior because of their sex and who were likely to be tomboys.* Those accidents which did occur during athletic activity appeared frequently to be among those who boasted of their powers ("you wouldn't think I had it in me when you look at me because of my size.") In speaking of their interest in machinery, these patients dwelt at length on its power, vast motion, and the problems of controlling it. For example:

Case No. F 28. A married man, aged 50, injured his back while working in a boiler room. A prior accident had occurred under similar circumstances, in which he broke an arm, when he had just changed from a better to a less good job. When talking about his pain the veins stood out on his forehead, and he would seem to be in the utmost agony. "This shooting pain drives me crazy, so I would like to shoot someone." But when talking about work with engines which had been his occupation since the age of 16, he was relaxed, became confidential, and seemed to forget everything else. He had spent his life in controlling engines, working up from little engines to big engines, all kinds of engines. He had had "good jobs with good engines" until the ice plant for which he had been working for fifteen years went into the hands of receivers, then after six months as a janitor he got a job "with a silly little engine in a hospital which couldn't hold a candle to any of the engines" he had controlled before.

Ninety per cent of the fracture patients had had strict *religious upbringing* and were still going to church. Characteristic remarks

* There were more tomboys among women in this group except for patients with rheumatic fever type A. (See Chapter VI.)

were the following: "I have a feeling it wouldn't be Sunday if I didn't go to church" (Case No. F 128). "Somehow I can't be regular in church but I send the child instead. I haven't been a very good Catholic but it helped me and I feel if I make the child a good Catholic that will help even more" (Case No. F 106). Of those with a history of previous injury, 53 per cent were Roman Catholic, 17 per cent orthodox Jews, and 20 per cent Protestants of a particularly devout type. Of the patients without history of previous injury, 50 per cent were Roman Catholics, 11 per cent were Orthodox Jews, and 30 per cent were Protestants. In both groups there were only 10 per cent to whom religion was not important. This presents a contrast to the general population and to patients on medical services. Only 50 per cent of the patients with cardiovascular disease gave a history of religious upbringing (21 Roman Catholics, 14 Protestants, and 15 Orthodox Jews). Only 8 per cent emphasized strictness in this respect (Chapters VI and VII).

Life Situation Immediately Prior to the Accident

The appearance of impulsive behavior in fracture patients has perhaps led investigators, including ourselves at first, to undervalue the situation in which the accident occurs. Many physicians say, for example, "obviously some people are all thumbs or just clumsy and so they are more likely than others to have accidents." But as has been noted previously, patients who are accident-prone do not have slow reaction time, poor co-ordination, or low intelligence quotient.

There does seem to be, however, a specific character conflict that is most frequently acted out, and in our patients accidents occurred in situations likely to activate this conflict. These situations are rarely dramatic and are very different in character from the type of traumatic experience usually reported by cardiacs as preceding the onset of illness or specific attacks. On the surface the situations seemed such usual ones that at first they appeared irrelevant.

Case No. F 111. A married man, aged 33, was admitted to the hospital for a fracture of the ankle and foot. He had an unstable work history (including running away from the farm, working as a shoemaker's apprentice, a few years at sea, work in a rubber factory and in a restaurant). The accident occurred on New Year's Eve when he was walking home with his hat pulled over his eyes. He did not notice an approaching taxi and in order to avoid being hit rushed forward and slipped on the ice. This was his third accident and both of his previous ones had resulted in fractures. The first accident was in an automobile. The circumstances of the second were as follows: A truck he was pushing slid back and in an effort to side-step it, he stepped on a banana peel and fell in such a way that he broke his left shoulder. The patient stated that he "was trying to hurry the cart along, and not paying much attention." Referring to the accident on New Year's Eve, he said that he was worried about what his wife and friends would say because he was late for a party. He later recalled an additional early accident when he chopped his finger with a meat cleaver during a hold-up.

Case No. F 130. An unmarried minister, aged 25, was steering a sled down a very slippery hill. His girl was on top of him and when he came to an embankment, he managed to get the girl off into the snow unhurt but sustained a fracture himself. He had been studying hard for an examination and stamped his foot when he mentioned this. He said that he got an A in the examination and was not particularly worried about it. (Subsequently it came out that he could not earn enough money to marry or even make ends meet without overworking.) This was the patient's second accident.

Case No. F 116. A married man was worried about being out of a job and particularly over the fact that his wife worked. He had been laid off from a job that he liked and on his way to apply for a new one he slipped on the ice and broke his leg. He was particularly worried about getting a new job because he had not told his wife about being laid off and was dreading the tearful scenes with her that would occur if he failed in his effort to obtain employment. He said spontaneously, "I'm always in a hurry even if I have plenty of time."

Case No. F 127. A married man, aged 47, for whom this was the second accident, had been worrying about a job until 4 o'clock on the day of the accident. The circumstances were particularly unpleasant because he had had a disagreeable talk with his brother to whom he owed money. At 9 o'clock he went out to investigate one more possibility and was knocked down by a car when he was crossing under an elevated train. His original accident in 1928 was being knocked down by a car while he was crossing under an Elevated.

Case No. F 126. A single man, aged 24, admitted for non-union after fracture of tibia, for whom this was the second accident, was watching children playing ball, and was struck by a car as he ran to pick up the ball for them. (Hospitalized four times by this accident.) He was depressed because six weeks previously the butcher shop where he had been working had closed down. He had been looking in vain every day for work, trying to get his mind off his troubles.

Case No. F 122. A single college student, aged 34, was admitted for fracture of tibia and fibula left. This was the second accident (the first was an injury to his forehead at the age of 10 or 12). He was skating for the last time at the end of a very much enjoyed vacation, when he fell.

Case No. F 132. A single man, 38 years old, was admitted for fracture of twelfth dorsal vertebra. He was working on Sunday morning, "which made me mad, but I couldn't refuse my boss." This had meant he had had to get up and go to 6:30 mass instead of staying in bed until 10, as usual on Sunday morning.

Case No. F 131. A married restaurant worker, aged 25, was admitted for subluxation of cervical two on cervical three. He was on night duty working from 6 P.M. to 4 A.M. which made him very restless and tense because of the irritability and criticism of boss and customers. He felt compelled to stick to it, however, owing to the necessity of making money, thinking that in this way he made more than he would at anything else.

Case No. F 133. A single man, aged 29, was admitted for fracture of the right tibia. He was trying to work off steam playing football, as had been his custom in the past when angry. He had had to leave Germany and a business that had been in the family thirty-seven years and had had trouble previously with authority—state, father, and older brothers.

Case No. F 119. A woman, aged 30, was worrying about money and the rush to do her housework and hold down her job. (Also she wanted to be a boy.) She fell in the kitchen when cleaning the floor.

Case No. F 118. A girl, aged 17, was worried because she was out playing in disobedience to her parents. She fell off a sled and it was not until the next morning that she allowed her family to learn that she was hurt. Two years previously she had sprained her ankle under similar circumstances.

Case No. F 115. A girl, aged 18, for whom this is the second accident, fell heavily on her outstretched right arm on her way home from a dance which she had enjoyed very much. She had been unable to get the kind of work she wanted and had been helping her father which she hated.

Case No. F 123. A woman, aged 24, was worrying about confessing her use of contraceptives and fell down the front steps on the way to church. (Although this was the first accident requiring hospitalization, she gave a history of many minor injuries.)

Case No. F 129. A woman, aged 49, for whom this was the second accident, was hit by a car while crossing the street going home from work. She was just opposite her church (Roman Catholic) and worrying about the fact that she had been too late to go in that morning. "I should have gone, it's a comfort; I think about all the members of my family who are dead."

Obviously these are just ordinary everyday worries and it does not seem likely that they should have had anything to do with the accidents in question. It is noteworthy, however, that in each case the worry has something to do with the patient's parental attitudes; worry about relation to an employer, not being given a job or being scolded by the wife for not getting one; worry about relationship to the church, as, for example, patient No. F 123's worry about confession of her use of contraceptives; and in a few cases worry about having or not having children.

Accidents among both men and women are likely to occur when a child is expected. Patient No. F 35, for example, had always wanted to have children but as soon as his wife became pregnant for the first time, had his accident. When he was seen three years later, he reported that one child was enough for him, but that it worried him to use contraceptives so that he now had a second child. He stated that his stomach always went back on him when his wife was pregnant, and he "couldn't sleep nights for worrying. I don't know just what about: but a cigarette usually quiets me the way a bottle quiets the baby." Accidents among women tend to occur not only in relation to conflict over pregnancy, but also in relation to the menstrual period.

Some specific worry in the life situation preceding accidents was reported by 80 to 90 * per cent of our patients. There are a few other types of accidents which do not seem to be related to any *specific* worry. One is the accident when the patient finally "gets caught" after a considerable period of deliberately taking chances. Another seems to result from absent mindedness or careless exposure accompanying a lack of awareness of the external environment which is characteristic of the introversive person (group B). A considerable number of patients also had phobias of falling or claustrophobia, and had accidents as a result of falling or being knocked down in the street. The following is typical:

Case No. F 104. A married woman, aged 29, was getting off a bus with her two children. They wanted to go ahead which she refused to permit, and herself slipped and fell down the steps. This woman had had a stereotyped nightmare throughout her life of falling down stairs. She said: "When I was little there was a big witch after me. Sometimes I ran and fell downstairs and

---

* Except for those with innocent accidents (page 177 ff.).

held on to both sides of the railing as I went down, telling the children to do the same thing, but I knew it would happen sometimes." It is interesting that this patient refused to come to the hospital after her injury because her marriage ten years previously had been a civil marriage. She felt the accident might have been a punishment for this and that it was absolutely essential to be married by a priest so that she could "receive" before she was taken to the hospital. While in the hospital her stereotyped nightmare recurred in the form: "I have a big weight on my back. A lot of plaster, or somebody else has it on in the image of me."

Reaction to Illness

Guilt and Resentment. The only striking characteristic of fracture patients which we have reported in previous publications [152, 153] was their marked reaction to the injury in terms of guilt and resentment during the first day or two of consciousness following the accident. The following examples indicate the typical emphasis as guilt. This guilt is frequently expressed in intense preoccupation with the question, "What have I done to deserve this?" And occasionally, "This happened to me because I did this or that."

Case No. F 2. A single woman, aged 32, working as secretary in a physician's office, slipped and fell on the floor fracturing her hip. She was given semiprivate care, the whole situation being covered by the physician's insurance, and her job was kept for her, so that there was little external cause for concern. Nevertheless, she became negativistic, insisting the hospital was breaking her morale, that occupational therapy was insulting, that she was brought up to do head work like her father, and now in the hospital she had nothing to do but think. As she brooded she became obsessed with a feeling of guilt: "I asked my friends why I must be punished so. I can't remember ever having done anything wrong, but I must have done something terrible."

Case No. F 16. A married man, aged 38, fell on the ice fracturing his right tibia and fibula. Having been out of work for five years he had just got a new job three months previously which he did not like, but on the strength of which he had been able to live apart from his wife. This patient was very nervous and apprehensive, having nightmares. While under the anesthesia he talked about some letters he had left in the drawer beside his hospital bed which would give him away, and he was convinced that the whole thing was a frame-up to get a secret out of him and to punish him for the way he had treated his wife.

Case No. F 64. An unmarried Puerto Rican, aged 16, said: "It was really my fault because mother had said supper was ready and I was not to go out.

I went out anyway, and got into a wrestling match and got my arm broken. Anyway I guess mother is sorry she is so strict with me."

Case No. F 76. A married, Irish-born housewife, aged 48, fell off a step-ladder, fracturing the os calcis of the right foot. She said she had been having a queer feeling that she had done something wrong. She wasn't sure what. "I always tell my children if they get hurt it's a punishment because they've done something wrong and they'd better confess."

Case No. F 87. "I got my hand banged up for disobeying Mother. She told me not to jump with long pants on but I did. God punished me for dis-obeying."

One patient who was punished for minor misdoings by being made to spend long times on her knees, commented on her accident—a fall in which she injured her knee: "Well, God brought me to my knees again, just like my parents used to do."

Sometimes the dominant idea was that the illness was a punishment for someone else. This reaction was characteristic of patients with strong repressed sadistic tendencies, and in our series all those fracture patients with hypertension gave this picture, as well as a few with marked fluctuations in the blood pressure reading. This would tend to confirm the findings reported under hypertension (page 257).

Case No. F 6. A married Irish waitress, aged 46, fell on the ice, fracturing the upper extremity of the right femur. She had never been in a hospital before but stated that she liked this one very much, that she was treated better than she deserved to be because she had disobeyed her "good angel." Something had said to her "don't cross in the middle of the street, it's too icy." But she took a chance and fell. "The wickedest part of it," she said, "is that it's not really myself but my husband that's hurt, by me not working all these weeks." (This patient had hypertension about which she had not known, discovered on this admission to the hospital, and a great deal of resentment toward parents and husband.)

Case No. F 20. A married woman, aged 54, who had led a gay life until her marriage thirty years previously which interrupted her career as a singer, fell and fractured her hip. "Walking home from the movies I just crumpled up. There wasn't even anything to slip on." She spent much of her time in the hospital trying to figure out whether she "deserved it because of the way she had treated her husband and brother with whom she lived after her husband's death, or whether they deserved it because of the way they had treated her. She blamed her husband who had interfered with her career and her brother who was usually out of work, for the fact that she, having been the first woman to have been given a military badge, had sunken to the level of having had to accept a job as a matron in a hotel just previous to her accident. She also had hypertension, discovered only after admission.

Sometimes more prominent than the idea of punishment is the idea of compelling parent or spouse to behave in some specific way.

Case No. F 11. A high-school girl, aged 17, injured her right knee playing football. She was an unwanted child of a mother who was trying to send her away to school so that she could marry another man. She could not bear to have the child around because she looked and acted so much like her father, the mother's divorced husband. The patient complained that her thoughts kept going round in circles, and the only thing she wanted to know was if her mother would not probably be too sorry for her to send her away: "She can't possibly send me away now when I'm so sick and may be crippled for life."

Case No. F 21. A married man, aged 31, injured his back while working. He had always been known as "mother's boy," previous to his marriage, and could not reconcile himself to the fact that his wife seemed to take less good care of him than his mother. "She'll have to take care of me now," he said hopefully. "I guess it serves her right."

Case No. F 23. A colored woman, aged 29, separated from her husband, was in constant fear of attack by him, and very much resented being imposed on by the Jewish women for whom she worked. Just before the Jewish holiday she went out to purchase a supply of food and slipped and sprained her knee. She telephoned her employer to say that she would send a friend to do her work while she went to the doctor to have her knee strapped, but her employer said that she could not get along without her and insisted that she return immediately. "I was so mad, I could have killed her." Before reaching the employer's house, she slipped again, fell, and fractured her leg. When her employer visited her at the hospital the patient frequently reminded her that if she had just had a little more patience. . . . "Now I guess she'll learn how to treat somebody."

Case No. F 59. A married woman, aged 27, was ashamed to relate the manner in which her accident occurred because she had "been acting like a little fool, and sliding down the banisters." She admitted that all her life she had worked off her annoyance with her parents, and now with her husband, by such tricks. "Perhaps I ought to know better but I wouldn't have been like that if they had had more sense, and had treated me more like a person instead of being so strict."

"Compensitis." Related to the guilt reaction to the accident is the marked tendency of these patients to exaggerate and to cling to the secondary illness gain, which makes them peculiarly difficult as compensation cases. Twenty-nine per cent of the patients in our series were actually compensation cases and it is of some interest that among them the percentage of previous accidents was slightly lower (52 per cent) than in the total group, although 45 per cent of them as compared to 35 per cent of the total group, were in the age range 35 to 55. It is interesting that of the compensation cases half were male and half were female, which corresponds with the sex distribution in the total group.

Of the compensation accidents, out of 31, 48 per cent (15) were automobile accidents; 26 per cent (8) were industrial accidents (of which half were falls on the job); and the remaining 26 per cent (8) were falls. (To compare this with the type of accident covered in the total group see page 185.) Forty-five per cent of these patients were hospitalized from one to six times subsequently for the same accident, and eleven others (about 10 per cent) had new accidents, whereas in the non-compensation groups which included an equal number of similar accidents, only 10 per cent of the patients had as many as two subsequent hospitalizations for the same accident.

The majority of these patients had had a conflict over earning their living and establishing themselves as independent human beings, and they were relatively naïve in their admission of it. If there is any such tendency in a patient it is usually increased by the accident in a way not characteristic of patients with cardiovascular disease. For example, patient No. F 39, stated that he wanted to get well enough to enjoy himself but not to work any more! These patients stood out from the group because of their tendency to have persisting pain and spasm, hence to require more follow-up visits and a longer period of disability.

Patients with cardiovascular disease are inclined to react to their illness by overdoing and trying to prove to themselves and others that they do not have to be taken care of. It is hard to teach them the importance of follow-up visits, in contradistinction to fracture patients, especially those in the compensation group, who are sometimes hard to keep away. Clinicians for many years have commented on this point, and more recently Drewry and Wall [129] have called attention to it even in psychotic patients with cardiovascular disease.

If, in addition to this, the religious upbringing of these patients is remembered, it becomes clear that they had had very high ideals set for them and they had been punished excessively for minor deviations. Furthermore, they had avoided facing their hostility and had not developed the habit of talking things over. When the pressure became too great they resorted to action. When their action resulted in injury to themselves the feelings of guilt and resentment from which they had been attempting to escape would come to the surface briefly only to be repressed again, in most cases with considerable expedition. Some patients then took comfort in a feeling that at last they had earned a right to be taken care of, and could enjoy the doctors and nurses who were playing the role of good parents to them, while others would find themselves overcome by a feeling of depression and complete hopelessness during the period of enforced limitation of activity.

The observations to follow shed some light on this reaction of guilt and resentment which characterized the first day or two following the accident, as well as on the later phase in which the patients tended to go to the opposite extreme and to protest their innocence, their lack of responsibility for the accident, and to stress a desire for compensation. This reaction was found in about 80 per cent of the accident patients on the fracture wards and in only 1 per cent of the patients with cardiovascular disease. It was absent even in cardiac patients who could be shown to have some responsibility for their incapacitation in the sense of having disobeyed instructions for limitation of activity, and so contributed to the next cardiac break, as well as in patients who had learned for the first time that there was something wrong with their hearts and so might have been expected to say suddenly like the fracture patient, "Why did this happen to me?"

It is our impression, it should be added, that this reaction would have been found in an even higher percentage of fracture patients had it been possible to see all patients immediately after the accident, that is, before this feeling had been repressed. This is borne out by the fact that it came to the surface on intensive treatment in some patients who gave no hint of it during the first interview.

IV. Dynamic Formulation

AREA OF FOCAL CONFLICT AND CHARACTERISTIC REACTION: AUTHORITY (AVOIDANCE)

A review of the histories of fracture patients impresses one with the fact that they have been in trouble with authority very frequently throughout their lives, first with their parents or stepparents, then with their schools, then with church and job, and finally in relations with wife or husband. Their characteristic response to these troubles has been to strive for independence and autonomy outside of authoritarian relationships, to minimize and avoid conflicts with authority wherever possible. The following material may serve to make clearer the childhood background of the patients in this group.

Most of them reported a stern parent, parent surrogate, or a strict school. A typical statement is: "Father was terrible; Mother was quite strict with the children too; she had to be, as there were ten of them. We helped to hasten her death." Another, whose father died when he was two, was brought up by a maternal aunt who was much the same as his mother: "I used to be under her orders all the time. Her husband was good but pretty strict."

Many patients reported severe beatings or punishment of what seemed to be disproportionate and unreasonable severity. Hence what is meant by strictness here is not so much a matter of discipline, although rules were in considerable prominence, as the production of a severe insecurity, a feeling of being unloved because the parents were cruel and unapproachable. Occasionally illness on the part of the parent contributed to this picture.

Case No. F 127. A married man, aged 47, was admitted to the hospital for fracture of his right clavicle, fracture of his left fibula, contusions and abrasions. He said of his father: "He beat me for anything. Gee, I was afraid. I thought he would beat my brains out with a heavy rope like they use for a cow, and dipped in water. When I was 15 I ran away. I forgive him now that he is dead. I ran away from home because I couldn't get on with my father. I go by myself to Germany to my brother, and ask him for something to do, and not to tell father. I carried water for the men in the mine. He took all the money from me. There was no one to look after me and buy me clothes. I was there for about a year, and then went away. I learned the carpenter trade. I worked for a man who fed and clothed me for three years. After I learned the trade I worked in a factory and made money. In 1913 I heard there was going to be a war, so I went on a trip and came over here." *

Fracture †

1. *Family History*. Relative frequency of accidents in the family and siblings (about 40 per cent), history of cardiovascular disease, however, not strikingly low (about 38 per cent). Little exposure to disease (about 46 per cent to accidents).

2. *Personal Data*. At least one strict parent. Average marriage rate. Few children, relatively many divorces (as compared with general population statistics or base line for groups studied).

3. *Health Record*. Excellent previous health record, few operations except appendectomy. Women good pelvic histories. Interest in health and vigor.

4. *Injuries*. Eighty per cent two or more accidents, majority three or more. Mainly the result of falls. Many childhood accidents.

5. *General Adjustment: Education:* Some tendency to interrupt in the middle, lack of planning, marked in group B which is predominantly male. Group as a whole nearer to base line than other groups studied. Generally good intellectual level, especially in group B. *Work record:* In types A and C tendency to stick to one job but without trying to advance status. Many and diverse jobs in type B. *Income and vocational level:* High. Marked by sudden changes in type B. Occupational distribution close to base line, with concentration in class III (clerks, salesmen, stenographers). Percentage in skilled labor same as coronary. *Social relationships:* "Good fellow." No marked tendency to dominate or submit. Tendency to aggressive self-reliance. Not likely to curry favor with either sex. Tendency to eccentricity in type B. *Sexual adjustment:* Superficially good. No tendency to emphasize sexual

---

* In another patient (No. F 36), development was retarded; menses did not come until the age of 18, and the patient was reported inhibited. In another (No. F 107), there was no definite history as to whether or not the parents were strict, but the father had arthritis. In another (No. F 81), the family was reported strict, but the patient was brought up in a Pennsylvania Dutch settlement, which is well known for its strictness; he had difficulty in talking as a child, because his tongue was tied. (It had to be cut by a doctor.) Another patient (No. F 53), had three accidents. There is no mention of strictness, but the doctor felt that there was pregenital conversion. In another (No. F 122), the mother was ill for some years with heart trouble. We do not know how young the patient was at this time. This seems to bear out what has been said above: that there is strictness and insecurity in the early life of these patients.

† In order to evaluate the distinctive features in this profile, reference should be made to Chapter IX.

problems, combined (especially in type B) with lack of real emotional contact. Careful to avoid infection in promiscuous relationships but without exaggerated fear. *Attitude toward family:* Dispersion of tendencies among groups A, B, C. Trend toward irresponsibility in group B.

6. *Characteristic Behavior Pattern.* Make up their minds definitely and quickly. Focus on immediate values rather than long range goals. Social rather than power interest. Striving toward integration and autonomy, outside of authoritarian hierarchy. Tendency to attach emotions to people and immediate concrete experience. Little emotional interest in intellectual values and verbalization. Defensive tendency to appear casual about feelings and personal problems. Group B marked adventurous trend and avoidance of responsibility. Living from day to day.

7. *Neurotic Traits.* High percentage of early neurotic traits, especially lying, stealing and truancy, sleep-walking and sleep-talking. Later life almost no obvious neurotic traits (some infantile trends) except for a small group, particularly women, with phobias, especially fear of falling.

8. *Addictions and Interests.* Tendency to use stimulants (coffee, cigarettes, alcohol) for pleasure or to let off steam. Marked interest in competitive sports or gambling (football, baseball, racing, auto-racing), and machinery. Practicing orthodox authoritative religion (institutionalized superego).

9. *Life Situation Immediately Prior to Onset.* Situation threatening individual autonomy in which direct release of aggression would be too costly. Often connected with actual or contemplated shifts in job.

10. *Reaction to Illness.* Bravado or fatalism about specific symptoms, or else exaggerated interest (insecurity) plus poor tolerance of pain, either one frequently combined with tendency to exploit injury for compensations, financial or other.

11. *Area of Focal Conflict and Characteristic Reaction.* Authority—avoidance. Attempt to establish personal autonomy to avoid authority relationships (marked passive-active conflict). Little identification with authority figures or concepts.

CASE ILLUSTRATION

Case No. F 74. A separated, unemployed Polish American truck driver, aged 28, was admitted for non-union of fracture of the shaft of the lower third of the left humerus, ankylosis of the ulna, radial palsy with repair of the left radial nerve.

Family History. The patient's mother died of flu when he was nine years old, and his father "from alcoholism," three years prior to admission.

Personal Data. The patient was the second child in a family of seventeen brothers and one sister. He had kept in touch with none of them. "Father and mother were too strict most of the time, till I was 18 I couldn't sit on my behind because I was beaten so much. When mother died it didn't help much because my stepmother was just about as strict. At 19 my father licked me for taking a straw ride. He said to stay away from girls until I was 25 or 30, that was the time he got married himself. After that I left home because I wouldn't take orders any more. It was the same way in the Catholic school. I was always getting licked. I would take my licking and holler and then go out and do it anyway."

He was married at the age of 21 but never got along with his wife because "she was Protestant and I was Catholic." She brought him into court several times on the grounds of non-support, but he was always able to convince the court that because his arm had been "out of commission" ever since he was married he could not do anything about it.

Health Record. Excellent.

Injuries. At the age of 17 the patient broke off the second finger of his left hand in a machine. A year later he fractured his left arm falling out of a second story window. He then twice fractured the same arm driving a car with his elbow out the window. His present admission was for the second of these fractures for which he had had eight open reductions and been treated in nine different hospitals in New York and New Jersey. There had been two more fractures of the same arm in the meantime as a result of "picking up things that were too heavy." After discharge from the hospital he refractured the same arm riding in a bus with his left arm similarly on the window sill.

General Adjustment. Vocation—education: Unlike many of the accident patients he had completed the educational unit undertaken, namely, grammar school. There was no necessity, however, of his stopping his education at this time. His family had urged him to continue, but he stated that it was only because of them that "I went as far as I did, then I rebelled and went to *work* as a carpenter's assistant. Pretty soon I left my job and became a mechanic's assistant. Then I became a boxer (he was classified as a third rater in the middle-weight class) by profession, but have had all sorts of odd jobs driving trucks to make money. I don't know what's the matter with people. I never could get along with the boss so I never worked for the same one very long at a time." The patient's *income* was good but irregular. *Social adjustment:* The patient liked to talk about his exploits as a prize fighter as well as his various close shaves and accidents in driving cars. He claimed he had a good many friends. *Sexual adjustment:* The patient was very scornful of his father's precept about "avoiding girls before you're married and being faithful to your wife." He saw "no relationship between sex which was natural and marriage which was unnatural, really invented by the priest." *Attitude toward parents:* See *Personal data.*

Characteristic Behavior Pattern. It is clear from this patient's history that in any situation of emotional tension his impulse was to do something reckless, to run away, or to forget about it. The patient himself said: "I never do what I'm told and I never change my habits."

Neurotic Traits. Like the typical accident patient this patient gave a long history of lying, stealing, truancy from school, running away from the family and so on, for which he was regularly punished without effect.

Addictions and Interests. He was addicted to coffee, tobacco, and alcohol. Also like the typical accident patient he was interested in competitive sports, particularly boxing and automobile racing. Again like the typical accident patient, this patient was Roman Catholic and continued to go to church in a perfunctory way.

Life Situation Immediately Prior to Onset. The first injury to the arm occurred immediately after the patient's introduction of his brother to the prize fighting business. The second injury to the arm occurred shortly after the patient's marriage when he had been berated by his wife for not supporting her adequately.

Reaction to Illness. The patient said: "If it don't heal take the whole thing off. Maybe its lucky that this has ended my career as a fighter. I never was as good as I wanted to be. What made it worse was I got my brother started and he turned out to be better than me." After this the patient spent most of his time in one hospital or another and showed little interest in recovering or going to work. He was preoccupied with the problem of collecting for his injuries but was unsuccessful. There was some suspicion that his frequent refractures and the failure of the arm to heal was somewhat influenced by this preoccupation.

Area of Focal Conflict and Characteristic Reaction. It is clear from the foregoing that this patient was always in conflict with authority. He left school, home, his various jobs, even his various doctors because of quarrels. His typical reaction was to avoid submission and assert his independence.*

DEGREE AND NATURE OF SOMATIC EXPRESSION OF CONFLICTS

In this chapter and those to follow the discussion under this heading will be mainly descriptive and suggestive because our resources were too limited to make possible a thorough analysis of this fundamental aspect of our problem. The questions to be borne in mind are: Is there anything inherent in the patient's sphere of major conflict, his characteristic reaction to it, or both which offers clues for understanding the degree and nature of his somatic injury? As has

---

* This may be considered a representative case of group B.

been stated already, patients found on the fracture ward stood out among all other hospital groups for the low percentage of overt neurotic symptoms. Even though fracture does not represent a clearly defined illness entity, as do most other disease syndromes in this book, there are several significant factors in personality and background which are common to nearly all fracture patients. Study of patients in the other illness groups who have accidents is recommended to readers who are particularly interested in this question.

By way of introduction a few comments on the sphere of major conflict and the patient's characteristic patterns for dealing with it would seem to be in order. If we remember that resistance to authority is particularly frequent in children strictly brought up, the preceding facts throw some light on the characteristic behavior pattern of these patients. It is also clear why they wish either to avoid parenthood or to become model parents and teach others to be so, and why they have such a marked tendency to take such good care of themselves in a physical sense, both in health and in illness except perhaps when compensation is involved. [Occasionally such a patient (i.e., Case No. F 74) will repeatedly refracture an arm that is not quite healed by disobeying orders, and lifting things that are too heavy for him, and so on.] This explains in part the apparent contradiction that in spite of the tendency to be overactive and to take chances, they make a point of getting enough sleep, and the right kind of food, to develop their bodies through athletics or regular work in a gymnasium, and so on.

General Tension Cloaking Aggression and Resentment

These patients have a good deal of pent-up aggression and resentment, but because of their life-long tendency to avoid facing their conflicts with authority they are essentially unconscious of their resentment, and sometimes unaware even of their tension. Illustrative examples are the following:

Case No. F 144. A clothing salesman, single, aged 20, was admitted for repair of an ankle after a previous fracture. He said: "I had this done to my ankle because I want to take the best possible care of my health. I eat well, exercise. If I think there is anything wrong with me I have it fixed up right away. I am the kind of fellow who just can't sit still. I have to keep going. I don't worry at all. What's the use. But it's being tense and in such a hurry that gets me into trouble." He showed marked tension, and tossed an orange back and forth as he talked. This patient had had three previous accidents. He was somewhat shy with girls, but went with them.

Case No. F 74. A married man, aged 28, was admitted to the hospital for non-union after fracture of the shaft of the left humerus, ankylosis of the ulna, radial palsy with repair of the left radial nerve. He stated that he had got *so low that he had lost all his tension*. He had reached the bottom and could go no further. There was nothing to do but wait till he was bumped off. This patient had had repeated injuries to his arm, refracturing it after it had been partly healed as a result of lifting weights he had been told not to lift. From some points of view he appeared to be a malingerer, but actually, as has been shown, this behavior seems better understood as a breaking through of the self-destructive tendency after the life-long tension had decreased.

An interesting example of a somewhat modified pattern follows:

Case No. F 141. A married man, aged 46, broke his leg while playing ball on the roof with some children. He had had two previous fractures, and his mother had had a fracture. His father was alcoholic, and both parents were strict. The patient, of pyknic build, was athletic, and interested in golf. He was strict with his children. There was conflict over the use of contraceptives.

He said: "To sit around would drive me crazy. Nothing is tougher than to sit down with nothing to do." He worked in a shop where he was very much interested in devising *ways of preventing accidents to himself and other people*. He said that accidents are just carelessness, but that he was a very fast driver himself.

As was noted earlier, these patients at first sight seemed to be relatively normal sexually as compared with other groups studied. The initial misimpression on this subject is analogous to the misimpression first obtained about their life adjustment as a whole. Actually they had serious conflicts over masturbation, sexual promiscuity, and married life, but they pretended to take these lightly as they did everything else. It was only when they came into conflict with direct authority, as for example, in being forbidden use of contraceptives, that they were likely to be worried about their sexual behavior. Otherwise they paid little attention to any social convention. (Frigidity among the women was less frequent than in any other group studied.) But perhaps because of their interest in self-care very few of them got into any serious sexual difficulties, that is, problems of venereal disease or illegitimate children. (This latter point is important if these patients are compared as a group with hypertensive patients whom they resemble in many ways. A very large proportion of them had the same tendency to promiscuity but seemed inevitably to get themselves into trouble as a result of it.) When, however, they did come to grief in their sexual life and were unable to "do something and forget about it," just as when "fate treated them unkindly" in their work adjustments, they were likely to have accidents.

Activity, Verbalization, Dreams and Fantasies

The tendency of fracture patients to be independent, active, and to focus on immediate concrete values is related to the fact that they are relatively inarticulate about thoughts and feelings. This probably had a bearing on the observation that there seemed to be few full-fledged psychoneurotics among them, and many eccentric characters. Furthermore, unlike asthma and hay fever patients, whom they resembled in the tendency to act out,[150] they reported *few dreams*. The prominence of these characteristics varies greatly in the three groups outlined, although the tendency to act in situations of particular stress is characteristic of all of them. In the initial picture of these patients it appeared that they had a relatively limited dream and fantasy life but later study showed that they had particular kinds of fantasy life and were less likely to reveal it.

Sherrington's analysis of the mind as essentially subserving an inhibitory function in relation to motor behavior is of interest in this connection. The greatest relief of instinctual tension is provided by action, the least by fantasy and thought, whereas speech stands half way between. If tension is expressed directly in action, the action is likely to be ill-considered and to create situations injurious to the patient. If, on the other hand, all action is repressed or entered upon only after considerable thought and the suppression of emotion, the development of a different type of psychic or somatic symptomatology or both is favored. Frequently when the patient began to discuss topics that were emotionally upsetting to him, he would become more tense and would move about in bed; he would often move his hands and feet which before had been quiet. The increased muscle tension and motion of a clumsy or ill-considered nature seems to appear in fracture patients under emotional excitement somewhat as palpitation does in cardiacs, or vomiting spells and diarrhea in gastro-intestinal patients. One example of an extreme case is that of a patient who became very tense and at intervals on the ward developed attacks of shaking. It was thought that she was acting, or possibly that this was the result of head injury. Later, when she was able to talk, she said that the sound of the brakes on a car under the window set her off this way. As she talked over the accidents, the attacks became less severe and less frequent.

Many of the fracture patients showed a marked inability to bear severe pain, the men particularly, and were likely to make the following statement: "You see, doctor, my nerve is in action; driving a car and taking risks. But when I have to stay still in one place I haven't any nerve at all." All these patients reported a feeling of discomfort when at rest either because rest was necessary as when they found themselves in the hospital, or simply when they were on vacation.

In recognizing this general urge to activity in these patients the fact should be borne in mind that a relatively small percentage of them resort habitually to action as a direct solution of their conflicts with authority. They reach a sort of equilibrium of adjustment to unpleasant situations and the sudden shifts and accidents occur when some external pressure has dramatized the conflict in concrete form. The need to take recourse to such behavior occurs most frequently in group B because they seem to have the most pent up hostility and the least satisfactory outlets through emotional contact with their environment. Hence, they have the most uniform distribution of high accident records.

There is no implication in the previous remarks that these patients are unwilling to talk. As a matter of fact they talk more readily than patients in some other groups, that is, they talk more readily about matters that do not concern them emotionally. But they would rather work off their *feelings* in action than talk about them. Even this, however, is not entirely a matter of avoidance. These patients actually are at a loss as to how to put their feelings into words, it is something they have never done and just as they have thought little about "the end and aim of existence" or about a carefully planned life work, so they have had little tendency to philosophize. Everything they do not understand is "fate" or "luck."

Patient No. F 106 said: "Look what God gives you. A sickness out of a clear sky. It seems pitiful that I have to go through all this. I never did anyone a mean deal in my whole life. I don't see why this should happen to me. . . . I have always been good at giving advice, and I could never understand why they didn't like it."

Patient No. F 126 said: "Why does it have to happen to me? But I figured my time was up. I'd never had anything happen to me before. I think I'm too afraid of hurting people."

Patient No. F 129: "I felt as if someone had wished it on me," and further: "To be close to the curb and to be knocked out, is sort of ironical."

Patient No. F 127: "If I only shouldn't go there that day, I wouldn't be here today, but maybe that'll give me my lesson. If you don't learn enough with one lesson, you have to have another."

It should be noted that they feel more intensely when they talk, which parallels the increase in muscle tension so frequently observed. Apparently, also, talking with a physician arouses resistance because it suggests the submissive role which is so abhorrent to them. The Rorschach test is a good indicator of the specificity of the reactions of these patients which intensifies their feelings in this situation (page 661).

It was brought out very clearly in the Rorschach review of this clinical material that where some groups of cardiacs would give only a vague, general, undifferentiated response to an emotionally stimulating condition, most fracture patients would give a selective, clearly perceived response reaction.

To go back to Sherrington: "The symbols, the fantasies, with which the patient occupies himself, represent a constant effort to translate the physiological energies of instinct into a form adequate for cortico-spinal expression, or at least into the dissipation of pure thought." [379]

One of the most difficult factors for the examining physician to evaluate is the fantasy life of a patient. It is particularly difficult in the fracture group because of their characteristic reticence about anything personal. We know these patients are all unlikely to reveal their fantasy life spontaneously, and that when their inner life fails them they resort to action. Our only conclusions regarding the extent and quality of fantasy in the first phase of this research came from psychoanalytical study of scattered patients. These impressions were confirmed and differentiated by the recent Rorschach review. The Rorschach test demonstrated that groups A and C actually have little or no fantasy life, but that group B is characterized by introversive traits of fantasy and inner living. Most clinicians use the concepts of fantasy and imagination extremely loosely. In our early work use of a "fantastic" image in a dream or day dream was interpreted as indicative of fantasy life. Hence some cardiac patients in whom such findings were frequent were described as having more fantasy life than was actually the case. In order to understand the role played by fantasy life in somatic terms, a more dynamic evaluation is necessary.*

If we realize the strength of the focal conflict in these patients, it is easy to understand their difficulty in finding a way of life that permits them adequate emotional expression. They find security mainly by avoiding conflict with authority, sometimes by shifting constantly from one type of job to another, and generally by focusing on immediate experience. Some of them who refuse to recognize any authority, concentrate all their feeling of hopelessness about coming to terms with authority in the inescapable absolute, "fate" or "luck," and sometimes also God and the church. They take chances somewhat as the criminal does with the basic feeling that "luck will end sooner or later but let's make the most of it while it lasts." The combination of their substitution of intense activity for adequate emotional expression in living, and the resentment piled up by their inability to dominate or submit to the authoritarian pressures with which they have to deal, or even to verbalize their personal experience or to find adequate satisfaction in fantasy life, favors the occurrence of accidents in moments of panic.

Patients with coronary occlusion also have personalities that have been molded by conflict with authority, but instead of trying to escape from authority altogether, their need to dominate stemming

---

* (For further discussion see the corresponding sections of Chapters V, VI, VII, VIII and Chapter XI, section IV.) "Speech, since it provides some degree of externalization of energy, may be regarded as standing between musculoskeletal behavior (i.e., action) and thought, and is also a manifestation of partial motor inhibition. The degree of availability of these modes of cortical expression to the instinctual levels is in direct proportion to the degree of motor inhibition, because of diminishing external risk, yet the degree of relief of instinctual tension depends on the degree of sheer motor component in the expression. Thus action gives the greatest relief, thought or fantasy the least. But instinctual action carries with it the gravest external threat and thought the least grave. Speech stands midway between them with regard to both considerations, and is thus a singularly happy medium of expression" (Sherrington [879]).

from their fear of submission drives them to become super-authorities themselves and gives them the power to keep all their resentment to themselves while they go through the various types of subjection to authority necessitated by their arduous climb to the top. The fact that these patients more than any other group with cardiovascular disease tend to have accidents (see Chaper V as to nature of these accidents) when they can no longer inhibit their fear and resentment, and what we aptly call vascular accidents when the strain of keeping everything bottled up becomes more than their bodies can bear, can be partially understood in terms of what has just been said. But why their reaction to the problem of authority is in the direction of an attempt to dominate authority instead of to escape from it is a point that will be discussed in the following chapter.

Comparison of the last two sections in this chapter with corresponding sections in the succeeding chapters will at least give some indication as to why fracture patients might find the most satisfactory somatic expression of conflict that of accident or injury. (For further discussion of this point see Chapter XI.)

There are points in the foregoing characterization suggestive of certain types of psychopathic and criminal personalities. And as a matter of fact there were many delinquents among the accident patients in group B. Statistics from one of our prisons where the average age of the prisoners was 22 years, give 86 per cent as having a similar history of parental sternness and lack of any older person one could talk with. Furthermore, 80 per cent of them gave a history of strict religious up-bringing but unlike our patients only 30 per cent of them continued to go to church after they left their homes. The patients with cardiovascular disease present a different picture. Although they frequently reported parental strictness, there was usually a very marked attachment to one parent.

These statements may suggest an attempt to correlate various external difficulties such as strict parents with different types of organic disease. Nothing is farther from our intention. In every case of illness one has both injury from the environment, whether from bacteria or from associates, and the patient's reaction to such injury in constitutional and psychological terms. An illustration of this is the fact just cited that both criminals and patients who have accidents give this history of strict parents and strict religious upbringing, yet other factors have entered into the picture in such a way as to make one group criminal, the other group accident addicts. And we all know people with this same history who are not accident prone, criminally inclined, or ill either mentally or physically, at least in any overt way. The strict parents are important only for the role they play in determining focal conflict and character structure of the patient. To bring about a somatic discharge it is always necessary in addition that there be a life constellation which reactivates the conflict in such a way as to render the patient's habitual defenses inadequate. Recognition of such factors as these, however, as they tend to be important from one disease group to another, is essential for a complete medical understanding of the disease process including especially therapy and prevention.

The psychological meaning of injury to the body has been discussed elsewhere and space does not permit its further discussion here.[17, 142, 143, 152, 153, 297] Only the following points will be noted by way of summary.

Alexander and others have made studies of the so-called neurotic criminal. They have been able to demonstrate that the degree of conscious anxiety in this type of criminal is relatively low. Thus he accedes to his need of punishment primarily through external means. He allows society instead of his own conscience to punish him. The fracture patient often shows a similar response suggesting the externalization of the punitive mechanism.

Incidentally, it has been reported by students of delinquency and criminology (Dr. Healy of the Judge Baker Guidance Center, among others) that a predisposing factor here is an inconsistent shifting back and forth from excessive severity to excessive spoiling.[15, 17]

In our series of cases psychopathic personalities were more frequent among the male patients. The delinquents seem to fall in group A but this point needs further investigation. Among both males and females the traditional conception of receiving injuries for "naughtiness" is strikingly prevalent. Interestingly enough, after the preliminary period there is a great deal of disowning of responsibility for the accident. This repression of guilt in a sense goes hand in hand with healing, and the patient frequently denies or disavows any claims to guilt despite remarks to the contrary in the preliminary period.

The fracture is not only self-punitive but also contains a fairly clear-cut hostile element. This hostility is characteristically directed against the authoritarian figure. The recognition of an aggressive hostile factor is necessary in the proper handling of the therapeutic problems. An important factor in group B is that a more archaic and regressive type of behavior has been called into play.[139]

In comparing the meaning of the fracture with the phenomenology of other psychiatric conditions, it can be seen that: (1) The neurotic criminal is not alone in attempting to solve his need of punishment by external means. (2) The individual who makes an attempt on his life is not alone in combining self-punitive measures with outwardly directed hostile trends.

SUMMARY OF CHARACTEROLOGICAL DEFENSES AND THEIR RELATIVE SUCCESS OR FAILURE

On the basis of our material then, it appeared that at least one factor in the personality which predisposes to accident is this tendency to solve the conflict between repressive authoritarian pressures and individual spontaneity by striving for satisfactions and security outside of the authoritarian hierarchy. By focusing their values on immediate concrete experience and by avoiding any marked submission or domination in vocational and social roles, they usually managed to minimize or avoid serious conflicts with authority. When thwarted, deprived, or subjected to some strain such as unemployment or a mother-in-law living in the family, patients who developed "accident proneness" had the tendency to *do something* either to modify the situation or to get away from it instead of just keeping their anger bottled up and boiling inside.

Cardiac patients on the other hand, under similar circumstances would sulk or become ultra-gentle and considerate, turning to philosophy or trying to repay injury with kindness. They would develop sensitive consciences. The impulse to "act out" their conflicts appears to be repressed or concealed at a relatively early age, usually in order to facilitate their conquest of authority.

When these usual defenses of the fracture patient fail and he can find no satisfactory escape from his hostility and guilt, his aggressiveness breaks out in an impulse to punish both himself and those responsible for his frustration. In the depressed individual the suicidal attempt is usually a conscious experience. In the person with an accident syndrome the process is brought about without conscious premeditation. The fact that ambivalence expresses itself through an injury is of prognostic importance to the patient because the implication is that a more divergent type of adjustment has been called upon. From the standpoint of therapy one can readily see that the problem of resolving such a difficulty is more complicated than if one were dealing solely with guilt punishable by external means.

V. THERAPEUTIC IMPLICATIONS *

For the physician who treats fracture and other bodily injuries several practical issues are of interest. By this time it should be clear that it is of utmost importance to ask the question as to whether the injury has elements in it other than those of pure accident. In some cases study of circumstances helps but in all cases a careful personality history is important. A patient who shows a majority of the characteristics outlined in this chapter is probably predisposed to accidents, no matter what the actual etiology of the present injury. If such patients could be carefully worked with, the probability of subsequent injury might be materially reduced, thereby simplifying financial and social problems for the patient and reducing the burden upon society which the clinics have to bear.

Another phase of the problem is the role of pain and healing in cases of injury. It is conceivable that much of the pain from injury is due not only to the resulting contraction of muscles in and around the site of injury but also to the tension produced through guilt. That the processes of healing go on more rapidly and successfully if extraneous demands on the circulation and muscles introduced by the psychoneurotic element were removed, has been demonstrated in many cases. The physician's management of this factor has a definite bearing on the duration of hospitalization. Examples are:

Case No. F 106. A married woman, aged 36, at first showed excessive tension, fear, pain, stiffened up all over, often shook with fear. This was precipitated by sounds of brakes grinding on a car outside, a stretcher going by the door, doctors getting ready to dress her wound, and so on. At first she could not talk about the accident. Later she was able to do so and

* See Chapter XI, section V.

she gradually improved. However, even after she went home she had spells of tension with difficulty in walking or crossing streets.

Case No. F 117. A married man, aged 31, was first extremely restless, tense and worried. He said that he had always been tense—so much so that he could not learn to swim. On the ward he noticed much tension when given water exercise. Three days later he said that he felt more relaxed with exercise and the nurse reported him more relaxed than usual. This patient was always glad to talk, unburdened much worry, and showed much fear. He reported pain associated with his tension.

Case No. F 2. A married woman, aged 29, was seen because of her tension and worry. She had excessive pain and was stiff and rigid all over, including her face which frowned. This she knew herself and she complained that her arms ached from it. Her ankle was excessively painful.

All these patients showed some relaxation and improvement with talking. The last two, especially, expressed appreciation for the chance to talk.

From the psychiatric point of view one could set up an experiment which might answer those first three practical issues, namely: (1) the determination of guilt motives worked out through external injury; (2) the study of pain and muscle tension; and (3) the problem of healing as influenced either positively or negatively by the nature of the personality involved.

From the point of view of therapy, certain complications arise. In the first place the patient quickly loses interest in the role of emotional factors as soon as he begins to feel well. The acceptance of therapy is, apparently, a form of punishment for the patient and it seems to mean: "I will bear up under anything as long as I am sick and frightened." In that sense the response to treatment is like the fracture itself, because as soon as the fracture is healed the patient goes on his way with little interest in gaining insight, only to become fouled again with some new injury. Sometimes the fracture has elements of the suicidal attempt in that there is spite and retaliation in the very accident. The following two cases are reported because of the importance which aggressive features lend to the prognosis.

Case No. F 63. A housewife, aged 21, was crossing an icy street with a bundle of groceries in her arms. Although she walked very cautiously, she slipped and fractured her left arm. The patient was reared in the South with relatively few deprivations. She is now living in the North, married to a man whom she has known since childhood. However, at times she seemed very angry because he has been unable to give her the things she wanted and to allow her to return to the South to the protected pleasant atmosphere of her family and friends. She was forced to get a job. Apparently she made numerous efforts without avail until she finally was accepted. On the day before she was to go to work she talked a great deal about the hard times, was not particularly overjoyed at the possibility of making a go of things, spoke somewhat resentfully of her husband, and went out of the house for the groceries. When returning she slipped on the ice and fractured her arm (left olecranon). She was enraged at the moment of injury because "no Northerner" rushed up to her side to help her. Finally an old man picked her up in his arms and carried her home. After a period of uncertainty concerning the proper hospital she was brought to this hospital where she acquired among some of the patients and nurses maternal encouragement and approbation. Her first remark on seeing her husband: "Well, I can't be blamed for hurting myself, can I?" A question which she asked the doctor frequently in the first few days at the hospital.

She was easily distressed by physical examinations, was quite flirtatious and assumed a somewhat exaggerated air of intimacy and attachment. She felt angry at herself for resenting her husband's vocational failure. She was apparently greatly dissatisfied and somewhat depressed about the state of affairs. This culminated in her injury, hospitalization, and final return to the South where recuperation was possible and incidentally where she had wanted to go ever since her marriage. This case is briefly quoted because it seems to bear out the observation that an ambivalence was apparent in the injury motive, just as is so often the case in suicidal attempts.

Case No. F 59. A married housewife, aged 27, broke her arm (fracture of surgical neck of the left humerus) when she was "playing tricks" at a party. She claimed that she and her husband were at a friend's house where there were numerous other people. All were drinking somewhat and carousing a bit. She decided to be the life of the party in contrast to her husband who was always sensible and proper. She slid down the banister, but on landing at the bottom fell on her shoulder, thereby fracturing her upper arm. Her husband chided her a good deal, asserting that she was always up to such tricks, and was not convinced at first that she was hurt. She was somewhat annoyed at him at this party because he was always doing the right thing and never letting himself go. Her attitude was that of a person who was willing to be a hero at any price in order to show up somebody else. In other words, she was willing to take the chance of injuring herself to show that she was courageous because she was annoyed with her husband's propriety. The glory of defeat, in this case, injury, was worth the price to her.

She had been married for five years and felt even from the start that her husband's virtues were mostly his calmness and timidity. In the last year or so she confessed that her love was waning, and that she was thinking of looking elsewhere. Even her friends admitted that her husband was somewhat stuffy and stodgy, although here again he never did anything which was actually to be criticized. Her injury had made a heroine of her. All her friends came to her rescue and there her husband, the white-haired boy, did not catch the spirit of the play and stood finding fault. No doubt, from her knowledge of her husband, she would have expected such a response from him, and the injury tended to corroborate her own feelings about him and those of her friends. It gave her an opportunity to make him out to be a worse person than he actually was. The patient's attitude at first was that she was a "little fool" for carousing in the way she did, and she assumed the responsibility herself. However, even in the first interview with the psychiatrist her spite motive was not particularly obscure.

The patient's past history revealed her to be a somewhat demanding, difficult person with a strong masculine component. Under stress she would always have to go off and take a vacation. Fainting occurred occasionally during the more difficult periods of her life, although there was nothing in the history or physical examination which revealed cardiac disease or any peripheral vascular disturbance. As a child she had a history of early neurotic traits in the form of nail-biting. She depended on her friends to place her in various vocations, would remain at inferior positions for relatively long periods of time, grumbling and feeling somewhat abused. Her marital life was satisfactory to her in the first two years because it increased her self-esteem and she could easily dominate her husband, although she considered sexual intercourse "a dull thing." She refused to have children because "it was disfiguring and makes one look sloppy." Her husband had always wanted children.

The family background was a difficult one in that both her parents had died when she was within the third year of life. She was brought up by an aunt, while her older and younger brothers were brought up by another aunt. Her religious training was in the Catholic Church and she went to mass every Sunday until she got married. Then the fear of the priest's censure for being childless made her feel that she could no longer continue the practice of her religion.

This case illustrates briefly the element of self-disgust and guilt, neurotically solved by injury. Through her injury her husband received the disapproval of others, no doubt a justification of her own waning affections.

Both these patients were peculiarly difficult management problems on the ward and became co-operative only after they had to some degree come to terms with their feelings of resentment and guilt as well as with their difficult life situations.

On the basis of such simple observations as these we may make at least the following recommendations to any physician who has such patients in charge, and which are of great importance to the general management of the somatic problem itself.

(1) Particularly to be avoided are excessive spoiling or severity by the physician during the period of illness, because it is well known that these things encourage resistance and delinquent tendencies just as they do in the child's bringing up.

(2) Special attention should be given to patients who give a history of early neurotic traits or previous accidents, or any considerable number of the characteristics described in this chapter.

(3) Attention should be given to the patient's emotional problem both immediately after the accident (as soon as consciousness returns, or even to what the patient says during delirium) and during the convalescent period. Relief of the first feelings of guilt or revenge before they become repressed often helps to decrease muscle tension, and concentration on the injured member, which may so seriously impede recovery from injuries.

(4) Special attention should be given to the problem of secondary illness gain in these patients. But it should be remembered that these patients are very rarely conscious malingerers and hence it is not advantageous to treat them roughly. If one is ultra strict one calls up the picture of the brutal parent and unreasonable authorities, and provides a further impulse for additional self-injury.

The latter three points are best handled by the consulting psychiatrist but the general physician with some awareness of the problem may help both the patient and himself. In any case he should be on the lookout for these reactions of guilt and resentment, and any patient who shows them in an exaggerated form should have psychiatric treatment immediately if this is feasible. Waiting until after discharge creates an exceedingly difficult problem involving additional expense and expenditure of time.

Case No. 34 FA (Type A). An unmarried female, aged 20, was admitted to the hospital for treatment of an old fracture of the left forearm, ankylosis of the left fingers, wrist and elbow, and keloid of the forearm.

Family History. The patient's father was 54 years old and in good health. The mother was in her late forties, worried a lot, and often complained of stomach trouble. She had had a "nervous breakdown" about 20 years before "when my brother was hit by a car." There were nine siblings living and well, five brothers and four sisters. The patient was the sixth born. There was no other history of illnesses or accidents in the family.

Personal Data. The patient described her father as "good to me" but quick tempered and fairly strict. Her mother she said "is grand and very understanding. . . . Things upset her very easily." The patient was unmarried and planned to marry at some future date.

Health Record. The patient gave no history of previous illnesses except for light cases of measles and chickenpox when she was 5 or 6 years old. She has always had a strong interest in her health—"I've always taken pretty good care of my health but I always was thin. A few weeks before the accident I was losing weight. . . . I tried to eat as much as I could and I force myself to drink milk. I make sure I get enough sleep, if I've had a strenuous day I go to bed and don't go out. I never stay out very late because I think it would be bad for my health." She told of taking vitamin tablets and various tonics. She spent as much time as possible outdoors and "loved" sports.

Injuries. Although the patient had been very active in athletics she reported no previous injuries or accidents. The present accident occurred when she caught her arm in a machine at which she was working.

General Adjustment. The patient completed her *educational* units. After graduating from high school she worked as a secretary for several weeks. She lost this job and had to take another one which she did not like as it was working with machinery in a factory. She said, "I would rather work for less at something I like than do factory work which I don't like at all. I'm most interested in stenography and clerical work."

The patient's salary was $22 a week. Her *vocational* classification is group IV (skilled labor) but she prefers the group III type of job (clerks, salesmen, stenographers). She was ashamed to mention to the examiner that her father was a janitor and that most of her siblings were working in factories.

In reference to her *social relationships*, the patient stated "I've had plenty of friends and I enjoy being with them." She was a member of a girls' club at this time, but most of her intimate friends had got married. She com plained of feeling very lonely since her accident, "The trouble is I have to do everything alone and I don't like to be alone. Everybody else is working while I'm playing." She did not seem to be inclined to argue or to take any aggressive role in her social life.

Little was revealed about the patient's *sexual adjustment*. She reported a normal menstrual history. She admitted that she had a boy friend but was reticent about saying anything more than that she wanted to marry sometime but had not considered marriage to this boy.

The patient revealed a strong emotional *attachment toward her family*. She said she was lonesome in the hospital, "It's all right, I can't complain, but it isn't like home. There are always a lot of people around there, my mother and father, all my sisters and brothers." She seemed to be especially fond of her mother and of one older sister.

Characteristic Behavior Pattern. The characteristic behavior pattern of this patient conforms quite closely to the fracture profile. She always made decisions quickly: "I'm pretty fast to make my mind up. Like other people would be scared to undergo an operation and I just made up my mind like that. It's the same way when I go some place." She was ambitious in the sense that she wanted a higher socio-economic status for both herself and her family. But like most fracture patients she focussed upon immediate values rather than long range goals. Her strong emotional attachments were to people—her family and friends, and to concrete experiences of the moment —swimming, tennis, horseback riding. She had no intellectual interests. In manner she was friendly and talked easily until questioned about feelings and personal problems when she would become reticent or choked with emotion. The depression and lassitude which were very noticeable during her stay at the hospital were apparently of fairly recent development in reaction to her accident. "I always was pretty active," she said; "I have always been happy-go-lucky in the past but now—. It's the sitting around and not doing anything that makes you feel low."

A summary of the *Rorschach* report follows: Intelligence is average. The subject is extremely ambitious. Inner creativity is limited. Affective responses to the outer world are unfree, unadapted, with hysterical elements. She is easily aroused, easily disturbed, but is afraid to respond spontaneously because she is unable to maintain intellectual control over herself when stimulated. She tries to repress strong feelings and especially to restrain her strong hostility. The cost of this effort is tension, irritability, indecision, and a sense of helplessness about determining her own fate.

Neurotic Traits. Unlike many of the fracture group, this patient reported no history of early neurotic traits, but gave the usual impression of being a "normal" person, with only slight tendencies toward depression and hysteria.

Addictions and Interests. The patient did not smoke or drink coffee or alcohol because she believed that all these things were bad for her health. She expressed the great interest in sports found among many of the fracture group: "I love all sports . . . any kind of sports." She said that she went regularly to the Catholic Church, remarking, "I feel more religious now than I did before [the accident]."

Life Situation Immediately Prior to Onset. Prior to the accident, the patient had been working at a job which she intensely disliked. Although she did not actually say so, it was obvious that she was ashamed to do this factory work just as she was ashamed of her father's position as a janitor and of the fact her siblings worked in factories. She said she had been losing weight because she "couldn't take it." She had finally been taken off the machines and was doing easier work; in a couple of weeks she expected to be transferred to a stenographic position which she preferred. Just before the day of the accident she had been away for the week-end and had returned, she said, "in high spirits."

She described the accident as follows: "In the morning that this happened a girl fainted on her job so I took it over. It was very smoky and she couldn't stand the smoke. It never bothered me, I never faint. . . . I have long fingers and my gloves got caught in the machine and it went right up my arm. I couldn't stop the machine and I just screamed and the machine jammed all of a sudden like. They rushed me to the hospital fast. I lost quite a lot of blood because I was bleeding so and nobody put on a tourniquet."

Reaction to Illness. The patient reacted to the illness with guilt and depression. She said spontaneously that she often thought the accident happened as a punishment. "I didn't like the work and I was always complaining to my mother. I wanted to rest," she said, "and now I've got a good long rest— too long." She also reported an increased irritability. "Since my accident things excite me and I get irritated very fast. When something happens or something is said that don't seem right to me, I just flare up." Thus she exploited her illness using it as a means to express her increased hostility. In "flaring up" she probably also was projecting some of her own need for punishment by punishing others. Like many fracture patients her reaction was somewhat fatalistic—the accident was a punishment by fate instead of something she did to herself. Also like many fracture patients she bore the resulting pain and discomfort of operations stoically.

Area of Focal Conflict and Characteristic Reactions. This patient's area of focal conflict was typical of that for the fracture group. She was striving for an autonomous self-development without adopting either a submissive or dominating role. She focused her values on immediate pleasures rather than on long range goals, thus reducing the importance of conflicts with authority. She could not, however, escape from the conflict about her own job and the menial occupations of the other members of her family, especially her father. In complaining about her own job she was indirectly criticizing her father, and thus resisting his authority. It is significant that she was in the process of being "raised" to a less menial position which would put her "above" her father. She had already been taken off the machines and the transference to the stenographic position might have taken place smoothly had she not voluntarily replaced the girl who fainted. There was an air of bravado in her offer; she could stand the smoky atmosphere—"I never faint," and she did not mind helping with onerous work since her superior status was already assured. She was probably a little more careless than usual and guilt reactions accompanying her feelings of superiority probably pre-cipitated the catastrophe. It is significant that as a result of her accident, the injury to her hand and arm may prevent her from ever doing the kind of work she would like to do. Very wistfully she remarked to the examiner, "1 would like to run a comptometer, but that takes too much strength in the hands."

Case No. F 78. A twice married woman, aged 41, was admitted to the hospital with fracture of the right fibula and tibia.*

Heredity, Actual and Pseudo. This patient's father had died twelve years previously at the age of 71, of a stroke. The mother had died nine and a half years ago of coronary thrombosis. The patient's only sibling, a sister, two years younger, was living and well, although she had been somewhat nervous since the death of their mother because the attachment had been particularly close.

Constitution. The patient was well built and somewhat small.

General Health. In spite of her heredity she had had no previous illnesses or functional disturbances. She herself said: "Disease" (by which she meant her accident) "took me by surprise. I suppose it had to come sooner or later. I was never in a hospital except when my child was born."

Early Influences and Traumatic Experiences. The patient stated that in general her life had been a happy one and she had not been much upset by the death of her parents because "fate decrees that parents must die." And she had never been very close to either of them. Later the patient related that her sister was the favorite and she thought her parents were too strict. She hoped she would be a better parent. At the onset of puberty she had slid down the banisters, and had accidentally fallen at the foot. When she was picked up she was "all covered with blood." She did not know at the time that this was only the beginning of menstruation, about which her mother had told her nothing.

Onset of Symptoms. The patient was crossing the street when the lights

* This case is not presented according to the profile. It can readily be seen that histories taken according to the profile are easier to evaluate.

turned against her and she was struck by an automobile. She said: "The driver was probably frozen to the wheel when he saw me appear all of a sudden out of nowhere."

Excerpts from the Medical Chart

The patient's chief complaint was the pain in and deformity of her right leg.

Five minutes before admission, while crossing the street the patient was struck by an automobile (the bumper struck her right leg below the knee). The patient was thrown to the ground and struck her head against the pavement but she did not lose consciousness. However, she was unable to get up.

The physical examination showed a deformity of the middle of the right lower leg with anterior angulation. There was marked tenderness in this region, as well as considerable swelling and a great deal of pain. She had also numerous ecchymotic areas and bruises on her body. There was no nerve damage.

The x-ray of the skull was negative. The x-ray of the right leg showed a complete slightly oblique fracture across the mid third of the tibia, and another across the junction of the mid and upper third of the tibia. The ends of the fragments were in partial apposition. There was also a transverse fracture across the junction of the upper and mid third of the fibula with displacements and overriding.

A Thomas splint was applied and the patient's leg suspended with enough traction to prevent angulation. Operation on the fourth day consisted of open reduction and the application of three Barrach plates for fracture of her right tibia. One plate was 8 inches with seven screws, and there were two 4-screw plates.

Outstanding Points in the Personal History

General Adjustment. Externally the patient was small, attractive, well adjusted and well liked.

She admitted that in order to get away from home she had married a man who was unable to support her and was unworthy of her. By this husband she had a daughter. When the daughter was 3½ years of age the patient was separated from her husband, and later divorced him. The patient worked as a law stenographer, and her sister took care of the child when she was away from home. When her daughter was 14 the patient married a man whom she had known for ten years. This man was very strict with the daughter who, he felt, was running wild. The patient stated that she had made a mistake in marrying this man at this time, but should have done so earlier or later, since her "headstrong" daughter was just old enough to resent a stepfather. The patient also became strict (too strict, she thought), trying to make her 16 or 17 year old girl come in at 10 o'clock on school nights and 12 on Saturdays, and also to pay more attention to her school work, which was not good. The girl resented discipline of any sort.

When the girl was 16 she fell in love with a boy 20 years old and making twenty dollars a week. The mother, feeling that the girl was about to repeat her own mistake, warned her against marrying him. The daughter would not speak to her any more. The daughter, she felt, was just like her father, uncontrollable and reckless. The daughter ran away from home, leaving a note to say she was going to live with her grandmother. The mother was much hurt, but thought the grandmother's discipline would be severe and hoped the girl would return. The grandmother could not handle the situation and sent the girl to live with her father and his mistress (who appears in the chart as the girl's sister).

At her first interview, the patient stated that she learned of her daughter's marriage to this boy just before the accident—on the same day. Later she said that she heard of it for the first time after arriving at the hospital, to which her daughter was brought for an appendectomy.

The patient's vocational record was grammar school, high school, one year of college, and work as secretary in a law office until her second marriage.

Characteristic Behavior Pattern—impulsive action. "I have had a lot of trouble and I cannot be sure I have done right by my daughter. Perhaps I should not have married again when she was only 14, but I guess everyone makes mistakes. When I am worried about such things I smoke or try to do something else."

Neurotic Traits—Early and Present. "It's funny I have always been sure fate would catch up with me. Since I was very little I have had nightmares of black shadows which would creep noiselessly up the stairs and sit on my chest and crush me. I guess that was fate. Now I don't have the nightmares so often but when I do I wake myself up and smoke cigarettes." From the time of her first marriage she had nightmares about being all covered with blood. She dreaded having her child because it reminded her of her fall when sliding down the banisters, and being picked up covered with blood. She felt guilty about having married a second time, both because the church forbids it and because of her child. She also worried about having a child by her second marriage, fearing to do so because it would "spoil her looks" and because of the blood fantasy.

Addictions and Interests. "I never have any particular interests. I just thought I would do what came along, but since my troubles started I have thought that religion might help me. I was starting to smoke too much and to drink but I am learning to overcome these things."

Life Situation Immediately Prior to Accident (See "General Adjustment"). The patient had left home just before she had her accident, and she was thinking about this, wondering whether it was her fault and if she had been a failure when she was walking across the street and "appeared out of nowhere to upset the driver of the car."

Reaction to Illness. "I have tried to avoid suffering all my life. I didn't mind the accident and coming to the hospital, but I am afraid of the operation. I have never liked to suffer. Perhaps I am being punished." In saying this tears came to the patient's eyes.

Summary. This patient gives a personality picture characteristic of the accident patient. She appeared generally normal, attractive, and pleasant. She had a marked jerky type of tension and an impulse to do something whenever she was in trouble. She had never been close to either parent because her sister was the favorite and she thought "they were too strict." She had a strong sense of guilt, feeling that the accident was a punishment. She had a small family—an only child. She had hoped she would be a better parent, but her daughter running away from home and marrying a man who was unable to support her recalled vividly her own earlier life. Worrying about whether she had failed in her ideal of being a good parent was the emotional background prior to her accident. She was worried also about whether she should have had a child by her second husband:

"But I just didn't have the courage. It spoils your looks and makes you ridiculous, especially when you're small. Ever since I was married I've had nightmares about being all covered with blood. I hated having my first child because it reminded me of my first accident when I slid down the banisters, and when I was picked up I was all covered with blood. It was only the beginning of menstruation, but I didn't know it then because mother hadn't told me. Anyway you shouldn't have children if your husband can't support them. The church says you shouldn't marry a second time and I guess that's what made all the trouble. My daughter has suffered too. After I had my accident she had to come to the hospital to have her appendix out, but when I first saw her she said: 'You have ruined my life. Don't ever talk to me again.' That's what my mother did to me, but I didn't want to do it to my daughter. I have an Irish temper too, and if you get me tied up where I can't move, I will fight my way out. My doctor is very nice but he is a bad psychologist. He keeps an unpleasant fact from you as long as he can and then springs it like the shadows that choked me in my nightmares. I would rather have it straight out than have it sprung on me. He is just like fate and I am sure I'm going to have another accident. I can never cross the street without getting palpitation and feeling in a panic. I am sure I will have another accident pretty soon. Perhaps I will get better when I get my compensation, but that won't be for another year, and I am afraid if I get well and get a job they won't give me what they owe me." She was like the female type of accident sufferer in having an anxiety hysteria.

This patient differs from the usual accident patient in her dual cardiac heredity. In view of this it is interesting that she had an accident instead of developing some cardiovascular disorder. One reason for this seems to be the acute activation of her focal conflict with authority as a result of her daughter's behavior, but it is interesting that after she left the hospital she did develop some cardiovascular symptomatology. Her nightmares of fate creeping up on her and of finding herself all covered with blood recall both her conflict with authority and her fears in relation to sex. "I hated to think my daughter was going to have to go through all that too, and that perhaps it was my fault." *

It would have been possible to choose a more dramatic case for illustrative purposes but the reason for the present choice is an endeavor to call attention to emotional factors in patients who on the surface appear to be more or less normal.

VI. COURSE AND FOLLOW-UP

The intimate relationship between the patient, his conflict, and breakdown of his defenses against the conflict and the initiation of an accident or the accident habit, is illustrated in the following cases. The question of recovery or non-recovery from accident-proneness should be discussed in terms of the personality type which will help to determine what therapy may be feasible or desirable.

Case No. F 50. A Roman Catholic boy, 15 years old, was admitted to the hospital for treatment of non-union after fracture of the femur.

Predisposition to Illness—Factors to be Evaluated

Organ Conditioning—Physiological and Psychological (Heredity, Actual and Pseudo). There were no positive points of interest.

Constitution, Age Range and Sex. The patient was an attractive boy, slightly small for his age.

General Health. The patient had had excellent health until the time of the accident. He had fractured his skull at the age of 8 because while riding on the handle-bars of a bicycle his feet had been caught in the wheel. Prior to the present accident he had had four serious falls in quick succession, one

* For comparison with individuals in other groups who have accidents, see the respective sections.

playing baseball, one playing football, and two skiing. After all this he had fractured his hip in trying to open the garage door to put away his skis.

Onset of Symptoms. The patient admitted some responsibility for the present condition in that following the fracture of his hip he had tried to pretend nothing had happened and had walked on it for nearly a day, in spite of the pain, before seeking treatment. He had then gone to an osteopath whose treatment had been to pull his leg, and it was not until after a considerable period of treatment of this kind that he sought medical aid.

Abstract from Medical History *

This is the third admission of a 15-year-old boy for flexion contracture of the left hip.

Present Illness. Nine and a half months ago the patient was first admitted with a history of injury to the left hip of two years' duration. Clinical and x-ray studies made a diagnosis of faulty union following epiphyseolysis of the upper extremity of the left femur. An osteotomy of the neck of the left femur was performed and a Smith-Peterson nail inserted. The patient was discharged seven weeks postoperative, wearing a non-weight-bearing caliper brace. Gradually he developed a contracture of the adductor muscles of the left hip together with a flexion deformity. His second admission, two and a half months ago occurred because of the deformity. At operation the Smith-Peterson nail was removed and a Scutter fasciotomy and myotomy of the adductor longus muscle was performed. A plaster spica was applied with the leg in 40 degrees abduction, and 10 degrees external rotation and neutral position of the hip anteroposteriorly. On the twelfth day postoperative the plaster was removed, the hip manipulated and a plaster spica reapplied in the same position. On the twenty-sixth day postoperative the second spica was removed and physiotherapy and active motion of the left hip was begun. On the fortieth day, the patient was discharged walking without the aid of support. Active and passive motion was equal in the two hips. External rotation 10 degrees on the left, internal rotation 5 degrees; flexion 110 degrees– 175 degrees; there was a 5 degree flexion deformity with the patient lying flat on his back. He had a slight lumbar lordosis when standing upright.

After discharge the patient was followed in the fracture clinic, and performed a series of prescribed exercises at home. Because of the shortening of the leg, the sole of his left shoe was elevated 1 inch and the heel 1½ inch. He gradually developed an increasing flexion deformity of the left hip with complete limitation and rotation of it. The patient was therefore readmitted to the hospital for further consideration and treatment.

* This medical history is included in such detail in order to illustrate the expenditure of medical resources and time which is necessary in treating accident cases.

Physical Examination. This was not remarkable except locally. The previous operative scars about the left hip were well healed. There was a 50 degree flexion deformity of the left leg. The internal abductor and external rotation of the hip were negative. The structures attached to the anterior inferior iliac spine were tense on attempted extension of the leg. The adductor muscles were not tense.

Laboratory Examination. The urine analysis was negative.

X-rays. Those taken just before this admission showed an anatomical rotation of the femoral head following the correction of the old epiphyseolysis. Bone production was noted along the inferior margin of the first innominate bone. Atrophic changes were noted along the articular margin of the femoral head medially.

Course. The patient was allowed to rest in bed for one week in order to overcome the muscle spasm about the left hip. On the eighth day a Kirschner wire was inserted through the lower extermity of the left femur and 10 pounds of traction were applied through this wire to the left leg at an angle of 40 degrees with the pelvis in order to relax the contracted muscle in the line of the deformity. On the ninth day the weight was increased to 15 pounds. On the tenth day an additional 5 pounds were added and it was found that after 48 hours of traction there had been a correction of 20 degrees in the flexion deformity. This amount of traction was maintained. On the thirteenth day the flexion deformity had been diminished to 10 degrees. On the sixteenth day, which was the ninth day after the traction had been begun, the left leg was parallel with the spine and the flexion deformity had been eliminated. There was but slight lordosis of the lumbar spine. On the twenty-first day on the ward, the thirteenth day of traction, the Kirschner wire was withdrawn and a plaster spica applied with the leg in 20 degree adduction and the leg flexed to 3 degrees on the pelvis. The plaster was extended to a point just above the left knee joint. On the twenty-second day the patient was allowed up to walk about with crutches. This proved to be too much strain on the plaster which cracked in its posteria portion. On the twenty-third day the first plaster was removed and a second spica reinforced with a ¼ inch steel rod was applied in the same manner. Flexion of the hip was no more than 3 degrees. An x-ray taken on the twenty-third day showed no change in the position of the head and neck of the femur. After twenty-four hours the patient was allowed up and about the ward and was able to walk comfortably with crutches before discharge.

Outstanding Points in the Personal History

The patient was attractive and sociable, but his parents were strict and set high ideals for him. He spent much of his time on the ward trying to

cheer up other patients, especially the older ones. He had never got on well
with his only sibling, a brother three years younger. His behavior toward him
had been an alternation of resentment and abuse and attempted reform. He
stated that his brother had got in with a criminal gang from which he had
had to rescue him, and the patient, then in the first year of high school, had
set his heart on going to Yale and law school to be a criminal lawyer. He
wanted to spend his life locking up criminals and protecting his brother.

The patient had always been active, fond of competitive sports in which
he was fairly successful "in spite of my size," although he admitted that this
was a handicap and he guessed it was just as well that he could not engage
in them any more because of his accident.

He had suffered from enuresis from the age of 6 or 7 and had taken up
pipe-smoking early as his only secret sin—except masturbation, which later
he feared might be responsible for his small size.

When seen in the follow-up clinic, two years later, after six periods of
hospitalization in the meantime, the personality picture was entirely changed.
The patient was fat and indifferent and had given up school. He stated that
he had tried various diets to keep up his good looks but he could not resist
beginning the day with soda pop, cake and bread and molasses, and continuing it in the same way with considerable eating between meals.

Although sports and reform had been his major interests he no longer cared
about them. "All I want to do is play with autos. If I ever go to school
again, it will be to commercial school. I think it should be possible to put
diesel engines into automobiles and then they would have much greater
power. *After all, there is much more power in machinery than in the greatest
athlete that ever lived.*"

Incidentally, whereas previously the patient's ideas about sex had been
extremely Puritanical, accompanied by an idealization of the female, he
now considered women uninteresting because of their weakness. His conflict
over masturbation continued as before.

Summary. This patient did not receive psychotherapy, but he illustrates
well the kind of deterioration that might have been prevented had psychotherapy been available to him in the hospital. The history shows an accident
habit of early origin, typical for accident patients of this age. It is also
typical that the injury occurred not while indulging in athletic sports but
while opening the garage door to put away his skis. The importance of the
athletic activity in terms of his self-esteem was clear, as was also his change
in attitude toward it after the accident. He was glad of an excuse to give
them up and substitute an interest in machinery. He was not, however, quite
satisfied by the substitution, and no longer had the courage to diet to keep
up his good looks, instead resorting to various exaggerated types of oral

satisfaction. His increasing lack of ambition turned out to be related to the change produced in his mother by the accident as well as in the care received in the hospital. He, not his younger brother, was now the son to be protected, and he stated that for the first time in his life he was really able to talk to her.

In view of the preceding remarks about the similarity of the family constellation in the history of criminals and in patients with accident habits, it may be interesting to note here that one family produced two boys, one who had criminal tendencies and the other an accident habit.

Case No. F 150. A boy, aged 17, broke his ankle while sliding with spikes on his shoes when playing baseball. He stated that he was angry because his side was losing.

Predisposition to Illness—Factors to be Evaluated

His family history was negative for diabetes, cardiovascular disease and nervousness, but his father had had an injury which may have been a fracture; he was also wounded severely in the war. One brother had had a severe injury and another many minor accidents. The father is now commander of the disabled veterans.

The patient was small, of linear build, and left-handed.

Except for an attack of jaundice, and an operation on his left arm when it became infected after scratching a mosquito bite, he had had no history of illness or operation. This, however, was his *eighth* important accident, although the first one in relation to athletics which was his major interest, and he reported in addition, that he was always having minor injuries; he "guessed because he banged around too much."

Outstanding Points in the Personal History

The patient was active, sociable, and happy-go-lucky about his studies although his mother and father held him to them pretty strictly. He had planned to go to college to study engineering but had forgotten that in order to do this he had to take languages in high school. He decided that it was not worth the trouble to make up for this oversight so settled on a course in aeronautics instead. He started going with girls at the age of 10 and would get a new one every six months or a year. He was unhappy at home.

This patient was extremely restless on the ward, jumping about in his wheel chair and rolling it back and forth while he talked. He made the usual comment that he was always in a hurry and had to keep busy.

He suffered from enuresis till he was 11, and sucked his thumb until the

age of 9; was addicted to walking and talking in his sleep, and was sensitive
to alcohol. He had started to smoke but had to conceal this from his parents.

His major interests were basketball, football, and track "because they
build you up physically." He added, "but I am always in the pink of condition, being in training helps to keep from doing things that are unhealthy.
I like to play with boys that are heavier than I am because those my size
don't play roughly enough. I like tough going." Other interests were air-
planes and photography. He used to devote considerable time to making
model airships.

Some time after the first interview it was learned that this patient was
angry at the time of the accident not only because his side was losing but
also because his mother kept him in so much, that he was not playing as well
as he should have been.

This patient became very much attached to his nurse because "she treated
me the way a parent should" and used to buy her candy. He was unwilling
to go home both because of his parents' strictness and because he did not
know how to get rid of his present girl: "She has already planned our honey-
moon house, and children, and I haven't the vaguest desire to marry her
at all."

Dynamic Formulation

The patient had always had trouble with authority both at home and at
school. Of his father he said: "He means business when he speaks at home."
He described his mother as relatively easy-going, although she had always
punished him severely and even at the present time would keep him in for
two weeks if he failed to return home at the exact hour she dictated, or if he
got bad marks at school. He was brought up a strict Methodist and forced
to go to church and Sunday school until he was twelve. He then substituted
the Y.M.C.A. but thought that sooner or later he would take up church
again.

The patient was to a considerable degree unconscious of his present conflicts, as indicated by his statement that his mother was easy-going which
was followed by complaints of her harshness, lack of understanding, and
unreasonable punishment. He said later: "Did I say mother was easy-going?
I am not quite sure that was quite the right word after all."

Again, like the usual fracture patient, although he walked and talked
in his sleep and sometimes waked up frightened, he could remember no
nightmares or dreams. He was impelled to act rather than brood.

It may be instructive to note here the way in which the characteristic constellation may bring about accidents in a patient with the

fracture patient's focal conflict, against which he has previously used quite different defenses, when these other defenses are suddenly taken away from him. A case in point is the following:

Case No. FP 5. A single woman, aged 29, came to the medical clinic complaining of headaches associated with fatigue of ten years' duration, precordial pain without relation to exertion, and pain in her back, together with nervousness. She related the fact that she had had an episode of numbness passing from the left arm to the right arm and involving tingling of the legs, lasting an hour or more, during which time she could not straighten the left fourth and fifth fingers and everything looked very small. A local physician stated that this was "just nervousness" which the patient refused to believe. In general, except for malnutrition and a club-foot the patient was an attractive normal-appearing girl with diverse interests who had kept a job as a clerk until the middle of the depression, a year and a half previously.

No organic basis was found for the patient's symptoms and she was referred to the psychiatric service. Her symptoms had started ten years previously when she gave up teacher's training because in her practice-teaching she suddenly got the feeling that the children were all staring at her club-foot, that this would always interfere with her management of children, that she was doomed to be a failure because of it, and that she probably should never marry. At this time she had an unhappy love affair for which similarly she blames the club-foot. She showed a great deal of hatred toward her parents because they did not know enough to have this deformity corrected at an early age, and because her mother bore her that way. The patient was also resentful at being seen by a psychiatrist, and although she gave a history involving a series of emotional traumata, she refused to recognize any emotional component in either her physical or her personality difficulties.

She made the following revealing statement: "When I was seven years old my sister had tuberculosis; I was told I mustn't let anyone know; it was something shameful. If I had to say anything I was to say she had a nervous breakdown but if mother had known what we know now about nervous breakdowns she'd have been *much more ashamed of that*." With discussion of emotional problems the patient became increasingly disturbed but unable to see any relationship between these and her symptoms. She was sure that she would be perfectly normal if it weren't for the club-foot. Her other conflicts, such for example as disgust at being a woman, "that awful weakness that makes me unable to keep a job because I'm a woman," which was expressed among other things in intense dysmenorrhea, were also blamed on the club-foot. She came to insist that nothing would help her except an operation to correct this deformity. The psychiatrist still attempted to point out that this was not the main problem, and then during a period when the psychiatric clinic was closed the patient injured her ankle and came back to the clinic in need of treatment. On the fracture service she insisted that the club-foot be cured at the same time. The operation was performed, the patient made a very slow recovery and there was marked persistence of pain and spasms in the foot. When finally she was allowed up on crutches she promptly fell downstairs fracturing in two places the extremity on which the operation had been performed.

Psychotherapy was not available for this patient at the time because her surgeon was convinced that it was unnecessary. She was a model patient. When "cured" this time she succeeded in getting an excellent job but was placed under pressure by necessity of aiding the tubercular sister who had suffered a recurrence. She then broke the other leg.

After this she was very much troubled by a sense of guilt: "I can't understand why I was so careless. It must have been my fault." And it became obvious that this had actually been a purposeful accident, among other things an expression of the patient's unconscious need to keep the deformed extremity as a defense against and cover for her more fundamental personality conflicts. With her recovery she became increasingly schizophrenic. On discharge psychotherapy was recommended but proved not to be feasible because the patient left town. She returned a year later, the foot and leg in perfect condition but with a full blown psychotic picture.

VII. Conclusions

(1) The group of patients with fracture has important similarities within itself, and differs from the other groups of patients studied.

(2) The patients in the fracture group stand out in certain respects from the population as a whole, for example, in their very low illness record, their high record for previous accidents, their high percentage of childless marriages, and the small size of the family.

(3) This group is the least homogeneous of all the groups studied, and appears to comprise three major personality types. This impression is borne out by application of the Rorschach test.

Type A, which includes a relatively high percentage of women, is composed largely of constricted personalities and its distinguishing characteristics are indicated in the "Profile." If the women in this group are excluded (they tend to have fewer accidents) the group has a lower accident rate than does group B, but nevertheless, includes some men who have a very high accident record.

Type B, which includes only a very few women, is characterized by strong introversive tendencies, and the distinguishing traits are more dramatically manifest. This group has a higher accident record than group A (with the women excluded) and a more even distribution of the accidents.

Type C, which also includes only a very few women, is characteristically extratensive and has less clearly defined personality traits. The group has a total accident record about equal to that of group A, but with a much less even distribution. *

(4) In addition, the following individual characteristics of the fracture group are outstanding.

(a) These patients generally present a normal appearance with few obvious neurotic traits, except for a small group (mostly women) with phobias and other signs of anxiety and hysteria.

(b) They manifest a jerky, restless type of tension, especially in group A. They show a tendency to hurl themselves into some form of ill-considered activity in situations of particular emotional stress.

(c) They have a tendency toward self-reliance and an equalitarian "good fellow" role in social relationships. They show a defensive tendency to appear casual about feelings and personal problems.

(d) They seem to be striving toward integration and autonomy outside of the authoritarian hierarchy. They show a marked tendency to make up their minds definitely and quickly, to focus upon immediate values, and they display little interest in intellectual values and verbalization. In group B, there is a marked adventurous trend and an avoidance of responsibility.

(e) They tend to have accidents when their strong aggressive hostility is aroused, or the pressure from authority becomes too great: for example, when their self-esteem is injured by a long period out of work and they are under pressure from husband or wife to get a job. An accident frequently occurs when they build up too much resentment toward their superiors, for example when they are required to

---

* In the original profile [142] the 20 per cent of the cases eliminated as atypical belonged to this group. This is partly because of the higher percentage of cases included in this group who had only one accident or an innocent accident.

do things that seem unreasonable such as working on Sunday, or when forbidden the use of contraceptives.

(f) Their initial reaction to an accident is in terms of guilt with an emphasis on destructiveness toward others or themselves which is followed by repression of all this and concentration on the injury itself.

(5) This personality pattern plays an important role in bringing about the accident itself. In patients with previous injury or with an accident habit, the factors just mentioned stand out even more prominently than in those admitted for their first accident. If careful evaluation is desired the three sub-groups must be differentiated.

(6) *The personality profiles selected to illustrate the points in this and succeeding chapters were chosen to illustrate the range of variations from the profile given which are likely to be encountered; they were not chosen to represent the cases that best fitted the profiles.*

Chapter V

HYPERTENSIVE CARDIOVASCULAR DISEASE, CORONARY OCCLUSION, AND ANGINAL SYNDROME

Le cœur a ses raisons que la raison ne connaît pas.—PASCAL.

Penalty is exacted, without remorse or opportunity for appeal, when man thrusts his works too confidently into the path of the major forces of nature.—*Science News Letter.*

Cardiovascular disease, the major cause of present day mortality, has the highest disability rate of any illness in the age period 25 to 64, and is exceeded only by nervous and mental disease,* orthopedic conditions, and accidents in the age period 15 to 24.

According to the National Health survey [286] (see also Boas [44]) 7,500,000 persons are disabled by cardiovascular diseases on any given day, and another 500,000 by other diseases of the circulatory system.† (Furthermore, nearly another 7,000,000 are disabled by rheumatism, a large part of which is rheumatoid arthritis.‡) These illnesses account for loss of more than 250,000,000,000 days annually out of a total of 800,000,000,000 days lost.§

"It is estimated that 23,000,000 persons in the United States have some chronic disease and that a minimum of 1,500,000 are disabled for such long periods of time (12 months or more) that they may be considered chronic invalids." [44] Of all the sufferers from chronic disease in the United States (of whom 70 per cent are under 55, and nearly half under 45) well on to 12 per cent are invalids because of cardiovascular disease (exclusive of rheumatic fever and rheu-

---

* For females, disease of the puerperal state.

† Including aneurysm except heart, gangrene, low blood pressure, and other diseases of arteries or veins, excluding diseases of the lymphatic system.

‡ According to this table rheumatism includes arthritis, gout, neuritis, neuralgia, lumbago, etc. (See Chapter VI.)

§ Rheumatism 97,200,000; heart disease 95,200,000; and arteriosclerosis and high blood pressure 56,900,000.

matoid arthritis). No illness ranks higher as a cause of invalidism except nervous and mental disease, which is responsible for eighteen per cent of all invalids. But in terms of days lost from work cardiovascular disease accounts for twenty per cent and nervous and mental disease for only seventeen per cent.[286] As the president of the Medical Society of the County of New York stated in his inaugural address: "In this country we are faced with the highest incidence of morbidity and mortality from the chronic degenerative diseases of middle life, notably the cardiovascular-renal groups, and the methods of prevention and the problems of treatment of these all-too-common maladies present a great challenge to the profession." [269]

HYPERTENSIVE CARDIOVASCULAR DISEASE

I. Nature and Magnitude of the Problem

STATISTICS

Three and one-half per cent of the total population of the United States (according to the National Health Survey[286]) suffers from high blood pressure and arteriosclerosis, but the percentages for the age period included in our study are about 6 per cent for the age period 25 to 34; 7 per cent for the age period 35 to 44; and about 11 per cent for the age period 45 to 54.

As noted in the introduction, hypertension is a major problem. According to the statistics of the Metropolitan Life Insurance Company, every other individual in the United States past the age of 50 years dies of cardiovascular-renal disease.[135] From other sources[170] we have evidence that probably half of these deaths are due to essential hypertension; that is, that almost one-quarter of all people past the age of 50 years die of the effects of hypertension on one or another of the vital organs. Thus essential hypertension becomes the greatest problem of middle adult life, not even excepting cancer.[226]

OTHER STUDIES

Weiss[414] has given an excellent and concise review of the literature relative to hypertension. There is, therefore, little need to discuss it here except to call attention to a few specific points.

Allen and Adson [21] discussing medical versus physical treatment of hypertension, point out that it is more common and more deadly than cancer. After dividing sufferers from this malady into four groups they give the mortality four years from the time of diagnosis as 42 per cent in groups I and II, 78 per cent in group III, and 98 per cent in group IV. They do not include in this study the effects of intensive psychotherapy. On this subject there have been recent contributions from Robinson,[355] Saul,[366] Alexander,[12, 13] Menninger,[298] and Renie [348] among others. Miller [306] has discussed the blood pressure findings in relation to inhibited aggressions in psychotics. Kraines and Sherman [276] have studied neurotic symptoms and changes in blood pressure and pulse following injection of epinephrine, and Anderson, Parmenter and Liddell [25] some cardiovascular manifestations of the experimental neurosis in sheep. Grollman, Harrison and Williams [213] studying the effect of various forms of treatment on dogs noted that sympathectomy lowered the blood pressure in five dogs for two weeks, and then it went up again.

Robinson and Brucer [357] noting that up to date there was thought to be no correlation between body build and the development of this illness, studied the insurance records of 3658 men and women. On the basis of this analysis they found hypertension seven times more frequent in the broad than in the linear type. This is in general accord with our own observations, but it is our impression also that when this disease occurs in a person of the linear type its course is likely to be more rapidly fatal, other factors being equal.

Davis and Klainer [110, 111] noted that the incidence of coronary disease is much greater in patients with hypertension. Our series is typical in this respect: 9 per cent of the patients admitted with hypertensive cardiovascular disease developed coronary occlusion in a period of from one to six years, and 27 per cent of our series of patients with coronary occlusion had hypertension. Davis and Klainer also noted that although hypertension is more common in women than in men, the incidence of coronary occlusion in women with hypertensive cardiovascular disease is about the same as in men with hypertensive cardiovascular disease.

In summarizing the treatment problem in relation to hypertension Hamburger [223] writes:

"In conclusion I should like to refer briefly to one practical point in treatment and mention the recent work of Alexander, Saul, Miller, Weiss and others on the role of the emotions in the genesis of hypertension and what may be done in a practical way toward amelioration. In a recent symposium on hypertension (*Psychosomatic Medicine*, Jan. 1939) Saul wrote on 'Hostility in Cases of Essential Hypertension' and Miller on 'Blood Pressure and Inhibited Aggressions.' From a practical therapeutic standpoint, however, Edward Weiss, I believe, states the situation in the simplest terms and I can do no better than quote his concluding paragraph completely:

'To advise the individual involved in mental conflict not to worry is absurd, especially when, as is so often the case, no concerted effort is made to find out what is disturbing him. Too often the physician is satisfied that there are no problems disturbing the patient after he has inquired, "Are you worried about anything?" and has received a negative reply. Most of the time the patient really does not know just how much he is disturbed, nor does he relate the factors actually responsible for his discontent. He is much more apt to project his worries into questions about his blood pressure, heart, brain, and kidneys. Careful inquiry will bring out that his fears are exaggerated and that the reasons he assigns for them are illogical. There is only one approach that has any merit; that is, to encourage the patient to talk about himself as a person rather than as a medical case. This will permit some insight into conflict situations and lead often to some relief of anxiety, which is closely related to the high blood pressure. Although this approach does not offer a complete solution of the hypertensive problem and does not even apply to all patients, it is a practical method of dealing with a set of important factors that may be modified, whereas the constitution of the individual cannot be touched. It is an approach heretofore not sufficiently practiced. We are too much concerned with physical measurements in hypertension—the blood pressure figures, the percentage of renal function, the size of the heart, the electrocardiographic tracing, the amount of retinal sclerosis—all of which are essential in the study of the hypertensive person but give incomplete information from the standpoint of the total evaluation of the patient. They should represent the beginning and not the end of study. We are too little concerned with the emotional life, which may hold the key to the satisfactory management of the hypertensive patient.' "

II. Onset of Symptoms *

In our series the onset of "symptoms" covered periods varying from one to eighteen years. The outstanding symptoms were headache, dizziness, and dyspnea. The period of duration of known hypertension varied from fifteen years to the date of admission.

A large number of these patients had early signs diagnosed as "cardiac neurosis," and went on to the development of hypertension. This serves to emphasize the fact that patients discharged as having no organic disease should be followed carefully.† Our material indicates that patients whose heredity, exposure, and early illness history is such as to be potentially predisposing to illness deserve especially careful watching.

III. Predisposition to Illness—Factors to be Evaluated

ORGAN CONDITIONING—PHYSIOLOGICAL AND PSYCHOLOGICAL

Heredity—Actual and Pseudo

About half (49 per cent) of these patients had a *history* of *cardiovascular disease* in the family (in parents, grandparents, parents' siblings), and in nearly one-sixth of them there was more than one case in the family. In half of the patients having a family history of cardiac illness there was hypertensive cardiovascular disease.

More than 98 per cent of these patients (and the remaining 2 per cent includes patients whose history was incomplete from this point of view) had been closely *exposed* to *serious cardiovascular disease* in parent, sibling or friends, and half of them to sudden deaths of parents, siblings or friends, at an early age. This fact is stressed here because of the marked effect of such exposure on the psychic component in the patient's preparation for illness. Cardiac heredity was relatively more important among male patients (58 per cent as compared with 43 per cent), but exposure to cardiovascular disease was equally prominent in the two sexes.

It is interesting that family history of cardiovascular disease was equally divided between the males and females of the family. The

---

* For further discussion see page ›65.

† "Psychic phenomena often give us the earlier, because more subtle, finer clinical signs, while objective phenomena give us the coarser, but the more unequivocal, data" (v. Bergmann [83]).

reason for making this note is discussed in later sections of this chapter.

Nervous instability was reported in the families of three-quarters of these patients (4 per cent had parents who had been committed to mental institutions).

Diabetes was reported in the families of nearly one-fifth of these patients. This figure would be increased to nearly one-fourth if diabetes in siblings were included. Of course diabetes is an illness often found in conjunction with hypertension and vice versa. (See for example Hutton.[244, 245] This subject is discussed further in Chapter X.)

The incidence of *injury* in the family history was about 10 per cent. If the patients' siblings are included this is increased to nearly 20 per cent.

Constitution—Age Range, Sex, and Marriage

Build. These patients tended to be athletic or pyknic in build. The same was true of patients with fracture or diabetes who showed hypertension (Chapter X).

Age Range.

AGE GROUP	PER CENT
15–24	12
25–34	14
35–44	44.9
45–55	28.6

The average age at the time of admission was 37 for males and 38 for females.

Sex. Of the patients in this group 39 per cent were males, and 61 per cent were females. It may be interesting to note that the respective representation of males and females coincided almost exactly with that for the total cardiovascular group which amounted to about two-fifths male and three-fifths female.

Marriage. Of the patients in this group 69 per cent were married.

	BOTH SEXES PER CENT	MALES PER CENT	FEMALES PER CENT
Total group	69	58	78
Of those 21 and over	72.3	61.1	79.3
Of those 25 and over	79	69	85

It is interesting to note that the marriage figures for our urban white population 15 years of age and over are 60.7 per cent males married, and 58.7 females married [393] (figures from 1930 census). In view of the relatively small proportion of young patients with hypertension in our group these figures cannot be used as a basis of comparison, but our impression is that the marriage rate for these patients is relatively high.

Of these marriages 24 per cent were childless. The average number of children per marriage was 1.79. It may be noted that this exceeds the average size of urban family in the United States (children 1.6— 1940 census), by about 12.5 per cent. It may be noted further that the females were inclined to have larger families than the males: 1.83 per cent and 1.73 per cent, respectively.

Previous Health *

The previous health record of these patients was in marked contrast with that of the accident group just reported, in that these patients averaged more than six previous illnesses per patient, instead of a little over one and a half. Only patients with anginal syndrome, rheumatic heart disease, and coronary disease had a worse health record prior to the onset of the illness for which they were admitted.

The *major operation* record gave an average of more than one major operation for every two patients. Only patients with anginal syndrome had a worse record for major operations. Characteristic operations were: cholecystectomy, appendectomy, ovariectomy, and hysterectomy.

All patients in this group had had one or more *major illnesses*, and half of these were pneumonia or pleurisy. Other prominent illnesses were typhoid, malaria, osteomyelitis, tumor; there was marked tendency to influenza, sore throats, sinus, gastro-intestinal upsets, nausea, vomiting, and especially constipation. The latter was present in more than one-half of the cases and half of these had severe hemorrhoids. One-sixth of the cases reported allergy.

Only patients with anginal syndrome and rheumatic heart disease had a worse record for *pelvic disorders*. In addition to the high incidence of pelvic disorders among patients in the group, we found also a very high incidence of *venereal disease* (20 per cent). Of all the groups studied only patients with coronary disease had a venereal

* See charts, Chapter III.

disease history (26 per cent) worse than that of these patients. But since five-sixths of our coronary group were male as compared with only two-fifths of the patients with hypertensive cardiovascular disease, and since in both groups venereal disease was less frequent among the females than among the males, the record in this respect is not quite comparable. If we compare males with venereal disease in the two groups we find patients with hypertensive cardiovascular disease 26 per cent, patients with coronary disease 26 per cent. In no other group studied was the percentage of venereal disease above 6 per cent for males and females combined, or above 20 per cent for the males alone.

Another prominent characteristic of the early history of these patients was *obesity*. More than half were definitely overweight and one-fifth had actually undergone treatment for obesity.

As was true of all the groups studied, the females in the group had a worse previous health record than the males, but the prominence of pelvic disorders in the group exaggerates the difference between the health records of the two sexes considerably. The previous disease record of the females in this group exceeded that of the males by 66 per cent. In only two groups was the sex difference greater; the previous disease record of the female patients with anginal syndrome exceeded that of the males by 75 per cent, and in the cardiac arrhythmia group by 68 per cent. In both these groups pelvic disorders accounted for a large part of this difference.

Because of the older age grouping, one is inclined to question the validity of comparing the health record of this group with that of the fracture group. Since the fracture group was almost equally divided among the three age periods in this study, we have therefore compared these patients with the fracture patients in the age period 35 to 55, the period of highest incidence for hypertension. On this basis we find again a marked difference in the illness history of the two groups; in the same age period that of the males with hypertension was three times that of the males in the fracture group; that of the females with hypertension was more than five times that of the females in the fracture group.

This illness record, then, were there no cardiovascular disorder at all, is several times what would be expected in the general population (page 18 ff). As just noted, it presents a strong contrast with the fracture group, whose disease record is markedly below that for the general population.

Statistics Concerning Previous Injury

Ten per cent of these patients had had fractures and about 30 per cent had had accidents (accidents were almost twice as frequent among males as females), but only 6 per cent of the patients (all of whom were male) had more than one accident, and half of these were patients who suffered also from diabetes, rheumatic fever or coronary disease. (For fuller discussion see Chapter X.) While the record for one accident is less than one-third of that for fracture patients, and the record for two accidents only one-thirteenth that for fracture patients, this is nevertheless the highest accident record in any of the other groups studied except for patients with coronary occlusion, whom these patients closely resembled, and patients with diabetes, which like coronary disease, was frequently found in combination with hypertensive cardiovascular disease. The record for two or more accidents exceeds that for patients with coronary disease. It is noteworthy, however, that these accidents were very different in nature from those found among fracture patients, with one exception, as follows:

Accidents were more frequent among those who developed an interest in "proving themselves" in terms of athletic superiority, although, as with the fracture group, the accidents did not occur in relation to athletic activities themselves, but rather "on the way to a ball game," or occasionally "on the way to see the boss," or "on the eve of return to work," these all being situations which brought acutely before the patient the "need to make good." The interest in athletics served a purpose similar to that served in fracture patients; e.g., patient H 96 said he took up boxing when his job got on his nerves because it gave him an excuse for fighting. It is clear, however, that the emphasis here is on expression of aggression rather than just running into activity.

The type of injury incurred by hypertensive patients resembled closely the type of injury incurred by fracture patients with hypertension, with the exception of those that seemed to be "innocent accidents" such as being hit by mistake when someone was aiming to hit a rock and aimed poorly (Case No. H 103). Fantasies of revenge and guilt were frequent in connection with them. The peculiar character of these accidents is discussed in the section on coronary occlusion (page 299).

Early Influences and Traumatic Experiences

Traumatic experiences were of importance in the lives of these patients, especially dramatic deaths of parents, siblings or friends from cardiovascular disease or accidents. The high record for operations and for major illnesses as well as for minor illnesses involving the vegetative nervous system is significant. Also the tendency to sexual promiscuity, including acquisition of venereal disease, illegal abortions, or pelvic disorders was important. In other words, from the medical histories alone it should be obvious that in this group of patients there was more physiological dysfunction than was found in the accident group and a worse health record prior to the onset of the illness in question than is found in the general population.†

OUTSTANDING POINTS IN THE PERSONALITY HISTORY

General Adjustment

*Vocation-Education.** These patients had a relatively low educational level, nearly 60 per cent of them were in the grammar school category, and only the patients with rheumatic heart disease fell below them in the college category.

*Income.** Consistent with their education level, these patients had a low income level. There were a higher percentage on relief and WPA than was the case with any other group studied, and a lower percentage in the category "comfortable or over."

*Occupation.** Although some of these patients were in groups I, II, III, and IV, and most of them had had ambitions in the direction of these occupations, 43 per cent of them were unskilled laborers and a higher percentage than in any other group studied were in group VI, although the percentage of females in this group was lower than the percentage of females in the rheumatic heart disease and cardiac

---

† For comparison, see this section for other groups, and also public health statistics.

* It will be remembered that statements under starred headings are based only on patients over 21, in order to make them comparable to national statistics.

arrhythmia groups. These patients were in the main cooks, maids, beauticians, corsetieres, painters, truck drivers, waiters, machine operators, firemen and signal men for the railroad, apartment house superintendents, bank clerks, brokers, foremen, inspectors, insurance agents.

Social Adjustment. Socially these patients were shy and kept to themselves except that they enjoyed alcoholic gatherings where they were inclined to become expansive. This seemed to be related to their constant feeling of being judged, their sensitiveness to criticism and fear of not making the grade.

Sexual Adjustment. Conflict over masturbation was important in the early history of all these patients and many of them had homosexual tendencies, sometimes acted out. They were markedly ambivalent. This element was borne out even in their sexual behavior, which was promiscuous and accompanied by a desire to avoid responsibility and at the same time to attain satisfaction or to follow the cultural pattern.

These patients seemed to have a compulsive need of demonstrating their superiority over their wives; that is, they were unsure sexually (Case No. H 32, page 273).

In general these patients had a poor sexual adjustment. They had a tendency to impotence and premature ejaculation, especially at home, and sometimes compulsive promiscuity. Their marriage rate and average number of children per marriage were greater than all other groups studied except patients with coronary occlusion.

Attitude Toward Parents and Children. The attitude of patients with hypertension toward their parents and families of their own was characterized by ambivalence and excessive sensitivity to criticism. There was a moderate rebellion against their parents because "they protected me too much and wanted to live my life for me." There was, on the other hand, a feeling that either their parents, or society as a parent-substitute, should take care of *them* if things went wrong. There was an urge to achieve the dignity of parenthood but simultaneously an urge to avoid the responsibility of too many children.

These patients rationalized their fear of being subject to authority on the one hand, and of assuming responsibility on the other, in terms of not being quite in the financial or social position in which they should have been. They were inclined to have large families

because this was expected of them, but they sought sympathy because of the financial hardships involved, and often resorted to abortion if they felt they could justify this.

TABLE IX

HYPERTENSIVE CARDIOVASCULAR DISEASE:

Parental Death in Relation to Patients' Age

	MALE AND FEMALE	MALE	FEMALE
Average age of patients at admission....................	37.8	37.3	38.2
Average age of patients at death of:			
Father..................	18.6	19.4	18.0
Mother.................	25.5	29.0	23.5
Parents living (at time of patients' admission):			
Both living at time of patients' admission........	12.2	10.5	13.3
Father living............	18.4	10.5	23.3
Mother living...........	38.8	36.8	40.0
Death of parents before patient was 16 years old:			
Either father or mother ...	30.6	21.1	36.7
Both father and mother...	8.2	5.3	10.0
Father..................	34.7	26.3	40.0
Mother.................	12.2	5.3	16.7

General Behavior. It was our impression (already reported
briefly), apparently given general confirmation by Alexander and
others, that patients with hypertensive cardiovascular disease present
a surface personality characterized by a considerable degree of self-
control and reserve. This is often riddled through by an emotional
reactivity and warmth, best described as a tendency to volcanic
eruptions of irritability, humor, or sentiment (page 280).

They all had compulsions relative to their jobs: Would something happen? Would they do it right? The signal man was constantly occupied with the thought that a storm "might" put out the
electricity and there "would be" an accident, and he "would be"
blamed. In these patients the *need to be perfect* had a dynamic importance paralleling that of the fracture patients' urge to activity,

and the coronary patients' drive to work. This need had much to do with keeping them from achieving their ambitions. Usually they chose occupations inferior to their actual capacity (Case No. H 351, page 286).

All of these patients were perfectionistically inclined, many abnormally afraid of dirt, and neurotically compulsive. They fall in between patients with fracture and patients with coronary occlusion from the point of view of their work record, being more stable than the former and less stable than the latter. They were inclined to feel driven by their work, to have trouble with their superiors. Although they were ambitious and had a definite goal they seemed never quite to "make the grade" because of moments of weakness or temper.

Characteristic Behavior Pattern: Compulsive Striving, Alternating with Impulsive Episodes

These patients being generally introversive, had a strong urge to keep peace and to seek satisfaction within themselves, as is illustrated in the following statements:

Case No. H 90. "I am a person who tries not to get angry because people don't like you when you're mad. As a child I *always tried to reason rather than fight.*"

Case No. H 351. "I was always afraid of not being loved, so I tried to do things perfectly and never be mad. Not to be loved makes you feel inferior."

These patients are usually not lacking in close contact with one parent, but they stress "never being allowed to talk back." The foregoing statements are in marked contrast with the easy expression of hostility frequently manifested by fracture patients, for example:

Case No. F 100. "You get a kick out of knocking another fellow down, it makes you feel good—as you know, American football involves a great deal of body contact."

The perfectionistic tendencies of patients with hypertensive cardiovascular disease and their concern for formality are characteristic of introversive personalities.

Case No. H 303. "I always keep things perfect in my bureau drawer. I straighten it out when I'm nervous and mad. I'm awfully quick tempered and sensitive. I get hurt when anyone makes cracks at me, and throw shoes around. Then I straighten everything out and start fresh."

Their conflict between passive and active impulses was revealed in their alternation between focusing on inner immediate values and striving toward long-range goals, as well as in an alternation between keeping the peace and occasional outbursts of hostility.

These patients combined some of the tendencies of both patients with fracture and patients with coronary occlusion (to be described in the next section) in their characteristic pattern of energy economy. Whereas the fracture patient discharged tension in active day-to-day interests and minor expressions of aggression and the patient with coronary occlusion found some release through hard work but bottled much hostility within himself, the hypertensive patient shifted from one pattern to the other.

Neurotic Traits—Early and Present

Early neurotic traits were reported by only 24 per cent of these patients and the early neurotic symptoms were in the main nightmares and temper tantrums, with nail-biting as the most frequent, but not truancy, stealing, enuresis or sleep-walking as with the fracture patients. The few patients in this group who reported these latter symptoms were in the main those who had accidents also.

The present neurotic traits of these patients have been indicated already; that is, the traits belonging to a compulsive character, especially their perfectionistic preoccupation. Their general tendency was to repress their feelings, sometimes becoming seriously depressed, but this pattern was punctuated by outbursts of aggression.

Addictions and Interests

More than half of these patients were excessive in their use of coffee and cigarettes. Many of them consumed up to ten or fifteen cups of coffee a day and several packs of cigarettes; and there was a marked tendency to alcoholism. Compared with the fracture patients, the former tendency was somewhat less and the latter somewhat greater. As has been noted already, a few of these patients had an interest in athletics—not football, baseball, basketball, hockey, track and racing as with the fracture patients—but rather tennis, golf, hunting and riding. They did not show the fracture patients' interest in machines, but they resembled the fracture patients in having some inclination to gamble.

This group of patients leads all the others here reported, in their interest in "wine, women, and song." The wine (and to a lesser degree the addiction to coffee and cigarettes) seemed to help them to feel that instead of being "almost but not quite," they had actually made the grade. The women seem to have been chosen as a compulsive reassurance in this regard, but like everything compulsively chosen, ill chosen, and hence likely to give them venereal disease. Similarly, the women patients seemed to have a sexual orientation likely to result in pelvic disorders. Neither group was willing to assume the responsibility of adult sexual life.

The "song" is the reverse side of their attempt to give an impression of reserve, which is not entirely natural to them. It is released by alcohol and in moments of elation.

In terms of this picture it is easy to understand their preoccupation with food, which seems to be their major means of gaining satisfaction and making themselves comfortable when other resources fail them. It is interesting that so many of them relate their hypertension to diet (since an interest in food represents a last defense against the depression which impends) when they are aware of the ambiguity of their lives and fear failure; and it is interesting that in the popular mind, as well as in the minds of many physicians, a primary role in treatment is played by diet, that is, by correction of a symptom, or in other words removal of the secondary effects of a symptom of the disease, rather than of the disease itself. It will be remembered that nearly one-fifth of these patients were actually treated for obesity, and two-thirds of them were worried about obesity without having actually sought treatment for it. The possible hereditary-constitutional-endocrine factor is of course to be borne in mind here.

In contrast with patients with fractures, a relatively low percentage of these patients had a strict religious upbringing. Only 33 per cent were Roman Catholic (of whom two-thirds were female), 22 per cent were Jewish, leaving nearly one-half (45 per cent) in the Protestant group. As these patients grew up, the Roman Catholics tended to become Protestant, the orthodox Jews and the Protestants to lose all interest in religion.

Life Situation Immediately Prior to the Onset

The situation prior to the onset of the illness in these patients was fairly uniform: Death of a loved one or separation from him, or financial stress and strain or both, factors rarely stressed by patients in the fracture group. It is interesting to note that although the traumatic death of relative or friend and disaster in the vocational field are reported by patients in the group with coronary occlusion also (as discussed in the next section), the former is usually given a minimal importance whereas in 90 per cent of the group with hypertensive cardiovascular disease the death or breaking off of relations with someone loved is related to the onset of the illness by the patient himself. Unlike some other groups studied, severe symptoms of illness seem to have been noticed only after several months to a year had elapsed after what the patient felt had been the precipitating factor or factors in his illness. This period was usually marked by nightmares related to death and separation, and waking up with attacks of palpitation or dyspnea or occasionally in a rage.

Usually the first symptoms were merely nervous headache, and a tendency to irritability and fatigue for a few months or two or three years prior to the discovery of the hypertension itself. It is probably significant that the hypertension developed as the patient's usual defenses against his conflict were weakened either by environmental strain or by the force of the conflict and the adverse effect of the defenses (alcohol, overeating, etc.) in themselves.

Reaction to Illness

There is probably no more characteristic expression of these patients' reaction to illness than that given by patient No. H 32: "The hospital should take care of me because I have done" this and that. From this point of view, the hypertensive patients fall into two groups; (1) those who follow the usual cardiovascular pattern (and this includes all hypertensives who later develop coronary disease), that is, trying to disregard their illness and go on in spite of it; (2) those who fall into the pattern of the compensation patient, that is, giving in to passive tendencies and insisting on being taken care of. This in itself would indicate that a major conflict is that between self-assertion and submission, active and passive tendencies.

These patients tend, when they enter the hospital, to say, "Now the responsibility is yours," and also to blame their previous doctors for not having helped them adequately. For example, patient No. H 32 said that much as it hurt him he had been dependent during his illness on his friends, but he could count on them no longer; now he expected the hospital to support him and his family. He was incensed when first the social worker and then home relief told him that he had to do something about it.

IV. DYNAMIC FORMULATION

AREA OF FOCAL CONFLICT AND CHARACTERISTIC REACTION: AUTHORITY (RIVALRY AND SELF-DEFEAT)

From the foregoing it is obvious that these patients, like the patients with fracture, have had a life-long conflict in the sphere of authority, but their difficulty relates not so much to a refusal to take orders from anyone as to a fear of criticism. They are constantly afraid of falling short. On the other hand, they have a tendency to feel that the criticisms of the superior are completely unjust although they dare not express their resentment. Their behavior is characterized outwardly by a desire to please combined with chronic rebellion. The typical formula often expressed in just these terms is, "I always have to give in, but afterwards I am furious."

In the sphere of work they are likely to recognize that they have ability but they are so much afraid of falling short that they choose an occupation below their actual capacity. They then seem to feel humiliated by having made this choice, to feel that it was forced upon them by lack of understanding of parents and superiors, and therefore to fail in this occupation also (e.g., Case No. H 351, page 286).

It should be noted further that as these patients' mothers ranged from gentle but strict to physically violent tyrants (see Chapter VI, page 434), the patients' preference ranged from strong emotional attachment to admiring fear with a fair amount of suppressed resentment.

Although chronic rage is characteristic of this group, and temper tantrums in childhood, the rage is later more or less completely repressed or expressed in less obvious acts of rebellion. These patients' major problem was working off their rage on the one hand, and on the other doing things well enough to keep themselves liked and admired. In this group the patients who died during the period of observation (22 per cent) were for environmental or characterological reasons particularly defective in this respect. Patient No. H 303, the youngest, who died at 19, had no outlet in athletics, work, alcohol, or sexual activity, but was constantly driven in on herself.

Even in the group of patients just mentioned, however, there was greater verbal expression than in the fracture group, *especially among those who did not have accidents* (pages 219 ff. and 673).

PROFILE

Hypertensive Cardiovascular Disease *

1. *Family History.* Cardiovascular disease in parents and siblings in 49 per cent. Accident history for parents and siblings in about 10 per cent. Diabetes in 19 per cent. Nervousness in about 75 per cent. Exposure to cardiovascular disease or sudden death in 98 per cent.

2. *Personal Data.* Both parents usually lived beyond the patient's adolescence, father usually died first and before the patient's majority. Both parents inclined to be strict, mother usually dominant. Average marriage rate. Many children, few divorces.

3. *Health Record.* Bad previous illness history, many operations with preponderance of pneumonia, gastro-intestinal upsets, major operations, allergy, and obesity. Women poor pelvic histories.

4. *Injuries.* Rarely more than one injury. Rate for one accident slightly above average but accidents tend toward fracture type, with many actual fractures. Almost equally divided between childhood and later accidents.

5. *General Adjustment. Education:* Relatively low educational level. This, however, is not consistent with intellectual capacity which tends to be average or above. *Work record.* Tendency to work to the top but constantly falling short. Inclined to choose an occupation below their capacity. *Income and vocational level:* Low. Represented in all classes but predominantly V and VI (unskilled laborers and WPA). *Social relationships.* Shy, sensitive, and fearful of not making the grade. Use of wine, women and song to compensate. Urge to fit conventional pattern. Lack of emotional adaptability in intimate relationships. *Sexual adjustment:* Attempt to follow cultural pattern as husband and father. Need to demonstrate superiority over wife, secretly and often compulsively promiscuous; insecure and frequently impotent or frigid. High venereal disease record, women many abortions. *Attitude toward family:* Ambivalent toward father, passive though often hostile and fearful toward mother. With wife and children attempt to be boss and "carry the burden" combined with demand for care and attention.

* In order to evaluate the distinctive features in this profile reference should be made to Chapter IX.

6. *Characteristic Behavior Pattern.* Urge to keep peace. Alternation between tendency to seek satisfaction within themselves and devotion to achievement of external long-range goals.

7. *Neurotic Traits.* Low percentage of early neurotic traits, and these in the main nightmares, temper tantrums, nail-biting. Present—obsessive doubts, compulsive traits, particularly perfectionistic inclinations, and outbursts of rage as a reaction against their passive tendencies. These latter come out in their dependence on food, and usually also on someone in a parental role.

8. *Addictions and Interests.* Excessive use of coffee, cigarettes, and alcohol. Some interest in athletics—not competitive sports but rather golf, hunting and riding. Major interest wine, women and song.

9. *Life Situation Immediately Prior to Onset.* Death of someone loved or separation from them, or set-back in the field of the patient's ambition, usually combined with greater indulgence in compensatory gratifications such as food, coffee, and alcohol.

10. *Reaction to Illness.* Usually a giving in to passive tendencies, using the illness as an alibi for failure, and insistence on being taken care of. Occasionally, however, like the coronary patient, these patients disregard health and attempt to keep on in spite of it.

11. *Area of Focal Conflict and Characteristic Reaction.* Situations involving aggression and passivity (rivalry and self-defeat).

CASE ILLUSTRATIONS

Case No. H 25. A married man, aged 41, was admitted to the hospital three times within a period of nine months, for hypertensive cardiovascular disease, cardiac hypertrophy and insufficiency. He was obese and there was considerable ascites and ankle edema. In view of the limitation of staff time, the seriousness of the patient's condition, and the complexity of his life situation, psychotherapy was not attempted, although the patient himself wanted it. The patient died six weeks after his third discharge from the hospital.

Family History. His father died when the patient was 12, of heart trouble, kidney trouble, and dropsy. His mother died of diabetes and stroke six years before the patient's first admission.

Personal Data. The patient stated that his father was very stern and that he never liked him. During the last year of life he was depressed, crankier than ever and wanted to commit suicide. His mother, on the other hand, was very gentle, and the patient was deeply attached to her. The patient was the oldest of three children and the only boy. He married at the age of 27 at a time when his mother was severely ill. He was much worried about the effect of his marriage on her illness and tended to blame himself for her death seven years later. After nine months of marriage his wife left him. He sold his furniture and went back to live with his mother. The wife then asked him to take her back which he did on condition that they both live in his mother's home. At the time of his marriage he had known that his wife suffered from petit mal but his physician told him that if she had a child this would stop. These attacks became grand mal during the first period of living with the patient's mother. After the first child, a son, was born she ceased having the grand mal attacks but continued to have the petit mal attacks. There was constant friction in the household between wife and mother and the patient found himself doing the housework for both of them. He claimed that doing the cooking was something he enjoyed as a sort of hobby. The patient's wife confirmed this statement saying that in all the years she had been married she had never prepared a meal for her husband and that he even took care of the babies, prepared their formula and changed their diapers. At one time when he was sick, the boy had to be sent to her grandmother, by whom she had been brought up, to be taken care of. She was panic-stricken at the thought of her husband's having to stay in the hospital because she did not know how to take care of herself or her children. The second child was born just prior to the patient's first admission to the hospital.

Previous Health. The patient had had pneumonia, and was subject to gastro-intestinal upsets and hay fever.

Previous Injuries. None.

General Adjustment. Vocational—education: After his father's death when the patient was 12 years old, he had to leave school and go to work. He said: "When father died it was a great relief except that I had to give up school and go to work." *Income and occupation:* He began as a messenger boy in a bank and went to night school. He worked his way up in the bank until he was earning $76 a week. He worked hard and was ambitious to get ahead. All went well until four years prior to his first admission when his bank was taken over by another bank and all the old employees were discharged. He then went on a prolonged drinking bout lasting one and a half years, after which he got a clerical job on Home Relief at $24 a week. He would not have been able to get along on this and support his wife and family had he not won $500 in the Irish sweepstakes.

(*Note:* This education, occupation and income record, which is very unlike the irregular records of our patients with fracture, is characteristic also of the patient with coronary disease, but the patient's reaction to the loss of his job, which occurred a little more than a year after his mother's death, resembled that of the accident patient rather than that of the patient with coronary occlusion.)

The patient's *social adjustment* was good. He belonged to the Elks and the Masons, but after his loss of job he gave up his social life entirely because he felt inferior among his friends. *Sexual adjustment:* Concerning his relationship to his wife he said: "Everything is all right. I use a condom to please her but I guess sex isn't very much fun in the home because there's too much responsibility."

Characteristic Behavior Pattern. The patient started out with a behavior pattern characterized by persistence, ambition, and an attempt to assert himself. He had made up his mind that he would show he had better stuff in him than his father, that he could be more responsible and not give way to childish tempers and depression. Nevertheless as he himself put it "fate was too strong" for him, "I had too much of my father in me." The achievement of his goal was interfered with by his tendency to outbursts of temper, his alcoholism, his dependence on his mother, and his unfortunate marital choice. His wife's epileptic character kept reminding him of his father and there was constant warfare. On one occasion she pulled the rocking chair out from under him when he was sitting "wondering what to do about his troubles," which so enraged him that he struck her in the face breaking her nose. "It cost me eighty dollars to get her face repaired and I just sort of felt that was too much to pay and everything was against me."

Neurotic Traits. Temper tantrums alternating with depression. "When things were too much for me I would go off by myself for hours at a time trying to figure things out. Sometimes I would talk to mother who was very gentle, but she couldn't help me much." These traits continued throughout his life.

Addictions and Interests. The patient smoked to excess, particularly at night when he would lie awake worrying and not knowing what to do with himself. He had always had alcoholic tendencies but became definitely alcoholic after the loss of his job. He had no interest in athletics but considerable interest in gambling. A note appears in the medical chart: "Patient always eats regularly and well." This seems to have been borne out by his weight of 216 lbs.

Life Situation Immediately Prior to Onset. It is clear that this patient's illness was preceded by a long period of wear and tear, conflict between mother and wife and with both of them, which culminated in his mother's death which was a great blow to him, particularly because he tended to blame himself for it, and in the loss of a job in which he had been working up steadily for a period of twenty-three years.

Reaction to Illness. The patient's first symptoms were dyspnea and epigastric pressure "not relieved by soda bicarbonate, rhubarb and soda, essence of peppermint, hot water, Eno salts, Sal hepatica or a hot water bottle." He was much upset by this. He called the local physician who told him he had heart trouble. He blamed much of his difficulty on inadequate medical care both before and during his three admissions to the hospital.

Area of Focal Conflict and Characteristic Reaction. From the above it is clear that the patient's major trouble throughout life was with his superiors, first father, then mother, then employer; and that he reacted to this by attempts at self-assertion alternating with submission to a passive role. Incidentally his first symptoms of dizziness occurred a few months after he had taken his wife back to live with him and his mother, although the first severe dyspnea and palpitation which led to the discovery of his cardiac enlargement occurred only after the death of his mother some seven years later. His acceptance of a female role in the household at the same time that he was "handling a million dollars in the bank" where he was becoming a person of considerable importance, caused a severe conflict.

Case No. H 305, a 47-year-old housewife, was admitted for headaches and convulsive attacks. The *admission diagnosis* was hypertensive cardiovascular disease with cardiac enlargement, obesity and convulsions on a hypertensive basis. The headaches had begun four or five years prior to her admission and just after her first convulsive seizure. After three weeks the patient was discharged very much improved. She was followed in the clinic. Her blood pressure remained in the vicinity of 290/170. Three months later she had another attack and was taken in an ambulance to a nearby hospital. There she felt better until another patient attempted to jump out of the window; this sent her into a confused state so that she was transferred to a mental hospital where she improved greatly and was sent home in two weeks. She was readmitted shortly after this, that is five months after her first discharge, and she remained in the hospital two months.

One month after her discharge she was readmitted for the third time for headache and vomiting of twenty-four hours' duration. Her mother had died of high blood pressure. According to the medical summary she had a previous history of progressive dyspnea for six years, with nocturia; there had been eight convulsive episodes in the past six months, with incontinence and foaming at the mouth.

At the time of this patient's first admission in November 1935, she showed obesity, retinal exudate, narrow tortuous vessels, and her heart was enlarged to the left with apical systolic murmur. Her blood pressure was 280/160. Her nonprotein nitrogen was 40, the phthalein test was 48, basal metabolic rate 27, urine analysis showed albumin and red cells. On a low salt and low caloric regime her blood pressure fell to 240/135. Because of the severity of her headaches and the convulsive attacks, the patient was seen in the Neurological Institute. Her recovery was uneventful and no neurological lesion was thought to be present.

The patient was then followed in Presbyterian Hospital where an interesting correlation was made between her headaches, her convulsive attacks, and her salt intake and the time of menstruation. A typical convulsive attack was induced at the time of menstruation by raising the salt and fluid intake. The patient was discharged on a low salt intake and followed in the out-patient department.

One month later, when her menstrual period was due, she began again to complain of headache and it seemed that a hypertensive attack was imminent. However, menstruation failed to occur and the patient again felt better until twenty-four hours before admission. She then developed headache and vomiting and slight blurring of vision. Her temperature was 100° F., her pulse 110, respiration 25, and blood pressure 265/180.

On admission the patient appeared to be a well-developed and well-nourished woman, with a facial mask reminiscent of that occurring with paralysis agitans. She was sitting up in bed, complaining chiefly of fatigue and heat. She had no cyanosis, her pupils were equal and moderately active. The fundi showed marked vascular sclerosis and exudation. Her nose was negative, her tongue moist, and she had a slight postnasal drip. Her neck was not stiff, and the trachea, thyroid and glands were negative. Her chest moved fairly well, and her lungs were clear and resonant. Her heart was much enlarged to the left with a forceful action, but there was no enlargement at the base, the sounds were muscular with snapping aortic second sound. She had no murmurs. Her blood pressure was 265/180. The peripheral vessels were moderately thickened and tortuous. Her abdomen was negative. The liver was just palpable, but there was no tenderness or masses. There was no weakness of the extremities, the ankle jerk, knee jerk, and Babinski reflex being equal and normal.

The laboratory tests showed a hemoglobin of 74; red blood count 4,300,-000; white blood count 14,000; blood non-protein nitrogen 40 to 60; serum chloride 587; plasma carbon dioxide 63 volume per cent; phthalein test 48; sedimentation rate 54; electrocardiogram showed left preponderance; urine, albumin 3 plus, specific gravity fixed at 1010.

On a low salt diet with fluids at 1600, the patient's condition did not improve. Without change in physical signs other than increased papilledema, the patient gradually became more and more irrational, until, because of the disturbance she created, it was found necessary to transfer her to another hospital. (There was no vomiting or nausea after the first day of this admission.)

The diagnosis was hypertensive cardiovascular disease.

Before the patient could be transferred her temperature rose to 102° F. and she became increasingly stuporous. The next day her temperature rose to 104° and the patient was not arousable. On physical examination no cause for pyrexia was found, her lungs, heart and abdomen remained as before, and the patient died that night of what seemed to be entirely a cerebral vascular difficulty of undetermined type—probably hypertensive encephalopathy. Autopsy was performed.

The more complete history of this patient was as follows:

Family History. The patient's father died when the patient was 27 years old, the cause unknown. Her "mother died of high blood pressure" when the patient was 35.

Personal Data. The patient was the second of four siblings.

Previous Health. The patient in general had good health except for an infection following an abortion. She went to a hospital where one of the fallopian tubes was removed.

General Adjustment. Vocation—education: The patient left school at the age of 13 in order to help support her family. *Occupation:* She worked in a bakery until she married at 16. At the time of the depression she was obliged to work again and continued to do heavy housework until she had to stop because of physical necessity.

Social adjustment: "I never was much for friends and parties. I'm always afraid of saying the wrong thing. My companions were my brothers and sisters, and then my children and grandchildren."

Sexual adjustment: "I used to enjoy sex but I didn't know enough not to get pregnant. After so many children and abortions so close together I sort of lost interest. With my second husband I never got pregnant and we never talked about it. A man who treats you right is more important than sex anyway."

Attitude toward parents and children: "I was never very fond of father but I prefer not to discuss him. I was devoted to mother. Her death was very upsetting. But I was always afraid she wouldn't approve of me. I was so afraid that I eloped with my first husband when I was 16. I knew they wouldn't like him and they didn't. My husband didn't turn out very well. He used to drink and be cruel." The patient's first child was born when she was 17, her next when she was 21, and the next at 23. She became pregnant again when she was 24 and induced an abortion with a catheter, which resulted in an infection. She went to the hospital and one tube was removed. While she was in the hospital her husband contracted gonorrhea so that when she got out she left him and went back to live with her mother. She found this difficult, however, particularly with her three children, and a year later married a man who was good to her. "He was like a father and a mother together. He may have wanted children. I don't know. But I never became pregnant. I think I'd had enough."

Characteristic Behavior Pattern. The patient was jolly, plump, and constantly smiling, even when she was discussing her troubles. She said: "I have had to keep down a great deal of feeling. Sometimes I think I am going to tell people just what I feel, but when I'm face to face with them I haven't the heart. I try not to blame my daughter-in-law for the way she brings up her children but they live with us in the same house and behave very badly. They seem to bring on my attacks."

Neurotic Traits. The patient bit her nails and was subject to temper tantrums as a child; the latter combined with occasional nightmares of family fights and of death recurred throughout her life.

She was at once extremely sensitive to criticism and extremely critical. "What hurts me more than anything is to be told I don't do things right. I try very hard to have them perfect, and I think my children should follow my example, but they didn't take after me. They are sloppy."

Addictions and Interests. Major addictions were coffee, aspirin, and cathartics.

Life Situation Immediately Prior to the Onset. "Five years ago just before I started to get sick my favorite sister died of cancer. This coming when I was just getting over mother's death was a terrible shock. At the same time we had financial troubles and I had to go to work."

Reaction to Illness. "It's been very hard to give up managing my home and to be taken care of by my daughter-in-law. It would be easier if I could get along with her. I keep feeling as if I ought to get up and go to work. When I'm not worrying about this I'm swallowing my rage and annoyance about my grandchildren and the way they behave."

Area of Focal Conflict and Characteristic Reaction. Although this patient said very little about her home life, her difficulty in adjusting to her mother and her fear of parental commands and disapproval were well illustrated in the reasons given for her elopement. It was also a factor in her second marriage. As her second husband she chose a man she could dominate but who at the same time would take care of her. From this time forth her difficulty was with her children and grandchildren, who, she felt, did not sufficiently recognize her as the head of the family. Her reaction to her difficulty in the sphere of authority was an attempt to establish herself as the manager of her own and other people's affairs. In this she was more or less constantly thwarted. In spite of her attempt to please and to follow her feelings, her resentment was constantly breaking through.

Case No. H 32, a 40-year-old Greek restaurant keeper, was admitted for the first time for slowly progressing dyspnea and edema over the past months. His admission diagnosis was hypertensive cardiovascular disease, cardiac insufficiency.

About two years prior to admission he had noted marked dizziness, palpitation, and a vague feeling of not being up to par. He consulted a physician who told him that he had high blood pressure. He had been gaining weight during the past five years, occasioned by overeating and drinking. About one year ago he became decompensated. At that time he also had bronchitis and phlebitis. He was at home in bed for three months, and then was taken to a hospital where he improved with digitalis. He resumed full activities, and did not take digitalis for six months, when his heart again began to decompensate.

Family History. The patient's parents were living and well at the time of the patient's admission; mother aged 79 and father aged 82. There was no history of heart disease. His mother tended to be somewhat nervous, and had stomach trouble. One brother had been killed in the war; two sisters died of pneumonia at the ages of 45 and 52, respectively, and a third, the patient's favorite, died in childbirth just prior to the patient's admission.

Personal Data. The patient was the youngest of seven children and devoted to his somewhat dominating mother. He obeyed his mother rather than his father although the latter was also strict. In general, he had been strictly brought up and never allowed to "talk back." The father had been quite severe, although the patient remembers being struck only once: he ran across a busy thoroughfare after his father who had told him not to; and his father had slapped him in the face.

Previous Health. The patient was very healthy in early life. He says that he had "acute rheumatism" fourteen years ago. At this time he was in bed for two months with fever. The patient's only other serious illness was pneumonia. Like so many patients with hypertensive cardiovascular disease he was troubled by obesity.

Previous Injuries. None.

General Adjustment. Vocational—education: The patient finished what corresponds to high school before he came to this country. *Occupation:* In order to avoid having to serve in the Turkish army the patient left his home and came to this country at the age of 18. The day after he landed, he began to work as a dishwasher, fifteen hours a night, at $29 a month and maintenance. He kept this job for one year and said he did not mind the work so much. He worked up until he became the proprietor of two restaurants, and until five years prior to admission was doing a good business. The depression affected the business and about five years ago he began to worry considerably. Finally one restaurant closed, and then the other. The second failure was associated with his cardiac break.

His *social adjustment* was good. There was a tendency to take recourse to drinking and night life under emotional pressure. *Sexual adjustment*: Again like the typical patient with hypertensive cardiovascular disease, the patient tended to gloss over his troubles at home. A full story was obtained from his wife. He showed the characteristic tendency to dominate his wife, pretending that he was the head of the house although in actuality this seemed not to be the case. The wife was a Greek woman who looked much younger than her husband. She spoke English with difficulty and seemed to resent the fact that her husband objected to her learning English. He told her she would never need it as she would never do anything but housework. She felt that this was a great handicap, and a bar to her ever getting a job. Apparently in contrast, she mentioned her father who spoke three languages besides Greek and was a Greek Protestant. The social worker felt an undercurrent of dissatisfaction with the fact that the patient was the head of the family, for even while in the hospital he must be regarded as such. The patient assumed all the responsibility for contraception because he could not trust his wife, and sex relations were not very satisfactory. "It's better to have all that outside the home where you can pay your money and be through with it."

Attitude toward parents and family of his own. He stated that the limitation of his family to one child was because of finances, he felt it was not quite the thing to do to have no more children, but on the other hand he could not feel it quite right not to be able to take care of them.

Characteristic Behavior Pattern. The patient said that he had been in the habit of keeping himself under control, and repressing his feelings. He never was a person to "speak out," although he admitted that he usually felt better if he did so. He was of the broad, round-headed type, and seemed to be a curious mixture of childish pleasantness and a rather aggressive and hostile personality. In the hospital he was told that he could do light work.

Neurotic Traits. Information relative to early neurotic traits was inadequate, but the patient did remember nightmares, especially of fights, which had continued more or less to the present.

Addictions and Interests. The patient reported that he "slept and ate well but had never indulged in drinking and smoking until things began to go wrong with his business five years ago. "Then I started to live high, going to parties, not getting much sleep, overeating, drinking from a pint to a quart every day." (In five years his weight increased from 180 to 225 lbs.)

Life Situation Immediately Prior to Onset. The patient himself made a very definite connection between his business worries and the occurrence of his high blood pressure. He began to worry about his business about six months prior to the finding by the local physician that he had hypertension. He worried a good deal, and could not sleep at night, and was sure that this caused his ill health. After his cardiac break, and the necessity for hospitalization, his restaurant began to fail because he was not there to attend to things. His business had been very exciting, requiring about *fourteen hours' work a day;* most of the time on his feet. The failing business, the hard work, and the attending financial worries all tended to make him feel worse physically.

Reaction to Illness. Although the patient believed that overwork and worry brought about his high blood pressure he stated definitely that if he could not find light work he would go back to his regular work and do ten or twelve hours a day. This he said rather defiantly.

The patient seemed to feel that he and his family had a right to be cared for by the hospital. It was not clear what the hospital represented to him but he kept repeating that he had been in this country twenty-two years and had served for two years in the Army. When the social worker explained the function of the hospital and the social service department he was still not convinced. He resented the suggestion that his wife apply for home relief, although he said they had no funds, and refused to let her go. In regard to his rating in the hospital, he said twice that he was not worried, he knew he would not have to pay.

The social service note continued: "This patient seems to be after all he can get, and seems anxious to shift the responsibility for his whole family on to Social Service, and thinks he 'deserves' special care. There may be additional resources, for the family are managing in some way and the patient is very unwilling to talk with the worker beyond demanding help."

Area of Focal Conflict and Characteristic Reaction. The area of life adjustment in which this patient seemed to have his major conflict was that of relationship to authority. First his parents, then the Army, then his wife. Here he attempted to manage the conflict by a combination of avoidance and the attempt to dominate. It is interesting that although he left home he tended to obey his mother; although he came to this country to avoid service in the Turkish Army he served for two years in the Army in this country; although at the age of 27 he married a girl of 17 whom he prevented from learning English in order to make her further dependent on him, she nonetheless was the more dominating of the two. In the sphere of business he followed the pattern of the coronary patient, working up to the top and becoming his own boss, but when during the crisis of 1929–1930 business conditions gave him a feeling of insecurity, instead of attempting to rise above them he took to living high and drinking.

Course. As convalescent care was advised, the patient planned to go to a friend in Staten Island where he could have complete rest in a family consisting of an elderly man and his wife. He had lent them money, and said he was free to go there at any time. He was taken there in a friend's car.

A home visit revealed that the patient did not go to Staten Island, giving the excuse that his friend was ill. He had been told on discharge to notify the hospital if his plans were changed, as a vacancy was available at a convalescent home a week later. At the time of the worker's visit, the patient was at Coney Island with his son.

The discharge note after this patient's first admission was as follows:

First admission of a 40-year-old Greek restaurant man for slowly progressive dyspnea and edema over the past month. He has always overeaten, and in the last seventeen years has gained from 130 to 225 lbs.

Past Health. He had flu in 1918 without sequelae. One attack of migratory polyarthritis in 1920; he was in bed two months with fever.

Present Illness. In 1933, because of palpitation, dizziness, and vague feelings of not being up to par, the patient saw a local physician who told him his blood pressure was high. He had no dyspnea or edema. One year later, he had bronchitis followed by dyspnea and swelling of his legs with subsequent tenderness called phlebitis. He was in bed three months without relief, then he was taken to another hospital where quarts of ascites were removed. His blood pressure was 150/110. He had blurring of vision. On salyrgan and digitalis he improved and he then resumed full activities without digitalis for six months. Three months ago there was gradual reappearance and progression of dyspnea, edema, and headaches. He had no paroxysmal dyspnea or precordial pain. A few days ago he had slight pain in the right anterior lower chest exacerbated by respiration.

Physical Examination. Temperature 100° F., pulse 84, respiration 22, blood pressure 160/128. A very obese, slightly cyanotic, orthopneic, and profusely sweating Greek. The arteries of the fundus varied in caliber, there were no hemorrhages. Many of his teeth were missing and broken. His lungs were expanded a little, probably because of abdominal distention. Rales at lung bases. His heart was enlarged to the right and left. The sounds were poor, distant, with gallop, and occasional extra systole; there were no murmurs. Pulmonary second sound greatly accentuated. The radials were not felt. The abdomen was distended with gas and there was shifting dullness in flanks. The liver was down a hand's breadth. The spleen was not felt. There was sacral and leg edema, but no clubbing or tremor. The reflexes were not obtained.

Laboratory Findings. Blood count: The hemoglobin was 98, red blood count 4,600,000, white blood count 9200, polys. 82. Urine: albumin 3 plus, occasional red blood cells, no casts. Sedimentation rate 51. Blood urea 45. The Wassermann was negative. The throat culture was negative. The blood culture was negative. X-ray of the heart showed enlargement in all the diameters. Fluoroscopy showed enlargement in the left auricular and ventricular curves, with feeble ventricular excursions. Film of the chest showed pulmonary passive congestion with a little thickening of the interlobar pleura on the right.

Course. This was particularly interesting inasmuch as the patient had hypertension apparently with little so called left-sided failure, but marked right-sided failure. He did remarkably well. Phlebotomy was done with a drop of 100 points in venous pressure. The patient was digitalized with progressive clearing of his insufficiency. The urine became clear. The phthalein test was 50 per cent. It was considered that he would do very well, provided he took the proper care of himself, but it seemed likely that overeating would be his undoing. He lost 40 pounds of edema in ten days, his blood pressure dropped to 116/98. There was no evidence that he had ever had any rheumatic heart disease.

Discharge diagnosis: Hypertensive vascular disease. Cardiac Insufficiency.

In reading the psychiatric follow-up note below it is important to remember that this patient had no psychotherapy except for the diagnostic psychiatric interview:

The patient has had one hospital admission, and seven or eight clinic visits. He has felt well since leaving here, that is, two and a half years, until last September. At this time he went out and drank too much. Following this "was not good." He has gained quite a little weight. He went to his local physician who advised him to go to bed for two weeks, and gave him two injections which took the water out of his system. After that he felt better again and went back to work. He reported that his business failed, and says that at that time he used to be out late drinking a lot, and was very tired. Since then he thinks he is better off, as he is a night counterman in a restaurant. He has cut down a lot on his alcohol, except for the one time mentioned. His breath smells a little now. He says that the work is quite aggravating to him, as there are a lot of low class people who come in there. "Before I used to get very angry, but now I just hold myself. Any time I get angry I get sick. You see, my whole system goes out of order. My heart pumps too fast, and my head gets too dizzy. I feel like 200 lbs. when I walk. At the time I got sick I had a lot of aggravation over worry. Now I don't worry so much. I have my job, and make $23 a week. I just have my wife and child to take care of." Going back to his early history, he says that he had a strict bringing up. His father was the boss, and when he came in "you couldn't say a word."

Case No. H 351 (page 286) presents a similar history.

In these case histories—and the same is true for the total series—
we find fundamental similarities irrespective of the patient's sex.
The only considerable variations were in the small percentage of the
series discussed in Chapter X, that is, the patients who were suffering
from two serious chronic illnesses simultaneously, as, for example,
hypertensive cardiovascular disease and diabetes or hypertensive
cardiovascular disease and coronary occlusion (pages 617, 619). These
similarities are notably:

(1) A history of unsolved conflict with authority extending into
all spheres of adjustment. Unlike the patients with fracture and
coronary occlusion, who had similar quarrels with authority, they
were unable to break away completely from parental domination.
This seemed to be largely because of a stronger affective relationship
to their mothers and a need for dependency.

(2) An attempt to cope with this conflict by making themselves
important and liked. In this attempt they were constantly defeating
themselves because of pent-up resentment which was constantly
breaking through at awkward moments, and a fundamental insecurity and lack of self-confidence for which they overcompensate
compulsively, notably in their perfectionistic tendencies.

(3) A tendency to brood about their difficulties or to escape from
them by overindulgence in food and drugs, contrasting with the accident patient's tendency toward impulsive action and the coronary
patient's attempt to banish all feeling, and in oscillation between active and passive impulses neither of which were able to satisfy.

(4) A preoccupation with ideas of destruction and death, particularly prominent in their nightmares, which usually antedated the
traumatic deaths among their own relatives and friends, to which
they so often ascribed their "high blood pressure." This of course
colored their reaction to these catastrophies and accounted in part
for their apprehensiveness relative to their own illness.

(5) A tendency when sick to continue their life-long pattern of
oscillation between active and passive tendencies, which was a major
problem in the management of the illness. Although they made excessive demands to be taken care of they were unable to enjoy illness
as many patients with fracture did, but they were also less successful
in disregarding it and going on in spite of it than were the patients
with coronary occlusion. They alternately overindulged and over-

disciplined themselves. For these patients there is no consistent path and there is no middle way.

In the minority of the patients who had accidents the fracture pattern is a little more prominent, particularly with respect to a slightly less regular work record, and a slightly greater tendency to avoid responsibility. In those who later developed coronary occlusion (9 per cent) the tendency toward self-discipline and the persistent endeavor to get to the top through thick and thin, was more marked (Chapter X).

DEGREE AND NATURE OF SOMATIC EXPRESSION OF CONFLICTS

Patients with hypertension have relatively weak defenses; when the defenses fail, work, athletics, sex, accidents, become inadequate as safety valves. They then take recourse to fantasies, but their fantasy life is disturbing to them because its predominant themes are either the need to kill someone who is loved, or the need to be taken care of. It is easy to see how this conflict, especially when neither need is given satisfaction, might bring about a discharge of energy into the somatic field, especially since both aspects of this conflict are inevitably accompanied by somatic changes such as increase in smooth muscle tension and of adrenalin or histamine in the blood with its inevitable influence on the fluid medium of the capillaries. It is probably significant that blood pressure is usually lowered temporarily if a patient regresses to a point where he can enjoy his need to be taken care of, or, on the other hand, after volcanic expressions of rage.*

These patients tend to give great attention to correct external behavior, and unless there is a marked accompanying symptom-neurosis they usually dislike too much attention to their symptoms, and tend to go on in spite of them. They are likely to deny that they are nervous. This seems to be in part because these patients are universally afraid of their aggressive impulses. Hence they are usually con-

---

* See Symposium on Hypertension, *Psychosomatic Medicine*.[403] Scupham, de Takats, Van Dellen, and Beck [375] presented the literature relative to Vascular Disease, noting that sympathin and epinephrine may be factors in the vascular spasm which is fundamental to hypertension, and that both are discharged into the blood stream with emotional excitement as well as with "hypoglycemia, cold, pain and vigorous muscular activity." It should be noted that the extreme tension of the skeletal musculature produced in the attempt to inhibit action (as well as emotional excitement), brings about this same effect. Thus, whatever the physiological mechanisms involved psychic factors may be of etiological importance.

siderate of others and are loath to arouse criticism of any kind so that they try to conceal their tenseness itself. The question arises as to whether the necessity of subjecting to special control the manifestations even of their tension, which itself is serving the purpose of keeping aggressive thoughts and actions in repression, may not have something to do with the development of smooth muscle spasm. The tension seems to be driven inward to involve also the vascular or gastro-intestinal systems. In any case, as patients are relieved psychotherapeutically of their symptoms we often see the process taking place in reverse direction. Easy blushing and other symptoms, as well as the fact that the resection of parts of the autonomic nervous system sometimes gives temporary relief, indicate the close interrelationship of the nervous system and the emotional reactions of the patients with the symptoms of this illness.

General Tension Cloaking Aggression and Resentment

With hypertensive patients, the conflict between the urge to be active and to dominate, and the urge to be passive and to be taken care of, is not very conscious, but they are usually somewhat aware of their difficulty in managing their aggression. They are unlikely to express anger, at least in the early stages (but when they do so, the expression is usually explosive), and they often relate traumatic experiences with a good deal of calm indifference. The marked aggressive tendency has been more or less completely repressed although it seems always to be "just below the surface," and the opposite characteristics have been developed by way of correction or defense.

Although the picture just given is the typical one (partly because in these patients the resentment is near the surface and little elaborated psychically), there are of course patients who present just the opposite picture, even to the extent of appearing to be libertines. In the typical case there is marked obedience to authority or the superego, as indicated, for example, in the characteristic statement cited: "I always say 'yes,' I don't know why. Afterwards I am furious." In a few cases where this element is less obvious there is still the marked conflict over passive tendencies and neither these nor the hostile impulses are given adequate expression. This can be shown to be important in the characterological armor or muscle tension which decreases as the inhibition of these impulses decreases.

Some patients with gastro-intestinal disease, for example, seem to have a similar focal conflict but their psychodynamic structure, especially their expression of and defense against this conflict, differs in several important respects, among which symbolization and fantasy are prominent.

Unlike the respiratory, gastro-intestinal, and genito-urinary systems the vascular tract is a closed system with no function which directly affects the environment.

Incidentally it is even easier to make these patients conscious of their fear than of their resentment. The fact that fear is relatively near the surface should be borne in mind by the physician. These patients, not knowing what the fear was originally, or really is, are particularly ready to attach to it an ill-advised remark such as "you have a very high blood pressure." Telling such a patient to be careful very often suggests to him that the slightest exertion might make him die of apoplexy. In this way the physician himself may become a pathogenic agent.

Activity, Verbalization, Dreams and Fantasies

The urge to *activity* in these patients, who are predominantly introversive (see p. 663), is mainly an outlet for inhibited aggressive tendencies, or for the need to attain distinction, compensating for feelings of inferiority or insecurity. When this fails they undergo an infantile regression, with an increase of oral tendencies, especially the tendency to overeat and the desire to be taken care of, unless they succeed in overcoming their sense of failure and go on to increased effort and often coronary damage.

These patients, like all those in the cardiovascular group, are relatively *articulate* and philosophically minded, although because of obsessive doubts definitely less so than the coronary patients to be discussed in the next section. Their defenses break down more easily. Many of them feel it is safer to be alone when they are angry. On the whole they have a greater tendency to stifle thought in athletic activity, sexual activity, oral enjoyment (with emphasis on alcohol), or fantasy, than do any of the other cardiovascular groups. There is a marked *fantasy* trend.

They report more *dreams* than do patients with fractures or with coronary disease, and in the early stages of the disease their dreams are characterized by fighting, and in the later stages by fear of death. The dreams are usually exciting: falling off buildings, seeing people sick or killed, dead people coming back to life, funerals, suffocation, and being chased. The latter is more characteristic of the females in the group.

These patients never find an adequate release of tension through activity, verbalization, or even fantasy. This fact may have a bearing on the manifestation of symptoms in an organ system which has no direct contact with the external world. In any case the gradually increasing tension represents a kind of deadlock between the need to dominate and be successful and the need to be taken care of.

SUMMARY OF CHARACTEROLOGICAL DEFENSES AND THEIR RELATIVE SUCCESS OR FAILURE

These patients are in a chronic state of ambivalence and obsessive doubt with which their defenses are inadequate to deal. They attempt an outlet in work but are never quite sufficiently successful to satisfy themselves. Then they swing back to a gratification of oral interests, to being taken care of, to alcoholism. They attempt to meet the conflict by being particularly successful in the sexual sphere and again are thrown back by a series of disillusionments or the acquisition of venereal disease. The major difficulty in both outlets is their fear of assuming responsibility.

As long as either of these two outlets is satisfactory they give an external impression of adequacy and reserve. As soon as the defense is broken through they become temperamental, alcoholic, obviously promiscuous, or simply children that need to be fed, and later have to be treated for obesity and put on a diet.

Their life history reveals indications of compulsive character and relatively few outspoken neurotic symptoms. If Alexander's experience differs here, it may be because he sees rather the exceptions than the general run of patients with hypertensive cardiovascular disease; that is, the exceptions in whom neurotic symptomatology is manifest. Seeing all patients with a given disorder, such for example as hypertension, sheds light on the role of the psychic factors in both the etiology and the course of hypertensive cardiovascular disease. Patients with "essential" hypertension seem to resemble those with serious arteriosclerosis or kidney damage in the constellation—constitucion, focal conflict, character defenses. The differences seem to be a matter of the relative prominence of psychic and somatic symptomatology, in terms of the inverse relationship on which comment has been made so often.[149] It seems that the degree of expression or inhibition of the focal conflict, as well as hypothetical constitutional and other factors, may play a role in the rapidity with which the disease progresses and becomes structuralized.

V. THERAPEUTIC IMPLICATIONS *

If the case of patient No. H 25 is compared with that of patient No. HP 3 (page 266 and page 107), several points stand out. Among these we may select first, the similarity in focal conflict and characteristic reaction to it; and second, the readiness with which relief of symptoms can be brought about if treatment is instituted before serious organic involvement has occurred. This fact is not surprising in view of the dissatisfaction of these hypertensive patients with all the channels of emotional discharge. Fracture patients in contrast get fun right along out of their many activities. Hypertensive patients play golf out of a sense of duty, or to keep up with their associates. Hence, these patients gain relief through the establishment of some direct contact with the outside world. Because they wish to dominate—be appreciated, and to be taken care of, they have a better immediate rapport with the physician. Or in other words, the physician-patient relationship does not activate the intense emotional resistance that is characteristic of fracture patients.

As yet no form of therapy has been found adequate in coping with this disease, and since patients with hypertensive cardiovascular disease usually come to the hospital only after the disease is far advanced and die very shortly, it is particularly important that the general physician who sees them first be aware of what may be accomplished by psychotherapy instituted early. In order to do this he should be familiar with what we have called the profile of the patient with hypertensive cardiovascular disease (page 265). Our observations suggest that patients whose history and behavior correspond in the main with this profile may be considered in serious danger from this illness, and furthermore the profile gives certain clues as to where to begin with treatment.

* See page 472 ff. and also Chapter II, page 107; and in addition Chapter XI, section V.

In the hospital the hypertensive patient is usually the hypersensitive patient. He is more afraid and more hostile than most patients. He reacts at a lower threshold and more intensively to various types of stimuli, such as noise, illness of other patients, and contacts with the medical staff. He may be able to cover this up and appear outwardly calm and so deceive the doctor or nurse as to how much he is really upset. These characteristics indicate that certain hospital situations are particularly upsetting to the patient and that he notices things which another patient would not notice. The quieter the atmosphere and the more cheerful and calm the staff, the better. It is advisable that patients should not be told very long ahead about tests or examinations (patient No. HP 4, for example, was very much upset twenty-four hours ahead of a cystoscopy and might well have been saved the strain). Another thing that is very upsetting is "doctors' rounds" and frequently it is noticed that a patient's blood pressure goes up at that time. A number of patients have expressed a distrust of doctors which is understandable in that they have been to a good many without help. The occasional, careful, interested check-up by one or two individuals at a time who appear in entire agreement (medical differences of opinion are very upsetting especially to these patients) together with a good deal of explanation and reassurance, as well as willingness to answer questions is definitely helpful. It is particularly important that there be no discussion at ward rounds in front of the patient and an examination should never be done in a group.

In the past there has been a tendency to keep these patients quiet. Study of some of them, sitting with every muscle taut and a frightened expression on their faces, indicates what "bed-rest" as it is carried out in a hospital ward often means. For some time it has been known that exercise such as a game of golf will decrease blood pressure instead of raising it. In the hospital, at least light activity, reading, occupational therapy or games, might be indicated. Where possible the patient should be up and on the porch or have some other such outlet.

There is frequently on the ward a tendency to keep the patient as quiet as possible as far as his conversation, and particularly the expression of any emotional material goes, because it is felt that this may upset him. We have observed that patients will talk over emotional events and show gradually increasing emotion (page 286) during the conversation, but afterwards they not only appear and are more relaxed but have shown an improvement in blood pressure. They generally say, "I feel so much better now I've gotten that off my mind." The use of sedatives may temporarily keep things off their minds and so lower the pressure, but as long as a patient is unadjusted to his conflict this benefit cannot continue unless the underlying difficulty is worked out.

Outside the hospital the same points are important. Patients have said repeatedly that they feel better when out in the country. They say they are very fond of such outdoor sports as hunting, boating, hiking, skating, rather than competitive games such as the fracture personality uses as an outlet. This is probably beneficial in that it is an outlet for tension and at the same time keeps the patient away from situations that tend to rouse his hostility.

Of course the patient's personality difficulties and the work situation is a factor in the illness. Many have been in positions where their hostility was often aroused but where it was not possible for them to express it. It is possible that in early cases, a change of job with relief from this strain would be a help, although relief from the inner conflict is obviously better when possible.

Many of these patients need help of one sort or another in regard to their sexual adjustment, which is usually poor. For example, an adult man may still believe that auto-erotic activity could cause his illness, and many need advice as to techniques (such as withdrawal) or contraceptives. The effects of sexual tension in both physical and psychological spheres are well known.

It is of the greatest importance in this group of patients to attempt to bring gradually to light and to relieve their hostility together with the underlying conflict that the patient represses. If the patient expresses this gradually, at an early enough date, and works the situation through in relation to his present-day environment and the early family difficulties which tended to build it up, he is greatly benefited. This is particularly true if he learns at the same time to modify his self-defeating behavior patterns. In cases where this has been tried the results have been promising.

When treatment of these patients is possible the first stage is characterized by fear of expression of aggressive impulses:

Case No. H 292. A married Negro doorman, 48 years old, was admitted to the hospital for paroxysmal nocturnal dyspnea. He said he used to get angry but as he grew up he acquired more control. He said: "I think I feel better giving way to my feelings. I first thought it made me worse. Now I realize it didn't. I just talk it off."

Case No. H 42. A married apartment house superintendent, 44 years old, was admitted to the hospital with a small myocardial infarct and hypertensive cardiovascular disease. He stated that he had "always been unable to turn over responsibility." He had "aimed at nothing but perfection." Brought up to work hard as a child he had kept it up ever since. He said: "I didn't use to rest but now I rest when I can. My wife says I have an inclination to be running around all the time. Being put out in the world at 16 and being in this country green. Even there, we used to work in the fields. There wasn't much vacation for us. When I was 12 I was behind a plow. The job was hard. I am glad I don't have it any more. Sooner or later it would have affected my nerves. It was nothing but aggravation."

Case No. H 97. A twice married housewife, 39 years old, was admitted to the hospital with hypertensive cardiovascular disease. She said: "I get excited easily, and get angry easily, but get over it. At times I am blue. I used to worry a lot. People told lies, and so on, but I don't worry so easily now. It rolls off my back. Now I am used to it. Maybe I am worrying underneath, and don't know."

As they lose their symptoms during psychotherapy, they are likely to show an increased nervousness and jerkiness. They may become quarrelsome, show a tendency to get into fights or to have accidents, but in the end they show poise and general ease involving a change in their breathing also, which is so striking that they themselves or their friends are likely to comment on it, usually in some such words as "Why, you look years younger." [146, 425] The nature of patients' tension is quite as significant for the somatic disorder as is quantitative predominance of specific trends and their expression through symbolically appropriate somatic channels.

With such expression, and relaxation of tension, there is a decrease in the need for oral gratification and the various substitute compensations so that it becomes easier for these patients to follow physicians' instructions about limitations of work and diet.

Case No. H 351. An unmarried Jewish boy, aged 22, was admitted to the hospital for precordial pain and palpitation of twelve years' duration which had become worse during the last two years. He complained also of vomiting daily since childhood. His blood pressure on admission was 180/105. Basal metabolic rate was plus 5. The heart was of normal configuration. An electrocardiogram showed an aphasic T wave in lead 4. The sedimentation rate was 5 millimeters per hour, the Wassermann was negative.

Family History. No family history of cardiovascular disease. No diabetes nor accidents.

Personal Data. The patient was born in New York City, the oldest of two siblings. "I think I had a bad start in life. I was always puny." The patient's father died of kidney trouble when he was 2½ years old. The mother was living and well at the time of the patient's admission. She had remarried five years previously. The stepfather was strict and left his wife shortly because she could not get along with his two daughters. Then, after marrying off both daughters, he returned, five months before the patient's admission.

Previous Health. Poor. Pneumonia in childhood. Vomited every day of his life.

Previous Injuries. "I tried my first experiment in being really independent. Mother didn't like dogs so I brought a stray one home. She made such a fuss I put it on the roof. Then I went up to get it after it was dark and the dog rushed up to me, I guess it was just glad to see me, but I was so frightened I fell down a whole flight of stairs. This reminded me of my first accident. I was trying to be independent then too. I stayed away from school and went out walking with a friend who had a reputation for petty thefts. It began to rain. I knew I would be beaten when I got home because Mother had told me to stay away from that boy. I walked and walked around the block and finally a laundry wagon ran over my ankles. Mother found me in the hospital. She told me it was a punishment for disobedience."

General Adjustment. Vocation—education: The patient completed grammar school, but asked to be allowed to repeat the last grade in order to avoid having to go to high school in the city. He nevertheless finished high school at the age of 17, but stated that he had never had any particular goal or interest. His mother wanted him to go to college but he could not see any point. *Occupation:* He went to work as an errand boy: "Although I knew I had more ability than to be an errand boy I was afraid to try anything more complicated for fear I might not measure up." Under pressure he tried a job as a mechanic but gave it up because he did not like to use his hands. "There is great difficulty in getting jobs, and after getting one I never like it. I took civil service examinations for postal clerk because they have written examinations and not oral ones. I got 90, but it didn't do any good because I'm not heavy enough. I need to weigh 20 lbs. more, but whenever I eat I vomit. Although I know it's beneath me I think I'd do better doing outdoor work, chopping trees or digging ditches. When I was in CCC camp I was my happiest. They offered me a job as assistant editor on the weekly paper with good wages, but I didn't accept it because I was afraid I couldn't make the grade."

This history is interesting in view of our general statistics showing the highest percentage of patients with hypertension in the unskilled labor class in spite of their conviction that they were made for something better, and the strong urge in most of them to get to the top. Their gradually downhill record for academic education in spite of their usual good intelligence has a bearing on this point.

After several psychiatric interviews this patient became aware both of his ambition and of his difficulty with authority. He commented spontaneously, "If it were not that I was like my father and predestined to be a failure I would have tried harder. I think I'm beginning to get an interest in life. I want to teach children. All repression is bad. Freedom is all-important. Given a child you could do almost anything with him. I think I'm much better but I get tense when I enjoy myself. There has always been a terrible confusion between my will and my subconscious. That's why you're helping me straighten out. That's what parents ought to do for their children instead of making it worse." His blood pressure went down to 125/86.

Social adjustment: The patient was always shy, but in general liked by both boys and girls. He commented: "I like to be a spectator more than a participator. I am always afraid people are indifferent to me. If they like me they don't like me enough. That leaves me in doubt and I don't know how to react. I like intimacy more than anything else. I want to know where I stand. It's hard for me to talk unless I have something definite to say. I'm afraid I might say something harmful. I might ridicule somebody. I don't know why but I can't help saying resentful things although I try very hard to keep it all in."

Sexual adjustment: The patient stated that he had never thought of masturbating until five months prior to admission when he noticed two dogs "fornicating in the street." He then added: "I don't know whether it was seeing the dogs or whether it was because my stepfather had just come back to live with us. Then the habit sort of got hold of me. I picture naked women. Sometimes my mother."

Attitude toward parents: "Mother was terribly strict. She was always either punishing me or making a fuss over me. We always knew we'd be punished when she got home from work. She spanked me until I was 15 years old.

Although she couldn't hurt me much then it was a great humiliation. She taught me that all the punishment and nagging was because of her love of me. . . . All my life I've always been angry with Mother because she lives her children's lives. She stuffs them with food and acts grieved and imposed on if they show any opposition. I used to vomit on purpose to even the score but now I can't help it."

Characteristic Behavior Pattern. "It is very difficult for me to face things. I try to shy away from all situations. I'm afraid of not being successful. I try very hard to get people's approval. I try to do things that won't show me up." (*Note:* One finds a similar situation in some other groups, but patients with diabetes, for example, although they behave in the way this patient describes, would not admit that they had any such feelings.) "I don't like jobs where you're told what to do and where you're judged. My brother had a goal. He's a musician and he's already making twenty dollars a week. . . . Instead of dreaming I talk to myself about questions of philosophy and ethics, questions like 'What is justice? What is good?' "

Neurotic Traits. Running away from school and home. All other *early* neurotic traits denied. *Present:* A perfectionistic drive: "I can't talk unless I feel someone understands me perfectly."

Addictions and Interests. Non-competitive outdoor sports. Coffee.

Life Situation Immediately Prior to Onset. The first attack of palpitation occurred when the patient was 10 years old. A dog barked at him and attempted to jump on him. His second attack was at the age of 15 when he was about to enter a foot race in high school. He commented on this: "Of course I expected to have it at the end especially if I didn't come out as well as I should. But it was funny to have it before I started. All these years I've had it before starting a new job or meeting new people." The exacerbation of symptoms, however, which brought him to the hospital followed the return of his stepfather to the household and increasing conflict with his mother.

Reaction to Illness. "I have weak hereditary factors from my father. I'm not excusing myself. My father was very sensitive; he had gastro-intestinal nervousness, and vomited a good deal, just like me. He and I are supposed to have looked alike. I feel that I will go the same way as my father. My father had consumption of the kidney even before marriage, and he was refused life insurance because of his organic illness. They tell me I have no organic illness. . . . Vomiting is due to trying to swallow all the things that distress me. My father vomited when he was upset. His weight was like mine. I always feel better after vomiting. In fact I really get hungry sometimes after vomiting even though I haven't vomited anything but a little fluid. I am always very tense and by vomiting I loosen up."

The patient saw a doctor in the medical clinic who told him not to vomit, but that if he could not help it, to swallow some rhubarb and soda. "I felt nauseated, but prevented myself from vomiting by self-control, and then when I left home I didn't vomit because one can't vomit in public. I feel that vomiting is a necessary part of my everyday life. I've done it so long that it's like setting up exercises. The very sight of the bottle of medicine stops me. The medicine is not hard to take, but since it's useless because my stomach is really all right why should I take it. The more bitter a medicine the more I like it. I don't take it in water because it takes away the bitterness."

Area of Focal Conflict and Characteristic Reaction. It is clear that this patient's conflict was in the area of authority characteristic of patients with hypertension. He was unable to cope with authority yet he had ambition. In spite of choosing jobs below his actual capacity he constantly defeated himself even in them because of his fear of not making good or living up to his perfectionistic ideas.

Case No. H 53. An unmarried woman, aged 36, was admitted to the hospital with hypertensive cardiovascular disease, cardiac insufficiency, and acute subsiding choleocystitis.

Family History. There was cardiovascular disease in her paternal grandmother who died of a sudden heart attack during the patient's childhood. The patient's mother died similarly at the age of 76, a year before the patient's admission. Her father had died suddenly six years previously of pneumonia. One brother died suddenly of influenza, one in an accident, and one sister of Bright's disease, and another in childbirth. The family history of this patient is thus typical of the patient with hypertensive cardiovascular disease—exposure both to cardiovascular disease and to a number of traumatic deaths.

Personal Data. The patient was brought up strictly in a family of six. Both parents lived well into the patient's adult life.

Previous Health. As a child the patient had fits and then developed asthma at the age of 10. She was ill for two years with "typhoid fever and malaria," at the age of 16. She had an appendectomy during pregnancy; at the age of 19 pneumonia; at the age of 36 ptomaine poisoning. For a good many years she was under treatment for syphilis.

Previous Injuries. Right after her mother's death the patient was bitten by a dog, an occurrence to which she ascribes much of her nervousness, although she stated that she never liked animals anyway.

General Adjustment. Vocation—education: The patient was forced to give up school at the age of 10 in order to help support the family. *Income and occupation:* She worked as a lady's maid. At the age of 13 she came to New York, where she worked as a cook up to the time of her admission to the hospital. In her early life her *social adjustment* was good but after the birth of her illegitimate infant, which died soon after birth, and the acquisition of syphilis she decided she had had enough of men. She had a few women friends but gave most of her attention to work. *Sexual adjustment.* The patient was brought up strictly and in ignorance. Her unfortunate early experience of the illegitimate child and the syphilis led her to try to cut sex out of her life although she was not entirely successful in this and there were various later relationships of an impermanent character. *Attitude toward parents:* The patient hated her father and liked her mother moderately. She stated that she got along better when she did not see too much of either of them.

Characteristic Behavior Pattern. Like her educational, income and occupational history, her behavior pattern also was typical of the patient with hypertensive cardiovascular disease. For most of her life she had planned to take a vacation some day but she had never been able to bring herself to it, partly because she was helping to support her mother and niece to whom she sent twenty dollars monthly out of her earnings of $75. On the surface she was jocular and good-natured but there was considerable tension underneath.

Neurotic Traits. Temper tantrums, fits, and nightmares in childhood. Nightmares, depression, and outbursts of uncontrollable rage in later years.

Addictions and Interests. Coffee, alcohol, epsom salts, food (patient weighed 210 lbs.), horse races, and ball games. She was brought up a Baptist but gave up religion at about the same time that she gave up men.

Life Situation Immediately Prior to Onset. The necessity of keeping at her job in order to support her mother in spite of working in an unpleasant household, the mother's death a year and a half prior to admission, and the necessity of still continuing to support her niece, indicate the type of situation which usually precedes the development of hypertensive cardiovascular disease.

Reaction to Illness. After the patient was forced to give up work because of her illness she went to live in a small apartment and took in an old friend named "Pop" as a boarder. According to the social worker's note "Pop" was a garrulous old man who took care of the patient's business affairs. The patient could not adjust herself to being taken care of, insisting that she had been a responsible person all her life and always stood on her own feet. This reaction to illness is more characteristic of the coronary patient or the patient with hypertension who later develops coronary occlusion than it is of the patient with hypertensive cardiovascular disease. It is interesting that during her stay in the hospital there was a question of coronary occlusion and that this diagnosis was definitely established two years later at another hospital.

Area of Focal Conflict and Characteristic Reaction. All her life the patient had had trouble with her superiors, particularly her father. She escaped this situation at the age of 13 by going to New York to work and help support her mother. Because of financial pressure she submitted to the authority of her employers but always with a great deal of friction. One of her reasons for not getting married, which was added to her unfortunate experience at the age of 16, she gave as follows: "All men do is boss you around, they don't take care of you anyway, so I'd rather take care of myself and be my own boss."

VI. Conclusions

(1) Patients with hypertensive cardiovascular disease are more homogeneous than patients in the fracture group. They have a personality profile that distinguishes them from any other group studied. Although they resemble the patients with coronary disease or anginal syndrome (to be discussed in the two succeeding sections), they differ in several important points.

(2) These patients stand out in several respects from the general population as a whole, for example, in their extremely high illness record, their high marriage rate, and their tendency to have large families. They have a relatively low accident rate and the majority of their accidents follow the cardiac pattern (page 256).

(3) Whereas, patients seen on the fracture ward are more or less equally divided among the groups constricted, introversive and extratensive, these patients are predominantly introversive.

(4) In addition, the following individual characteristics of this group are significant:

(a) Their appearance is superficially normal except for signs of strain and anxiety which are often obvious in their facial expression and bearing. Many have classical neurotic symptoms, mostly compulsive in nature. There is a marked perfectionistic tendency combined with obsessive doubts. When their feelings find expression it is usually in an explosive manner.

(b) They show a generalized tension of both smooth and skeletal muscles and a tendency to take recourse to "wine, women, and song" in situations of particular stress.

(c) They are extremely ambitious but constantly fearful of not making the grade. In social relationships they are shy and conventional except when off guard. They talk readily about their feelings and personal problems and relax when a free expression of feelings is given social approval.

(d) Their basic conflict is between authority identification and their need to be taken care of—active-passive drives. They are constantly ambivalent and hence experience obsessive difficulty in making decisions or determining a course of action. This is often verbalized in a preoccupation with intellectual pros and cons. They tend to court much more responsibility than they are able to carry.

(e) Unlike patients with the accident syndrome, in whom tension from repressed aggression varies intermittently with specific external pressures, these patients become, over a period of time, gradually surcharged with tension for which they find no adequate outlet. Although they may relate the first discovery of high blood pressure to some particular traumatic event, investigation shows that this event represents the climax of a long history of accumulating tension.

(f) In their initial reaction to the discovery of high blood pressure their usual ambivalence is reflected in the combination of exaggerated fears and relief in having an alibi for failure. This "alibiology" is very noticeable in these hypertensive patients.

(5) This personality constellation plays an important role in the development of the illness syndrome and has a bearing on prognosis and therapeutic management. Great care must be exercised by the physician in order to avoid increasing the patient's dilemma.

CORONARY INSUFFICIENCY AND OCCLUSION

I. Nature and Magnitude of the Problem

STATISTICS

Coronary occlusion is of course an important entity in our high mortality and disability statistics for cardiovascular disease. On the basis of three sets of statistics, it has been estimated that at least 500,000 attacks of coronary artery occlusion occur annually in the United States. This is an approximate incidence of one attack per 54 males and 189 females over 40 years of age.[292] Furthermore, it is the one subdivision in the group of cardiovascular diseases that seems to have increased most rapidly in prominence.

Hedley[229] writes: "The mortality rate among white persons increased from 36 per 100,000 in 1933 to 84 in 1937, an increase of more than 100 per cent. The mean annual mortality rate from acute coronary occlusion among white males was 76 per 100,000 population while among white females it was only 37 per 100,000 population, less than half the rate among white males. The mortality rate from this disease among the Negro population was 25 per 100,000 population, while in 1937 it had increased to only 28 per 100,000, and it showed a tendency to fluctuate during the intervening years.*

"Furthermore, while acute coronary occlusion accounts for 26 per cent of the total recorded heart disease mortality in the 50–59 year age period, with each succeeding age decade it is responsible for a smaller percentage of the total mortality from heart disease. In the age group over 80 years of age only 5.5 per cent of the recorded mortality from heart disease was due to this cause.

"Recently, Gordon, Bland, and White [207] studied the incidence and degree of significant coronary disease among 600 private patients examined post mortem as compared with 2,800 ward patients examined post mortem at the Massachusetts General Hospital from 1925 to 1937. In the age period between 40 and 60 years they found that 24 per cent of the private patients examined post mortem had acute coronary occlusion or myocardial infarction as compared with 12.2 per cent among ward patients.

"In the 35–44 year age period the death rate was highest among professional men (47 per 100,000 persons in that occupational group) and lowest among workers, who had a mean annual occupational-specific mortality rate of only 29 per 100,000)." †

---

* It should be noted that among white persons the mean annual age-specific mortality rate among males was nearly four times as great as that among females in the 40 to 49 year age decade, over three to one in the 50 to 59 year age decade, and over two to one in the 60 to 69 year age period. This relationship does not prevail in the Negro population, where the ratios between males and females were more nearly equal in each age group.

† "Levy, Bruenn and Kurtz [280] on the other hand, in a study based on the number of cases of coronary disease found at autopsy among all cases examined post mortem at the Presbyterian Hospital in New York City from 1910 to 1931, found that coronary disease occurred slightly more often among foremen and skilled workers than among other occupational groups, but that, in general, occupation did not appear to play an important role in the occurrence of arterial damage" (Hedley [229]). Our own observations, also on a series of patients at Presbyterian Hospital, are not in accord with this conclusion (see Occupational Chart VI). It is possible that the discrepancy could be accounted for by the fact that so many of the patients with coronary occlusion work up through the skilled laborer class to the rank of officials, managers, or professionals, and then after the first attack of illness adjust themselves to a lower occupational level rather than give up working entirely. Hence in studying this question it is important to base figures on the occupational level just prior to the onset rather than that in which we find these patients after their first or second attack.

OTHER STUDIES

In a recent article published in the *U. S. Naval Bulletin*,[409] attention was called to the frequency of coronary accidents during the seventy-second Congress. The statement appears: "Since the secondary cases all died, and three of the primary died instantly, or almost immediately, the specter of sudden death became a formidable one." *
A group of patients with coronary occlusion were studied for possible similarities that would distinguish them from congressmen of the same age and type who did not succumb to this disease. Six facts were noted:

"1. The metabolic disturbance because of improper endocrine balance."

"2. The failure to balance the energy-work-waste elimination with the food intake.

"3. The improper use of their physical machines."

These three points compare interestingly with our observation of patients in this group (page 296).

"4. Low oxygen carrying power of the blood, or as better expressed, low oxidizing power of the blood.

"5. Low carbondioxide combining power and high blood-fat content.

"6. The metabolic disturbance as the result of anger, worry, fear, and other acute emotional storms."

Our observations provide an interesting comparison here also (page 309).

The report concludes: "We also believe that we have progressed far enough to state that a man is not likely to have a coronary occlusion, in the dangerous age (45–55), barring toxic effects, if he:

"1. Makes a daily sustained, moderate physical effort.

"2. Balances the food-fuel value with the energy-work output.

"3. Practices the hygiene of a quiet mind.

"4. Obtains 8 hours rest in bed every night."

In the preceding section comment was made on the incidence of coronary occlusion in patients with hypertension. In the article by Davis and Klainer [110] attention is called to the general increase in coronary occlusion especially among women.

* *U. S. Naval Bulletin*, page 385.

Cecil [78] stated that the causes of coronary occlusion "are those of vascular hypertension and arteriosclerosis. . . . Most of its victims give a history of having previously suffered from the syndrome called angina pectoris." He says further: "Heredity is of considerable importance in indicating a familial tendency to chronic vascular disease."

Master, Gubner, Dack and Jaffe [292] reported that 415 patients were followed from six months to fifteen years after the attack of coronary occlusion. More than half returned to work on full or part time. Half of this group assumed work three months after discharge; three-fourths within six months; and nine-tenths within one year. The percentage of patients returning to work was higher in the younger group, particularly among those under 40 and those recovering from an initial attack. The percentage was about the same in males and females. Professional and white-collar classes resumed their work more frequently than did patients in other occupations. About half of those that went back complained of pain, dyspnea, or weakness which were not of a sufficient degree to cause disability.*

II. Onset of Symptoms

In the coronary group the onset of symptoms covered a period varying from two hours to fifteen years prior to admission. An illustration of the frequently sudden discovery of this condition is the following:

A few minutes after he was examined and rated 100 per cent physically, Patrick J. McLaughlin, 37, of New Britain, fell dead in the employment office of Colt's Patent Fire Arms Manufacturing Company. Because of his excellent health, a job had been promised to McLaughlin, starting Monday. He sat down, and then died. The medical examiner said death was caused by a coronary thrombosis. *New York Times*, Hartford, Conn., March 1, 1941 (U.P.).

In half of the cases the first pain was felt for less than six months before admission to the hospital, and in half of these, for less than a week. In another 25 per cent there was pain on exertion or excitement for from six months to a year prior to admission; and in the remaining 25 per cent, for from one to fifteen years. (In this

---

* For classification of coronary disease, see Chapelle, C. E. de La, and Levy, R. L., Bull. New York Acad. Med. 19:201–223 (Mar.); 273–290 (Apr.) 1943.

latter group other symptomatology, such as cholecystitis and operations, was particularly frequent.)

In a high percentage of cases the onset of symptoms immediately
followed eating or drinking, and was often ascribed to too much
of one of these, usually combined with too much smoking. In this
connection it is interesting that these patients reported a marked
weight gain or loss during the period of onset, and a great many of
them had difficulty in keeping to their diets. In others the onset
was in the middle of the night following a nightmare.

III. PREDISPOSITION TO ILLNESS—FACTORS TO BE EVALUATED

ORGAN CONDITIONING—PHYSIOLOGICAL AND PSYCHOLOGICAL

Heredity—Actual and Pseudo

In the families of 42 per cent of these patients there was a *history*
of *cardiovascular disease,* and in 18 per cent there was cardiovascular
disease among the patients' own siblings as well. It is interesting, furthermore, that 79 per cent of this cardiovascular history occurred
among females of the family, and almost always in the patient's
mother. Only 9 per cent of the cardiovascular history consisted of
hypertensive cardiovascular disease, which is a lower percentage than
was found in the preceding group.

In nearly all these cases the patient was *exposed* to one person in
the family with the illness in question, and the exposure to cardiovascular disease was always to the mother or to both parents. In
addition, one patient with no cardiovascular heredity had a wife
with "heart trouble"; 8 per cent had siblings who had accidents (one
of these belonged to the 50 per cent with cardiovascular heredity);
16 per cent complained of nervousness in the spouse.

Furthermore, the exposure factor was particularly prominent;
either close friend, parent, spouse, or child had dropped dead on the
street, or had died in the patient's arms of "heart trouble." One man
had lived in constant terror since a physician had told him that his
wife would probably drop dead "in a day or so of heart disease,"
although the lady lived to see him in the hospital fifteen years later.

There was *diabetes* in the family history of 9 per cent of these
patients, and *injury* in the family history of 4.5 per cent, exclusive

of the patients' siblings, and 9 per cent of the siblings are included. *Nervous illness* was relatively prominent in the families of these patients (but only 27 per cent as compared with 73 per cent for the group with hypertensive cardiovascular disease); particularly there was a tendency to instability, mood swings, and in 14 per cent of the cases a parent committed suicide or was sent to an institution.

It is noteworthy, nevertheless, that the history of nervousness in parents or family was less frequent than in the group with hypertensive cardiovascular disease. Although the *accident* history was less (9 per cent including siblings), the history of traumatic death was more frequent. The cardiovascular heredity, however, is almost uniform for the two groups.

Constitution—Age Range, Sex, and Marriage

Build. In the patients with coronary disease the pyknic type predominated, although in a quarter of the group the physique was definitely asthenic or athletic.

Age Distribution. For the males the distribution was: ages 25 to 34, 5.3 per cent; 35 to 44, 36.8 per cent; 45 to 52, 58 per cent. For the females the age distribution was 35 to 44, 67 per cent; 45 to 52, 33 per cent.

Sex. In this group there were six males to every female. If patients in other disease groups who developed coronary disease be included, we get five males to one female, a rate which corresponds with the male-female distribution of coronary disease in the general population as given by National Public Health statistics.

Marriage. Of the patients in this group 95 per cent were married, and this figure includes all of the females. Of these marriages 19 per cent were childless. The average size of the family was 1.9. This is the highest record for marriage of any group studied and except for patients with diabetes, these patients have the highest record for size of family. It is interesting to note that the females were inclined to have smaller families than the males.

Previous Health *

Like patients with hypertensive cardiovascular disease, these patients have a poor health record. Although the chart shows an only slightly poorer health record than that for patients with hypertensive

* See charts Chapter IV.

cardiovascular disease, the low percentage of females in the group
is a factor to be evaluated. It should be noted also that the difference
in health record between males and females in this group is less than
in any other group studied. This might or might not be changed
were the number of females larger. Reference to Chart VII where
this group as well as patients with hypertensive cardiovascular disease
are compared with patients with fracture and patients with diabetes
in the same age period, brings out the fact that this difference cannot be accounted for in terms of age distribution.

Of these patients 27 per cent had a previous history of hypertensive cardiovascular disease. Patients having a previous history of
hypertensive cardiovascular disease include 33 per cent of the females
and 26 per cent of the males. These patients are discussed in detail in
Chapter X.

In this group slightly less than one half of the patients had a
history of major operation. The combined major and minor operation figures give slightly over one operation per patient. Characteristic operations for this group were appendectomy, tumor, diverti-
ulectomy, cholecystectomy, hernia repair, excision of fistula-in-ano
and hemorroidectomy.

The major illness record gives an average of nearly two per patient; and if minor illnesses are included, a total of more than five
illnesses per patient. Typical illnesses were: pneumonia, pleurisy and
bronchitis (one of which was reported by nearly half the patients in
this group), malaria, tuberculosis, influenza, cholecystitis, jaundice,
typhoid, scarlet fever, otitis, cholelithiasis, diphtheria, ulcer of stomach
or duodenum, and diabetes (one case). There were also histories of
frequent sore throat, nervous breakdown, allergy, constipation, sinus,
migraine, erysipelas, psoriasis, grippe, colds, genito-urinary trouble,
and headaches.

It will be noted that this past history resembles very closely the illness history of patients with hypertensive cardiovascular disease except for the great prominence of intestinal disorders, urinary disturbances, and bad teeth. It is in marked contrast with the illness
record of the group of patients with fracture.

Statistics Concerning Previous Injury

The previous injury history for patients in this group is slightly
worse than that for the group with hypertensive cardiovascular dis-

ease, and the nature of the injuries is even more characteristic. Although more of these patients had had fractures—46 per cent had had one or more injuries (47 per cent of the males, 33 per cent of the females)—only 4.5 per cent had had more than one injury (all of whom were males). Thus the first figure exceeds the figure given for patients with hypertensive cardiovascular disease, whereas the second figure is markedly lower.

More than half of these injuries were the result of something done to the patient by someone else, in contradistinction to the fracture pattern, in which accidents were usually the result of falls or traffic accidents. Many of these injuries were the result of being hit, stabbed, shot, or knocked off of something. There is of course the question as to whether or not the patient himself provoked these injuries, but in any case the difference in type remains. Cuts were prominent among the remaining accidents.

There were no cases of definite fracture. The only possibilities are patient No. CD 223 who "had a little fracture or something" when he stepped under a car, and patient No. CD 197 who "sprained or fractured" his wrist when he was a child.

The following examples are illustrative of this difference in type: Patient No. CD 311, at the age of 9 was hit in the right shoulder with a ball bat, and at the age of 15 was bitten by a dog; patient No. CD 339 was hit by a car; patient No. CD 213 was stabbed while watching a baby parade; patient No. CD 309 was stabbed with a pitchfork in the abdomen in childhood when he was hiding in the hay; patient No. CD 328 was injured in her right eye by a bullet. Other injuries were as follows: Patient No. CD 316 became frightened and fell out of a tree and landed on his neck; patient No. CD 295 cut the third left phalanx with an ax.

Early Influences and Traumatic Experiences

In brief then, all patients with coronary occlusion, like patients with hypertensive cardiovascular disease, had been exposed to cardiovascular disease in some dramatic way, although only half of them— that is, fewer than in the hypertensive cardiovascular disease group —had cardiovascular heredity. There was also a relatively frequent history of severe shock as a result of death of a person to whom they were closely bound emotionally, usually by cardiovascular disease or occasionally by accident. Although unlike patients with hypertensive cardiovascular disease the cardiac heredity was mainly among females of the family, such traumatic deaths as occurred were mainly among the males of the family.

Furthermore, nervousness in family or spouse was complained of by three-quarters of the patients with hypertensive cardiovascular disease, but by only 27 per cent of those with coronary occlusion.

Even more prominent than these factors, however, was the excessively strenuous work history; the patients worked long hours without vacations under considerable stress and strain. There was regularly a sudden reverse just after achieving the goal for which

TABLE X

CORONARY OCCLUSION: PARENTAL INFLUENCE AND LONGEVITY

	MALE AND FEMALE	MALE	FEMALE
Average age of patients at admission...................	44.6	44.8	43.7
Average age of patients at death of:			
Father...................	25.6	24.9	36.
Mother..................	30.7	32.5	10.
Parents living (at time of patients' admission):			
Both living at time of patients' admission.......	9.1	5.3	33.3
Father living.............	18.2	15.8	33.3
Mother living............	40.9	36.8	66.7
Death of parents before patient was 16 years old:			
Either father or mother ...	27.2	26.3	33.3
Both father and mother...	0	0	0
Father...................	22.7	26.3	0
Mother..................	4.5	0	33.3
Mother dominating and preferred:			
All coronary patients.....	27.3 to 45.5	26.3 to 47.4	
Coronary patients with hypertensive cardiovascular disease................	50.0 to 66.7	40.0 to 60.0	100
Coronary patients without hypertensive cardiovascular disease	13.7 to 27.3	15.8 to 31.6	

they had been working. A sudden traumatic "ruin" was regularly reported by these patients and rarely by patients in the group with fracture.

General Adjustment

*Vocation—Education.** Reference to Charts I, II, and III in Chapter III will recall the fact that patients with coronary disease have very unusual educational records, showing a marked tendency to complete the academic unit undertaken and a generally high educational average.

*Income * and Occupation.** Reference to Charts IV, V, and VI makes clear that the income for these patients is correspondingly high, in fact the highest for all the groups studied, and the occupational grouping is similarly high and characteristic. As has been noted in other studies, the majority of these patients are found in group II (proprietors, managers, and officials), which is consistent with their tendency toward persistence and their drive to get to the top. Their most frequent occupations were shop-owner (20 per cent of the patients in the series; e.g., one patient worked up from newsboy to butcher boy to owner of a chain of butcher shops), broker, foreman, salesman, headwaiter, and night-club owner and entertainer. Coronary occlusion is prominent among physicians and professional men who for a good or bad reason tend to burn the midnight oil. It is interesting to find this same tendency among waiters and butchers with the same illness, who would seem to be under less obvious necessity to behave in this way.

General Behavior. In terms of general adjustment the major difficulties of these patients with coronary occlusion seemed to fall in the spheres of family and of sex. They had unusually stable work records, most of them with histories of beginning at the bottom and working up to the top.

Social Behavior. These patients were always well liked and sociable except that they tended to have difficulties with their superiors and to keep others at a distance. The technique of keeping others at a

---

* It will be remembered that statements under starred headings are based only on patients over 21, in order to make them comparable with national statistics.

distance, however, was one that made them popular: they dramatized, they joked, they did things for people. For example, patient No. CD 223, having stated that he made friends easily, went on to say: "That's why I'm sick. I always want to do things for other people. That is, I don't like to be asked to do things, so I do them without being asked; that keeps them from thinking that I'm lazy or falling down on the job." When asked if anyone ever accused him of that, the patient said: "No, but I want to be sure. What everybody says is: 'Gee, I've never seen a Jew work like that.'" The following statement of one patient is typical: "My disposition was always a little worrisome but good-natured."

Sexual Behavior. In contrast with patients with fractures, of whom only 73.5 per cent were married, and with patients with hypertensive cardiovascular disease, of whom only 75 per cent were married, 95.5 per cent of the patients with coronary disease were married. Although sex had always been important to them (and their impulse had been stimulated early), very few had made what they regarded as a satisfactory sexual adjustment. Half had not bothered to secure adequate contraceptive advice and continued to practice withdrawal although they disliked it. The women in the group were frigid, and the majority of the men had frigid wives, or suffered from premature ejaculation, or both. The following comments are characteristic:

Case No. CD 223. This patient married at 26, had four children and was not anxious to have more. He practiced coitus interruptus until his wife got contraceptive advice, "some kind of rubber and a salve." When asked if his earlier sexual practice had been satisfactory he said characteristically: "Well, there's no use thinking about that, it had to be. With the new method I don't like it either, but I just forget about it. As long as it is safe I don't care either way. My wife never cared much about sex any way."

Nevertheless these patients tended to have large families, and were excelled in this respect only by patients with diabetes. It will be remembered that the fracture patients frequently avoided the responsibility involved in having children and had the lowest record for number of children per marriage of any group studied.

Attitude Toward Parents. Although patients in this group had some tendency to prefer mother to father they showed little tendency to rely on their mothers, perhaps because in general their mothers were less dominating and although usually the center of attention in the family, less effective as human beings. (The only patients who showed any preference for their mothers were among the 27 per cent in this group who had hypertensive cardiovascular disease also.) These patients developed a tendency to outdo their fathers and to dominate their mothers. Both parents lived well on into the patient's adult life.

Characteristic Behavior Pattern: Compulsive Striving: Urge to Get to the Top Through Hard Work, Self-Discipline, and Mastery of Others

As has been noted, traumatic events of considerable seriousness, deaths in the family, financial disaster, or the sudden ruin of ambitious plans were prominent in the histories of all the coronary patients, constituting a sharp contrast with the patients with fracture, whose troubles were more of the ordinary everyday variety: difficulties with jobs, especially. But the patients' reactions to difficulties were never a matter of impulse of the moment.

Patient No. CD 57 (page 321) illustrates the difficulty of these patients in sharing responsibility. This man had been perfectly well as long as he was his own boss as the owner of a butcher shop. He ascribed his first attack to having had to take a partner because the business was too much for one man. He said: "After having worked all those years to be my own boss I suddenly wasn't my own boss any more." After the first coronary outbreak this patient was able to work long hours and did fairly well until the return of his partner from vacation. Although the return of the partner made it possible for him to work fewer hours and to obey doctors' orders about rest, a second attack occurred two or three months later, which the patient ascribed to the irritation resulting from sharing responsibility with the partner.

These patients are strongly governed by their principles and their sense of propriety. For example it could be said that in all other cardiovascular groups the "variables" of the coronary emotional pattern are: (1) the degree in which a sense of "propriety" exists, and (2) the direction of their masochistic tendency: viz., in the patients with coronary occlusion the direction is egocentric, they are martyrs to their own principles, and enjoy being "cruel" to themselves. In other groups the direction is allocentric, as shown in their tendencies to be martyrs to principles they do not like, to wives or husbands whom they consider vile, and they prefer to be cruel to others.

Neurotic Traits—Early and Present

In contrast to patients with fracture, less than one-third of these patients reported early neurotic traits. Among this group, characteristic difficulties were temper tantrums, dreams of fighting, of injuring and being injured, and conflict over masturbation. Nail-biting was sometimes reported but usually denied. The nightmares were of a stereotyped nature, occurring over considerable periods of time. A characteristic nightmare of this type was that reported by patient No. CD 57—falling off a cliff and being butted by billy goats. Characteristic also was his comment relative to his nightmares: "No, I never had nightmares. Quite often I used to dream of falling off a cliff and being butted by a billy goat. Sometimes I had this dream so often that it really worried me. Usually I forget all my dreams."

As children these patients were known as being self-willed and stubborn, with a tendency to brood. They suffered regularly from constipation. In later life we found suicidal fantasies, and also compulsive character traits like those shown by the patients with hypertensive cardiovascular disease. But perfectionistic tendencies were less marked, perhaps because these patients felt more security in accomplishment and achievement of their goal. These patients, furthermore, showed more control relative to their eating habits and were not generally obese, although the onset of the illness was often ascribed by them to a dietary indiscretion.

Addictions and Interests

More than half of these patients admitted excessive use of tobacco and coffee. Patient No. CD 307 said: "I smoked too much before. More work, more smoke. It was like a narcotic. I can't work too much if I don't smoke." Their spontaneous statements about this, however, were: "I do it to keep myself alert on the job," or "awake"; in contrast to the patients with fracture who did it to work off tension: "Because I feel restless."

The coronary patients in our series were more interested in gainful occupation, especially intellectual, than in sports or machines. They were more interested in power than in enjoyment. They were interested in power in the field of vocation, sex, and family. In general they had a keen sense of responsibility, had relatively large families from a "sense of duty" and were good parents, although not particularly good husbands in any sense other than providing for the wife's support.

These patients consistently neglected their health, principally through lack of sleep, working long hours, taking no vacation or recreation, going contrary to doctors' orders, excessive use of tobacco and coffee, consolation in food, either forbidden or thought to be harmful. The only exceptions were among those who tended to have accidents. Patients with fracture, it will be remembered, tended to protect their health. The notes of the attending physician frequently mentioned incidentally as characteristic of the patient, stoical self-denying temperament and tendency to self-neglect. Appropriately enough, these patients showed a tendency to depression and a third of them reported suicidal fantasies of long duration.

As will be clear from the histories, as well as from the preceding discussion, these patients had exaggerated oral interests. Not only did attacks tend to come on after eating but they were specially related to eating; or, as with a patient who was a butcher, to cutting red meat. When they occurred during the night, they usually followed dreams of fighting. Patient No. CD 307 said: "The only dreams I've ever had are of war, fighting, and prisons." This same patient went on to say: "When horses are kept on straw they get soft and have to have oats to work. I'm the same way; I can't eat vegetables. Tea makes me sick. It's coffee and meat that give you power." He complained bitterly about the hospital diet because it made him feel soft and took away his power. He constantly begged for meat and even though he had been warned against excesses in this direction, continued his old habits as soon as he got out of the hospital.

In general these patients had a religious upbringing to which they soon began to feel superior, although they continued an interest in philosophical speculation about the nature of the universe, and approved of religion as an institution for the less enlightened. For example:

Patient No. CD 307 stated: "I was brought up in the Greek Catholic church and taught right and wrong. I still go to church on holidays for the social side but I don't believe in it. That is, I think there probably is a God but I don't believe in priests."

Taking males and females together only 14 per cent were brought up as Catholics, including Roman, Russian and Greek Orthodox (as compared with 60 per cent of the accident group); 59 per cent were Jewish; and 27 per cent, Protestant. There was not the preponderance of Catholics among the females which was found in the group of patients with hypertensive cardiovascular disease, but this observation may not mean much because of the small percentage of females in the group.

Life Situation Immediately Prior to the Onset

As is obvious from the case histories (page 313), the situation prior to the onset of the illness in these patients was always an acute one, although preceded by a long period of overexertion and worry with inadequate rest. The major emotional factor was usually a disappointment in relation to vocational life: "After working so hard all those years, I had just reached the top and was happy, when this happened, and it was all taken away"; or, "I wasn't my own boss any more." Although death or illness of parent or spouse was usually mentioned as having occurred just prior to the onset of the illness, the patient was inclined to minimize the emotional importance to him of such events; instead, the specific reference was likely to be to eating or nightmares about fighting or to financial reverse.

Reaction to Illness

When ill these patients attempt to deny the fact. If activity is curtailed they become depressed and lonely (see pages 330–31).

IV. DYNAMIC FORMULATION

AREA OF FOCAL CONFLICT: AUTHORITY (ATTEMPT TO SURPASS OR SUBDUE AUTHORITY)

In contrast to patients with hypertension, the focal conflict was peculiarly repressed in patients with coronary disease. Careful study of these case histories makes it clear that although, like patients with fracture, patients with coronary disease had trouble with authority, the fundamental pattern was the attempt to surpass or subdue superiors. These patients felt that they must be as good as the superior, appreciated by him, superior to him, and that they must be in a dominating situation in relation to others. It was not enough to be fathers of children; they must be rulers of men. They were easily hurt by their superiors, but instead of leaving them, they curried favor and tried to dominate them.

The identification with the father is of special interest in view of the nature of the patients' illness. Although the cardiovascular disease to which these patients were exposed occurred most frequently in the mothers, sudden death, including cardiovascular and other accidents, occurred primarily in the males of the family, and it was with the male that the identification together with the domination pattern was established. A large number of these patients had a dual psychosomatic conditioning: exposure to cardiovascular disease in the mother including early focusing of attention on the heart, to which was added the shock of sudden death in a male relative. It is noteworthy that a death during or immediately after an operation was almost always described in some such words as "his heart went back on him" or "his heart just couldn't stand the strain."

In this group a typical statement concerning the relationship to the father is the following:

"My father was strong; my mother was very soft, we could talk to her like a friend. I was ashamed to smoke in the room with my father when I was a full grown man. If we needed something from father, we would go to mother and ask her to talk to him. School was also like that, strict."

As in other patients with cardiovascular disease, the mother was the focus of attention in the family group, usually maintaining some contact with the patient even in cases where she was either strict or inadequate. She was never, however, the dominant member, as with the rheumatic fever patients. The father died before the patients' adolescence in only two instances, both times being replaced by a stepfather. In no case did a patient report a good relationship to the father. When patients left home, the father or stepfather was primarily to blame. Having left home, however, instead of starting on a career of wandering, these patients threw themselves into a life of extreme ambitious activity aiming to become "as good as the old man or better."

PROFILE

Coronary Insufficiency and Occlusion *

1. *Family History.* Cardiovascular disease in parents and siblings about average for the groups studied (42 per cent). Accident history for parents and siblings, about 9 per cent. Diabetes, 9 per cent. Nervousness, about 27 per cent. Exposure to cardiovascular disease or to sudden death in about 90 per cent of the cases.

2. *Personal Data.* Both parents usually lived beyond the patient's majority. The father usually died first. Both parents typically strict. High marriage rate. Many children, few divorces.

3. *Health Record.* Bad previous illness history with predominance of vegetative symptoms and many operations. Anginal symptoms frequent. Tendency to self-neglect. Women poor pelvic histories.

4. *Injuries.* Rarely more than one injury. Rate for one accident above average, but these accidents were of a specific type: result of action by another person, typically cutting, shooting or stabbing. Few childhood accidents.

5. *General Adjustment. Education:* Marked tendency to complete educational unit undertaken. Planned career. *Work record:* Sticking to one job, working to the top. *Income and vocational level:* Highest of all groups studied. Characteristically class II (executives and officials). *Social relationships:* Generally respected. Tendency to dominate. Argumentative with men, attentive to women. *Sexual adjustment:* Role of exemplary husband (and father) combined with frustration and often secret promiscuity; high venereal disease rate. Emphasize sexual problems (overt anxiety). *Attitude toward family:* Hostile toward father, better toward mother in early life, with marked tendency to cut off both later. Dominating, proud and responsible toward wife and children.

6. *Characteristic Behavior Pattern.* Compulsively consistent action. Tendency to work long hours and not take vacations. Tendency to seize authority; dislike of sharing responsibility. Conversation an instrument of domination and aggression. Tendency to attach emotions to ideas and goals. Articulate about feelings. Living for future.

7. *Neurotic Traits.* Few early neurotic traits, tendency to brood and keep their troubles to themselves. In later life inner tension and a tendency to depression which is rarely admitted to others, together with compulsive asceticism and drive to work.

* In order to evaluate the distinctive features in this profile reference should be made to Chapter IX.

8. *Addictions and Interests.* Tendency to take stimulants to help keep on working (overwork). Little interest in sports, few hobbies. Skepticism about religion. Marked interest in philosophy.

9. *Life Situation Immediately Prior to Onset.* Exposure to shock—especially in job or in relinquishment of authority.

10. *Reaction to Illness.* Tendency to minimize symptoms and self-neglect.

11. *Area of Focal Conflict and Characteristic Reaction.* Authority—attempt to be and subdue authority; identification with authority and authority concepts.

(*Note:* The coronary occlusion patient with pre-existing hypertension or anginal symptoms usually diverges from this profile in the directions indicated in the two respective profiles, especially in categories 4, 5, 6, and 10.)

DEGREE AND NATURE OF SOMATIC EXPRESSION OF CONFLICTS

Tension, Aggression and Resentment

Unlike patients with hypertensive cardiovascular disease, patients with coronary accidents are mainly extratensive (page 280) which means that they have imposed an extreme repression on the inner promptings of instinctive drives and creative imagination. The few who had had a preexisting hypertensive cardiovascular disease differed from the others in this respect. They had more of the introversive traits characteristic of the patients with hypertensive cardiovascular disease and would be called more "dilated," that is with more affective and inner spontaneity. It may be difficult for the physician unfamiliar with these concepts to grasp this distinction, but the point is made here because of its prognostic significance. The dilated personality with hypertensive cardiovascular disease or coronary disease is likely to live longer with his illness than the patients in either group who run true to form. From this it is easy to see that a somatic short circuit is favored by any extreme repression of spontaneous impulses.

These patients were characterized by aggression and resentment which was always fairly near the surface, but volcanic outbursts were rare. They showed an extreme sensitivity and readiness to be insulted. Only one patient in the group was timid, although in several fear was mingled with hostility and the tendency to dominate. Many of them were considered great fighters, although the fighting was not so much a matter of ill-considered outbursts as a matter of subtle scheming. When thwarted in any active expression of their aggression they became sullen or suicidal.

They were all more than usually reactive, although they tended to wear masks or to become stoics. This reactivity involved the whole vegetative system, as is suggested by the diseases which preceded or were added to their cardiovascular disease. They blushed or became pale easily, were subject to palpitation, nervous indigestion, gall bladder disturbances, and so on, and were easily aroused to anger or tears.

All this suggests the hypertensive patient, except that with the latter, vegetative disturbance seems more nearly to control the emotional tension. With the patients with coronary disease, both vegetative symptomatology and activity, especially acting out in an impulsive way, sometimes with a tendency to accident, are called into play as well.

Activity, Verbalization, Dreams and Fantasies

The intensity of conflict in these patients is fairly accurately measured by the intensity with which they throw themselves into work without regard for health or rest. Although they resemble the fracture patients in having an urge to *activity*, it is very differently expressed. The more difficult things become and the more unhappy they become, the harder they work. They would rather die than fail, and many of them develop suicidal fantasies as a reaction to a fear of "not making good." Since they are unable to become aware of their conflict, if work as a defense fails them, and if in addition, joking fails them, and if in addition, as is usually the case, their sexual lives are inadequate, they seem still unable to give much expression to their difficulty either verbally or in dreams and fantasies. They rarely allow themselves to find solace in drugs or alcohol. They depend for security on external success. They lack the satisfaction of inner creative living—for enjoying immediate pleasures.

Verbalization is also used as an outlet by these patients but again the manner in which it is used is determined by their personality types. They tend to generalize about their experience, saying, for example, "A person who cannot control his temper does not deserve to achieve success." They are good at telling stories, do a lot of "kidding" on the ward, and generally are cheerful and sociable. One said the more he was worried, the more he "kidded" and made jokes about it. Another said: "When people think I am the most happy-go-lucky and the life of the party, I'm always the most worried." Another said: "I like people, but I don't want them to know my troubles, and joking is a good way to keep them at a distance." Another, "To be quite frank, I despise humanity and love ants!" Beneath the surface, the preoccupation is in philosophy —what is the end and aim of life? Many of them when serious discuss Plato, Marx, Hegel, etc. In contrast with fracture patients, they all had marked neurotic tendencies of either compulsive or depressive type. Not only are they unable to enjoy most immediate experience as the fracture patients do, but also they have given up all hope of enjoying it. Hence they search for answers to the "riddle of living" and try to convince themselves that life is worth while. They have too little inner security to dare to be fatalistic.

Such *dreams and fantasies* as they had usually expressed intense fear and impulses to self-destruction. This is not characteristic but is related to periods of anxiety about achieving their goal. When all else fails them, these patients may take recourse to an impulsive accident as do fracture patients, but as was noted earlier, the accidents are of a different type. They are mainly a matter of getting themselves injured by someone else, even being bitten by a dog, rather than slipping and falling, and they are likely to result in self-mutilation by way of serious cuts, burns or amputations, rather than simple fractures. Even in their accidents they cannot expose themselves to the accusation of being stupid, of having lost control. Nevertheless, these patients do a great deal of solitary thinking, hence such accidents are not the rule. Patient No. CD 307 hit the nail on the head when he said: "I *never* do something quick before I think."

By way of stressing further the necessity of looking for specificity in material such as this, rather than in case history material representing factors of which the patient is conscious, the following two histories of patients with anginal syndromes are given. One had coronary disease, the other showed no organic damage. These case histories seem identical down to the most minute details, yet in terms of such factors as those here mentioned there are some important differences. They illustrate also the fact that descriptively and psycho-economically, patients with similar syndromes, including psychic and somatic symptomatology, have important similarities in personality and history at least on superficial study, whether or not organic damage has taken place. The second case, patient No. AS 184 (page 315) may serve as an introduction to section III of this chapter, "Anginal Syndrome."

Case Illustrations *

With Organic Disease:

Case No. CD 298. A married man, aged 32, pyknic in type (Jewish), was admitted to the hospital after dinner one evening. He had severe pain, substernal radiating to the episternal notch and the right elbow, which was relieved only after "three hypodermics" (Magendie).

Onset. On the day of admission he had supper at his mother's house. The mother, in her customary oversolicitous manner had inquired about his health. He said: "I never felt better in my life. I feel as muscular and as strong as can be." "Strangely enough," he added, "that night I got sick."

The first symptoms had been substernal pain and oppression with belching, four months previously. Since which time he had been treated by doctors for "heart trouble," indigestion, or some other illness.

Heredity, Pseudo or Otherwise, and Family Adjustment. The patient's oversolicitous mother, aged 60, had thought for sometime that she might have heart trouble because she had pains in her chest. The patient's father died at 27 when the patient was 3 years old, having suffered from sunstroke one year before his death. Both the patient and his mother had strong feelings about this.

Neurotic Trends. The patient, an only child, was always sickly, suffering frequently from sore throat and upper respiratory infection. He bit his nails until the age of 15 or 16. The patient always smoked a great deal, and claimed that he knew something would happen to him for smoking so much. This smoking was of a rather compulsive kind, in that he did not really enjoy it; it frequently made him feel nauseated, but he "did it to avoid getting something to eat between meals when he was hungry" (i.e., compulsively), and he stated that his mother always felt that he might get sick from smoking. The patient also had a particular attitude toward eating. Even when he had no appetite if his wife made a good steak he would eat. He thinks that eating when he was not particularly hungry may have harmed him, also that nocturnal emissions probably weakened him. During his

---

* These cases were treated by Dr. Edward S. Tauber under the supervision of Dr. Theodore P. Wolfe and the author.

For further case illustrations see pp. 321–335.

stay in the hospital he used to be awakened by erections and asked to have salt peter in his diet.

Sexual Adjustment. The patient suffered from premature ejaculations and impotence. His marriage was patterned after his relationship with his mother. He married a few years before his illness. He had begun masturbation at the age of 13, and had had heterosexual relationships, "never with a nice girl." His marriage was essentially against his wishes ("I disliked losing my freedom"). He married because he "felt obligated," in view of the fact that he had "strung along" the girl, and she had requested him finally to marry her. The patient stated: "I think of her more as my mother, really, than anything else. She treats me like a little boy, and I like it. She tweeks my nose, and tickles me, and has had a baby picture of mine enlarged which she calls 'Bubi.' " She is very protective and on one occasion she wanted to beat up a man who was about to get into a fight with her husband. The patient has had no extramarital relations because he thinks it is cheap and because *if his wife found out she would "beat him up."* In view of his liking for being babied it was not surprising to find that after awhile the patient stated that he was beginning to enjoy hospitalization and did not feel eager to leave the hospital. He had a stereotyped dream: while in the midst of business negotiations, he would look at his watch and say, "It's late. I have to get back to the hospital."

Vocational and Social Adjustment. The patient worked in the insurance business and when he lost his job (apparently through no fault of his own) he took odd jobs, and in June 1936 was given the position of gym teacher in a WPA project.

He always liked outdoor sports, but disliked hunting and fishing, stating that he *could not bear to kill an animal.* He said that if anyone ever harmed an animal he would kill him, because he hates to see blood—that is, "animal blood." He told of an incident in which a shepherd dog that he used to walk through the fields with in summer, caught a bird and killed it. He tried to get the bird away from the dog because he *hates to see one animal kill another.* An interesting incident occurred several years ago when the patient was in a bakery shop, and a dog belonging to the baker growled at him and took a nip out of his leg. The patient told the baker to call off his dog, but the baker was amused and did nothing about it. The patient grabbed a large knife lying on the counter and started for the dog. A short time later a girl in the neighborhood was bitten by the dog, and the patient was called to court to testify against the defendant. He was almost given thirty days for *contempt of court* when he became flippant with the judge. The patient described himself as being very quick to anger and extraordinarily *sensitive to pain,* enraged by the slightest inconsideration. He never gave expression to his anger in a straightforward manner, however, but in such devious ways, as for example calling a man who had changed his name to Stedman Coles, "Simon" or "Kohn" in the presence of groups of people. He held grudges for a long time, and enjoyed revenge. His repressed aggression showed up constantly in his dreams which were full of fighting and arguing. One night he dreamed that he was walking along the street, and that some friends were fresh with him. He ran over and struck one in the jaw. A policeman came up and the patient said that he had just got out of the hospital and was weak, otherwise he would *really have been able to beat up the whole bunch.*

Course of Illness. The patient was discharged from the hospital three months after admission. The discharge note says: A case of classical coronary thrombosis, unusual in such a young man. Blood pressure was 155/110. He returned to the hospital at the end of two weeks and then again after three more weeks at which time psychotherapy was undertaken. He was seen seven times and has been followed at intervals of a few months for nearly two years. He has remained without symptoms during this period and able to be somewhat more active.

Without Organic Disease:

Case No. AS 184. A single man, aged 24, asthenic in type (Jewish), was admitted to the hospital suffering from precordial pain radiating to his right arm, so severe that it made him double up.

Onset. The immediate onset had been after dinner while he was seeing a war movie with his girl friend. He began to develop a slow insistent stabbing type of pain. This patient also made the comment on the evening of admission that he never felt better in his life, having just returned from a vacation which he had taken in order to recover from his previous attack which he describes as follows: "I was at a roadside restaurant with Mother and Father, and suddenly developed this awful pain. I remember I was eating a cheese and ham sandwich, and had a glass of beer, something I never drink."

First symptoms. In this patient, also, the sudden onset of sharp precordial pain was the beginning of a series of painful experiences with the medical profession (although interestingly enough his "heart condition" was taken more seriously than in the former case). He went immediately to see a doctor in the neighborhood (1) who told him it was "probably indigestion" and "it was all right," and gave him some medicine. A week later, still having his pain, the patient was seen by his family doctor (2) who said "It's your heart" and ordered two weeks bed-rest. After these two weeks, he went to see a specialist (3) who told him "his heart was all right." Several weeks later, however, a complete work-up and an EKG showed "slight irregularities" which were interpreted to the patient as meaning that he had "a muscle strain leading to his heart." He was told to stay in bed for an additional seven weeks, after which period of rest he was told that there was much improvement in his heart. However, the patient became "worried sick," tense and restless. Nevertheless, he went back to work and continued more or less uninterruptedly until a year and a half later when he had a mild attack lasting several days of the same type of precordial pain. He went to see his local physician (4) who told him that his heart had developed a bad murmur in the last two years. The patient was advised to go on a strict diet and to get a good deal of rest. Again he became very much worried over his health, and lost it as he always did when he worried a great deal. He saw two other doctors (5, 6) who reassured him, telling him that his heart condition was functional, and that most of his trouble was "nerves," but by this time he was so scared he was unwilling to believe them.

Heredity, Pseudo or Otherwise, and Family Adjustment. The patient's mother, aged 48, was oversolicitous and complained of pains in her chest which she thought *might be heart trouble.* The patient was an only son (having one older sister who was married just prior to the patient's admission to the hospital). The patient's father, 48 years old, in the insurance business, had an emotional make-up so much like that of the patient that a friend remarked: "It is clear they could not get along together." Although he had always been well, the father some months before the patient's admission to the hospital had been brought home from the golf course in a state of *mild sunstroke,* concerning which the patient said: "I could feel my own stomach contracting, and was nauseated. I felt as if things were moving from my abdomen up to my chest." A paternal uncle, aged 56, dropped dead of heart disease just after the onset of the patient's symptoms.

Neurotic Trends. This patient also bit his nails and had temper tantrums which, however, he said did not last long. "They were beaten out of me by my father." He noted that when he was upset he had *urinary frequency* and gas that formed in his stomach so that he would have an urge to defecate, although he had always suffered from severe constipation. He was inclined to relate his troubles to eating.

Sexual Adjustment. This patient also took up casual heterosexual relationships at the age of 15, after a period of masturbation, and suffered from *premature ejaculation.* In this connection it is interesting that the summer before his admission, a heart specialist advised him to get married.

The patient had been engaged for two years prior to his illness to a wealthy girl to whose mother he was very much devoted. The girl's mother, however, robbed him of some three thousand dollars' worth of commissions to which he was entitled for handling her investments, and gave the responsibility to someone else. He never mentioned his anger over this to either mother or daughter. He separated from the girl, gave up working with his father, and developed precordial pain. The fact that the patient never gave vent to his feelings toward his father may deserve stress. "I would just get burned up inside. Shut up and not say anything for days at a time." This has apparently something to do with his temper tantrums at the age of 5 which "were *beaten out of him by his father*." This situation is a common finding in the anginal syndrome: hatred and resentment which is being kept repressed instead of being given expression. The situation with the father was accentuated by his experience with his prospective mother-in-law who cheated him out of the proceeds of his hard work. Here again, he got all "balled up inside," not saying anything about it to anybody. Then came his sister's marriage, his father's sunstroke, awakening his sense of guilt, his uncle's death, and the confusing statements made to him by doctors.

Life Situation Immediately Prior to Onset. In addition to the above it should be noted that the patient's first attack of pain, although it occurred immediately after a meal, occurred also immediately after he had given up working for his father in the insurance business because they "couldn't agree." There were many violent conflicts which bore a relationship to his symptomatology.

Area of Focal Conflict and Characteristic Reaction. This patient, like the one preceding, had had difficulty in the sphere of adjustment to those in authority. One important difference to be noted is that instead of trying to rise to the top under his own steam he attempted to imitate his father, be as good as his father in the same business. (See section III of this Chapter, page 349, for this as characteristic of the patient with anginal syndrome and no organic disease, as contrasted with the patient with coronary occlusion.)

Course of Illness. Admission diagnosis was rheumatic heart disease, inactive (?), subacute endocarditis (?). The patient was discharged two weeks later as having no organic disease. Pneumothorax of the left apex was discovered during the hospital admission, after the patient had been in for about ten days. He had psychotherapy from the start, and remained free of somatic, although not of psychic, symptomatology for nearly two years. His economic condition and the necessity of going back to work made it impossible for him to have more than eight periods of psychotherapy.

Such case histories as these show clearly the need of more than superficial psychological study. These two patients were similar in heredity, position in the family, type of mother, attitude toward the father (both fathers even suffered sunstroke). These patients were similar in their marked oral component, oral dependent attitude, sexual conflict and inadequacy. Both were compulsive. They were similar in having been exposed to relatives with cardiovascular symptomatology, and in the situations which were the precipitating factors in the attack that led to their hospitalization. It should be noted that both patients have remained symptom-free, apparently as a result of psychotherapy, which, however, was obviously inadequate and directed toward merely the symptom complex most closely related to the organic symptomatology.

There were the following overt differences: The case without demonstrable organic damage was eight years younger and of different constitutional type, but he had actual cardiac heredity whereas the one with organic disease did not. In the case with organic disease the father died when the patient was three years old, whereas in the case without organic damage the father was living and in consequence the patient's hostility toward him was constantly brought to the surface and to some extent acted out. Did this have anything to do with the fact that in the latter the hostile and sadistic impulses were nearer to consciousness than in the former with his more passive attitude and his fear of blood? Berliner [35] has suggested that "there are deeper conversions which affect not only the functions but also the structure of organs and which apparently come into action, when a strong superego drives the ego into deep pregenital regressions, to a level where psychic and physical functions are less differentiated." And the literature contains many suggestions to this effect. Furthermore, the patient with organic damage had sufficiently repressed his difficulties to allow himself to be married, although "against his wishes," and to accept a completely passive role; the patient without organic damage, although constantly forced into a passive position, was still fighting. This is not at variance, as might appear, with the fact that the hypertensive patient's blood pressure decreases when he gives expression to either his aggressive or his passive impulses.

These two patients illustrate, also, the difference in behavior between the patient with organic heart disease and the neurotic patient with cardiac complaints to which attention is often called. Whereas the patient without organic disease always expected the doctors to find evidence of organic disease, the patient with organic disease stated that after discharge from the hospital he wanted to check up the diagnosis because he did not feel convinced that he had heart trouble even though he thought that "the doctors at the hospital were very capable"!

Do these differences have anything to do with the course of illness in the patients concerned? Is it possible that the second patient will return some time within the next few years with coronary damage? We can only agree with Pascal that *"La cœur a ses raisons que la raison ne connaît pas."*

SUMMARY OF CHARACTEROLOGICAL DEFENSES AND THEIR RELATIVE SUCCESS OR FAILURE

Coronary patients are remarkable in the apparent strength and extreme brittleness of their defenses. They are strong only in the sense that the highly unified and rigidly crystallized life role is culturally well adapted and very rewarding. When this life role, which has served as a major defense against inner poverty or insecurity, is threatened or mutilated through extreme circumstances these patients become psychologically self-destructive and experience somatic accidents. There is slightly more resilience and capacity for repair in the dilated than in the extratensive group. Patients in the latter group usually fall "never to rise again."

A major characterological defense was hard work. These patients were always up early or late to bed or both, working sometimes for forty-eight hours at a stretch, often seven days a week, and usually with no vacations. For example, patient No. CD 223 said: "I've been working all my life seven days a week, 8 A.M. till 12 at night. I've always thought that work would never kill anybody. What kills you is when customers say things to you, and the customer always has to be right even when you know he's not." One of the patients in the group who died had worked from the age of 11 until his death at 50, at first in a meat market and later with a business of his own, never having taken a vacation. There was a feeling of discomfort when not working toward some specific goal: usually favor with the boss or getting riches or power. In contrast with patients having an accident syndrome, these patients could not relieve their tension by smoking or athletics. About this drive to work these patients said: "I have to keep doing *something useful*. I have to be concentrated or worries come into my mind." Whereas the patient with fracture said: "I have to keep doing *something, it doesn't matter what,* sometimes because I'm mad, sometimes because I'm just restless." Although patients with hypertension, like the patients with coronary disease, were also ambitious and tended to work long hours, they were less successful in achieving their goal and when thwarted or disappointed, they were more readily satisfied with a position somewhat below the top. There was, however, little tendency to change from one type of job to another.

V. Therapeutic Implications*

The therapeutic problem presented by the patient with coronary disease is in many ways similar to that presented by the patient with hypertensive cardiovascular disease, and it will be remembered that a relatively high percentage (27 per cent) of the patients had a pre-existing or accompanying hypertension. Of course the physician's impulse is to start with the correction of these patients' unhygienic habits, particularly their excessive use of coffee and tobacco, their tendency to disregard sleep and recreation, their irregular eating habits, and their compulsion to work at top speed. Relative to these things, however, advice alone is rarely effective. Even the patient who pretends to co-operate is likely either to go his own way, thinking he can manage his affairs better than the doctor can; or to find himself completely unable to change these habits without a degree of emotional rebellion which in itself is as dangerous to his health as are the habits which he is attempting to give up. It is important to realize, furthermore, the coexisting self-destructive tendency of these patients which is frequently reflected in their moods of depression, although generally strongly repressed. Unless the patient is helped to understand himself in these respects and at the same time to find a better solution for his conflict, a direct attempt to correct his behavior pattern is likely to accomplish little.

Unlike most patients with the accident habit, however, the coronary patient is a particularly satisfying person with whom to work therapeutically. His life-long habit of working things out for himself makes it easy to enlist his interest and co-operation. His interest in ideas and concepts makes it relatively easy for him to understand what the physician has in mind, and the traumatic effect of the illness itself, usually reinforced by a preceding traumatic emotional situation, creates a disequilibrium in his own inner adjustment which makes it relatively easy to relieve his life-long repressions and in-

---

* See Chapter XI, section V.

hibitions. The danger relative to this latter point is the intensity of the emotions repressed, hence the physician must proceed cautiously in order not to place an undue strain on an already damaged heart. In our series, however, there were few patients in whom therapy was contraindicated for this reason, and in none of the cases in which therapy was attempted were the results anything but favorable (e.g., Case No. CD 213).

The physician should guard against being taken in by the frequent cheerfulness of these patients, their tendency to joke and take it like a good fellow. This is not an indication of "a good adjustment to the illness," as is so often assumed, but simply one more expression of the patient's characteristic, and in terms of emotional economy, damaging behavior pattern (for illustrations, see page 312). In our series the patients who were the "best sports" about their illness were the ones that died.

Another point to be borne in mind is the patient's difficulty with his sexual adjustment. His tendency to promiscuity, or to sexual indulgence, is something toward which he is likely to have strong guilt feelings, because it is in some degree in conflict with his ideals and his principles relative to being a good father. Hence he is likely to ask the doctor if he should not give up sex altogether now that he is sick. This should be recognized as another expression of his need to discipline and punish himself. Instead of agreeing with the patient that his sexual life should be restricted, it is better to relieve the patient's sense of guilt. In many cases it may be well even to encourage continuation of normal marital relations, because this in itself is a relief of vegetative tension, provided the patient feels no conflict about it. Of course such encouragement, if the patient's conflict has not been relieved, may be harmful rather than helpful.

The following cases should be read in the light of these statements:

Case No. CD 57. A married butcher came to the hospital complaining of a peculiar feeling around the heart.

Heredity. The patient said that all his ancestors lived to be past 80, and that his mother had once had high blood pressure but got over it. There was no other family history of serious illness.

General Health. This patient was pyknic in type. He had always had a tendency to have sore throats. For five years prior to admission he had suffered from indigestion and had taken mineral oil for the last ten years.

Onset of Symptoms. The patient suffered a very severe attack of substernal pain radiating down his left arm while he was cutting a steak on a very cold day after a hearty lunch. He went to a doctor who gave him a powder which did not help. The pain continued, and after ten days his wife persuaded him to come to the hospital.

He stated that he had always been afraid that there might be something wrong with his heart, that he had never been able to sleep on his left side and that he had not slept well for two years. He had noted a burning pain over the left upper chest following excitement or exertion over a period of twelve years. But this usually passed off in ten or fifteen minutes. Five or six years ago he had had slight rheumatism in his left wrist which soon passed off.

Four months prior to his admission the cardiac pain became so severe that the patient consulted a doctor who declared the trouble was his gall bladder. Since the doctor did not help him he visited a second one who told him that he had hardening of the arteries. He then consulted a third doctor who said he had aluminum poisoning and gave him a powder which relieved him.

Physical Examination. The patient, aged 48, was well-developed and well-nourished, he appeared chronically ill and was extremely pale. He was apprehensive and in pain. Examination revealed that he was dyspneic, orthopneic, and slightly cyanotic. His pupils were equal and reactive; the sclerae were muddy, possibly icteric; the fundi showed sclerosis. His ears, nose and throat were negative. His mouth showed a moderate pyorrhea. His pharynx was clear. His tongue was coated. The trachea was in midline. The veins on his neck were slightly distended. His chest was very emphysematous. His heart borders were not made out. The heart sounds were regular and rapid, of fair quality. No heart murmurs were heard. Aortic second sounds were greater than the P_2 phase, but not accentuated. The lungs were clear, emphysematous, with some basal râles. The abdomen was soft and non-tender. The spleen tip was felt just below the costal margin. The liver was one finger down, and not tender. Examination of the extremities revealed marked varicose veins of the left lower leg and minimal edema. The dorsalis pedis was barely palpable, the radials were thickened. The reflexes were physiological.

Laboratory Findings: Hemoglobin 97; red blood count 4,320,000; white blood count 7,700; polys. 78; venous pressure 85. The Wassermann test was negative and the urine was negative except for occasional white blood cells. The electrocardiogram revealed a sinus tachycardia, a bundle branch block, and a ventricular premature beat with low voltage, suggesting a considerable degree of myocardial damage with some slight changes occurring in repeated electrocardiograms, but not typical, however, of coronary occlusion. X-ray of the chest showed some passive congestion and a small amount of fluid at both bases and a moderate enlargement of the heart. On admission the serum phosphatase was found to be 8.2, inorganic phosphatase 3.1, non-protein nitrogen 43, bilirubin 2; two weeks later the serum phosphatase was 5.2, non-protein nitrogen 26, bilirubin showed a faint trace, cholesterol 217, phthalein test 48 on 400 cc., and the sedimentation rate was 4.

Reaction to Illness. The patient was not very much disturbed about his illness at the time of admission and said he was sure he would get well. But when his 17-year-old son, who has a job in a law office, visited his father in the hospital and found him in bed, the boy fainted.

Outstanding Points in the Personality History—General. The patient's work record was excellent. He was sociable and always got along well with people, except his superiors. His family adjustment was on the basis of obedience until he decided to leave them, and his sexual adjustment was never adequate.

Drive to work. The patient stated that he had got into the habit of getting up at 6 in the morning and working until 8 at night. He said: "My ambition in life was always trying to get ahead. I didn't want to be as poor as my people were. I always worried about my family, and I feel that I owe my own children something because I brought them into the world. We care about each other so much that whenever any one of us is sick, all of us are sick. Sometimes everything looks bright and then again everything looks gloomy. I always worry about tomorrow, but if I set my mind on something I have to do, I can do it."

After three years in "a little white school house" in New Jersey the patient ran away from home and started to sell newspapers. He said that he inquired from other boys what to do and how to go about it as soon as he got to the city. He paid $1.25 for a bed in a newsboys' home. He sold papers for three cents in the morning for which he paid only a cent. Throughout the day he would sell other papers. He did this for a year and then worked in a meat market for $3.50 a week, plus board. He was here for four years and then left for a better job at $7 with board. He stayed for a year, and then got $14 a week with no board. At this time he took his grandmother in and supported her. He lived like this until he married, at 21. He had saved $300 out of the money he earned, and he bought himself a business, borrowing $250 to do it. He made about $18 a week in his own business after this. He then kept on improving his business and never took a vacation. Fourteen years ago he decided to have a partner. The business has gone very well since then but he looks back with longing to the days when he had no one to consult but himself in business affairs.

Addictions and Interests. The patient was always interested in marbles, baseball and swimming, and now plays with his children. He is very much interested in food, and smoked one to two packs of cigarettes a day. He drank a good deal of coffee, but said, regarding alcohol, that a drink or two would make him tipsy. Although he was brought up strictly, he no longer went to church. But he said, "I feel I am doing right if I say my prayers at night and send my children to church."

Early Neurotic Traits. The patient denied early neurotic traits except for biting his nails, "not from nervousness but just to even them off." He had nightmares of falling off cliffs or being knocked down by billy goats, but on the whole tended to forget his dreams.

Sexual Adjustment. This patient had tended to take sex rather lightly. He masturbated early and steadily, but said to himself that it was natural and that if he said his prayers it would be all right. He was married at the age of 21 to a girl one year older and had four children to whom he has devoted his life. After the birth of the last child his wife was treated with radium and lost her interest in sex. The patient stated that this did not really matter since he had his children to devote his life to. This change in his wife came at just about the time that he took a partner in business and antedated the onset of his symptoms by about two years. Of his children he said: "I never gave them a piece of bread that it wasn't divided equally. I would like to send them to college but I won't send one until I can send them all."

Articulateness. This patient is relatively articulate and in spite of his lack of academic education has done a great deal to educate himself.

Situation Prior to Onset. It will be noted that this patient had taken a partner a little prior to the onset of his symptoms and had regretted the necessity of doing so, because he said it made him irritable for anyone but himself to have a say about how things should go. He had felt he had to do it for the sake of his business and his children, but added: "After all, a lot of business is personality and if you get irritable you can't do much anyhow. Having a partner makes it much more difficult not to get irritable." He then spoke of his sensitiveness to fighting, mentioning the fact that when another patient on the ward had got into a fight with somebody else it made him much worse.

The pressure of business had been particularly severe four months ago at the time of the exacerbation of his symptoms because his second son had just graduated from high school and wanted to go to college, and his principles of equity made it impossible to send him, so he decided to get him started in a law office and work all the harder to see whether he could not put himself in a position to send them all to college.

Focal Conflict. The patient was an only child. His father was killed in a railroad accident when the patient was two months old. Some years later the mother married a second time. The patient was unable to get along with his stepfather and after seven months decided to run away to the city. He was then 12 years old. He said: "I figured I could look out for myself without bothering them." The mother's second husband died after twelve years and she then married a man twenty years younger than herself. The patient violently disapproved of this but decided to forget about it and try to get married himself, which he did promptly, although it was necessary to use considerable persuasion with his wife-to-be because she thought they were both too young. He is now on good terms with his mother and stepfather and feels he has proved himself the better man.

Aggression and Resentment. It is clear that this patient's life experiences gave rise to a good deal of aggression and resentment, particularly his family's poverty, the death of his father, and his mother's two remarriages. He reacted to this by extreme ambition, the attempt to become an ideal father to his children, and the development of social theories.

Follow-Up. When this patient was discharged after three weeks in the hospital during which there had been no psychiatric consultation, he seemed definitely better. He said: "I've made up my mind to go home and be all right because my family needs me." Less than a year later he was readmitted with severe decompensation and died in an oxygen tent.

Summary. It will be noted that this patient followed the general pattern of our coronary group in history of diverse vegetative symptomatology, his tendency to forget what bothered him, urge to work, addictions and interests, sexual problem, and articulateness. His focal conflict was rivalry with the father, the urge to be a better father to his children than either of his two stepfathers had been. Things had gone well until he associated himself with a partner to whom he had to defer in important business matters, and then his resentment became harder to control. He differs from the general pattern in that his own father died before he was two months old so that his father ideal was rather imaginary than real. He had more fantasies and continued more interest in religion than any of the others. It is interesting also that he was freer sexually until his wife's sterilization.

A summary of the report on the second admission of this patient is as follows:

Physical Examination. In appearance he was a pale, ashen, cyanotic and orthopneic, middle-aged white male, in apparent discomfort. There was no jaundice. Examination of his ears, nose and throat was negative. His teeth were dirty and there was resorption of the gum margins. The chest was symmetrical. The heart was at the nipple line, and had a rapid gallop. The aortic second sounds were equal to the pulmonary second sounds, and there was no murmur, but one extra systole was heard. There was no fibrillation.

The pulse was rapid, of poor quality, and not alternating. The lungs were clear and resonant, there were no râles. The abdomen was soft, with no masses or spasm. There was a slight tenderness in epigastrium. In an upright position the liver was down two to three fingers and was tender. The spleen was not felt. Examination of the extremities revealed the nailbeds to be cyanotic, but there was no edema. The reflexes were equal and active, showing two plus. There was no Babinski reflex. A rectal examination was not done. Examination of the spine was negative.

The laboratory findings were: hemoglobin 13.5; red blood count 4,750,000; white blood count 8,600. Examination of the stool was negative for guaiac, ova and parasites. The urine specimen showed acid, two plus albumin, 5–50 white blood cells, and rare to 5 red blood cells; it was loaded with hyaline and fine granular casts. The serum phosphatase was 6.1, inorganic phosphatase 3.8, non-protein-nitrogen 50, and bilirubin a trace. Electrocardiogram revealed a sinus rhythm, ventricular premature beats, a bundle branch block which was unclassified. Since his electrocardiogram taken ten months ago, there have been changes taking place which indicate extensive heart muscle damage. An x-ray of the heart showed the thoracic diameter to be 20 cm., and shadows were seen which were suggestive of fluid at both bases. Sedimentation rate was 65.

On admission the patient presented a picture of marked cardiac insufficiency with cyanosis, orthopnea, but no edema, and was complaining bitterly of epigastric pain. His venous pressure was 212 and his systolic blood pressure was 110. He was placed in an oxygen tent and remained there throughout his stay in the hospital. He was given large doses of morphine for relief of epigastric and left upper quadrant pain. It was felt that he probably had a coronary infarction with emboli to the spleen and perhaps the liver. The patient lived ten days, and never seemed to improve.

The anatomical diagnosis was: arteriosclerosis of aorta; arteriosclerosis of coronary arteries, advanced, with occlusion of circumflex and anterior descending branch of left, and stenosis of right; infarcts of heart—left ventricle and interventricular septum—healed; thrombus in heart—left ventricle—organizing; embolus in splenic artery; and, infarct of spleen.

Case No. CD 181. A 48-year-old, married, Russian Jewish tailor was admitted to the hospital in relative comfort as a result of hypodermics administered by a general physician for severe precordial pain which had roused him from his sleep two nights previously.

Heredity. There was no family history of cardiovascular disease, diabetes, injury or nervousness, and also no family history of other major disease, such as cancer or tuberculosis. The patient's father had died twelve years previously of pneumonia at the age of 61. The mother and all but one of his five siblings, who was killed in the war, were living and well.

General Health. The patient was athletic in type. He had had malaria two successive summers at the ages of 6 and 7, but no subsequent attacks. He had had a hernia repaired at the age of 23, and an anal fistula incised following an ischiorectal abscess, at the age of 43. During adolescence he suffered from nose-bleeds, and throughout his life from headaches. For two years prior to his admission he had been bothered by buzzing in his ears with each heart beat. For some years he had had a chronic "cigarette cough" which disappeared if he stopped smoking. He had had neuritis in his left shoulder for years and had been told that he had high blood pressure. Blood pressure on admission was 140/90 and on discharge 100/75. In addition he had suffered for some time with psoriasis.

Onset of Symptoms. Until six days prior to admission the patient had been feeling relatively well. That evening, walking home from the station, he felt a severe squeezing pain under the precordium and became dyspneic. The pain radiated down his left side, down his left arm to his hand. He stopped walking and the pain became less severe but did not disappear entirely. He continued walking home, stopping frequently, and when he arrived he lay down. After a half-hour the sharp pain disappeared but a substernal ache persisted. He went to work the following day and again walking home from the train he had a similar attack. The substernal ache continued but there were no further attacks until he was awakened in the middle of the night on the day prior to his admission to the hospital.

The patient said that for thirteen years he had dreaded coming home because every time he expected to find that his wife had "dropped dead." This was because, following the birth of his second child, his wife, then 27 years old, began to complain of heart trouble, a pounding which made it impossible for her to lie on her left side, and which constantly woke her up. He told of having got all his savings together in order to see a doctor who was "really a big shot." The doctor had said to him: "I hate to tell you this but probably your wife will be dead in a day or two." The patient took his wife home in a taxi, put her to bed, put the house in order, and waited for her to die. Shortly after this his father died of pneumonia but his wife is still living and well except for frequent attacks which necessitate his sending for a doctor. Physicians subsequently have told him that there is nothing much wrong with her, but he could not believe this, and so for thirteen years he tried to save her from any type of exertion including work around the house, and to give her every luxury.

Physical Examination. The patient revealed a temperature of 100.4° F.; his pulse rate was 104, respiration 22; and his blood pressure was 100/75.

In appearance he was a well-developed and well-nourished male. He was restless and apprehensive. There was no cough or cyanosis, and no dyspnea. His skin showed psoriatic lesions on elbows, chest, and shins. Examination of his head was negative. His pupils were equal and reacted; the fundi was poorly visualized but the vessels appeared normal. The mouth showed pyorrhea. The throat was red and the tonsils were large. The thyroid was normal. The lungs were clear. The heart sounds were of fair quality; the rate was rapid; aortic and pulmonary second sounds were equal; and there was a soft systolic murmur but no rub. Examination of the back was negative. The abdomen showed no masses, spasm, or viscera. The genitalia were normal. Rectal examination was negative. The extremities showed no clubbing, tremor, or edema; radials were soft and equal. The reflexes were normal. There was no precordial hyperesthesia.

The laboratory findings were: red blood count, 6,000,000; white blood count 15,000; polys. 87. The smear was normal. On admission, sedimentation rate was 7, then rose to 32, decreased to 14, and then to 3. The stool was negative. The urine was negative. The electrocardiogram revealed a sinus tachycardia; Q_4 absent, T_1 inverted; T_2, T_3, T_4 upright. The T waves in leads 1 and 4 definitely indicated presence of heart muscle damage. An electrocardiogram taken three days later revealed marked changes, which consisted of T_1 becoming upright, and there was marked inversion of T waves in leads 2, 3, 4. The right T interval in leads 2 and 3 was of the so-called cove-shape. The phthalein tested 35 per cent with the dye excreted in two hours. The blood non-protein-nitrogen on admission was 45; subsequently became normal. The blood Wassermann was negative.

The patient's temperature, which was 100.6° F. on admission, remained elevated for the first three days in the hospital; thereafter it returned to normal and he was afebrile the rest of his stay in the hospital. His blood pressure was consistently about 100/65 or a little below. His white blood count returned to normal after five days in the hospital. At no time during his stay did he have precordial pain, and the rather marked apprehension that the patient showed on admission rapidly disappeared on repeated reassurance.

Summary. This is a case of coronary occlusion in a male, aged 48, with no previous cardiac history. His convalescence was uneventful, and he showed all the classical signs of a coronary occlusion.

On discharge the diagnosis was: coronary occlusion, arteriosclerotic heart disease with coronary sclerosis.

Reaction to Illness. This man showed the characteristic apprehensiveness of the coronary patient, and remarked that he did not see why this serious sickness should come to him because he had always thought it was his wife who had the bad heart. He was co-operative and gave up smoking after leaving the hospital.

Outstanding Points in the Personality History—General. The patient's work record was excellent. He was sociable and always got along well with people except his superiors. His family adjustment was on the basis of obedience until he decided to leave, and his sexual adjustment was never adequate.

General Behavior. As is already clear, this patient had the characteristic drive to work. He was the oldest of six siblings and went to a Hebrew school in Russia. He was confirmed at the age of 12 and worked with his father as a men's tailor until he came to this country. He came to New York City at the age of 24. In this country he worked as a ladies' tailor, and a good deal in factories. He had a great ambition to get ahead and had been disappointed by the hard times during the depression. He had always worked long hours and was happiest when working, except that he found his work in this country aggravating because of constant contact with the boss and foreman neither one of whom was anything like his father whom he admired greatly. Hard times had thwarted him in his ambition to have a tailor shop of his own like his father's in Russia, only better.

Addictions and Interests. As already noted, this patient had the characteristic addiction to cigarettes and coffee to give him more "pep" for work. He had no interests outside of his work and his urge to get ahead.

Early Neurotic Traits. The patient denied all early neurotic traits; he was always conscientious, and strictly religious in an orthodox way until he grew up. Although he sometimes had nightmares he never remembered any dreams. He said he regretted this because he had always thought that if he could only dream about his father it would help him to be more like him.

Sexual Adjustment. He did not talk freely about his sexual life, but apparently was strongly repressed until his marriage at the age of 27. His wife was never much interested in any physical relationship and for the last thirteen years he had felt he should spare her because of her condition. He claims, however, that this has never bothered him. He had three children.

Articulateness. The patient was highly intelligent, well educated, with a somewhat mythical trend which had replaced his early interest in religion, and very high ideals.

Situation Prior to Onset. The pain started when this patient was walking home wondering whether or not he would find his wife dead. The attack which brought him to the hospital started after a nightmare which he could not remember except that he thought it had to do with death. Five years after the patient started to worry about his wife's supposedly fatal cardiac illness, the depression came and he was no longer able to supply her with a maid to do the housework for her. He, and his son and daughter helped, but he could never escape the idea that through some failure of his he was "knowingly killing her." Three years later his son, with whom he had attempted to develop the same relationship that he had with his father, developed mastoid and then pneumonia (the illness of which his father had died) and he had felt as if everyone were dying around him. He had tried to be philosophical about this, throw himself even more energetically into his work to forget everything else.

Focal Conflict. As the patient talked further it became more and more clear that his father was his ideal. On the other hand his resentment of his father's strictness and his desire to be on his own, and a real man like his father, led him to leave his father in Russia and come to this country to get established. His adjustment to the different work conditions here, and especially the replacement of his father by foremen to whom he was forced to be subservient, had been very difficult. In the course of about six years he had established a certain equilibrium when he suffered the shock of his wife's illness and his father's death. He then focused all his interest in his work and in his son, only to have the son near death from the same illness that had killed his father. He said: "I try not to think of these things, but it hurts you sometimes somewhere, no matter how you go away from it and forget it."

Aggression and Resentment. It should be unnecessary to comment on the aggression and resentment generated by these life experiences. From the foregoing history it should be clear that the patient, in spite of his intense emotion, never allowed himself to be led into any impulsive behavior by these things. He never showed his anger with the boss because it might interfere with his going ahead. He forgot his feelings about his father's death and the illness of his wife, and instead of looking for sexual satisfaction elsewhere he forgot about sex when his wife's sickness led him to think that sexual expression was bad for her. One wonders what degree of unconscious insight, or what degree of truth there may have been back of his statement following his admission to the hospital for coronary occlusion: "Somehow it hurts you sometimes somewhere no matter how you go away from it and forget it."

Follow-Up. This patient has been followed for four years during the course of which time he has added various visits to private doctors to his clinic visits. He has had an attack of shingles lasting for two months during the whole of which time he continued to work. He has also had paralysis of the left side of his face, apparently Bell's, which cleared up with electrical treatment. He continues to work as hard as ever, although he "tries not to worry so much." He says: "Sometimes you feel you're lost. It's on your conscience because you can't do all you want to, can't do even as much as before. You feel blue and all alone. The only thing that does me any good is to be with a lot of people. Then I forget myself."

(*Note:* This patient was given no psychotherapy and the only effect of the initial work-up was to convince him that it was bad for him to get angry and worried. He tried to co-operate in this respect, as in all others, but finds there is little he can do about it.)

Case No. CD 213. A married man, aged 44, was admitted to the hospital with a diagnosis of coronary occlusion. He was in the hospital for four or five weeks, the diagnosis confirmed by electrocardiogram, and left ventricular aneurysm confirmed by x-ray. He was admitted again two months later, and again three years after his first admission with the same diagnosis.

Family History. His mother died of stroke, his father of typhoid and pneumonia. No other cardiovascular disease, diabetes, or accident reported in the family.

Personal Data. The patient was born in New Jersey. His birth and early development were normal. He had lived his life in New York City. He was married at the age of 19.

Previous Health. He had had pleurisy and gonorrhea, the latter as a result of one of his extramarital affairs.

Previous Injuries. Just about the time of his first marriage he was stabbed six times while he was watching a baby parade. Details are lacking concerning the reason for this, but it may be noted that this is a characteristic coronary type of injury.

General Adjustment. Vocational—education: The patient completed high school and two years of college, planning to study medicine. During his second year of college his father died and the patient had a severe attack of pleurisy which kept him in bed for a considerable time. *Occupation:* Financial straits resulting from his father's death necessitated his giving up his ambition. He then went into aviation and in the World War was listed as a commissioned officer and quickly promoted to the rank of first lieutenant. In the Army he had a supervisory job in engineering mechanics. After leaving the Army he went into equipment and supplies for hospitals, working up in this field for sixteen years. His *income* was about $500 a month. He saved considerable money, most of which he lost in the 1929–1930 crash. In 1931, three years before his first admission, his firm went bankrupt. He then made a fresh start and became sales manager for a liquor company.

Social adjustment. The patient was always well liked and enjoyed people although he assumed the superior attitude toward them characteristic of the coronary patient: "My father taught me the only way to get along with people is to treat them as you expect to be treated and never let anyone put anything over on you."

Sexual adjustment. This patient maintained that he was very happy with his wife and greatly upset by her death, which precipitated his second attack. He saw nothing wrong in "sexual pleasure outside the family as long as you could take care of your wife and children."

Attitude toward parents and children. Although this patient's mother had lived in the same city, he had seen her only a half dozen times in the last twenty-five years, since the death of his father when he was 20 years old. He stated that he was always on good terms with his family but they never meant much in his life. He was not affectionate with them. The patient had two children by his first wife, a boy who died in childhood and a girl who died in childbirth. He stated that he was really just as glad because he had done his duty by having children and had taken good care of them, but their deaths had relieved him of a burden which would have been too much for him after he got sick. "My second wife wanted a child so I thought I should let her have it but she had a miscarriage after three months."

Characteristic Behavior Pattern. "It's best to keep people in their place without fighting. You can usually do it with words. But if there's a reason I fight." He stated that only once did he have to have a real fight: "I was in the subway with my wife when a drunken man who had picked up a small American Legion flag began to wave it around saying that America had never been any good to him. He didn't have any use for the country. He was making a lot of commotion walking up and down and bumping into people. My wife said to me it was strange that it was always the foreign born who always criticised America the most. The man overheard it and sat down on the other side of her, frowning and trying to get her into an argument. I sat there quietly until the subway reached 72nd Street, then I picked a fight with him near the platform and shoved him out of the door. He fell and tried to rush back onto the train but the doors had closed. So he was just able to pound the windows with his fist."

(*Note:* The patient showed great emotion in discussing this episode. His face became suffused with blood and his pupils dilated as he lay in bed discussing it.)

He commented, "Although I have disciplined myself to get the upper hand at people by words, because it's better policy, it certainly does give you satisfaction to have a real fight." He then went on to express his ideas about life, stating among other things that the trouble with the United States and the world in general was lack of discipline. All groups of people like the C.I.O. should be wiped out. If discipline were maintained in the world there would be no more trouble. "Just to show you what I mean, I saw a little boy standing in front of a vendor's cart urinating. His mother tried to drag him away saying this was improper. The boy called her an s.o.b. I felt like killing him. If it had been my own son I would have killed him. Much as I liked my own son I would rather have him dead than have him speak to his mother like that." (See further under *Addictions and Interests*.)

Neurotic Traits. Early—temper tantrums. Present—none superficially obvious.

Addictions and Interests. The patient had always been a heavy smoker, and coffee drinker. He stated that it cleared his brain for work and quick decisions. He had slightly more than the usual interest of the coronary patient in sports, particularly in his early life. He said watching fights relieved his pent-up feelings. "I have never had much use for religion. If you have a mind of your own you can discipline yourself. But the way the world is the Catholic Church does a lot of good. People need to be disciplined."

Life Situation Immediately Prior to Onset. The first attack was apparently precipitated by the emotional trauma involved in the bankruptcy of his firm, settling affairs, and attempting to get a fresh start just as he was getting where he wanted to be in life. The second attack was precipitated by the death of his wife; and the third attack by financial difficulties and by the illness of his second wife whom he married eight months previously. She had a miscarriage. He was glad not to have the child; "I was upset because my second wife was going to die too, and because of the expense which I didn't know how I was going to meet."

He had an earlier traumatic experience of significance in terms of his emotional and somatic reaction pattern. Just after the war he was standing near a railroad when a workman was walking up the track and a train was coming. The workman slipped on a tomato can so that he fell onto the track and the train cut off both his legs and arms. In the second when he realized what was going to happen he had a sharp pain in the region between anus and testicles: "The feeling was so tremendous I felt as if my legs were glued together and I had to put my hands down to protect my testicles. I couldn't move for several minutes. Since then whenever I see anything that shocks me I get a spasm like that. I had the same kind of spasm there and in my heart when my wife died."

Reaction to Illness. The patient was stoical about his pain and showed considerable scorn of the people on the ward who complained and behaved like babies. He had an impulse to take the matter of ward discipline into his own hands and threatened to get out of bed and thrash the next patient who showed he was such a weakling. It became necessary for the house officer to request this patient to leave ward discipline to the doctors. In response the patient talked at length about his philosophy, as suggested above, and attempted to convert the doctor to be a better father of his children. A note appears in the chart: "The patient is a rather high-strung intelligent fellow who is inclined to resent too much medical attention and gives one the impression that he prefers to manage his own affairs. However he is rather attractive and affable."

After the patient's savings were nearly used up, and because of his illness he was not allowed to return to his regular job, it was suggested that he might have a WPA job. Characteristically, he resented this suggestion and stated that he had always managed for himself and he intended to do so. He thought with his intelligence his body could be disciplined.

Area of Focal Conflict and Characteristic Reaction. It is easy to see that for this patient the area of major conflict was that of authority, and also that his typical reaction to it was along the line of being his own boss and the boss of others. (An illustration is the incident on the ward under *Reaction to Illness.*) The patient also commented: "It's harder to keep doctors from putting things over on you than anybody else because they have the authority. That's one of the reasons I wanted to be a doctor myself. They lie to you and it makes you swell with anger because you can't fight them and don't know enough to show them up."

This patient was given brief psychotherapy to which he responded relatively well. He was followed for four years after his admission for his third attack and at the time he was last seen things were going well with him. X-ray showed no further development of his left ventricular aneurysm. He had, however, succeeded in acquiring another venereal infection.

Case No. CD 204. A married woman, 42 years old, was admitted with a tentative diagnosis of coronary thrombosis which was confirmed in the hospital. The onset of the illness was characterized by backache and fatigue, together with a tendency to palpitation and choking. Her first anginal attack occurred one month prior to admission.

Family History. Her parents were both living and well at the age of 70.

Personal Data. The patient was born in Austria, came to the United States at the age of 17. She was the second child, first girl in a family of sixteen, of whom only six lived beyond infancy.

Previous Health. The patient was always sickly. She had had one minor operation—tonsillectomy and adenoidectomy—at the age of 34; pneumonia at the age of 28, and one other major illness; severe dysmenorrhea, all her life; and an abortion. She had a tendency to gastro-intestinal attacks, bad teeth, and allergy.

Previous Injuries. None.

General Adjustment. Vocation—education: The patient always liked school, graduated from what corresponded to high school in this country, all the while working hard on her father's farm. Her sudden decision to come to this country was because she did not like her family and she wanted "to better" herself. Her parents were "terribly strict." She was married at 24, but continued to work as a waitress. In addition she was very thorough and energetic about her own housework. Her ambition had been to work up to the dignity of head waitress and she had just accomplished this when her unwanted pregnancy "spoiled everything." *Social adjustment:* Good. She was humorous and likeable. *Sexual adjustment:* "My husband says I shouldn't have married at all. Sex is disgusting to me. I never had any sensations." Her first and only child was born when the patient was 38. She was upset by the birth of the child because after that she was unable to work and it was just at this time that her husband lost his job also.

Characteristic Behavior Pattern. Compulsive need to work.

Neurotic Traits. Early nightmares of being chased with knives, of falling and particularly of the death of her parents. Present—none obvious except frigidity.

Addictions and Interests. Coffee and "Ex-lax." She thinks these things clear her system and keep her going. The patient was not much interested in religion.

Life Situation Immediately Prior to Onset. Her only child, concerning whose birth she had had a serious conflict, died from a streptococcus infection following an operation for removal of tonsils and adenoids. "I almost broke down altogether. Then my heart started to hurt."

Reaction to Illness. "Having the child spoiled my job. Then my husband lost his, and we lost most of our money. Then I lost the child too."

Area of Focal Conflict and Characteristic Reaction. This patient left home because of the strictness of her parents. She married a husband who was more like a mother than a father but still resented the fact that he held the purse strings. She said: "I like to manage things for myself. He might not have lost those bonds if I'd been taking care of it." Her reaction was to try to better herself, for which reason she came to the United States, and then to work outside the home as well as inside. Even though her occupation was more humble than that of the typical coronary patient she had the characteristic urge to work hard and become the boss. The defeating of her ambition through the unwanted pregnancy was a serious blow.

VI. CONCLUSIONS

(1) Like patients with hypertensive cardiovascular disease, and in contrast with the fracture group, patients with coronary occlusion

are relatively homogeneous. They manifest an especially clear-cut constellation of personality traits.

(2) These patients stand out from the population as a whole in their high previous illness record, their high marriage rate and their large families (in average number of children per marriage they exceed even the record for patients with hypertensive cardiovascular disease). In their educational record they are unique in the tendency to complete whatever unit is undertaken.

(3) They are predominantly extratensive, not introversive like the hypertensive cardiovascular disease patients; but the small percentage of them who show in addition a strong introversive tendency usually have some concomitant hypertension.

(4) The following individual characteristics of these patients stand out as most significant:

(a) They have a generally "distinguished" appearance with considerable evidence of control. Few classical neurotic traits are manifest but their typical life pattern of asceticism and hard work cloaks and rationalizes many compulsions.

(b) These patients present a surface calm with little of the appearance of strain that is evident in patients with hypertensive cardiovascular disease. The tension, until a crisis arises, seems to be mainly a smooth muscle tension. In times of stress they tend to brood and seek solitude.

(c) They have a general air of self-sufficiency and tend to dominate in social relationships through superior argumentative skill. They rarely allow themselves freedom in emotional expression but talk readily about themselves and describe their own feelings insofar as they can find some respectable formula or precedessor for them through Schopenhauer or the Bible, for example.

(d) Accepting the idea of hierarchy they identify with authority figures and strive to become super-authorities. Unlike the hypertensive patients, they make up their minds quickly because they have a definite frame of reference in their long range goals. The resemblance to the fracture patients is only superficial because the fracture patients' decisiveness is based upon a response to immediate values.

(e) The coronary accident in these patients is precipitated by an apparently irreparable mutilation of their picture of themselves through external threats to their authoritative role.

(f) Their initial reaction to illness is despair combined with a compulsive need to deny any need for change in their pattern of living, hence, their tendency to overdo and disobey instructions or to develop extreme depression.

(5) This personality constellation plays an important role in bringing about the coronary accident and has a bearing on prognosis and therapeutic management. With the typical extratensive coronary patient the prognosis is relatively poor unless some appeal can be made to his creative impulses. Emphasis should be laid on the creative outlets still open to them without accentuation of the necessary curtailment of their usual activities.

ANGINAL SYNDROME

I. Nature and Magnitude of the Problem

STATISTICS

It is impossible to give adequate statistics relative to the frequency of the anginal syndrome because this entity is so much less well defined than those discussed in the two preceding sections of this chapter. A definition of this syndrome together with a review of differential diagnosis problems, is given in the 1942 "Year Book of General Medicine." [202a] It is generally stated that the anginal syndrome is found most frequently after the age of 40, predominantly in the sixth decade. Males outnumber females four to one. It is a common disease in Jews but rare in Negroes.

OTHER STUDIES

There is considerable literature on interrelationships of coronary disease, hypertensive cardiovascular disease, and angina pectoris. The following recent contributions are illustrative.

Davis and Klainer [110] have compared anatomical findings in 40 cases of angina pectoris and hypertension with those in 21 cases of angina pectoris without hypertension. They found an extreme degree of coronary disease involving two or more major arteries was present in 95 per cent of the patients without hypertension and in only 39 of the patients with hypertension. The incidence of myocardial infarction was correspondingly very much higher in patients without hypertension. Angina pectoris often develops with less coronary disease in patients without hypertension. Factors other than coronary insufficiency which are important in the production of angina pectoris in hypertensive heart disease are (1) cardiac hypertrophy and (2) increased cardiac work.

In a recent study, Rytand and Holman [364] gave the results in 40 patients who underwent section of the splanchnic nerves with the removal of three pairs of lower thoracic ganglia. Criteria usually given for selection of patients were ignored. In general the results were poor. Only one patient gave brilliant results. Five others showed some reduction of blood pressure. Six felt better with no change in blood pressure. Eight died in two weeks. Nine had no change and 11 died in a year and a half. The authors concluded that the main role in deciding the outcome seemed to be played by the presence or absence of malignant hypertension as evidenced by renal and retinal arteries.

In an experiment with dogs by Green and Gregg,[209] calculation made on this basis indicated that following an increase of cardiac work through simple elevation of aortic pressure, the available coronary bed becomes smaller. On the other hand, in ischemia and in augmented cardiac work because of increased output, the bed increases because in the former the diastolic flow increases less than the pressure differential while in the latter, the reverse is true.

Bourne [46] reported that patients may present symptoms of angina of effort as a result of coronary thrombosis. Pain starts suddenly, is maximal at its onset and may be the only symptom.

Cohn [90] reported studies on the relation of the clinical manifestations of angina pectoris, coronary thrombosis, and myocardial infarction through the pathological findings in 125 consecutive autopsy studies. The numerous attacks of prolonged anginal pain were presumably due to partial ischemia which developed on exertion or excitement, because the collateral circulation while capable of meeting ordinary requirements was not sufficient for increased needs. Among the factors which increased the work of the heart and therefore its metabolic demands are exertion, arterial hypertension, emotion, valvular obstruction or insufficiency, anemia, and so on. The results suggest that constant undernourishment of specific areas in the heart may favor coronary arterial sclerosis. Exertion or emotional tension may produce still greater anoxemia and lead to necrosis and definite fibrous change.

Master, Gubner, Dack, and Jaffe [292] reported cases of coronary infarction without occlusion due to coronary insufficiency. They found that there were two types of infarction: Occlusion of the coronary artery is the end result of a progressive process in the sclerotic vessel and is followed by relatively large area of infarction extending from endocardium to pericardium. Coronary insufficiency exists whenever a disproportion arises between the oxygen requirement of the heart and the blood flow. It is produced by factors which increase the work of the heart or reduce coronary circulation, and produce a different type of infarction, usually disseminated foci of myomalacia, and is largely subendocardial. Often the clinical findings and symptoms are identical but the electrocardiograms are different.

Blumenthal and Reisinger [42] stated that prodromal attacks of pain vary from case to case as regards duration, character, and length of the period by which they preceded the obvious manifestations of coronary occlusion. Generally, the attack appeared suddenly without precipitating causes when the patient was in good health. Pain usually developed while the patient was at rest; sometimes it developed after exertion, but in these instances it usually stopped after exercise or else came on with a cessation of exercise. Some patients were able to do fairly strenuous work on the day when the attack of pain occurred. It was stated that cardiac pains other than those associated with effort may precede typical manifestations of coronary occlusion. There are undoubtedly many factors which contribute to the production of prodromal pain and subsequent coronary occlusion. Of these, it appears that hemorrhage may be especially important.

The psychological mechanisms involved in the production of anginal pain are discussed in the following articles.

Robertson and Katz reported in 1938, that by keeping the blood pressure cuff on the left arm at 50 mm. above the systolic blood pressure, pain was produced in the arm and was followed by anginal paroxysms in 19 out of 24 patients who were subject to angina. After this was repeated in the right arm, attacks followed only if the pain radiated to the right arm, in spontaneous attacks. The mechanism is not known.

Morrison and Swalm [309] in a symposium on the relation of gastro-intestinal disorders to angina pectoris and other acute cardiac conditions, write that stimuli arising from the esophagus and stomach can induce dangerous cardiac changes. Four patients with angina pectoris were studied with balloon distention of the esophagus and stomach, with recordings of the muscular activity and with corresponding electrocardiogram readings. In one there were no changes; in two there were marked changes in the RT segments including marked evidence of ventricular irritability; one patient had complete auricular ventricular standstill and nearly died. It was found that removing the gall stones from a patient who had inverted RT waves brought about a return to a normal reading in six weeks. These authors believe that the use of morphine is unwise because it upsets the gastro-intestinal tract and they recommend it only for very severe pain. It causes increased intraductal pressure in the biliary tree and spasms leading to gastro-intestinal symptoms. In six cases of angina pectoris, concentration on the gastro-intestinal tract with non-surgical drainage and antispasmodics diet, and so on, stopped the angina pectoris symptoms.

Breyfogle [49] stated: "There were 1,493 autopsy studies indicating a positive association regardless of age or sex, between gall bladder and coronary artery disease where the latter is regarded as a direct cause of death or the contributing factor."

Stressing more particularly emotional factors we find such articles as the following:

Mainzer and Krause [287, 288] write that while investigating the effect of an anesthetic, they came on the observation that fear of impending operation produced remarkable changes in the electrocardiogram of many persons with normal hearts. They mention the work of others on psychic stimuli, including fear, on the cardiovascular system. They note that there is such a striking parallelism between the tracings of these patients and the tracings obtained in coronary insufficiency or myocardial damage that a discussion seems justified. A series of tracings were made before the patients knew that they were to have an operation, again just before the anesthesia was given, then under the anesthetic, and finally some time after the operation.

No drugs were given before the electrocardiogram was taken. None of these patients had vascular disease. Patients with coronary sclerosis were not excluded. There were 40 females and 13 males. Twenty-four patients showed a changed tracing owing to fear of impending operation. The changes were of three types: Type 1a, Changes found most frequently in coronary insufficiency. Type 2b, Changes found in persons with neurocirculatory asthenia and hyperthyroidism. Type 3c, Consists of both types. In five patients, these changes disappeared immediately after the psychic stress was over. It may therefore be assumed that the fear reaction of type A corresponds to reduced coronary circulation; type B may be produced by sympathetic stimulation. Many of these patients may in fact present fear reaction and clinical fear may become apparent (fear or nervousness) or remain hidden. This is important clinically in cardiac conditions in which reasons for the changes in tracings sometimes are not clear. Sudden death from operation may represent only extreme cases of fear reaction increased by excitement under anesthesia and coronary reaction may be the main factor.

By way of review Mainzer and Krause state, "The electrocardiogram as induced by psychic emotion has been investigated by psychologists (Astruck, 1923: Landis and Slight, 1929: Weinberg, 1923). The results, which are mostly reported in the archives of psychology or psychiatry—including the paper of Blatz (1925) who is the only one to have studied the influence of fear on the electrocardiogram— are unfortunately not at our disposal. Bier (1930) found high P.R. and T waves after pleasant excitement in some of his experiences. The majority of workers used hypnosis to provoke emotional excitement.

Boas [48] noted that many writers feel that because coronary thrombosis comes on when the individual is asleep it is not a result of undue effort. He feels that trauma or bodily effort may produce coronary occlusion or angina. He discusses the pathology of coronary thrombosis and quotes Patterson, who found internal hemorrhage due to rupture of capillaries in the coronary heart wall; and also that during periods of physical stress the rise in the pressure in the capillaries of the intima may cause rupture. Hours or days later this may lead to thrombosis.

Wirth [423] stated that if as a result of physical effort or emotional stress cardiac activity is increased, there is a correspondingly increased demand for coronary flow. Because of pathological changes this increased flow cannot occur and there may result temporary relative myocardial ischemia and anoxyemia.

Regarding the differentiation of benign and fatal angina pectoris, Cornwall[103] writes that two factors, the cardiac and nervous, are important. He mentions cases of angina in which lessening of the blood supply is due to spasm—in some it is on a pathological basis. In others it varies with excitability of the nervous system. The factor of nervous hyperexcitability plays a major role in excitation of the angina in the benign cases. Benign angina is apt to predominate in early life—to be grave in later life. Benign angina is more common in women. It is more likely if there is a neurotic family history.

II. ONSET OF SYMPTOMS

In the group of patients having anginal pain without coronary disease, the onset of pain referred to the heart covered periods varying from two to fifteen years. In this group, as in the group of patients with coronary occlusion, symptoms related to gall bladder and to operations were particularly frequent. Although habits of eating, drinking and smoking were blamed by the patient in relation to the onset of these symptoms, the onset was ascribed by him to, and in all cases followed shortly after, the death of a person to whom the patient had strong emotional attachment: father, wife, mother, or friend, in this order of frequency. The first symptoms were likely to be felt on the way home from work, or occasionally on the way to work, or after a meal, or on awakening from a nightmare in the middle of the night.

III. PREDISPOSITION TO ILLNESS—FACTORS TO BE EVALUATED

ORGAN CONDITIONING—PHYSIOLOGICAL AND PSYCHOLOGICAL

Heredity—Actual and Pseudo

In the families of 51 per cent of these patients (grandparents, parents, parents' siblings), there was a *history of cardiovascular disease*; a rate which is nearly identical with the 42 per cent for patients with coronary occlusion and the 49 per cent for patients with hypertensive cardiovascular disease. If patients' siblings are included, this figure is increased to 65 per cent (the percentage among the

siblings was 24 per cent—30 per cent males, 14 per cent females);
thus the exposure factor is definitely increased.

Seventy-seven per cent of these patients (a slightly lower percentage than was found with the patients with coronary occlusion)
were *exposed* to at least one person with *cardiovascular disease*. The
heredity and exposure was about as frequent on the male as on the
female side, with a slight preponderance in favor of the former,
which may be significant in view of the preponderance in favor of the
females in the group of patients with coronary occlusion. There was
no clear history of hypertensive cardiovascular disease in these families
(which may be compared with the 9 per cent found among patients
in the group with coronary occlusion and with the 24 per cent found
in the group of patients with hypertensive cardiovascular disease).

The *diabetic heredity* and *exposure* was 12 per cent, which may be
compared with 9 per cent for the group of patients with coronary
occlusion, and 19 per cent for the group of patients with hypertensive
cardiovascular disease.

Unlike the groups of patients with coronary occlusion and hypertensive cardiovascular disease, there was no *history of injury* in the
families of these patients, except for 6 per cent, all among siblings of
male patients.

In 24 per cent of these patients *nervousness* was reported in the
parents. This is slightly lower than the figure for the patients with
coronary occlusion and much lower than that for the patients with
hypertensive cardiovascular disease. Nervousness was reported more
than twice as frequently in the families of male patients as in the
families of female patients.

Constitution—Age Range, Sex, and Marriage

Build. In this group the linear type predominated.
Age Range.

Age	Total Group Per Cent	Males Per Cent	Females Per Cent
15–24	18	30	0
25–34	53	40	71
35–44	12	10	14
45–54	18	20	14

It is clear that this group represents the youngest of the three groups
included in this chapter.

Sex. This group was 59 per cent male, and 41 per cent female.
Marriages.

	TOTAL GROUP Per Cent	MALES Per Cent	FEMALES Per Cent
15 years and over	71	70	71
21 years and over	75	78	71
25 years and over	86	100	71

Of the first group, 17 per cent of the marriages were childless (males, 14 per cent; females, 20 per cent); 33 per cent had one child (males, 43 per cent; females, 20 per cent). The average number of children per marriage was 1.5 (males, 1.3; females, 1.8). Although these figures are not below the marriage figures for the urban white population, the size of family is definitely below that for the first two groups reported. The younger age distribution must be evaluated relative to this point.

Previous Health *

This group surpasses all the other groups studied from the point of view of number of illnesses, and, in addition, the difference between the health record of males and females was the greatest found. There was an average of two-thirds of a major operation per person, and including minor operations, one and one-third operations per person. They also surpassed all other groups studied in terms of frequency of major illness—nearly three per patient—and of pelvic disorders. The venereal disease history was 5.9 per cent (males, 10 per cent, females, 0 per cent), less than one-third that for patients with hypertensive cardiovascular disease or coronary occlusion.

The types of operation and illness were the same as those given for patients with coronary occlusion. It is interesting to note that in both these groups of patients the number of severe illnesses and operations is several times greater than would be expected by comparison with general morbidity tables; whereas in the patients with fracture it is many times less. Review of these illnesses, furthermore, shows considerably more involvement of the vegetative system and a striking amount of vegetative symptomatology prior to the onset of the cardiovascular disease itself.

* See charts, Chapter III.

Statistics Concerning Previous Injury

The accident record in this group was in contrast with the record given for the patients with coronary occlusion, since only 29 per cent reported previous injuries. In this respect they resembled the patients with hypertensive cardiovascular disease but differed in that accidents were more than twice as frequent among the females as among the males. Six per cent of these patients (all of them male) had had more than one accident.

The accidents resembled the type of accident found among patients with hypertensive cardiovascular disease, although nearly half of them (as compared with 95 per cent of accidents to patients with coronary occlusion) were of the "coronary type" (Case No. AS 157, page 358). It will be remembered, however, that there were no fractures reported by patients in the coronary group, and in the anginal group 50 per cent of the accidents were fractures. These patients differed from patients with coronary occlusion in that the majority of their accidents occurred in childhood.

Early Influences and Traumatic Experiences

The average age of these patients at the time of admission was 32 as compared with 45 for patients with actual coronary disease. Hence, as might be expected, 23 per cent had both parents living, as compared with only 9 per cent of the patients with coronary occlusion. But although the group was almost equally divided between males and females, none of the parents of the females were living at the time of the patients' admission, as compared with 40 per cent of the parents of the males. This situation is the reverse of that found in patients with coronary disease where only 5 per cent of the males as compared with 33 per cent of the females had living parents; although as already noted, the small percentage of females in the group of patients with coronary disease makes this point of doubtful comparative value.

It may be significant, however, that the tendency of fathers to die relatively early was more marked in the group of patients with anginal syndrome than in the group with coronary occlusion. The average age of the patient at the time of the death of the father was 21 for this group, as compared with 25, for the patients with coronary disease; these figures being the same for patients of both sexes.

Susceptibility to maternal influence and domination was greater in this group than in the group with coronary occlusion.

As has been noted earlier, possible heredity of cardiovascular disease in this group was about the same as for patients with coronary occlusion, but the exposure was much less. The exposure to traumatic deaths as a result of accident or injury was prominent in nearly all cases. (Occurrence of cardiovascular disease was equally divided between male and female ancestors, whereas, as will be remembered, in patients with coronary occlusion occurrence of cardiovascular disease was predominantly among female ancestors—79 per cent as compared with 21 per cent.) Hence, in general, the patients in our series with anginal syndrome were less exposed to cardiovascular disease and were subjected to fewer traumatic events in their early lives (but not in adult life) than were patients with actual coronary occlusion. In their sexual lives also traumatic experiences such as venereal disease were less prominent, although the record for illegal abortions was very high, and pelvic disorders were characteristic of the females, just as in the preceding group.

Unfortunately information is lacking as to the age of these patients when first exposed to serious illness in their parents. Should studies similar to this be carried out elsewhere this point should be observed carefully.

OUTSTANDING POINTS IN THE PERSONALITY HISTORY

General Adjustment

*Vocation—Education.** As will be remembered, this group was outstanding among all the groups studied for the high percentage of patients with college education, although it is noteworthy that of those who went to college proportionally fewer were graduated than was the case with patients with coronary occlusion. Furthermore, in none of the groups studied, except patients with diabetes and patients with cardiac arrhythmia, was there so small a percentage who stopped their academic education in the grammar school category.

*Occupation.** The type of occupation chosen by these patients was closely parallel to the occupational record for the patients with

* It will be remembered that statements under starred headings are based only on patients over 21, in order to make them comparable with national statistics.

coronary disease except that there were even more of them in group II, and relatively fewer in all the lower categories, with the sole exception of group VI, in which the larger percentage of females (housewives) accounted in part for the difference. Their most frequent occupations were: hotel manager (one patient, after school at an orphanage, worked up through waiter, elevator starter, etc.) trained nurse, chief laboratory technician, secretary (frequently officials in investment trust companies and banking departments), restaurant cashier, newspaper columnist, lawyer, vice president of supply corporations, night-club entertainer, professional singer. One patient was a veteran on government compensation for non-existent heart disease. It will be noted that these occupations are fairly parallel to the occupations chosen by patients with coronary disease except for the considerable percentage of musicians and night-club entertainers (23 per cent).

*Income.** The income of these patients places them in the upper half of the groups of patients studied, but it is definitely below that for patients with coronary disease although markedly above that for patients with hypertensive cardiovascular disease and patients with fracture.

General Behavior. The general behavior pattern of these patients was similar to that of the patients with coronary occlusion, with two exceptions. First, the drive to work was slightly less intense and the ability to enjoy a little greater. Second, although the major tendency was to repress conflict, impulsive expression was a little more frequent in action and in writing and artistic endeavor. Similarly, the tendency to dominate was expressed more indirectly than directly, often through esthetic channels. Patients in this group who had no artistic outlet were inclined to be nervous and gave much less impression of poise and assurance than did patients in the coronary group.

Social Adjustment. The social adjustment of these patients was relatively good. Their tendency to dominate was expressed through their ability as entertainers rather than through intellectual domination as with the coronary patients. Like the patients with coronary disease, they tended to preserve a distance between themselves and their associates.

* It will be remembered that statements under starred headings are based only on patients over 21, in order to make them comparable with national statistics.

Patient No. AS 225, for example, said: "I love people. I am a good mixer. I generally give a good impression of myself. Every bar I've been to I always make friends; although I don't go out very much with men I'm not a lone wolf. I like respectable fun. I never gamble and I don't like jazzy girls. I like to go to a place like the Waldorf where it is quiet and where they have good music. I know all the operas and I like classical music better than popular songs. Time away from the job means nothing to me unless I can do something I really enjoy. I'd just as soon be working."

Patient No. AS 344 said: "Since my illness I've lost all my self-respect. Now I have to wear shabby clothes. I used to make good money. For your self-respect you need a lot of clothes."

Patient No. AS 269 said: "I always get along with people because I'm always friendly and never fight. Not that I wouldn't like to some times." (*Note:* This patient considered herself pleasant and placid, but there was marked pent-up emotion in her voice.)

Sexual Adjustment. These patients followed the pattern of the group of patients with coronary occlusion in their sexual adjustment, except that the women were somewhat less likely to be frigid and the men less likely to acquire venereal disease in their extramarital relationships.

There was also a considerable tendency to try to get along without sex. For example, patient No. AS 238 made the following statement:

"I mostly stave off intercourse with a remark such as, 'Listen dear, I've got to go to work tomorrow. What do you think I'm made of? I can't do that sort of thing.' " He said that he did not like to have his wife masturbate him simply because it is an artificial process, and he felt that artificial means of getting pleasure were improper.

Attitude Toward Parents and Children. Most of the patients in this group, like those in the two preceding tended to prefer the parent of the opposite sex, but from this point of view patients with anginal syndrome fell between patients with coronary occlusion and patients with hypertensive cardiovascular disease, in that the former admitted no considerable attachment to either parent, and completely refused domination by either, whereas a considerable percentage of patients with anginal syndrome admitted being influenced by the mother. Since these patients seemed to be less bound by a sense of propriety than were patients with coronary occlusion, they were a little more open in expressing feelings of hostility toward both parents, and a little less violently hostile toward their fathers. In no case did a patient report a good relationship with his father. As with patients who had coronary occlusion, the father represented a sort of ego ideal to these patients. They strove to be like him but were less determined in their struggle to outdo him.

Patient No. AS 215 stated that he and his "father were often taken for brothers. Physically we are both heavy and muscular, very good-natured, not easily aroused to anger, hard-working and energetic."

As to families of their own, the sense of responsibility from the point of view of having children was somewhat less than in any patient with coronary occlusion although the general pattern was the same and in marked contrast with that of the fracture group.

Characteristic Behavior Pattern: Compulsive Striving; Urge to Get to the Top Through Hard Work in a Non-competitive Field

It will be seen from the case histories which follow, that these patients, like the patients with coronary occlusion, had a strong drive to work, but their work records were slightly less stable, and they tended to choose occupations where they could be their own boss and achieve distinction without too much administrative responsibility. Their inclination toward the arts gave them slightly more opportunity for emotional expression and enjoyment. On the whole they showed more external nervous tension, more neurotic symptoms, and an inclination to panic.

Case No. AS 289. A married woman, aged 48, was admitted for cardiac pain of the anginal type of one week's duration. The onset was sudden. She stated later that for a period of eight years she had had milder attacks of a similar type, which she had always associated with gas in her stomach. The electrocardiagraphic study indicated auricular fibrillation and moderate heart muscle damage. The blood pressure was 150/110.

She said: "I never played. At the age of 10 I went to work at a dollar a week. I've worked all my life and I like it, except it was hard while I was married, what with taking care of the children (four of them and three abortions) who kept coming and a drinking husband who didn't support me. I left him sixteen years ago, and have supported myself, three sons and a daughter. They are all grown up and healthy, two of them married. When

I think of anything that's to be done I'll do it or I'll die. I think if I sat still for a minute I'd die."

After this patient was discharged from the hospital she was told not to return to work. A week and a half later she went back to her job. "I went staggering to work but I stuck it out. It would be better for me if I wasn't that way but I can't help it." Although there was question of infarct while this patient was in the hospital she was well and working four years later, at the time of the last follow-up visit. Her blood pressure was within the normal range.

[*Note:* This patient was given brief psychiatric treatment. In general patients with records of this type and little outlet in play or fantasy are more likely than others to develop coronary occlusion (page 319). Whether or not the brief period of psychotherapy had anything to do with preventing this development of course we cannot know, but it did result in considerable diminution of tension from pent-up feelings and a way of living which allowed a little more room for enjoyment. It helped also to bring about a reconciliation between this patient and her only daughter with whom she had not been on speaking terms since her elopement, just prior to the patient's first development of symptoms.]

Neurotic Traits—Early and Present

These patients differed from the group of patients with coronary disease in that a somewhat higher percentage of them reported early neurotic traits. This was in accord with the observation that they were slightly less repressed than the latter, or perhaps more exactly, less sternly governed by their ideas of propriety. But the type of trait reported followed the coronary pattern except for the fact that there were more phobias and fewer compulsive traits among the patients with anginal syndrome. In later life these patients were somewhat inclined to depression like the group of patients with coronary disease, but more of them, and particularly those who had no emotional outlet in esthetic channels were inclined to be nervous. Unlike patients with coronary disease, nearly all of them reported dreams, particularly of animals, fights, death and suffocation.

Addictions and Interests

Like the patients with coronary occlusion these patients were heavy smokers, and had many food idiosyncrasies. Very few of them were interested in sports or athletics. They talked at great length about making money and had relatively little interest in parenthood.

Patient No. AS 216 said: "I suppose I'd like to be married. I miss it some-times. I'd like to try it for a couple of years but it's not worth spoiling your life for."

These patients differ from the patients with coronary occlusion, however, in having relatively more interest in enjoyment and a marked interest in the arts.

In general, these patients were not interested in religion at the time of admission, although the religious interest was slightly more marked than among the group of patients with coronary occlusion. Forty-one per cent had been brought up Roman Catholic (40 per cent males, and 43 per cent females); 18 per cent were Jewish (10 per cent males, 29 per cent females); and 41 per cent were Protestant (50 per cent male and 29 per cent females). Attention should be called to the higher percentage of Roman Catholics and markedly lower percentage of Jews in this group as compared with the patients with coronary occlusion.

Life Situation Immediately Prior to the Onset

In 80 per cent of the males and 85 per cent of the females the onset of the illness was preceded by death of parent, wife, or close friend. These patients differed from the patients with coronary disease (and resembled those with hypertensive cardiovascular disease) in that they reacted with much greater shock to such deaths, and quite regu-larly ascribed their illness to them.

Patient No. AS 344 said: "On my birthday I was coming home to celebrate. A friend met me at the door and said, 'Don't go upstairs; your father is dead.' I had to go up. I was terribly frightened. I was sure his body had been mangled. A policeman was standing there. Mother said father had a severe pain in his chest and left arm, felt nauseated, and when she was helping him to the bathroom he fell and pulled her down too. He was dead by the time the ambulance came. Mother said he hadn't been mangled but I couldn't believe it. I pushed the policeman out of the way and pulled off the blanket to see. I never could believe he was dead and kept on dreaming he was alive. He was always so healthy. I was sure mother would die first, but before he died I always used to dream about his being mangled." The patient's symptoms, that she described as the same as her father's, began shortly after this. She had to give up work and commented: "Father had just lost his job when he died. I wonder if I'll die too."

In this story we see the effect of traumatic exposure to a cardiac death, the ambivalent feeling toward the parent who died expressed particularly in dreams and fantasies, and the preoccupation with ideas of death which is more overt in the patient with anginal syndrome than in the patient with coronary occlusion. It will be remembered that although traumatic deaths were a regular occurrence in the histories of these latter patients also, dreams and fantasies relative to them were rarely reported. The tendency of the patient with coronary occlusion is to deny his fears and try to pretend that nothing has happened to change the course of his life. Thwarting of ambition or financial reverses often were mentioned as secondary factors but were usually considered the result of the illness instead of a factor in bringing it on as was the case with patients with coronary occlusion.

Case No. AS 93. A 28-year-old single woman was admitted for cardiac pain of an anginal type, which had begun a little over two years ago. The pain had begun "two or three months after father's death. He died of heart trouble. He had had a stroke before and partly recovered. I never liked him much so I don't see why his death upset me. Besides it was better for him to die than to see him lying around the house suffering. But since then I have waked up nearly every night with a pain in my heart and a feeling of dying. I have awful nightmares of dying. All this trouble spoiled my job. I was selling a thousand dollars worth of hats a week and working up. Then the shop went out of business and I was too sick to make a fresh start. We lived on savings for two years. Last year the savings were all used up and we had to go on relief. That turned my hair gray."

(*Note:* This was true to the extent that the patient, aged 28, at the time of admission, had markedly graying hair. It is interesting that the mother described the patient as having been devoted to her father although the patient herself denied it. The patient's mother was her father's second wife and there had always been friction in the home.)

Case No. AS 333. A 30-year-old married man was admitted with symptoms of anginal pain and palpitation. The first symptoms had occurred nearly two years previously, following the death of his mother "who died of heart trouble." (At the same time his wife had a miscarriage.) After this he gave up drinking which had caused a great deal of friction with his wife. His attitude toward his mother was characteristically ambivalent. "She prevented my education through mother-love." Just prior to his mother's death a man who had been a great friend "and a father to my wife, died of rheumatic heart trouble. I keep having dreams about him. I see him lying dead."

Case No. AS 224. A married man, aged 43, was admitted to the hospital with pain of the anginal type. Just prior to the onset a close friend had died suddenly of "hardening of the arteries. I began to be afraid to go out alone and dream about death. Then my doctor told me I had heart trouble. This seemed likely because ten years ago they turned me down for the Army because of a murmur." As a matter of fact there was no evidence of heart disease in this patient.

Case No. AS 225. A widower, aged 45, with two children aged 12 and 20, was admitted with a squeezing knife-like pain all over the front of his chest, most severe in the precordial region. He ascribed his illness to his wife's death five months previously. Immediately after her death his son ran away from home, so he sublet his apartment, took a furnished room for himself, and put his daughter in a Catholic institution. Then he began to drink, lost his position and became preoccupied with ideas of suicide. He then pulled himself together and went back to work, but in a much lower capacity. This fact always rankled.

Reaction to Illness

Although these patients do well socially and are well liked, with the onset of their symptoms they tend to become afraid of being alone and fear that they may lose their friends. The reaction of these patients to their illness is ambivalent, as is that of the patients with hypertensive cardiovascular disease. They are constantly torn between their urge to make light of it, laugh at it, go on in spite of it (Case No. AS 289, p. 349), and an exaggerated sense of suffering and the need to be taken care of. They are likely to make severe demands on their physicians and to be alternately very critical and very grateful.

If the illness has resulted in financial hardship they have great difficulty in admitting this or accepting charity. If, however, they decide to accept help they are likely to become more difficult than ever. For example:

Patient No. AS 344. A single girl, aged 28, said: "I refuse to accept charity. The relief check bothers me. I've always made good money. Dr. —— was cross to me this morning. A doctor shouldn't speak to you that way. I knew if I was paying him he wouldn't talk to me that way. I was here on charity and had to take it."

IV. Dynamic Formulation

AREA OF FOCAL CONFLICT AND CHARACTERISTIC REACTION: RIVALRY
WITH SUPERIOR (ATTEMPT TO EQUAL RATHER THAN SURPASS)

Study of the psychosomatic histories for patients in this group
(page 356) reveals the sphere of major conflict as life relationships
involving authority, just as in the three preceding groups. But the
behavior patterns developed in the attempt to deal with this conflict
resemble those developed by the coronary patient more than those
of any other group. The following excerpts are illustrative.

Patient No. AS 238 said of his school work: "I never gave a damn. I
would never take anything from anyone better than myself. I got into
trouble because of this just after I graduated from military school with the
rank of sergeant. I was demoted for being out late. But they took me back
because I had so many good points. I learned that to get ahead you had to
obey your superiors. But I decided I could never stand army discipline and
studied for the law. I planned to be a G-man but I found that then I'd have
to take orders again so I went to work on the stock exchange instead." This
patient had the degree of bachelor of law, and in addition a master's degree.

In other words, this patient's reaction to his difficulty with authority
was not that of avoidance, as with the typical fracture patient; nor
was it working up in a specific chosen line and submitting to discipline until he reached the top as was the case with the typical patient
with coronary disease. Instead he worked hard to find himself a place
in a field where he could have distinction and still be his own boss.

This patient also, interestingly enough, married a girl much below him
educationally and socially in spite of his mother's violent objections and
repeated threats to kill herself if he did. "She hasn't come near us since I've
married, but I'm glad of it," he commented. "I'd rather be with my wife,
she's timid and does what I want. She's my kind."

There was definite indication in the further pages of his history that
he had chosen her in order to be sure to have his authority unchallenged in the home. For example, on one occasion he stated:

"I like her because: She respects me; she never makes demands; she appreciates me; she never objects to anything; she admires me; she does as I say
and never argues. It was lucky I found her when I did because I had made

up my mind I would marry when I was 25 and that was just when she came along."

This patient showed also marked altruism, mainly verbal, toward people who were underdogs, but was at considerable pains to repress his hostility with people who were his equals or superiors. His general behavior pattern in this respect is well illustrated by the following dream which is characteristic of his dreams and his everyday life: He was present when a child was knocked down by an automobile in the street. The child was lying in the street bleeding. The patient rushed to a telephone booth, called the police, told them of the accident and where it happened, but refused to give his own name. The police over the telephone were angry with him and said: "Why won't you identify yourself?" He replied, "I won't do anything of the kind." Outside the booth the crowd was grouping itself around him. The patient got angry. He shouted to them, "Instead of standing around criticising why don't you do something for the child?" The patient explained this dream as something rather realistic in his everyday life, namely, his need for helping people in distress and at the same time his tremendous fear of being implicated. For example, he never wanted to get into any general situations which involved fights, accidents and all that, because he was afraid that something might happen to him, that if he told what he knew somebody might come to shoot him or shoot his wife.

In general then, the anginal patient finds it more important to be his own authority or to be in a situation where his authority is unchallenged than to be the boss of others.

In terms of general adjustment, the anginal patients' major difficulties seemed to fall in the spheres of family and sex, although their work records were not quite so stable or so outstanding in distinction as those of the coronary group.

PROFILE *

Anginal Syndrome

1. *Family History*. Cardiovascular disease in parents and siblings, 65 per cent; accident history for parents and siblings, about 6 per cent. Nervousness, about 24 per cent. Exposure to cardiovascular disease or to sudden death, 77 per cent.

2. *Personal Data*. Both parents usually lived beyond the patient's majority, the father usually died first. Both parents typically strict. Average marriage rate. Few children, few divorces.

* In order to evaluate the distinctive features in this profile reference should be made to Chapter IX.

3. *Health Record.* Worst previous health history of all groups studied, with preponderance of major illness and major operations. Tendency to self-neglect. Women poor pelvic histories.

4. *Injuries.* Rarely more than one injury. Rate for one accident low; accidents about equally divided between coronary type and fractures. Majority of accidents in childhood.

5. *General Adjustment. Education:* Tendency to pursue academic education to a high level but less tendency than coronary group to finish unit undertaken. *Work record:* Sticking to one job but usually in a more individualistic field than coronary group. *Income and vocational level:* High, with leaning toward artistic pursuits. *Social relationships:* Generally liked. Tendency to dominate indirectly. *Sexual adjustment:* Similiar to coronary patients with more anxiety and insecurity. Venereal disease high but lower than coronary group. *Attitude toward family:* Ambivalent toward both parents and toward spouse and children.

6. *Characteristic Behavior Pattern.* Similar to that of patients with coronary occlusion, but more outlet in artistic channels, and enjoyment of, as well as a much more vivid, dream and fantasy life; also a greater awareness of anxiety and fear.

7. *Neurotic Traits.* Same general type as in patients with coronary occlusion but more phobias and nightmares, and relatively fewer compulsions. In general more outspoken neurotic traits. Tendency to dream about accidents involving death of someone.

8. *Addictions and Interests.* Tendency to take stimulants to help work. Little interest in sports or hobbies. Aesthetic interests. Skepticism about religion. As compared with the coronary group more Roman Catholics and fewer Jews.

9. *Life Situation Immediately Prior to Onset.* Exposure to shock, death of relative or friend, secondarily, financial reverses or relinquishment of prestige.

10. *Reaction to Illness.* Tendency either to minimize symptoms and go on in spite of them or to make excessive demands for care.

11. *Area of Focal Conflict and Characteristic Reaction.* Rivalry with authority but more important to be as good as superior than to surpass him—tendency to imitate rather than outdo father and tendency to be one's own boss (in a field indicating superiority) rather than the boss of others.

CASE ILLUSTRATIONS

Case No. AS 319. A married man, 43 years old, was admitted to the hospital with a diagnosis of angina pectoris.

Family History. The patient's mother's brother had heart trouble, and his sister had diabetes.

Personal Data. The patient was the oldest in a family of five. His birth and development were normal. He was born in Russia and came to the United States at the age of 20. Fourteen years prior to admission his mother, sister and brother were all killed by Polish robbers. His father was severely injured, his arm crippled and skull fractured. He was in the hospital for a year and then the patient had him brought to America to live with him. Five years prior to the patient's admission his father was run over by an automobile and killed. It was two and a half years later that the patient's son was killed (See "Life Situation Immediately Prior to Onset") and immediately thereafter that his wife left him. He married at the age of 17, and was divorced one and a half years ago. He had three children.

Previous Health. He had had two major operations, including the Beck operation for angina just prior to admission; pleurisy and many minor illnesses such as colds, gastro-intestinal disturbances, and severe pyorrhea of many years' duration.

Previous Injuries. None.

General Adjustment. Vocational—education: The patient finished what corresponds to high school. His father wanted him to become a Rabbi. *Occupation and income:* This he escaped by coming to America where he worked in the clothing business, rising quickly to the position of assistant foreman and finally to that of supervisor of the factory. His *social adjustment* was relatively good. His only real recreation was enjoyment of music. The patient's *sexual adjustment* had never been good which seems to have been partly the fault of his wife. The patient stated that he had more or less cut sex out of his life in the interest of work. *Attitude toward parents and children:* He said that he never got along well with his family because of their strictness: "I had to get away to live my own life." He nevertheless expressed affection for them. He had three children, the third, unwanted, died at the age of 11 months of rickets.

Characteristic Behavior Pattern. The patient's life had been characterized by a desire to succeed. The necessary hard work and discipline "got on my nerves quite a lot. Music is the only thing that quiets my nerves and rests me. I guess some men are happier at home than I've been. My wife always blamed me for everything that went wrong, including my son's death."

Neurotic Traits. No early neurotic traits remembered. The patient dreamed of fighting, accidents and death, in both early and later life.

Addictions and Interests. Considerable tea and coffee "to keep the mind alert" until the onset of the illness when this was cut down to three cups of tea and one of coffee. Cascara and mineral oil daily for years. No particular interest in religion although strictly brought up. Little interest in sports; marked interest in music.

Life Situation Immediately Prior to Onset. Two and a half years ago the patient's 20-year-old son was killed in an accident and the patient experienced a tingling sensation in his feet so severe that he was unable to walk. It was five months later that he first felt "a queer pain" underneath his sternum: "It wasn't exactly a pain but something had made me feel as if I had lost the world, or like disappointed love with frequent sighing." About a month later while taking a Turkish bath he felt the blood rush to his head, he developed an awful headache and started for home. A half a block before he reached his house he felt a sharp stabbing pain radiating to his back and both shoulders. He felt suffocated and "barely managed to reach home, lie down, and call for help." When his physician arrived he gave the patient an injection of amyl nitrate and told the patient he had angina pectoris.

One year ago he had had the Beck operation after which there were no severe attacks until thirteen hours before the present admission. He had been returning from work in the subway when he received a sharp jab from an elbow at the point over his heart where the rib had been removed in the operation. This was immediately followed by sharp precordial pain radiating to the left shoulder, extreme dizziness, and dyspnea. He went to bed but the acute pain persisted all night. Characteristically, he attempted to go to work the next morning but about half way up the stairs to the elevated train he had a severe attack so that he had to lie down on the floor because he was unable to stand. A policeman told him later that he was unconscious for a short time.

Reaction to Illness. As is evident from the preceding paragraphs, this patient's reaction was to keep on working in spite of his illness in order to recover the place in the scheme of things that he had lost, and to make light of his symptoms.

Area of Focal Conflict and Characteristic Reaction. This patient had trouble with authority throughout his life and came to this country to avoid conflict with his too strict parents as well as the necessity for becoming a Rabbi. His reaction, nevertheless, was to work hard until he achieved a position of authority, as is indicated by his steady work record up until the onset of the illness, and his behavior thereafter.

Case No. AS 157. A 27-year-old married woman was admitted to the hospital for attacks of precordial pain radiating down the left arm, and shortness of breath of two years' duration. The electrocardiogram showed slight changes in T 4. Basal metabolic rate varied from -10 to -16 per cent.

Personal Data. The patient was the eleventh in a family of twelve. Her birth and early development were normal. Her mother was living at the time of admission, "and healthier at 68 than I am at my young age." "Mother was a strict Catholic and never let me go to dances. When I would go she would wait up for me, make me undress and then beat me. Once she hit me so hard with a strap on my left arm that it was disabled for several days. It broke out into boils all over. Mother was funny," the patient continued laughing, "she couldn't stop beating me even after I was married. I would never cry out but I cried afterwards. My husband gradually put a stop to it." She had been married eight years, her husband was living "and too well."

Previous Health. The patient had had attacks of nausea and vomiting, and frequent headaches from childhood on. A kidney stone was removed following her fifth abortion. She had had many colds and sore throats and severe sinus trouble. In connection with her present attacks she had twitching and numbness of the left eyelid and the left side. She had had five abortions.

Previous Injuries. No serious accidents, several minor ones of the cardiac type; arm injured when her mother beat her with a strap; slightly bitten by a dog, and so on.

General Adjustment. Vocational—education: The patient stopped school at the end of the first half year of high school because she had to work, but she continued for two years in night school. *Income—occupation:* From 14 to 17 she worked in a silk mill and then left her family to take a job as cashier in a New York restaurant, and also worked in her spare time as a model. She held this position till her marriage at the age of twenty.

Social adjustment: "I like people and always get along well with them. I laugh everything off that bothers me, and people like my sense of humor. I can make jokes about myself too." She always went to a lot of parties, was admired by men, and had a gay time. She never cared for women and never made a woman friend. "I was always a tomboy as a child and even now I'd rather go with men than women. My little girl's just like me, she is always going out dressed up in her brother's suits."

Sexual adjustment: The patient stated that she never knew anything about sex. "I guess I was scared into menstruating when I was 16 by the stories I heard from other girls." She tried to conceal the fact from her mother and succeeded in doing so for some time by washing her own clothes. At the time of her marriage she knew nothing about intercourse. There were seven pregnancies with five abortions. The patient said: "I've always been in trouble. I didn't want any children." Her first abortion was prior to the birth of her first child, three came between the first and second child, and it is to the fifth that she ascribes the onset of her illness. She commented: "In the beginning I enjoyed sex, I am ashamed to say, but I got over it when I had the last abortion. Now it's repulsive." "I always used to like it best when I was bleeding. I guess that isn't very nice." She would never undress in front of her husband or sleep without a nightgown, which was an occasion for constant friction with her husband.

It is interesting that this patient was given a Rorschach test and persistently interpreted all the pictures as parts of the body, especially the female genital organs, adding: "I guess that's how it looks, I've never seen it."

Attitude toward parents and children: She said, "I never cared much for mother and father; they were very strict. My brothers and sisters never meant much to me either. I felt better when I left them. Two years after I left home father died of a stroke. He never kissed me in all my life. It was right after that I got married." "I never wanted children. They drive me crazy. I scold and beat them and yet they won't eat. But I love them. I could just eat them up when they are asleep. I never say a cross word to my husband though because I'm afraid he might get angry. Mother was the same with father. I guess women have to swallow their anger with men because men are stronger." One day when the patient's children were quarreling her son bit his sister. The patient told the girl to bite her brother, when the child would not do this the patient did it herself.

Characteristic Behavior Pattern. This patient left home in order to better herself. She had a good job as cashier with the possibility of advancement, and a steady work record until her marriage. After this her social outlets were more or less cut off as a result of seven pregnancies in five years, and she had no particular artistic outlets: her childhood temper tantrums returned. Nevertheless she continued to swallow her resentment toward her husband.

She developed hypertension and manifested the hypertensive patient's tendency to self-defeat, especially in the sphere of child-bearing; that is, she did not want to have children but refused to use contraceptives and had abortions instead. As has been stated earlier, it is hard to make a sharp distinction between the patient with hypertension who develops coronary occlusion or anginal syndrome, and the patient who develops either of these disorders "out of the blue." On the basis of our material it would seem that early thwarting of ambition plus a somewhat weaker ego organization and a greater tendency to submit to externally imposed suffering is a major determinate of the difference.

Neurotic Traits—early: Nail-biting, temper tantrums, fear of animals and nightmares disturbed this patient's childhood. These continued more or less to the *present*. She had a compulsion to lock all the doors and look under the beds whenever she entered or left the house. Recurrent nightmares were: "I always seem to be burying my father, and last April, I began to dream that Buddy (the patient's favorite son) got hurt and sure enough he fractured his clavicle, skull, and shoulder blade." She said further: "I can't understand why I keep hitting the boy on the head, particularly since he's had a fractured skull."

Addictions and Interests. Alcohol, about which she felt as guilty as about her early enjoyment of sex, tea, medicines, especially laxatives, and food. She liked meats and sweets but hated vegetables and cereals. She ate much between meals. She had no interest in religion from which, having been brought up a Roman Catholic, she tried to escape by marrying a Jew. Nevertheless she could not quite escape from her Catholic conscience and this apparently was a factor in her refusal to use contraceptives. When questioned about this she said: "I know both are forbidden, but you don't have to sin so often if you have abortions as if you use contraceptives every time." On the other hand she said that she "didn't believe in religion anyway."

Life Situation Immediately Prior to Onset. The patient's first symptoms occurred after her fifth abortion, while she was having almost continuous bleeding for a period of six months. She had lost interest in sex, decided she should not have got married because she could not take care of her children, that she might have amounted to something in the world if she had gone on with her job but now her health and her chances were ruined, and there was nothing left for her.

Reaction to Illness. In her reaction to illness this patient shifted between the attitude of going on and working in spite of it, keeping her house unnecessarily neat, etc. (she was always brushing and scrubbing her children and pressing her husband's suits), and enjoyment of her suffering. She could never organize her emotions along either line. In the course of treatment she resented the relief of the anginal syndrome, decreased breathlessness, palpitation and pain, and as these symptoms subsided, began to return to the clinic with large bruises on the left arm for which she could never give any cause. She insisted that they just appeared and must come from her bad heart. These were not petechial hemorrhages and appeared exclusively on her left arm until a doctor told her that she would have them in other places too if they came from her heart. After this she did get them in other places too!

Area of Focal Conflict and Characteristic Reaction. The sphere of this patient's major conflict was her relationship to those in authority; father, mother, husband, and church. She attempted to escape from these conflicts by leaving home because she could not avoid being beaten while at home and she wanted to better herself. She worked hard, first carrying both night school and her mill work, and then carrying her job as a cashier and modeling. After her marriage the situation changed. She lost the freedom she had achieved and was thrown back into the early atmosphere of violence to which she reacted by submitting to her husband, beating her children, and suffering: "That seems to be all there is left for me. With my broken health, I can never amount to anything."

In the course of treatment this patient herself pointed out several important facts relative to her illness. She said: "It's funny it's always my left shoulder and arm that has the pain. I wonder if it was brought on by my mother's beating me? But that's a silly idea because that's the kind of pain you get with heart trouble. Father's left arm was paralyzed when he had the stroke and died." At another time she said (beginning with the characteristic, "it's all very funny,"): "The one thing that relieves me is to have the children sick. When my boy was in the hospital with the fracture I was perfectly well. As soon as he got back home the pain and breathlesness began again. The only thing that would relieve it was to beat him."

Although this is not a clear-cut case like the one preceding because this patient had hypertensive cardiovascular disease, it seemed worth giving here because of the patient's own comment on the relationship between her emotional conflict and her symptoms. It is suggestive also from the point of view of the difference between patients who develop hypertension plus anginal pain, and the patients who do not. It is our impression that the weaker the ego organization, and the less successful the patient is in organizing his energies in the direction of his major goal, the more likely he is to have hypertension as well as anginal syndrome and/or coronary occlusion.

DEGREE AND NATURE OF SOMATIC EXPRESSION OF CONFLICTS

Tension, Aggression and Resentment

Of all the personality profiles here given those for the anginal syndrome and coronary occlusion are the most similar. From the point of view of the internist this might be expected because basically angina pectoris and cardiac infarction or coronary occlusion are so closely related that some investigators consider them different manifestations of the same disease process. The major difference is that the former represents a reversible process and the latter an irreversible process. As already stated, a considerable percentage of our anginal patients went on to the more or less irreversible phase of coronary occlusion. A first point to be noted is that the more closely these personalities resemble the coronary profile the closer is the likelihood of a somatic accident. Several heart specialists with whom this problem has been discussed suggested that in young patients presenting an anginal picture the prognosis (relative to the development of coronary damage) depends considerably on the vago-sympathetic equilibrium. This, they think, varies with the degree of crystallization of a rigid life pattern and the extent of accessory emotional outlets. As might be expected, these patients seem to resemble the coronary group in being predominantly extratensive. As yet there is too little evidence from our research review of this problem to substantiate the likely hypothesis that they are more dilated than the typical coronary patient, that is, have greater spontaneity. Should this be so these patients would be distinguished from the hypertensive coronary patient in respect to prominence of the active-passive conflict. This conflict is much more marked in the hypertensive coronory patient than in the coronary patient with a long antecedent anginal history.

These patients, like those in the two preceding groups, have trouble with their aggressive impulses, and suffer from a generalized tension. They are more likely than the patients with coronary occlusion to show this on the surface. In general they are somewhat less repressed and they are much more likely to be aware of their fears.

Activity, Verbalization, Dreams and Fantasies

These patients also have an urge to *activity,* but this urge is not expressed exclusively in work as is the case with the typical coronary patient. Patients suffering from anginal syndrome, although they work hard, take time off for enjoyment, particularly the type of enjoyment which gains them the appreciation of their rivals or superiors. Usually they have "parlor tricks," they sing well, or are experts at doing "take-offs." One patient, for example, prided himself on his prowess as a juggler which enabled him to command the center of attention in social situations.

Whereas patients with coronary occlusion are extremely *articulate* in the field of philosophy and argument, patients with anginal syndrome seek outlets in artistic channels also and are better entertainers. Their *dream* and *fantasy* life is vivid and profuse.

From the psychiatric point of view the difference between the two groups could be described as a greater prominence of phobic mechanisms in the one case, in the other a greater prominence of compulsive mechanisms, although of course, both are found in both groups. Furthermore, in both groups these mechanisms are a little elaborated in the direction of obvious neurotic symptomatology, which together with the extreme tension may be a factor in the somatic involvement. In any case, the group with anginal syndrome, which is characterized by more obvious neurotic symptom-formation than the group with coronary occlusion, has, when considered as a whole, less somatic damage. (See for example, Federn.[176])

SUMMARY OF CHARACTEROLOGICAL DEFENSES AND THEIR RELATIVE SUCCESS OR FAILURE

The defenses of these patients are for practical purposes stronger than those of patients with hypertensive cardiovascular disease and coronary occlusion. They lack the intense passive-active conflict of the former and the brittleness of the latter. They are more flexible and resilient.

V. THERAPEUTIC IMPLICATIONS *

All that has been said relative to general management of patients with coronary occlusion applies also to this group of patients. But there are some important differences.

(1) Because of the greater elaboration of conflict in neurotic symptoms, these patients are somewhat slow to respond to the simple process of being made aware of their conflicts and of the relationship of the conflicts and of their characteristic behavior pattern to their tension and their symptoms.

(2) When they know that their pain has no demonstrable basis in organic pathology they tend to cling to it all the more tenaciously.

(3) Because they have to accept the absence of organic damage and are deprived of a defensive alibi, psychotherapy should not be introduced too abruptly. A good procedure is to take their symp-

* See Chapter XI, section V.

toms seriously, using palliative drugs if necessary, and to introduce them to psychotherapy gradually as a means of interrupting the syndrome and preventing possible future organic damage (page 472 ff.).

Because so many of these patients do develop coronary occlusion as time goes on, it is the more important from the point of view of prevention to treat them early, and if possible to interrupt the personality trends that are leading them in the direction of increasing invalidism.

VI. CONCLUSIONS

(1) The patient with anginal syndrome, then, resembles the patient with coronary occlusion in both his personality structure and his symptom complex. Attention has been called previously to the fact that patients with similar symptomatology in the physiological sphere, no matter what the organic basis or etiology is found to be, tend to resemble each other more closely from the point of view of personality structure than patients with very different physiological disorders.

(2) Like patients with coronary occlusion, these patients stand out in certain respects from the population as a whole. But they differ from patients with coronary occlusion mainly in their lesser tendency to complete educational units undertaken, and in their higher general educational average. They are somewhat less likely to undertake responsibility, to have large families.

(3) Although the general profile for this group suggests a certain degree of homogeneity, it is probable that, like the profile of the fracture group, it should be subdivided. Such subdivision if properly worked out might have an important bearing on differential diagnosis and prognosis. The typically extratensive patients seem the most likely to go on to coronary damage. But this may appear true with other personalities also, in cases where channels for release of emotional energy are inadequate.

(4) The individual characteristics of patients in this group resemble so closely those of patients with coronary occlusion that there is little point in listing them in detail. The difference is mainly one of emphasis. It is noteworthy that both anginal syndrome and coronary occlusion are found frequently in combination with hypertensive cardiovascular disease. In patients suffering from any com-

bination of these three syndromes there seems to be a greater scattering of emotional energy. The tendency toward passive dependency on the mother seems to be stronger than in patients suffering from anginal syndrome or coronary occlusion alone.

(5) In any judgment of the role played by these traits in bringing about the illness syndrome, the personality constellation must be carefully evaluated. In general the more these patients diverge from the hypertensive or coronary profile the better the prognosis. Carefully oriented therapy may bring about such a divergence if undertaken at a sufficiently early stage.

Chapter VI

RHEUMATIC DISEASE

Rheumatic fever, perhaps because we know so little of its causation, seems at the moment an excellent example of a disease on the borderline where exogenous and endogenous factors are closely balanced.—GEDDES SMITH, *Plague on Us.*

INTRODUCTION: GENERAL NATURE AND MAGNITUDE OF THE PROBLEM *

STATISTICS FROM THE POINT OF VIEW OF PUBLIC HEALTH

Unfortunately public health statistics are not satisfactory on the subject of rheumatic fever and rheumatic heart disease, not only because of confusions in terminology and classification, but especially because, as Coburn [87] pointed out, rheumatic disease is so protean in its manifestations that accurate diagnosis is difficult. After commenting on the well known geographical factor in the distribution, as well as in the symptomatology of this disease, he states:

The spring season and with it the high incidence of rheumatic disease has just passed the peak in New York; nevertheless in more than one-fourth of the general medical ward beds of the Presbyterian Hospital the rheumatic state is now manifesting its protean nature. In some patients the disease is characterized by well-recognized carditis, polyarthritis, or chorea. In others, however, bizarre lesions of the skin, strange solidified areas in the lungs, vague symptoms referable to many viscera compose the foreground of the disease picture.†

---

* Cecil [78] points out that rheumatic heart disease occurs especially in the temperate zone. The polyarthritic form of the disease is relatively more prominent in the North Atlantic States. Longcope and McLean noted, he says, a greater relative frequency of cardiac compared with arthritic manifestation in Baltimore and Birmingham, Alabama. In central United States polyarthritis is very rare, but mitral stenosis is common. It is twenty times as prevalent among the poor as among the well-to-do. Multiple cases in a family are fairly common; this tendency is greater the more intimate the contact. Most cases occur within the first three decades—polyarthritis within the first four decades.

† Coburn,[87] page 2.

A census .. . . of rheumatic patients in the medical wards of the Presbyterian Hospital . . . showed variations between a minimum in the early
fall and a maximum in the early spring. In October, 1928, of the patients
on the medical wards of the Presbyterian Hospital, only 8 per cent were
known to have rheumatic disease. This incidence steadily rose until in 1929,
during March, April and May, rheumatic disease occupied 30 to 40 per
cent of the medical beds. By the following September, this had fallen to 10
per cent.*

Even apart from the more unusual manifestations of this disease
we know that rheumatoid arthritis † ranks high among causes of
disability today, and that rheumatic heart disease is one of the major
factors in the disability and mortality resulting from cardiovascular
disease.[286] Cecil [78] notes that rheumatic heart disease is relatively more
frequent among men. Females, on the other hand, suffer more from
mitral stenosis as adults, and from chorea in their early years. Sheehan
and Sutherland [378] make the following statements:

Acute rheumatism or chorea is found most frequently in the young. It is
twice as common in females as in males. After 35 there is a striking increase
in pure mitral lesion mainly in women, and pure aortic lesion mainly in men.
The significance of recurrent endocarditis is especially doubtful. It is a
terminal condition.

Is it an occasional development in the presence of certain exciting factors,
or an intermittent process coming and going unsuspectedly for many years
without any particular causation apart from the continued presence of rheumatism—or is it a serious complication?

It will be seen that every attempt at correlation of chronic valve lesion
with acute or recurrent endocarditis breaks down in some fundamental
aspect and no satisfactory explanation can be offered for the sex and age
difference of the various lesions. Nevertheless the difference appears to be
important and of some definite significance.

May G. Wilson, in analyzing available statistics, states that 3
to 7 per cent of all hospital admissions are rheumatic patients. Atwater and Swift estimated that there are 170,000 cases of rheumatic
fever a year in the United States. Cohn estimated that 20 per 1000,
or 1 in 50 persons in the adult population of the United States are
affected with heart disease. Furthermore, 60 to 80 per cent of the

* Coburn,[87] page 73.
† See Boas.[44]

heart disease in persons under 40 years of age is of rheumatic origin.[422] "In New York City during the four-year period 1933–1936, mortality from heart disease (mostly rheumatic heart disease) exceeded that from all other causes of death among girls 5 to 14 years of age, while among the boys it was exceeded only by accidents. Hedley assesses the mortality rate of rheumatic disease in Philadelphia during 1936 as 17.6 per 1000 of the population. In this city during the year studied, rheumatic heart disease resulted in more deaths in persons under 20 years of age than pulmonary tuberculosis and all the following diseases taken together: pertussis, meningococcus meningitis, measles, diphtheria, scarlet fever, and poliomyelitis." [422]

OTHER STUDIES

The literature relative to patients with rheumatic fever differs from that for the other cardiovascular groups discussed thus far, in that very little has been written about emotional factors as predisposing to this illness. Our impression, however, is that even though the chain of cause and effect may be somewhat different the emotional factor does play a prominent role.

Reference should be made to the study of chemical and other factors in determining resistance to an illness and in effecting a change of a virus from a relatively harmless form to a pathogenic one. If, as is constantly reasserted, an actual form of streptococcus has been isolated as always present in rheumatic fever, the question remains as to whether its pathogenicity may or may not be determined by the physiological equilibrium of the organism. In most patients with cardiovascular disease, for example, metabolic processes and the energy exchange in general are taking place at a relatively high level.

McGregor [294] gives a digest and discussion of some previous papers asserting a psychological factor in chronic rheumatism, but no satisfactory data is presented. Silver,[385] a state hospital psychiatrist, reports a careful psychiatric study of 21 girls with rheumatic heart disease who were residents for a year or more at a school for cardiac patients. Verbatim interviews (a social service investigation) and two personality tests were used. In these girls, he found no evidence of personality difficulties that could be related to their chronic heart disease. He observed that their social adaptability was much better than could be hoped for in a group of children visibly handicapped with other chronic disease (see p. 413). Where neurotic behavior was manifest, parental over-solicitude could be blamed. The author, thus, could not detect the presence of any particular emotional conflict in the rheumatic girls. His study did not include a search for psychological contributing factors in rheumatic exacerbations. Neustatter [314], however, who made a more extensive study, reached a different conclusion. By the questionnaire and parent-and-child interview method, the author tried to determine the incidence of "functional disorders" in rheumatism, their differences in the various manifestations of the disease, whether functional disorders precede or postdate rheumatic processes, and whether psychological situations are etiologically related to the rheumatism. He was interested also as to how far social factors might be related to both rheumatism and "nervousness." Three experimental groups of 40 children were examined: (1) those with clinical rheumatic fever; (2) those who had a history of chorea, with or without other manifestations; (3) children with "growing pains" without evident non-rheumatic etiology, who showed no objective signs of rheumatic fever. For controls, three groups of children: (1) with "good physique," (2) with very poor physique, and (3) with proved tuberculosis, were examined. Each child was seen once, and the parents twice; a questionnaire was used in the interviews with the mothers. The children were asked questions pertaining to "fear of the dark, of parents and teachers, worries, etc." An estimate of the child's personality was made at the same time, as regards "timidity, shyness (depression, secondary gain from illness), aggressiveness, obstinacy, defiance." A similar estimate of the child was obtained from the mother; she was questioned regarding behavior, mood, sleep, feeding and excretory habits, the presence of incontinence, somnabulism, vomiting, night terrors, tics, timidity, anxiety, restlessness or backwardness, and on the time relationship between the onset of such "nervousness" and the appearance of rheumatic symptoms. The diagnosis "not nervous" depended on the absence of these symptoms in the history and on interview.

The data in this study showed: (1) The sum total of features supposed to indicate underlying "nervousness" rises steadily in frequency in the various groups in the following order: controls of good physique, tuberculous controls, controls of bad physique, clinical rheumatic fever group, subjective pain group, chorea group. (2) Although there is a higher incidence of nervousness in the rheumatic patients, as compared with the unhealthy controls, this difference is not statistically significant. (3) Forty-two per cent of the nervous children in all groups were nervous before the age of 2. (4) Tics occurred in 7.5 per cent of non-rheumatic and in 31 per cent of the rheumatic groups. (5) Tics alone are specifically greater for rheumatic than other diseases. (6) Although there was a high incidence of nervousness in the subjective pain group, no psychological factors could be found to suggest that growing pains are a conversion symptom. (7) The author explained these pains as being, rather, on the basis of prolonged fatigue and emotional strain lowering resistance to the rheumatic process. He does not state whether he found growing pains in the non-rheumatic groups. (8) There is no evidence that psychological factors might be responsible for precipitating rheumatic manifestations. (9) There was suggestive, but not conclusive, evidence that "bad home conditions" may play a part in producing nervousness. (10) Psychotherapy could at times be usefully employed. (11) The features under the general heading of nervousness which are significantly greater in the rheumatic as opposed to the non-rheumatic groups are: restless sleep and night terrors, worrying disposition, timidity, mood swings, emotional instability, tics.

There was some confusion as to the meaning of the various criteria of nervousness used. The brevity of the interviews and the poor cultural status of the children, of course, made inconclusive the finding of no specific psychological factors in rheumatic exacerbations.

Gordon [206] refers to a study made by Cecil and Angevine and states that "it is obvious from these conclusions, that no one factor is going to prove responsible for various forms of chronic rheumatic disease." He describes the manner in which emotion may contribute to the condition: (1) Changes through abnormal action of the autonomic nervous system on circulatory and secretory organs and on the tone of plain muscles. (2) Respiratory exchange, urinary and sweat excretion, circulation, endocrine activity and blood. (Leucocytes can be increased and decreased by emotion without change in the differential picture. Serum calcium, potassium and chloride changes.)

(3) Derangements of bodily function by modification of the postural tone and activity of the skeletal muscles, unconscious gestures, defense, defiance supplication.

A promising study of children with rheumatic fever is being carried out at Babies Hospital by Hilde Bruch who did some of the Rorschach studies of patients recorded in this chapter.

RHEUMATIC FEVER AND RHEUMATOID ARTHRITIS

I. Introductory Comment

The reason for dividing this chapter into two sections is that in the course of our study we became impressed with certain personality differences between the patient who comes in with acute rheumatic fever characterized by polyarthritis, or with a history of several such attacks of considerable severity, but with little or no actual cardiac damage; and the type of patient who comes in with heart disease, with no history of acute rheumatic fever or merely with a history of vague growing pains on some occasion or occasions in the past. Furthermore, in the former group there seem to be two personality types, one of which is much more likely than the other to go on to the development of rheumatic heart disease.

These two types in the first group, we have called A and B. Type A has certain personality traits suggestive of the group of patients with accidents and is definitely accident-prone. These patients in spite of their many attacks of rheumatic fever, including cardiac involvement, are likely to recover with little permanent cardiac damage and many of them later develop rheumatoid arthritis. Type B, which we have called the cardiac type, have many personality traits suggestive of other cardiacs. They are not accident-prone. Our follow-up of these patients over a period of time indicates that they gradually swell the ranks of those diagnosed as having actual rheumatic heart disease.

II. Onset of Symptoms

In the majority of patients in our series the first symptoms appeared in childhood in the form of growing pains, polyarthritis, or chorea (15 per cent of the cases). Seventy per cent of them had had one or more attacks of rheumatic fever prior to the present admission. In 78 per cent of the cases (type A, 65 per cent; type B, 96 per cent) there was cardiac involvement during the period of hospitalization. The number of hospital admissions for these patients varied from one to twelve. As nearly as could be ascertained the average duration of rheumatic fever with or without cardiac involvement prior to the admission during which the patient was seen, was 9 years for type A males and 13 years for type B males with closely parallel figures for the females.

The familiar cold (Coburn,[81] pp. 155 ff.) was frequently stressed as preceding the illness or its recurrence and these patients showed a very high susceptibility to colds. This point has a special relevance to allergy psychosomatically considered (see Dunbar,[150] Wilson [418]).

In general the attack of rheumatic fever had been preceded by an upper respiratory infection or sore throat, but the attacks of joint pain had also been preceded by such diverse operations as cholecystectomy, appendectomy, erysipelas due to draining sinus from mastoid or a tetanus injection following an infected cut hand.

III. PREDISPOSITION TO ILLNESS—FACTORS TO BE EVALUATED

ORGAN CONDITIONING—PHYSIOLOGICAL AND PSYCHOLOGICAL

Heredity—Actual and Pseudo

Of these patients more than one-half (type A, 58 per cent; type B, 52 per cent) gave a *history of cardiovascular disease* in the family (i.e., in parents, grandparents, parents' siblings, or their own siblings). A family history of rheumatic disease specifically was given by nearly one-quarter of these patients (type A, 25 per cent; type B, 23 per cent) and if the patients' siblings were included this figure was somewhat increased (type A, 37 per cent; type B, 25 per cent). Exposure to cardiovascular disease was 60 per cent (63 per cent, type A; 55 per cent, type B). There was a more equal division between male and female heredity or exposure than in the coronary group; that is, there was only about 54 per cent of the patients in whose families the male rather than the female represented the heredity or the exposure. In type A the ratio of paternal to maternal heredity of rheumatic disease was one to one and one-third; in type B one to one.

A history of diabetes in the family was reported by 9 per cent of these patients whether or not the patients' siblings were included, and the figures were the same for type A and type B. That is, the history for diabetes was lower than in any of the groups discussed in the preceding chapter, except for the coronary group.

A *family history of injury* * was reported by 10 per cent of these patients (type A, 13 per cent; type B, 7 per cent). These percentages remained the same whether or not siblings were included. Among type B patients there was no additional exposure to accident, but in the type A group 2 per cent had a history of exposure to injury in a close friend or spouse. The family history of injury was higher than that for any one of the groups in the preceding chapter except patients with hypertensive cardiovascular disease, which was the same.

Nervousness was important in the families of 35 per cent of these patients (type A, 33 per cent; type B, 37 per cent). Five per cent in the type A group and 2 per cent in the type B group reported insanity or suicide in the family. Furthermore, there was a relatively high percentage of chronic alcoholic addicts in the family background of these patients (type A, 8 per cent; type B, 4 per cent).

Constitution, Age Range, Sex, and Marriage

Build. These patients were mostly of the linear type.

Age Range. The age range was 15 to 50. More than 41.7 per cent of them fell in the group 15 to 24, and about 73.1 per cent in the age group 15 to 34.† As would be expected they constituted the youngest age bracket in our cardiovascular study.

Sex. Nearly two-thirds of the group were female (37 males and 71 females). It may be of some interest that half of the male patients fell in the first age group 15–24, and three-quarters of them in the

---

* For example, three patients had fathers who died as a result of an accident; one patient had a father who had been an invalid for eight months because of an accident; one patient's brother died of burns; one patient's uncle was killed in an accident; two patients reported brothers who had serious motor accidents (in one of these patients this news coincided with her onset of illness); two patients had brothers and one a father who had had fractures, and one a brother who drowned.

† The number of patients in each age group was as follows: 15–24: 45; 25–34: 34; 35–44: 21; 45–50: 8. Total: 108.

first two decades, thus suggesting a slightly earlier onset in the male than in the female.

Marriage. Of the males slightly less than one-third (30 per cent) were married and of the females slightly more than one-half (55 per cent), resulting in an almost equal division of the group between married and single. Of those over 24 years old, 58 per cent of the males, and 77 per cent of the females were married, that is 71 per cent of the total number in the series over this age were married. Thus the tendency to marry in these patients, even when corrected for age, seemed to be slightly less than in the patients with anginal syndrome and hypertension, and markedly less than in those with coronary occlusion. The average number of children per marriage, however, was relatively high, being 1.6.

Previous Health

These patients had a better health record than other cardiovascular groups studied with the exception of those with hypertensive cardiovascular disease. They had notably fewer major operations, i.e., less than 25 per cent had had major operations although 60 per cent of the males and 70 per cent of the females had had minor operations (15 per cent gave a history of fracture, 49 per cent of the males gave a history of accident, and 13 per cent of the males had more than one accident). Twelve per cent reported appendectomies and 3 per cent splenectomies. Other operations were thyroidectomy, cholecystectomy, salpingo-chophrectomy, mastoidectomy, hemorroidectomy, removal of ovarian cysts, sinus operation, induced abortion, cesarian section; and one each of the following: amputation of toe, amputation of finger, removal of chest tumor, removal of nasal polyps, removal of nodules in neck, removal of unspecified growth from throat, unspecified operation on foot. In addition, 46 per cent reported removal of tonsils and adenoids, and 3 per cent dilatation and curettage. This operative record is lower than that for any other group studied except patients with diabetes and fractures (where the age distribution is more nearly comparable), although still triple that for the latter and more than that for the general population.

Over half of these patients had had at least one major illness. Almost half of them had pneumonia, pleurisy or severe bronchitis, and several of them had all three. (It will be remembered that half of the patients with hypertension and nearly half of those with coronary disease also gave this history of pneumonia and pleurisy.) Perhaps the most interesting aspect of their illness history is the wide range of illnesses reported without a high frequency of any particular diseases. The following illnesses were all reported but in no case by more than 5 per cent of the total group: diphtheria, epilepsy, lymphogranulomatosis, tuberculosis, jaundice, malaria, typhoid, gastro-intestinal ulcer, polyserositis, septicemia, subacute hemiplegia, facial paralysis, appendicitis, and neoplasm. About one-seventh of them had allergies of diverse types (especially asthma) and there was a marked susceptibility to upper respiratory infections, influenza, colds, sinusitis, sore throat, pharyngitis, grippe, headaches, and skin eruptions. More than one-quarter of them had bad teeth or pyorrhea, and almost half of them reported gastro-intestinal disorders. Other illnesses were: liver trouble, fibroma of the breast, lymphangitis, cellulitis, phlebitis, neuralgia, low back pain, scarlet fever, hernia, obesity, dizzy spells, gall bladder disorder, kidney disorder, disorder in eyes, nose and throat, anemia, bursitis, alcoholism, low blood pressure, fainting spells.

As to disorders of the cardiovascular system: 12 per cent had hypertension, 0.8 per cent had an anginal syndrome as well as hypertension, 1.6 per cent had coronary disease and 0.8 per cent of these had hypertension also. Seven per cent had had chorea. Twenty to 25 per cent of the patients reported "nervous breakdowns."

Most noteworthy among these patients is the fact that they exceeded all others studied, except patients with diabetes, in the frequency of pelvic disorders. (In this respect they resembled the patients with hypertension, but not in their history of venereal disease.) Only 5.7 per cent of the total group reported venereal disease. The ratio of males to females was two to one. One male reported having had both syphilis and gonorrhea.

Statistics Concerning Previous Injury

Fifteen per cent of these patients gave a history of fracture, and 30 per cent of them (40 per cent of type A, and 16 per cent of type B) a history of accident (49 per cent of the males and 27 per cent of the females), but only 7 per cent (all of them type A) had more than one accident, the ratio of male to female being three to one.

These accidents followed the pattern of the fracture patients' accidents—falls and sprains; rather than that of the coronary patients' injuries—cuts and stabs done to them by other people. There is evidence that nearly half of these accidents may have been innocent accidents. Still this figure is surprisingly high in that one might expect these patients, because of their limitation of activity, to be less exposed than the general population. It is of some interest, however, that nearly one-half of the patients having accidents fell in the age group 15 to 24, and, as with the fracture patients, this age group includes only one-third of the total number of patients. Also, half of the patients who reported more than one injury were in this age group.

Early Influences and Traumatic Experiences

Whereas traumatic events such as deaths from cardiovascular disease in the family were slightly less prominent than in the group of patients in the preceding chapter, the heredity and exposure factor was no less marked than in these three groups. It is interesting that although the percentage of cardiovascular heredity is about the same as that for the preceding groups, the exposure to traumatic death from cardiovascular disorder or accident was markedly lower than for patients with coronary disease or anginal syndrome. The percentages for such exposure are as follows: hypertensive patients, 98 per cent; patients with coronary disease, 90 per cent; anginal pain without coronary disease, 77 per cent; patients with rheumatic fever and rheumatoid arthritis, 60 per cent.

Traumatic situations resulting from injuries played a particularly prominent role in the type A group. For example, two patients had sons with fractures; one patient lived in the same apartment house with a man who committed suicide by jumping out of the window and she also saw a man who had been burned to death; one patient's husband was lame as a result of an injury received in his youth; and one patient's husband was in an institution for mental disorders as a result of a fracture of his skull.

These patients had particularly unstable home lives and had not been successful in establishing satisfactory lives of their own. Much has been said about the frequency of rheumatic fever among members of poor social groups with unstable homes, families traveling from place to place, and living under poor conditions. This factor was extremely prominent in our series and has its importance from the emotional angle as well as in the more external environmental sense (page 432 ff.).

Furthermore, like the patients with hypertensive cardiovascular disease, these patients tended to have traumatic experiences in the sphere of sex, not so much, however, as a result of sexual promiscuity but rather as a result of auto-erotism, homosexual practices and difficulty in adjusting to their sexual role. With the girls, onset of menstruation was a traumatic experience in practically all cases. For example:

Case No. RFB 2. A girl, aged 13 years, came to the cardiac clinic for treatment following her discharge from the ward of another hospital in October 1934, after three months' hospitalization for rheumatic fever and pericarditis. Her complaint was attacks of palpitation and dyspnea. These attacks came on with exertion but also when she was sitting at home quietly or in the middle of the night.

Personal Data. The patient was a school girl, 13 years old, living alone with her mother.

Family History. The patient's mother was living and well, aged 40 years. The patient's father died in 1932 following an appendectomy. There was no other history of serious organic disease in direct or collateral lines. The parents were of Italian stock, having come to this country with the paternal grandmother just before the patient was born. The father had been a carpenter. The family remained somewhat aloof, took its place in an Italian community on the "lower East side," considerably dominated by the paternal grandmother.

Personal History. The patient was an only child, born in New York City on the "lower East side," in 1922. Delivery was normal. There were no previous pregnancies. The patient had the usual childhood diseases. She suffered from fear of the dark; she was left much alone by her parents and on one occasion fell out of bed and cut her head on the chair so that a scar persists to the present time. Her first memories are of quarreling between her paternal grandmother and her mother, the former claiming that her son gave better furniture to his wife than to his mother. On these occasions the patient used to side with her mother and father against the grandmother, or more often she would run out of the house in fear. She described this grandmother as an ogress, and used to have fantasies of being eaten up by her like the old witch in Hansel and Gretel which she had seen in the movies.

The patient had a normal school record, getting on well with other children until her illness in August 1934, since which time she has become seclusive "because of her heart trouble." When questioned further she explained this by saying that other children tell dirty stories so she prefers not to associate with them either in school or out of school, besides, these stories affect her heart. Other important elements in her history will be covered in relation to her treatment.

Personality. The patient was of average intelligence; friendly, sociable, excitable. Since her illness she has developed a tendency to stay at home and listen to the radio, as noted above. She dominates her mother after the following formula: "If I don't win out I set up a holler and then mother always does what I want."

Physical Findings. A slight systolic murmur was heard at apex. Otherwise the physical examination was negative. The patient is of pyknic type, slightly overweight.

Treatment. The patient was seen four times during January and February 1935. At the end of this time the attacks of dyspnea and palpitation had ceased and she was allowed to return to school, not in the cardiac class, as had been intended at first.

Preparation for Illness and its Course. Physiological: No definite physiological preparation for illness during the two days preceding her illness could be elicited (see below). *Psychological:* There was a definite psychological preparation as will be indicated. The patient's early environment had developed in her a deep-lying fear and guilt.

The patient had gone alone to the movies on a hot summer day. All of a sudden she looked down and saw blood on her dress and leg. In terror she jumped up and ran out of the movie house, only to find that it had turned cold and was raining. She ran top-speed five blocks home and up the three flights of stairs to her apartment. She arrived pale and panting, much to the terror of her mother who put her to bed and tried to comfort her. She was convinced she was going to bleed to death and stayed in bed for four days. On the second and third days the joints of her hands and feet began to swell. She developed fever and general pain. On the fourth day she went to the clinic and was transferred immediately to the ward. The rheumatic fever followed more or less the usual course, but the attacks of dyspnea and palpitation continued, after the patient returned home. In addition, the patient was very much worried over the fact that she had not had a second period. She said she had always been afraid of blood, she "didn't know why." She blamed her mother for her illness, but not daring to confess this had set out to reform the mothers of her friends, telling them "they'd better tell their children about being sick before it happened, or else they'd get heart disease, too." Considerably more material was elicited from this patient, especially in relation to her fear of the dark, of attack, and of boys who told dirty stories. The details here are of significance in relation to the guilt feelings which lay back of her terror when her first menstrual period began. The relationship between this group of fears and her physical symptoms was made clear to her in discussing nightmares of terrible monsters attacking her, or of choking in fire and smoke.

This history is typical of several in the "potential cardiac" group. The dyspnea and palpitation were relieved by such therapy as that indicated.† Incidentally, with the relief of the anxiety the patient had her second menstrual period.

Many women in this group ascribed the onset of their first attack to an unwanted pregnancy.

Other traumatic experiences were after the following pattern:

Case No. RF 118, a married woman, aged 35, remembered being very much frightened by a doctor when quite small. The doctor had been called to see her younger sister, and at the same time to vaccinate the patient. When she heard her younger sister screaming, she crawled under a couch and could not be found. The doctor left, and the patient did not come out for fear of being whipped. Two people sat down on the couch, which sagged under their weight, and almost suffocated her; still she remained, until her boy cousin caught sight of her dress and got his mother, the patient's aunt, to pull her out, as he knew she would not punish the patient. The patient was "blue" with fright when she was pulled out. She had always been afraid of doctors since and had to be driven to consult one when she was sick.

OUTSTANDING POINTS IN THE PERSONALITY HISTORY

General Adjustment

Vocation—Education.* These patients had an educational record which was pretty close to the average of the groups studied. As in so many other respects, they resembled the accident patients most closely.

---

† The influence of emotions on the heart rate is a matter of everyday experience. Schwab [874] expressed it: emotion is "the most common heart accelerator." It is important, he states, to exclude the emotional factors in evaluating heart disease.

* It will be remembered that statements under starred headings are based only on patients over 21, in order to make them comparable with national statistics.

Their companions with actual rheumatic heart disease, like patients with hypertension, were definitely below them educationally. We found among these patients two rather distinct groups in terms of the tendency to complete the educational unit undertaken. Those with the accident habit followed the pattern of the fracture group in having a positive deviation for incomplete units, a minus deviation for the completed units. The remaining patients, however, and interestingly enough these were the patients with greater cardiac involvement, resembled the coronary group and showed a marked positive deviation for completed units, together with a negative deviation for incomplete units.

*Income.** In terms of income also these patients fall close to the average. But there is a relatively high percentage of them in the marginal group, with relatively fewer in the dependent or the comfortable categories. This figure again needs to be interpreted in the light of the two distinct patterns found among these patients.

*Occupation.** Consistent with their income record, rather than with their educational record, the majority of these patients belong to the third and fifth occupational groups. That is (a) clerks, salesmen, ticket agents, telegraph operators, insurance agents, bookkeepers; and (b) unskilled workers including waiters, and unskilled laborers in general. The percentage of males and females in each of the higher categories was about equal. The fact that there were twice as many females as males in the group becomes evident only in the number found in class VI, which includes retired persons and housewives, and was exclusively female.

Their occupations were for the most part as follows: nurse, orderly, pharmacist, merchant, jeweler, clerk, stenographer, salesgirl, cashier, printer, dairyman, elevator operator, furniture mover, truck driver, office boy, factory worker.

General Behavior. In terms of general adjustment these patients' major difficulties seemed to fall in the sphere of the family, although as just noted, their work records were not particularly good; also they had difficulties with sex.

They seemed to have traveled a good deal from one place to another and to have had great difficulty in adjusting to new surroundings.

* It will be remembered that statements under starred headings are based only on patients over 21, in order to make them comparable with national statistics.

Even twenty or thirty years later they talked about "going home" as their one great longing, and some of them had refused to marry or postponed marriage because they wanted to marry "someone from back home."

Social Adjustment. These patients were likely to be shy and not well liked socially. It should be noted, however, that when they became ill they tended to become much more likable in a childish way (e.g., Case No. RF 208, page 385).

Sexual Adjustment. Interestingly enough, even in children and adolescents suffering from their first attack of rheumatic fever, the conflict over masturbation and fear of mutilation or death as a punishment therefor, together with conflict over sexual role, male or female, as the case may be, is very prominent. Girls are inclined to be tomboys and boys to be passive or "sissy." They uniformly hate sex, whereas the first three groups discussed pretend they like it, even when this is not actually the case.

Attitude Toward Parents and Children. These patients were markedly ambivalent in their attitude toward their parents. They were as a rule well aware of their resentment, felt they had plenty of reason for it, but at the same time tended to conceal it when they felt that it might have an adverse effect on other peoples' opinion of them. They resented their children, whereas the patients in the coronary group tried to be proud of them and accept them as important responsibilities. For example:

Patient No. RF 6. A married woman, aged 42, said: "If I ever think of sewing clothes for my daughter I get a pain in my heart."

In general, these patients were afraid of assuming responsibility and wanted to be taken care of.

The preceding statements are general. Relative to parents, however, there was marked difference between type A and type B in this group. First of all, 11 per cent of the parents of type A patients were divorced (22 per cent of the males) and there was serious friction plus periodic separation between parents in 40 per cent of the cases (nearly 50 per cent for the males). This is a higher record for separation and divorce than was found in the families of any other group except for the patients with fracture, and was much higher than was found in type B patients with rheumatic fever. A typical statement is: "While father and mother threw things at each other all I could do was to sit and weep."

Characteristic Behavior Pattern: Acting a Role Combined with Diplomacy and Appeal for Sympathy

These patients on first impression were the quietest of all the patients studied. They were not very communicative except in the manner of the fracture patients, that is, they would talk readily about their interests and their hobbies. Those of the rheumatic fever group, however, who followed the cardiac pattern rather than the accident pattern, although at first reticent, tended to talk at considerable length about their emotional conflict as soon as confidence in the physician was established. The fact that neither group was lacking in emotional sensitiveness, nevertheless, was shown clearly by the skill with which they covered up their worries and answered questions in terms of what they thought was expected of them, even to the point of actually lying in an attempt to curry favor. On first impression such traits appeared to be compensation for a sense of inadequacy because of their illness, but it is probable that the conflict between parents and the moving about from place to place played an important role.

Usually these patients had a few good friends (almost always of the same sex) but disliked being with many people. The relationships even with a few good friends were likely to be somewhat ambivalent.

Patient No. RF 283, aged 15, said sadly that he really "didn't have many friends. Only two boy friends but we always have fights. I never had any girl friend. Never want to have any. Girls are soft and sissy. I do everything the fellers do, even play football. Next to football I like shooting craps." (*Note:* Playing football was definitely against doctors' orders.)

In terms of the urge to activity they fell somewhere between patients with fracture and patients with coronary occlusion. A characteristic statement is the following:

Patient No. RF 31, a married woman, aged 31, said: "If I sit my brain starts, and that bothers me. My heart, liver, and all my body gets worse. When I have to think all my body is worse."

The urge to activity was more in the direction of work than was the case with patients with fracture. Patients with rheumatic fever were less persistent and less prone to follow one clear-cut course than were the patients with coronary occlusion. But they had to keep doing something.

Neurotic Traits—Early and Present

This group of patients ranks next to the fracture group in prominence of early neurotic traits, and, as has been noted already, their accident record is worse than that of any of the other groups studied. Although they resembled the fracture group in prominence of early neurotic traits there was a slight difference in type in that temper tantrums and nightmares were relatively more frequent, and truancy, lying, and stealing less frequent. Like the patients with fracture, however, talking and walking in their sleep were characteristic. Next to temper tantrums came finickiness about food and nail-biting. Tics were relatively frequent. These patients also show strong hysterical tendencies, particularly during adolescence and later life.

Case No. RF 357. A married man, aged 39, who had had five accidents all the result of falls, stated that he was under a good deal of emotional strain at home, because of the children and continual bickering. "If I hear something fall I always jump and then I get a pain. The children get me excited and I go after them but I don't mean to be angry." He had temper tantrums and bit his nails and this habit has continued to the present day. He also walked and talked in his sleep until he was 16 and had nightmares more or less continually. The recurrent dream was of a small object coming toward him and enlarging as it came. He would wake up screaming.

His work record was also after the accident pattern. He was interested in machinery and after grammar school started as an apprentice in an automobile repair shop. But he drifted from one repair shop to another looking for better conditions and a more congenial boss. At the end of nine years he became discouraged and a friend helped him get started in elevator work. In this he advanced rapidly from helper to assistant mechanic, mechanic and foreman, which suggests a shift to the cardiac pattern.

Marked mood swings were characteristic of these patients in later life, as well as a continuation of the tendency to have nightmares. They were in general, tense with considerable guilt and depression, usually related to masturbation. Their tension, however, except for those with the accident habit, was not of the jittery type. It was rather a matter of lying still and showing pallor, increased quietness and control when resentment was aroused.

The sexual lives of these patients were characterized by auto-erotism and homosexuality with a considerable sadistic element, especially on the part of the women. Anxiety neurosis was generally present.

Case No. RF 208. A woman, aged 20, married, stated that when she was a child she liked to kill chickens by squeezing their necks and pushing them into a drain pipe. She said she liked to do it because they looked so cute. She enjoyed doing the same thing with snakes, crushing them in the middle with forked sticks. This patient insisted nonetheless that she was "fond of animals, and also her husband." She had been married for three months but had refused to have intercourse with him until two or three days before she came to the hospital. She felt as if intercourse would tear her apart and blamed her illness on bleeding following defloration.

Incidentally, this patient suffered from enuresis until the onset of menstruation at the age of 13. She had been much of a tomboy and fractured her arm falling out of a tree. She was addicted to beer, and drank four or five glasses at a time, in addition to two cups of coffee and two cups of tea daily; she smoked one and a half to two packages of cigarettes a day.

In many cases at the time of admission these patients had developed a strong reaction formation against their sadistic tendencies, which showed itself in excessive concern about the health of others even to the extent of making their perfectly well friends or children feel sick, after the pattern of: "My dear, you look as if you must be exhausted. You certainly will break down if you don't take it easy." "Doctor, you're certainly going to die young because you work so hard."

Case No. RF 135. A married Roman Catholic woman, aged 38, who stated that she went to church "because of a sense of duty although I really never saw why I should, and resented having to," was greatly preoccupied with the health of the Pope. She said that it kept her awake at night worrying about him because he had edema of the ankles and kidney disease. "He must suffer a great deal and I am sure God will take him very soon."

Case No. RF 218. A girl aged 17, single, who had nightmares and talked in her sleep, wanted to be a nurse in order to take care of people, particularly babies when they were suffering. She said she was very much afraid of fires and closed her ears and her eyes whenever she heard fire engines on the street because she could not get her "mind off the burning bodies, all writhing and black."

In addition she was afraid of water, heights and the wind, because she could not help thinking of drowning or buildings falling in a heap with everybody crushed underneath.

This patient was afraid of being looked at, speaking in the presence of others, and always blushed when told she looked nice in her clothes. What she called her modesty went so far that she could not buy clothes in a store because it was too embarrassing to try them on. Her mother had to make her dresses for her and no one was allowed to know about her underclothes. She would fly into a tantrum if her mother sent her brother upstairs to bring her her laundry.

Although her mother tried to explain to her about sex when menstruation began she would never listen to it. Then someone else told her about intercourse and she refused to believe that anything of the kind had happened between her mother and father. When she was finally goaded into asking her mother, and her mother admitted to having sex relations with her father, she developed a violent revulsion against her mother to whom she had been very much devoted. She said she "never would have expected such a thing and she ought to be ashamed of herself."

In addition to their urge to work these patients were very much preoccupied with cleanliness and being on time, and were characteristically perfectionistic. For example:

Case No. RF 186. A single male, aged 26, who was a starter of subway trains, thought it was this job that wore him down because there were so often tie ups and he could not endure having the trains even a few minutes off schedule.

Addictions and Interests

These patients tended to have rather diverse and scattered interests. About two-thirds of the men had an interest in athletics, and the 13 per cent who had had more than one accident are all in this group. The interest in athletics followed the pattern of those among the patients with fracture who felt themselves small or not quite masculine enough, and there was the same impulse to athletic activity beyond their strength. This element was even more marked among the females than among the males. They were tomboys, proud of their athletic prowess, and proud of exerting themselves contrary to doctor's orders. Over half of the females in the group who followed the accident pattern were interested in athletic sports and tended to exert themselves beyond their strength, whereas less than 27 per cent in the cardiac group showed an interest in athletics and less than one-half of these showed a tendency to over exertion.

Case No. RF 232. A girl, aged 16, said: "Before I got sick I was a tomboy. I was always tall for my age. I was the head of a gang of seven boys. I beat up my older brother. I still have marks on me from those days. This was until I was 7. After that I got sick. Every week I would pick out a different girl to go to a baseball game with me. They don't like to go. I like to watch six-day bicycle races. I love to watch basketball. Sometimes I get in and throw a basket. I love swimming, and swim too far. The doctor doesn't know how far. I like rowing and handball which is terrible for me, but I play doubles."

There was some addiction to tea, coffee, smoking, although this was not particularly striking. A tendency to seek cure by trying various patent medicines was characteristic, and there were several drug addicts.

Again, like the patients with fracture, most of these patients had a strict religious up-bringing, although there was a small group whose homes were so much broken up that they seemed to have heard little or nothing about religion. Fifty-two per cent of these patients (a higher percentage than in any of the groups in the preceding chapter) were Roman Catholics (39 per cent males and 59 per cent females); 21 per cent were Jewish (32 per cent males and 16 per cent females); and 27 per cent were Protestant (29 per cent males and 25 per cent females). Unlike the fracture patients, however, they became early disillusioned with religion or simply lost interest in it.

Life Situation Immediately Prior to the Onset

The situation prior to the onset of illness was characterized by extreme tension not only in terms of the external situation (page 377) but also in terms of inner tension, as will be obvious from the case histories themselves.

The majority stated that they were well until they came to the **United States**, or well until they came north from the south, or well until they came to the city from the country. Each change of residence seems to have been the result of a search for better living conditions, often after a period of extreme privation. For example:

Case No. RF 110. A woman, aged 31, came to this country following a period of starvation during a Turkish war and developed rheumatic fever after three months' residence in the United States.

A characteristic statement is: "Nothing ever seems to have gone quite right with me" (Case No. RF 38). This statement relates in general to a long period of early insecurity from which the patient found no way out.

The onset is often related to fights between parents followed by their separation and divorce. Patients illustrating both these factors are:

Case No. RF 198. A woman, aged 32, after returning from Germany to New York at the age of 7, was told that she had heart trouble. She came to live with a "very disagreeable stepmother, who wasn't much relief from my actually devilish mother." She reported "variable stepfathers" and a husband "who is absolutely no good," and did not support her.

Case No. RF 200. A woman, aged 26, the illegitimate child of an alcoholic mother, developed rheumatism a few weeks after her arrival in the United States from Ireland, and each of her ten admissions to the hospital for a rheumatic flare-up *followed a severe beating*. The last attack followed the serious illness of her fiancé who had nearly died of pneumonia, which terrified the patient because "he was all I had." Even her relationship to him, however, was marked by extreme insecurity because he insisted on having intercourse with her and then each time blamed her for having "led him into sin."

Recurrence of the illness was blamed on similar events: leaving home to get married or trouble with spouse. Among the women: the onset of menstruation, pregnancies and miscarriages were very regularly given as causes of the illness or its recurrence.

It is clear, in other words, that the early insecurity of these patients is not only in the social and environmental setting but also in all their close human relationships. It will be noted that this period of early insecurity is similar to that found among the fracture patients. The patients with rheumatic fever, however, are usually unable to leave home, and the constant exposure to ambivalent relationships with parents and relatives of both sexes probably increases the difficulty of adjustment to their own sexual role, a point which will be discussed later.

Case No. RF 146. A man, 28 years old, a clerk in a jewelry company, was admitted to the hospital with his third attack of rheumatic fever. He gave a history of pains at the age of 12 but his first actual attack occurred when his family discussed moving next door. He stated that he did not want to move with them because there were two great Danes in the house. It was his subsequent sickness that kept them from moving. The doctor who cared for him during this attack told him his heart muscles had wasted away. This frightened him so much that he was unable to sleep and began to have attacks of palpitation. The patient stated, however, that he had been subject to such attacks as well as stomach upsets all his life. His second attack occurred at the age of 21, following his father's death of angina. This was particularly traumatic because it was the age beyond which, according to the doctor, he would not live. Prior to the present attack he reported a long period of stress and strain because he was living with mother, brother, and sister, all of whom were nervous and irritable and in constant conflict with each other. The mother attempted to order them around like children. He spoke also of a similar strain in connection with his business because of a boss who was much the same way. He thought this last attack was brought on because the boss committed suicide.

Reaction to Illness

In general their illness meant for these patients an excuse for getting out of things they did not want to do, while it in no sense deterred them from forbidden activities that appealed to them. The only exception seemed to be in the case of patients whose symptoms recalled early frights or unpleasant experiences, as, for example, patient No. RF 118 (page 380). Characteristic statements are as follows:

Patient No. RF 58, a man, aged 48, did not stop working until his doctor, after many times advising him to do so, told him that he would die within two or three days if he worked one hour more.

Patient No. RF 31, a woman, aged 31, who was seriously decompensated, said: "I am too active. If I don't read I write letters or I do crochet work. I cook in bed. I call my children and they bring it to me."

A frequent statement was: "My hands can't be idle because it gives me time to think." When definitely confined to bed these patients were always doing something with their hands, knitting, crocheting, drawing or making things.

Patient No. RF 120, a woman, aged 28, stated that she never worried, that is when she was doing something. If she ever sat down she started to think and that bothered her.

Patient No. RF 34, a woman, aged 48, said: "I probably did too much. The minute I could keep going after my last attack I kept my fingers in action."

Patient No. RF 35, a woman, aged 35, said: "When I sit down I think of everything."

Like patients with diabetes, and unlike the other cardiac patients discussed, they have a tendency to enjoy their suffering.

Patient No. RF 41, a woman, aged 42, said: "My husband is always saying to me, 'Why do you put yourself in the grave for the children? You give them all you've got, and then you let them ask for more.' "

Patient No. RF 198, a woman, aged 32, who would not carry out her physicians' recommendation to give up her job as a waitress and not have so many children, kept on, but was constantly reproaching her mother with her suffering, saying: "If you'd treated me better I wouldn't be so sick."

Patient No. RF 314, a woman, aged 29, said: "I am a glutton for punishment. I keep on going when I can hardly crawl."

The tendency to get satisfaction out of suffering, or to bear illness with excessive patience is one of the most common characteristics of these patients, and is noted by the social workers in their notes and by nurses as well as by the psychiatrist. In some of these it is especially outstanding: Patient No. RF 118 seemed to take pleasure in telling how long she went without a doctor and how much she suffered. She had a martyr attitude which was seen also in patients No. RF 31, RF 41, RF 110, RF 121, RF 183, and RF 200.

Carried even further, this tendency goes to the point of excessive self-neglect. In some this is unconscious, in others conscious, and is in marked contrast to the group of patients with fracture. From the point of view of the nature of their self-neglect they differ also from the coronary patients who show the same tendency but always in the interests of achievement of their goal, whereas with these patients the self-neglect is in the interests of pleasure, often of martyrdom.

IV. Dynamic Formulation

AREA OF FOCAL CONFLICT AND CHARACTERISTIC REACTION: SEXUAL ROLE—IDENTIFICATION WITH OPPOSITE SEX; AUTHORITY— AVOIDANCE OR SUBMISSION

Again, resembling fracture patients more closely than those in any other group, these patients reported strict parents. Conflict between the parents, however, was a factor of great importance. There was a tendency to temper tantrums on the part of the father in the majority of cases, and on the part of the mother frequently. Unlike the fracture patients, they tended to become involved in this conflict themselves and to take sides, unless they were terrified to tears.

Case No. RF 121. A woman, aged 22, said that her mother and father hurled things at each other, used abusive language, and were always scrapping. "When I was a child I used to stand in the corner and cry as they belabored each other."

The father was rather easy in general but "would lose his temper and beat us children with his belt. I was the only one who never got spanked, except once when I was 10 years old for having come home from a wedding by myself at midnight. Father *put blankets over my body and then started to beat me with the belt*, so that I would not feel it very much."

In contrast with the preceding groups of patients with cardiovascular disease, these patients were all brought up primarily by females, mothers, grandmothers, aunts, and occasional housemothers in orphan asylums. In 30 per cent of the cases the father died or deserted the mother before the patient's adolescence, and usually when the patient was very young. In the other cases the mother, or occasionally the grandmother, was the dominating person in the household, sometimes ruling tyrannically (reported by one-fifth of the cases) and "wearing the pants," but more often ruling from behind the scenes, or as patient No. RF 146 said: "Mother always had a way of putting things so everyone had to do them her way." Of the patients who complained of strictness on the part of both parents, all reported a grandmother, aunt, or sister to whom they could run for comfort and understanding. In spite of the predominant role played by the females in the families of these patients, the father usually left his mark on them. These fathers were erratic, prone to tempers, and best remembered by the severity and variety of the punishments they meted out.

Case No. RF 140. A man, aged 24, a "soda jerker," was admitted to the hospital for the fourth time with a diagnosis of acute rheumatic fever. (The first admission seven years previously had been with polyarthritis; the second, six years previously, polyarthritis and fever; the third, four years previously, with acute streptococcus pharyngitis and joint pain.) The patient's mother died when he was 4 years old and his father remarried when the patient was 9. At this time the patient had a tonsillectomy and then got himself struck by a beam and that fractured his skull. Although he first described his father as easy-going, he nevertheless stressed that he was the kind of "feller you always had to obey." "If you didn't it was a matter of a thrashing, and if he didn't want to bother with that he made me chew up Epsom salts."

In the light of these facts it is easy to understand the conflict developed by these patients relative to their sexual role. Although both boys and girls preferred the mother, the girls developed male characteristics partly to protect the mother, and partly as a defense against submission to the father. The boys, on the other hand, were blocked in the development of their masculinity by the fact that even more than their sisters they needed protection from their mothers, and, on the other hand, their fathers made their own natural masculine tendencies abhorrent to them, and of course in any case competition with the father was impossible. Both sexes were markedly narcissistic and their sex life had a strong auto-erotic element. When they did reach out toward a sexual relationship this was likely to be homosexual in character. Homosexual relationships in which the patient was the aggressor were characteristic of the accident type, and passive homosexuality was more frequent in what we have called the cardiac type. Some of the former, especially some of the men, showed a reaction formation against their homosexual impulses in the direction of promiscuity. They spoke of this as a demonstration of their sexual prowess and boasted about the number and intensity of their affairs but said at the same time that the whole business meant nothing to them, and that they got no satisfaction.

Case No. RF 228. A bookmaker, aged 27, unmarried, "was admitted to the clinic for the third time one week ago, with symptoms of fever, and an elevated sedimentation rate following an upper respiratory infection, which turned into hemolytic streptococcus pharyngitis. His first hospital admission was in 1928 when he had just completed high school and was preparing to go to New York University. How long he was in the hospital at that time he does not recall, but says that it was for many weeks. The original symptoms were primarily joint pains, with fever and relatively little evidence of cardiac disturbance on a rheumatic basis. On the *second admission,* in 1933, the cardiac aspect became apparent, although no mitral stenosis was seen at that time. On this admission he was essentially well except for his fever, but while he was in the hospital he developed a flare-up of joint pains, perhaps the most serious he has had so far. The pain was primarily centered in the knees and shoulders, but there was also pain in practically all the other joints, particularly the cervical region of the spine."

The patient said: "I can never get interested in a girl. I'm not the loving kind." The patient said that he had intercourse a great deal. He had no difficulties whatsoever in this line, and when he got "a good number" he could have three or four orgasms in an evening. He does not plan to get married. He said that there is no sense in it.

He reported that he began school at the age of 6, and that he went through grammar school and high school. He finished high school in three and a half years. The patient claimed that he was never particularly interested in his work, and never did any studying. He had a job three days a week as a cashier in a drug store.

He had never been interested in athletics.

After a certain amount of loafing after his original illness in 1928 he became a "bookie," and had been one ever since. He had had good and bad times. He described in detail many of the experiences he had had with the police. He had been arrested innumerable times, but never put in jail for more than a few hours. He had bought back his finger prints for fifty dollars. "Many of the police come around and milk me for money."

The women in the group who followed the accident pattern were tomboys and tended to avoid pregnancy. Those who followed the cardiac pattern were likely to submit and then have miscarriages and abortions. Of the married women in the group 50 per cent had had at least one abortion or miscarriage and 15 per cent two or more. It may be noted that the 50 per cent corresponds to the 50 per cent of these patients who followed the cardiac pattern instead of the accident pattern. The following case illustrates the accident pattern type:

Case No. RF 190. A married woman, aged 35, with one child, stated that her whole social life consisted of staying home and taking care of the baby. "It's too bad it's the woman who has to have the child, because I was really cut out to be the man of the family." She said that sexual relationships with her husband were satisfactory but left her tired. She asked for contraceptive advice because "it would be terrible to have another child." She said she and her husband were very happy, although she kept him waiting a good many years just to be sure. She "thinks that he is not very bright," on the whole inferior to her, but that's the kind of husband she ought to have. "One you can manage." She supposed she should allow him intercourse now and then "because men like those things and as long as there are no more children it's probably all right."

PROFILE *

Rheumatic Fever and Rheumatoid Arthritis

1. *Family History.* Cardiovascular disease in parents and siblings type A 58 per cent and type B 52 per cent (half of this rheumatic disease). Accident history for parents and siblings 10 per cent. Extreme nervousness about 35 per cent. Exposure to cardiovascular disease or to sudden death in about 60 per cent.

2. *Personal Data.* Many broken homes, poor social and economic background, poor contact with parents, although fairly frequent dependence on mother. Low marriage rate, many children per marriage, few divorces.

3. *Health Record.* Poor previous health record with tendency to minor operations, and minor and major illness and allergy. Women have poor pelvic histories. (In type B, marked susceptibility to respiratory infections.)

4. *Injuries.* Accident record about average (type A high, type B low). Accidents preponderantly fracture type. Majority of accidents in childhood.

5. *General Adjustment. Education:* Average record (type B tendency to complete units undertaken, type A opposite tendency). *Work record:* Variable. *Income and vocational level:* Characteristically classes III and V (stenographers and unskilled workers). *Social relationships:* Shy, childish and not well liked. *Sexual adjustment:* Fear of sex and marriage. Average venereal disease history. *Attitude toward family:* Marked (inadequately expressed) resentment toward both parents with tendency to exploit them. Identification with parent of opposite sex and homosexual trend in later relationships. Resentful of children.

6. *Characteristic Behavior Pattern.* Posing as good sport combined with diplomacy and appeal for sympathy. Quiet, sensitive, a few good friends

* In order to evaluate the distinctive features in this profile reference should be made to **Chapter IX.**

but uncomfortable in groups, especially type B. Realization of ambitions in dreams and fantasy.

7. *Neurotic Traits.* Second only to fracture group in history of early neurotic traits, particularly temper tantrums, nightmares, sleep-walking, sleep-talking, finickiness about food, nail-biting, tics. As adults, marked mood swings, continuation of nightmares, guilt and depression often related to masturbation, homosexual tendency; absorption in cleanliness, being on time, and general perfectionistic trend.

8. *Addictions and Interests.* Addictions not particularly striking, except to patent medicine and drugs. Impulse to athletic activity beyond their strength, especially among girls and small men (especially type A). Early disillusioned with religion.

9. *Life Situation Immediately Prior to Onset.* Disruption of emotional attachments through change of environment; separation of parents; extreme hardship, and so on.

10. *Reaction to Illness.* Tendency to get satisfaction out of suffering (type A); or to overdo and disregard doctors' orders (type B). Increasing escape from reality in dreams and fantasy.

11. *Area of Focal Conflict and Characteristic Reaction.* Sexual role—identification with opposite sex; authority—avoidance or submission.

CASE ILLUSTRATIONS

Rheumatic Fever—Type A

Case No. RF 64. A married woman, 34 years old, was admitted with a diagnosis of inactive rheumatic heart disease. She had had an attack of rheumatic fever at the age of 13, and a second attack of "rheumatic arthritis" at the age of 21. After this she became pregnant, pleurisy and septicemia developed after forty-eight hours of labor, and at this time her heart was affected. The onset of this, her fourth attack, was two weeks previously, with a chill and fever.

Family History. Both parents died of tuberculosis when the patient was in her infancy.

Personal Data. The patient was the second child. She was of linear build. She was born and lived in Philadelphia until the age of 18. The only girl in a family of three, she was adopted when her parents died when she was a little over a year old. In the foster family she was the oldest of four, two boys and a girl. "We always used to fight. They sided against me except for my foster brother six years younger who was my favorite."

Previous Health. Mumps and an appendectomy in childhood. First attack of rheumatic fever at 13 (see above).

Previous Injuries. Two months prior to admission the patient was out walking with her terrier dog and thinking about her troubles, particularly her problem son, aged 12. "He pulled me in front of a car crossing the street. I didn't even see it coming. I was knocked unconscious; for two days and two nights I couldn't remember being hit. When I came to the first thing I thought of was my son. My other accident happened a good deal the same way. I was riding very fast. I had a feeling of getting away from everything. I was just enjoying it and not paying attention or bothering much to hold on and the horse shied. I was unconscious for half an hour."

General Adjustment. Vocation—education: "I went to public school and didn't like it, then had a year in prep school and went to boarding school where I graduated at 18. Then I decided to study music at the Damrosch school and stayed till I was 21. I should have finished the course but I got ambitious and wanted to work at once, to be independent, so I got a job as an organist in a theatre at $90 a week which I kept for nearly eight years when the radio took it over. The radio spoiled my field. Since then the only jobs I've had have been modeling."

Social adjustment: "I used to like to be one of the gang. I played specially with boys. Now I have one or two real friends who are girls and stick to you in all kinds of weather. I think I changed when I learned what people were like."

Sexual adjustment: "Mother handed me a book with so many diagrams I couldn't make head or tail of it. She never explained anything from it. But I collected what I knew from boys and girls at school. I was more or less indifferent to it all. Mother scared me a little by telling me I had to go to bed every month but I rebelled. I felt much better when I found I could just disregard it and play anyway. I played football with the boys on the street in a rather tough way. Mother used to pester me. She said I would either have to come in or put on my brother's clothes if I behaved like that. Both Mother and boarding school were so unbearable I planned one night to elope with a boy. He had a horse and sleigh outside but I told a girl friend and she told the teacher. They found him shivering and waiting for me and sent him away. It made me so upset I couldn't eat. I married to get away from the family. My husband was Jewish and very erratic. I was working and supporting us while he studied at Bellevue. He drank, took dope, and had another flame on the side. I was pregnant when we separated after six months. I kept on working. My family never took me back. But I wouldn't have gone back anyway. I have supported myself and my son ever since. Lately I have had a friend who is divorced and seventeen years older who wants to marry me but I don't think he would be a good father for my son. He says he would give me everything I want, money and a ranch. I would like security but I think it's safer to depend on yourself than to depend on a man."

Attitude toward parents. "My foster parents were very strict. Now I see as little of them as possible. I shouldn't say that. My foster father is a very fine, reserved, cultured man, very serious. He is a Yankee Congregationalist and naturally strict. So was his first wife who died two years ago of spinal meningitis after picking a pimple on her nose. He then married her sister who was not much less strict. My foster mother was so nervous and high strung that if you dropped a spoon she would jump and yell at you and pull your ears. She would sit by me when I was practicing and pinch my arm when I made a mistake. It made me frightfully mad. We had awful scenes. When I was 6 or 7 they told me I was an adopted child and I was not at all upset. I guess I was glad of it."

Characteristic Behavior Pattern. All her life this patient had attempted to be a good sport "and not to submit to the frailties of my sex." There were frequent outbursts of impulsive inner struggle for independence. Note the accidents, leaving school without finishing the course in order to get a job, an so on.

Early Neurotic Traits. Nail-biting and sleep-talking.

Addictions and Interests. Major interests were in competitive sports, basket ball, tobogganing, etc. "I never cared much for dancing. Of course I had to go to church as a child. I never got much out of it. As soon as I was free I gave all that up. Since I've been sick I've experimented with 'Unity.' I think it helps."

Life Situation Immediately Prior to Onset. "My first attack of rheumatic fever came right after my first period. I guess that must have weakened me. It isn't nice to be told you have to go to bed once a month and can't play football with the boys any more. I had been very miserable in school, too, and I thought I had just got free because I had left school to go to prep school connected with a University, and I thought I wouldn't be treated like a child any more. But the teachers were just as strict." It will be remembered that the patient's second and third attacks like the first followed traumatic experiences in the spheres of sex and vocation. The second attack occurred when she discovered almost simultaneously her pregnancy and her husband's unfaithfulness, and separated from him, facing the necessity of supporting herself through the remainder of her pregnancy.

The third attack was precipitated by the long and difficult labor and having worked up to the last minute, as well as by the fact that she had just heard that her husband had committed suicide and she had been left in doubt as to whether or not they would keep her job for her, and was faced with the necessity of supporting herself and her child. "I was terribly afraid

I would have to ask help from my foster parents and I didn't know whether they would help me or not, and I didn't want them to anyway."

The fourth attack, during which she became part of the present study, was precipitated by the conflict over whether or not to seek security for herself and her son in marriage to a man who, she felt, would not be a good father to her son. In addition, there had been a further traumatic experience in the sexual sphere because she had decided to clarify the situation by the experiment of living with him and had found intercourse with him unbearable. "I was sitting with one of my friends, a girl I like and talking about what I should do. We were sitting in the back yard and I looked across at the hospital and said to her: 'Well, anyway I suppose I am better off than if I were lying sick over there.' Then I got the chill and here I am."

Reaction to Illness. This patient associated her illness with the proverbial suffering which is the lot of woman, tended to deny it, and to overdo. There was very little of the attempt to submit and get enjoyment out of suffering and fantasy characteristic of what we have described as the rheumatic fever, type B, personality until the present illness during which she took recourse to "Unity," about which she said: "I have decided not to try to run my own life any more. Unity teaches you to leave all that to God. If it is right for me to find security and a good husband He will arrange it for me, otherwise if He wants me to suffer I will submit."

Area of Focal Conflict. The major conflicts in this patient's life had been in the sphere of (a) her sexual role: the conflict between having to recognize that she was a girl intensified by the onset of menstruation, and her tomboy personality, the partial solution of this conflict in marriage to a man who was dependent on her, but then deserted her for other women when she became pregnant, and so on; and (b) in the sphere of relationship to authority: the long struggle with foster parents, and several sets of teachers, partially solved by leaving the Damrosch school to get a job, but then rendered more acute by her marriage and increased responsibility. It will be noted that each attack of rheumatic disease was precipitated by an acute phase of conflict in each sphere.

Rheumatic Fever—Type A

Case No. RF 232. An unmarried Jewish girl, aged 16, was admitted for symptoms suggestive of subacute bacterial endocarditis. Her illness had begun two weeks previously when she woke up feeling stiff all over and in a good deal of pain. There was swelling in her knee which spread to her shoulders. On admission she had mitral stenosis and insufficiency and aortic insufficiency. She had had four attacks of rheumatic fever since the age of 12 and had had chorea at the age of 7. During her third attack of rheumatic fever she spent two months in the hospital and during her fourth attack, four months.

Family History. The patient's father was living and well at the age of 42, and her mother was also well at the age of 41. However, two brothers were markedly accident-prone and a third brother had a cardiac disease.

Personal Data. The patient was the second child, only girl in a family of four. She was born and lived all her life in New York. She was of linear build, tall (5 feet 8 inches) and lanky. Although both parents were strict she said that the father was known in the household as "the spoiled kid. Every Sunday we all get into bed together and tussle."

Previous Health. She had mumps and chorea at the ages of 6 and 7; her adenoids and tonsils removed at the age of 8; first attack of rheumatic fever at the age of 12; dysmenorrhea which she tended to deny: "I don't believe girls should be handicapped. I just pretend I am all right, swim and play ball and forget about it" (see introductory note).

Previous Injuries. "I was always falling all over. Just before I got sick this time I broke my toe kicking the side of the swimming pool. I manage to kick into everything. I am always falling too. Just before I got sick the first time I fell downstairs and broke my wrist."

General Adjustment: Vocation—education: "I went to kindergarten when I was 4 because my older brother went and I had to do everything he did. . . . I'm supposed to be the brightest in my class in high school (the patient was finishing her third year), and I think I'll go to college. I write poetry and like English. If you do one thing better than anybody you don't have to bother with the grind. We are all very bright in my family. My older brother picks up philosophy books for me to read. The trouble is I want to be independent and have a job but there's nothing I want to do. I wouldn't work for Father the way my brother does because I wouldn't want to be told what to do. I've had enough of that. I wouldn't want to be a nurse for the same reason. I couldn't be a bookkeeper because I can't stick to anything consistently; I'm too unstable. The only thing I want is to travel all over the country in a car and have adventures, then I could say that I had really lived. Maybe then I could be a newspaper writer."

Social adjustment: "We live on the East side and I go down to the docks, sometimes five or six or twenty of us. It's a hard neighborhood and the water smells are bad but there is lots of material there. I wrote a poem on the dock once. Everything was gray and mysterious, and there was a heavy fog and a fog horn. I called it the 'Opera of the Foghorn.' The foghorn was the stage, and my thoughts were the main orchestra. You couldn't see the bridge, but just the lights suspended in the air like dew drops. Boats from Canada come in there." The patient was always very active. "Before I got sick I was a tomboy. I was always tall for my age. I was the head of a gang of seven boys. I beat up my older brother. I still have marks on me from those days. This was until I was 7. After that I got sick. Every week I would pick out a different girl to go to a baseball game with me. They don't like to go. I like to watch six-day bicycle races. I love to watch basketball. Sometimes I get in and throw a basket. I love swimming and swim too far. Dr. —— doesn't know how far. I like rowing and handball which is terrible for me, but I play doubles."

Sexual adjustment: "I just disregard menstruation. I don't like physiology, it's too realistic. I don't regard boys as being any different from girls. The ideal girl is a tomboy anyway. I don't intend to get married though. I've been tied down three-quarters of my life already and if I ever got married there would be complications about getting a job, my husband might not want to be in the same place and there would be dishes. It would be like having an extra piece of luggage along if I were traveling. When I want company I'd rather take a girl with me they are less trouble."

Attitude toward parents: "They are both strict and keep me tied down. I am scared of them but when they get mad we try to turn it into a friendly tussle."

Characteristic Behavior Pattern. "I daydream about travel and about writing. I see something beautiful; a thought or a feeling. Little by little I will daydream over it, and write a poem. Right then and there, on the dot, I would have the words of the poem in me. I had a foghorn as a solo instrument. A person might say something—it might strike me. My feelings are very easily hurt. I don't know why. I try to cover it up, and keep quiet for a long time. Usually I laugh as much as possible. If I make up my mind it is terrible for me to change it, even if I want to. It is very silly. A lot of times I argue with my brother. I argue as long as I can. Then little by little I will see that he is right, and give in. I hate to give in. I argued against a friend and said that man is superior to woman. Little by little she gave in to me, and when she did I walked away and said that she was silly to give in. 'After all you were right all the time.' Sometimes I say very nasty things, and afterwards regret them. I usually do things on the spur of the moment. I can't stand monotony. If I am not doing anything, I am daydreaming. I have a marvelous time at that. It is usually little things that make me angry. I can manage big things, but the little remarks that girls make, or if someone tells someone else that her dress is marvelous, when it is really terrible— that burns me up. Also if someone talks to another person as if they were an inferior. On a trip I will be free, free from friends and conventional things. I hate convention, and that is why I say things that I shouldn't. If I am walking with a boy, and I say how silly for him to switch, and come over to the side of the street. We are led around by the nose. The Jewish religion is a very beautiful story; that is all that impresses me. It annoys me to have my mother say: 'With God's help you'll be out of here soon.' I don't take it that way. Boys are more free, and that is why I envy them."

Early Neurotic Traits. "I always walked and talked in my sleep. I would go downstairs to the table and sit down and get up. Once I found myself under the shower in the bathroom. I talk a lot and usually laugh and yell. I don't remember my dreams, but I guess they are the usual thing, going somewhere." There were marked mood swings from gaiety and aggression to despondency.

Addictions and Interests. The patient's only marked addiction was to candy: "On the whole I like to eat a lot." Relative to religion the patient said: "I doubt if I believe in God. That stuff is all right for women. Mother is religious and goes to the synagogue. The house is kept Kosher."

Life Situation Immediately Prior to Onset. "It's funny I always have an accident before I get an attack. I was feeling fine the night before Labor Day except for the trouble with my toe and before I went to sleep I thought a long time about not knowing what I wanted to do. You have to have a job to be free like a boy, but a job ties you down and I've been too much tied down at home. Some people get married to get free but I'm too bright for that, marriage ties you down even worse. It's silly but sometimes I even pray I won't ever be tempted. It's a vicious circle whichever way you look at time. I got sort of despondent. Then I decided that I would run away somewhere because tomorrow is a holiday, and just forget about everything. Then I woke up stiff all over."

Reaction to Illness. "Being sick makes me depressed then I feel like rebelling. At other times, inside, I fell like shooting off. I say 'Why?' 'Why am I sick?' I have always told myself that if I were well all the time I wouldn't appreciate it. Now when I am sick most of the time I appreciate it somewhat when I am well. But that doesn't work very well."

Area of Focal Conflict. Little insight is required to deduce from this patient's history the spheres of her major conflicts. She gave them in her own words repeatedly. See, for example, her outlining of the two vicious circles, one relative to her sexual role, the other relative to authority; that is, her urge to be free and to be her own boss. In her general behavior pattern, impulsive episodes and difficulty in formulating any consistent course of action stand out, accompanied by the fear that there may be no solution and that in the end she will have to submit.

Summary. This patient is easily recognized as the personality we have described for type A rheumatic fever. As is consistent with her accident tendency, her previous health record is somewhat better than that found in the type B group. The patient had less tendency to respiratory infection than is usual with these patients. Furthermore, she had done a little better than most such patients in coping with her parents, although she did this with the help of her three brothers: "We sort of ganged up on them." One has the impression, however, that the severity of this fifth attack of rheumatic fever together with the cardiac involvement may be in part related to her increasing fear of defeat in her struggle for freedom.

Rheumatic Fever—Type A *

Case No. RF 144. A married woman, aged 30, was admitted for pain, tenderness, stiffness in the left hip which spread to knees, ankles, shoulders, elbows, wrists, and fingers, with nodules about her elbows and knees particularly. These symptoms were of sudden onset, accompanied by fever, four years previously. She spent three weeks in the hospital and after her discharge the pains continued, particularly in wrists and shoulders. The admission note described this patient as "a sweet-mannered, mild young woman, who evidently is not worried about her condition or the economic situation." The social worker commented that "she appreciates interest taken in her." The patient was seen for the first time in connection with this study on her sixth admission over a period of five years for the same complaint. The admission note at this time stated "the patient is happy and has become increasingly handicapped by her disease. The patient has lost the neurotic element thought to be present last summer and carries activity limitations very well." During this admission she was seen very briefly but she returned again nine months later with cardiac decompensation accompanied by trancelike states.

Family History. The patient's father who was a carpenter died at the age of 77 of old age. The mother was living and well at 60, when the patient entered the hospital, except that she "was slightly troubled by two bullets in her chest," and suffered from high blood pressure.

Personal Data. The patient was born in Porto Rico, the fourth child, second girl, in a family of five. The two brothers died, one at 17 of typhoid fever, the other was drowned at 23. There was also the poor social and economic background and constant warfare in the home from which the patient attempted to escape by coming to this country at the age of 14 (see below).

Previous Health. The patient had had tonsillitis off and on throughout her life. In general this patient had the poor previous health record characteristic of the rheumatic fever group, with a tendency to upper respiratory diseases and pelvic disorders, including dysmenorrhea, leucorrhea, and abortion. A year prior to her first hospital admission for rheumatic fever she had pneumonia following spontaneous abortion.

* For other illustrations see Chapter X.

Previous Injuries. None.

General Adjustment. Vocation—education: The patient finished elementary school, went one year to high school and one year to business school. She studied Spanish because her parents spoke it, and obtained a *position* as translator at *twenty-five dollars* a week which she held until her marriage at the age of 22.

Sexual Adjustment. "I never knew anything about sex until I was married. Then my husband gave me a book." Patient had been frightened by her first menstrual period at the age of 15—"I didn't know what it was, what had happened to me." She suffered from severe cramps until an abortion two months after her marriage. She had known her husband for some time prior to her marriage but had not intended to marry him. Then she developed rheumatic fever. She said: "I was so sick I was afraid I couldn't work any more so I got married." (See also *Life Situation Immediately Prior to Onset.*)

Social adjustment. "I was always shy. I think it was partly Mother's fault. Then I was in a new country and making friends was hard, and then pretty soon I got sick and that interfered."

Attitude toward parents and children: The patient said she disliked her mother who was exceedingly strict, and constantly kept her home from parties in order to do housework. To get away from her she came to this country with her older sister at the age of 14. Her mother then followed her, and since her marriage has spent much time with her. "She is cross with my child. I can't do anything about it. It makes me crazy. I don't want my daughter to be frightened the way I was as a child." When first seen the patient had had one child. She had a second cesarian section and sterilization by resection of the ovarian tubes a year later.

Characteristic Behavior Pattern. This patient showed initiative in her attempt to escape from her mother, but her mother caught up with her and she was completely unable to cope with her. During her adolescence she was active and attempted to appear a good sport although at the same time she was uncomfortable in groups and felt that she was not really liked. With the onset of her illness the appeal for sympathy became marked and there was an increased enjoyment of suffering with an active dream and fantasy life. Note also her insistence on having children contrary to medical advice and in spite of her fear of both the sexual relationship and pregnancy.

Neurotic Traits. Temper tantrums and nightmares as a child as well as nail-biting. As an adult, marked mood swings, continuation of nightmares, and preoccupation with ideas of neatness and cleanliness. "I know I'm awake —see myself in different places (Mexico) and know I'm in my bed. Then I can't move—I pray hard that I might be able to move. I get frightened; the heart stays quiet." These "dreams" occur only at night, and not at the hospital. She "can't stop it" by herself, "praying is the only thing." "Sometimes when I pray hard that it should go away from me—then many times I felt something was near me that didn't like the praying." Many times she leaves the light on because she is frightened. Many times she "sees" a person—"ghost-like." "A person comes near me—I feel somebody is biting me —sometimes I've been kissed, sometimes I've been slapped in the face. Here in the hospital I could tell I was transferred to the Tutankhamen Tomb" (this was an oxygen tent).

During one of these trances she saw a gorilla come up and put his paw on her left breast and start to drag her away. She could not feel it even though she knew he was there. She could see his hairy chest and glittering teeth; he was fierce and hoary. Patient told her husband about this the next day, and besought him not to think that she was crazy. She says that she remembers very well trying to be nice to the gorilla so that he would not hurt her, because she was so frightened. Her dreams have been somewhat strange. She says that she prays to prevent herself from dreaming, and to save herself. In her dreams she keeps going to get mail; the letters seem very old as the paper is yellow with age and spider webs have formed over the envelope. She never finishes the dream, and does not know exactly what the letters are.

She dreams of receiving letters and of seeing a tomb open up. In the letter it says: "I wish my ——." In the dream she asks why she is to be buried alive. This dream occurred in January, before her illness, and again several weeks ago. Patient dreamed last night that she had a newborn baby she was caring for. She did not know how it came, or who its father was. Patient says that the baby, even though newborn, talked to her. Patient dreamed that she was at a funeral, and that the mother of the deceased girl was shedding tears. "The house was always kept so neat and the floors so shining, and the girl was so good and kind." The patient said that she decided in her dreams that the girl had died of heart trouble from scrubbing the floors so much.

Addictions and Interests. No particular addictions except for considerable reliance on drugs to make her sleep, which began in early life and was increased after the onset of illness. She was brought up a Roman Catholic but after leaving home did not take religion very seriously.

Life Situation Immediately Prior to Onset. "I always wanted to get ahead. I had high aspirations. I studied Italian, French, English, Portuguese as well as Spanish. I wanted to be an important person and took a man's job, that's how my illness began. *I never wanted to get married* but I got sick and so I had to. But my husband never could earn as much as I did."

Reaction to Illness. As is clear from the above this patient tended to get satisfaction out of suffering and to disregard doctors' orders. Her increasing tendency to escape from reality progressed to the point of occasional trance-like states which the attending interne considered psychogenic in origin.

Area of Focal Conflict. As is clear from the foregoing this patient's major conflicts were in the sphere of her sexual role. She started out with a male identification and a complete unwillingness to think about sex at all. She had intended never to get married but her illness with the accompanying fear that she would not be able to support herself resulted in a sudden decision to get married. In marriage she considered herself still the man of the family because she had a greater earning power than had her husband and was a better manager. On the other hand, she felt that she must pay for the security she got in marriage by acceptance of the female role, including childbearing, incapacity and suffering. In the sphere of relationship to authority also she had conflict, her first reaction was the attempt to escape; thwarted in this by her mother's pursuit and "the necessity of marriage" she submitted more and more but always with episodes of rebellion.

Summary. It is easy to recognize in this case history a rheumatic fever patient starting out as type A and developing rheumatic heart disease. The points in her history which are not characteristic for type A are the lack of accidents and injuries in her early life (but it should be noted that her mother had an accident history); her early neurotic traits which followed were those of type B (for example, there was not sleep-walking and sleep-talking characteristic of type A patients); and the gradual swing from an active aggressive personality of five years preceding her first cardiac decompensation. Consistent with the lack of accident history is her relatively good educational history and her ability to keep a job.

Rheumatic Fever—Type B

Case No. RF 146. An unmarried man, aged 28, was admitted with acute rheumatic carditis. He had had an attack of joint pains at the age of 12, at which time a doctor told the mother in his presence that his heart muscles were all wasted away and there was not a chance of his living after he was 21. He had had a second attack a year previously with joint pain; first, the right knee, then the right shoulder; then the other shoulder, ankles, wrists and fingers. He suffered also from cardiospasm and he had had gastro-intestinal symptoms more or less throughout his life.

Family History. The patient's father died at the age of 68 when the patient was 21, of angina pectoris. A maternal aunt had rheumatic heart disease. The mother was living and well at the age of 66 the time of the patient's admission.

Personal Data. The patient was the younger of a pair of twins, the fifth in a family of six, five boys and one girl. He was born and lived in New York City.

Previous Health. The patient had always "been weakly": pneumonia and empyemia at the age of 7, thoracotomy six months prior to the admission, and a great deal of trouble with his teeth for three to ten years. He had had periodic gastro-intestinal onsets since infancy, and from adolescence on, attacks of palpitation.

Previous Injuries. The patient stated that he was bitten and dragged by a greyhound at the age of 4.

General Adjustment. Vocation—education: "I never liked school. I would have done better if I'd applied myself. I went through two and a half years of high school and then decided to get a job." *Occupation:* "I worked as a clerk for a year and a half and went to night high school at the same time then I went into the jewelry business. It's always worried me to carry fifty to a hundred thousand gems around. I never carried a gun because you're surer to be shot. I used to get drunk and misplace gems and then I'd be scared that I would be accused of stealing them." He recounted one or two episodes when this had actually occurred although the matter had always been straightened out and he exonerated later.

Social adjustment: "I never liked people much, but I used to go around with my brother. But I had to give that up because he was always getting into scraps with people and I was afraid something dreadful would happen. Somebody would get smashed up or hurt."

Sexual adjustment: "I used to go around a good deal with boys but they led me into masturbation. I'd never heard of it before but I knew it wasn't right. I don't care much for sex. I've given up women, too, because I found there was nothing in it. Sometimes men speak to me on the street but I never go with them. I shall never get married."

Attitude toward parents: "Mother was kind. I am like her. Father had temper tantrums and scared us all to death. My twin brother is just like him. All of us are nervous. But Mother had a subtle way of controlling her children. She still has. She has a way of putting things so you have to do her way. She wants to mold our lives to suit her. It's just another case of a silver cord."

Characteristic Behavior Pattern. Continuing the statements about his mother just given, the patient said: "Mother made rebels of all my brothers and has ruined my sister's life and runs her children. I have tried to be more considerate, to give in and avoid trouble. But I think it's been good for me to be away from her in the hospital. I'm beginning to realize that this was not good for me. Things are going to be different from now on. I shall take matters into my own hands. It will be easier to do this if I go to California."

Neurotic Traits. Early neurotic traits, nightmares especially of drowning. After hearing the doctor speak of his impending sudden death he "was unable to sleep at all for three years." He feared dogs and had dreams about being attacked by them which he related to an episode of being bitten and dragged by a greyhound at the age of 4.

Addictions and Interests. No particular addictions.

Life Situation Immediately Prior to Onset. The patient gave a history of pains at the age of 12, but his first actual attack occurred when his family discussed moving next door. He stated that he did not want to move with them because there were two great Danes in the house. It was his subsequent sickness that kept them from moving. His second attack occurred at the age of 21, following his father's death of angina. The doctor who cared for him during this attack told him his heart muscles had wasted away. This frightened him so much that he was unable to sleep and began to have attacks of palpitation. The patient stated, however, that he had been subject to such attacks as well as stomach upsets all his life. Prior to the present attack he reported a long period of stress and strain because he was living with mother, brother, and sister, all of whom are nervous and irritable and in constant conflict with each other. The mother attempts to order them around like children. He spoke also of a similar strain in connection with his business because of a boss who was much the same way. The thought was that this last attack was brought on because the boss committed suicide.

Reaction to Illness. Prior to his therapeutic interview this patient's reaction to illness was the characteristic one: enjoyment of being taken care of, somewhat of a martyr attitude, and relief because his illness had made it necessary to give up his job which released him from conflict with his boss, worry, and responsibility. Later his reaction was that given above.

Area of Focal Conflict. The spheres in which this patient had had his major conflicts were (a) his sexual role: there was a strong reaction versus his homosexual impulses and an aversion to woman, marriage, and sex in general; (b) relationships to authority: first, that of his mother and father, later that of his boss. His reaction to the former conflicts was a pretty thoroughgoing aversion; and to the latter, submission. His improvement in the hospital ran parallel to his shift from the passive submissive attitude of the rheumatic fever type B patient to a decision to take matters into his own hands.

Rheumatic Fever—Type B

Case No. RF 222. A married man, aged 34, was admitted to the hospital with a diagnosis of rheumatic heart disease, mitral and aortic stenosis and insufficiency, auricular fibrillation. He had had one earlier attack ten years previously which kept him in the hospital for a week with painful swollen joints.

Family History. The patient's father had died three years previously at the age of 68, cause unknown. The mother was living and well. No family history of heart trouble, diabetes, fracture, or nervousness.

Personal Data. The patient was tall and lanky and the fourth child in a family of six boys. He was born in Czechoslovakia.

Previous Health. Always subject to colds and tonsillitis. First attack of rheumatic fever at the age of 24.

Previous Injuries. The patient fell while playing baseball as a child; he said, because the other boys pushed him. He thought he fractured his right elbow, it would not flex until about six months later. His older brother "pulled it out" for him and he had no trouble after that.

General Adjustment. Vocation—education: The patient went to school from the age of 7 to 12, but was kept home a good deal to take care of his father's cows, which got him into trouble with the teachers. "I was always being scolded by one of the two of them—father and the teacher—for neglecting the other." "I got sick of it and came to this country." *Occupation:* After making a start as a bus boy in a restaurant he became a window cleaner which has been his means of support ever since: "I work all the time in a private building and not in a union. I no like the way they butt into your private affairs and tell you when you got to work and when you got to stop." *Social adjustment:* "People don't mean much to me. I just keep busy minding my business. I like museums and to walk in the park." *Sexual adjustment:* "I never cared much for girls, maybe because we were all boys in our family. I married my wife because I liked her mother on the other side, and it seemed like the thing to do. I don't care much about sex." Although the patient had been married for twelve years he had only one child, his wife was in perfect health and although he denied any use of contraceptives this had been his wife's only pregnancy. His attitude toward his wife was rather negative. "She's all right. I let her run things her way. We never fight." *Attitude toward parents and children of his own:* "Mother had a bad temper, but I liked her better than Father. . . . The boy's all right except he runs around too much. I let his mother worry about that."

General Behavior Pattern. Patient says: "If you eat all right, you don't have to worry whether the Germans go into Czechoslovakia or not. . . . I am not mad or angry at people. I don't talk; I listen, but all the time I am friends with people. I don't get mad. I never go away; I let them have it if they want anything. I just want to be healthy and happy. Sometimes somebody wants to grab everything; I never. I am easy; I don't rush, unless I have to."

Neurotic Traits. Enuresis for several years. Nightmares. "Now I like my own thoughts better than anything else. The only place you can really have a good time is in your own head."

Addictions and Interests. No addictions, no particular interests. Brought up a Greek Catholic and still goes to church occasionally "because the Sisters are nice and help you if you are sick or in trouble."

Life Situation Immediately Prior to Onset. At the time of the patient's first attack of rheumatic fever he had been in this country for six years. His wife had just given birth to her first and only child, which worried him because he had been temporarily out of work and he did not like the idea of another mouth to feed. At the time of his second attack he had been working late, washing windows and had been in a draft. He had been worried about his son because he seemed to be irresponsible. "At his age I was working for my father besides going to school. And all he does is to run around."

Reaction to Illness. "If you're sick, you're sick. Somebody takes care of you; you don't have to worry."

Area of Focal Conflict. Although this patient, like other rheumatic fever patients had had conflicts relative to sex and authority, his passive reaction to these conflicts stands out throughout his history. Even in his escape from home he took little initiative, having been more or less brought over by an uncle. In connection with his job he avoided authority situations including, for example, his refusal to join the union; when he could not avoid them, he submitted. In general he avoided girls but he submitted to marriage because it was the thing to do, and married a woman who would take care of him like a mother. The reason for this continued interest in religion was "because the Sisters help you out." Nevertheless his attacks were precipitated when these techniques of avoidance and submission were inadequate.

DEGREE AND NATURE OF SOMATIC EXPRESSION OF CONFLICTS

In view of the lack of success of these patients in attempting to work out a solution to their problems, one would expect an early development of a somatic short circuit, which, of course, fits in with their illness history. The type A patients showed some resemblance in their early history to fracture patients, both in their activity and in their tendency to have accidents. Type B rheumatic fever patients followed the cardiac pattern more closely in their early history of generalized inner tension, allergic reactions, and vegetative symptomatology in general. Both groups, however, remained caught in an emotional dilemma which was insoluble to them, instead of developing their independence as fracture patients did, or finding a means of controlling authority like the patients with coronary occlusion. It seems probable that this condition gradually disturbed their physiological functions, rendering them more susceptible to disease, especially diseases affecting joints and the cardiovascular system. (Jones.[253] See also section II of this chapter, page 429.)

Tension—Cloaking Fear and Resentment

From the point of view of muscle tension these patients followed the fracture pattern of the type A fracture patients rather than the coronary pattern in that they were generally restless and frequently showed jerky movements. There was also the tendency to tics already noted. Guilt was also more prominent than in the groups with cardiac syndromes. Sometimes, however, particularly when resentment was near the surface, they showed a generalized tension. This tension differed from that shown by the preceding three groups, however, in that it appeared to be less an inhibition of aggressive impulses than a matter of being on guard. There seemed to be an accompanying capillary pattern resulting in pallor and sometimes showing itself even in the difficulty with which blood was obtained for blood count.

Although these patients, especially type A, occasionally fought if they thought their chances were good, they were more likely to boast about fighting than to become involved in brawls.

Activity, Verbalization, Dreams and Fantasies

The group of patients which we have termed rheumatic fever, type A, had an early history of *activity*. Not infrequently they revealed a well established accident habit which was abruptly terminated by the first attack of rheumatic fever. Type B patients in this group rarely had accidents and were generally less active. The recent Rorschach review suggests that type A patients resemble at least in their early life the constricted (type A) fracture patients. A few of them seem to have more introversive development. In contrast Type B patients, who are more prone to develop cardiac damage, seem to be less generally constricted with a strong active-passive conflict in which the passive masochistic tendency usually wins out.

From the point of view of *verbalization*, type A is inclined to follow the type A fracture pattern. These are the patients who will talk about their interest in sports for example, yet they show marked resistance to close emotional contact with the physician. Type B patients, in contrast, talk freely about themselves but usually with a plaintive note and a demand for babying. They show little tendency to generalize their experiences or to philosophize. Type A patients concentrate on immediate values, while type B dwell mostly on their sufferings.

Unlike patients with hypertension, or patients with cardiac arrhythmia, patients whose symptoms were mainly joint pain showed a tendency to symbolization of the sites of pain, and a rather distinctive *dream* and *fantasy* life. The following excerpts from the analysis of such a patient are characteristic:

"I dreamed that a cat jumped up and clawed my right arm so that I thought I would bleed to death." When the patient woke up her arm was paralyzed. She had shown a tendency during the past week to rub her feet together, to rub her fingers together, to rub the hair on her head in little circles, but no comment had been made on this behavior. On this particular day the patient said: "I suppose you think when I do this I am masturbating, but I don't see why you don't say something about it." She said: "Doing this with my right hand really hurts because of my arthritis, but it hurts *just enough to be comfortable.*" In this patient the feminine role was bound up with suffering. Mutilation was an important theme in her dreams and to some extent acted out. She had suffered for six years with fairly severe arthritis, especially in the right arm and hand so that she was unable to write. This was the masturbation hand. Also her grandfather had lost this arm and hand and an uncle had lost a finger of his right hand because of being scratched by a cat. She herself had lost part of a finger on this hand because of having allowed an infection to go uncared for.

In association the patient said: "I've spent hours this week in trying to write. I can't get anything out. I nearly go mad faced with blank stretches of hours. I must but I can't. I feel like doing some real injury to myself, biting my little finger to break it the way mother broke grandmother's finger when I was born." Later she dreamed:

"I gave mother an overdose of sleeping powder and then it seemed as though someone had given it to me and then just as everyone thought I was dead my right arm began jerking and it jerked so hard it waked me up."

At this time the patient's arthritis was so severe that she was unable to turn a door knob or to eat with her right hand. Shortly before the arthritis finally cleared up (and there has been no reccurrence of it) she had the following dream:

"A disembodied arm is lying in my lap and I am admiring it. Someone has just said how strong it is and I am surprised to have an arm with so much muscle. I was particularly surprised because it was my right arm in which I never used to have any strength. Then I noticed that the arm was solid gold and I said that perhaps I had found the pot of gold at the foot of the rainbow. Just then I heard a moaning voice say, 'Who's got my golden arm? Who stole my golden arm?' I was filled with horror and thought it was a ghost creeping down the hall like the ones I used to be afraid of in grandmother's house."

This dream is sufficiently obvious to need no interpretation. This association of arthritic pain with masturbation and restraint or punishment is a general finding in both men and women, the focal conflict, like that of the asthmatic, being related to the sexual role.

SUMMARY OF CHARACTEROLOGICAL DEFENSES AND THEIR RELATIVE SUCCESS OR FAILURE

It is misleading to generalize about the characterological defenses of patients with rheumatic fever. They develop no definite system of defenses but tend to waver from one type to another. It may be said that their defenses break down so easily that a somatic short circuit is favored early in life. With the progress of the disease, the symptoms themselves provide a particularly satisfactory defense which is used to the utmost; hence, the clinician's confusion as to how much of the emotional picture is a reaction to the disease and how much was antecedent to the disease.

In the patients in this group who are designated as type A, the defenses follow, in general, the pattern of the type A fracture patients. But, as the range of freedom becomes limited, there is concentration on joint pain. The incapacitated member assumes significance as a symbol of both personal and sexual inadequacies. They tend to become preoccupied with a swollen wrist, for example, dwelling on its importance as an interference in their activity. They underestimate the limitation of activity demanded by the somatic impairment; but they exaggerate its importance in relation to all their frustrations in life. This is frequently evidenced in dreams. In such cases subsequent attacks seem particularly likely, other things being equal. In some cases, however, there seems to be a reorganization of energy. The patient may go on without further attacks but may succumb to a different illness (Chapter X). This seems to be particularly likely in young patients. The general therapeutic management both during and after discharge is of utmost importance in determining the course of the somatic history.

In the rheumatic fever patients termed type B, the defenses are still weaker. These patients are more dominated by their passive masochistic tendency. They find a more diffuse solution for their sexual problem. In a personality study of a group of "potential cardiacs," that is, young patients between 10 and 20 years of age who were known to have had attacks of rheumatic fever were kept under observation in order to see whether cardiac damage developed. Although evaluation of the emotional disturbances in these patients was difficult because of the factor of adolescence, several distinguishing characteristics stood out. There was a marked and consistent conviction that they were different from other people, which was especially hard on them because of their impoverished inner life and extreme dependence on external approval. There were conspicuous martyr fantasies and enjoyment of suffering, exaggerated fear and guilt—all with a sexual emphasis. They either avoided companionship with the opposite sex and banished ideas of marriage, or accepted both as part of what was expected of them, preparing themselves for increased martyrdom. This attitude was particularly prominent in girls, because social pressures play into the hands of the syndrome.

Characterologically rheumatic fever patients resembled what has been termed the phallic character type (e.g., Fenichel,[178] pp. 424 ff.), and a general observation in the personalities of these patients is the "overcoming of an aggressive impulse directed against some person through an identification with this person," an important factor in the genesis of homosexuality. In general the defenses characteristic of these patients are inadequate. And of course they are seriously undermined by the illness itself, so that we see them regressing from thwarted identification (i.e., identification with the opposite sex) and strong reaction formation to a pregenital character level.

These traits tend to explain the relative weakness and the peculiar form of defenses in these patients. If there is added the frequent lack of opportunity for intellectual development or the repression of it, particularly in the girls, the binding of energy in somatic symptoms becomes almost inevitable and increases the likelihood of organic damage. Rheumatic fever seems to be predominantly a disease of the lower middle class, hence may be expected to be in some way associated with their mode of life. Diseases associated with a given mode of life usually have a particularly prominent psychic component, as for example tuberculosis. It must be remembered that mode of life includes not only physical conditions but also psychic relationships, habits of everday life, and cultural patterns.

V. Therapeutic Implications *

Strictly speaking, patients suffering from acute rheumatic fever should be treated separately instead of being classed with patients who have rheumatoid arthritis. It must be added, however, that there do not seem to be very important differences in the psychosomatic constellation, especially the character defenses, except in those with cardiac involvement as compared with those without it.

The first essential with these patients is to give them a sense of security and the opportunity for an active outlet in a personal relationship with the doctor, then gradually with their social contacts and in some vocation. Cultivation of hobbies and occupational therapy are not satisfactory because instead of relieving, they emphasize the feeling of difference and afford no chance for expressing aggression. The artificial ideal of being a good person in the family and having to swallow rage should be modified. The latter points are of particular importance in the type B group of patients and those with serious cardiac damage.

Attention should be directed to control of environment for these patients at least until they have gained a little more ability to cope with environmental difficulties. From this point of view the present tendency to handle these patients in special classes in schools and in special institutions is particularly desirable especially if full advantage is taken of the opportunity for simultaneous psychotherapy which is thus offered. Observations of groups of children under such conditions have shown that there is usually a marked increase in blood pressure and pulse rate, and frequently even exacerbations of

* See Chapter XI, section V.

the illness in situations involving criticism or competition—examinations for example—or in situations arousing their sense of guilt. Yet such factors are not usually evaluated or given psychotherapeutic attention.

Although a major need is relief of the guilt relative to sexual difficulties it is dangerous to attempt this too early. The guilt is so deep-reaching and so likely to be expressed somatically that establishment of some sense of security is a necessary preliminary to the attempt to assist them with this problem.

RHEUMATIC HEART DISEASE

I. Introductory Comment

Study of the cases reported in this section will show many resemblances to rheumatic fever type B just described, and as a matter of fact no sharp line can be drawn between the two groups. Nevertheless, these patients are discussed separately because they offer a more clear-cut illustration of the typical rheumatic heart disease picture.

Concerning rheumatic heart disease Boas (pages 4–5)[44] writes: "Rheumatic heart disease is usually contracted in childhood before the tenth year of life. Many die from repeated rheumatic infections in childhood. Those who survive to adult life and marry and assume their place in society, usually have contracted their infection later, on the average at age 17. Then, ten or fifteen years after the onset of their disease their hearts begin to fail, and after another five or ten years of increasing invalidism they die between the ages of 35 and 40, in the prime of their lives, leaving young dependent children." (See also DeGraff and Lingg.[118])

II. Onset of Symptoms

The average age of these patients at the time of admission was 32 years, as compared with 27 for rheumatic fever type A and 21 for rheumatic fever type B. The number of previous admissions to this or some other hospital ranged from zero to ten. The age range at time of onset was 5 to 51 years, the average being 23 for males, 28 for females, and for both 26.

Unlike the group of patients discussed in the preceding section, the period between the onset of symptoms and admission, whether long or short, was one of more or less steady incapacitation, rather than a series of acute episodes. The earliest and most prominent symptoms were severe dyspnea, palpitation, and fatigue. The symptoms were likely to lead to hospitalization after an upper respiratory infection.

III. PREDISPOSITION TO ILLNESS—FACTORS TO BE EVALUATED

ORGAN CONDITIONING—PHYSIOLOGICAL AND PSYCHOLOGICAL

Heredity, Actual and Pseudo

In the heredity of these patients, rheumatism or cardiovascular disease was found in 44 per cent of the cases, diabetes in 20 per cent and nervousness in 36 per cent, including 12 per cent institutional cases and suicides. In addition to this, allergies of various types were relatively frequent in the family background. In comparison with the other groups studied, these patients seemed to have a relatively lower hereditary handicap. The accident history for parents and siblings was 8 per cent.

Exposure to serious illness was relatively slight but exposure to nervousness and sudden death from accident or suicide was high. The total exposure to cardiovascular disease was about 80 per cent. Suicides in husbands was about 4 per cent.

Constitution—Age Range, Sex, and Marriage

Constitution. These patients were predominantly dysplastic or linear in type, although there was a sprinkling of pyknics. In general they were small and thin.

Age Range. The age distribution was 28 per cent in each of the three first decades and 16 per cent in the decade 45 to 55. Seventy-six per cent of these patients were either the oldest or the youngest in the family; this figure includes 16 per cent who were only children.

Sex. Only 36 per cent of the patients in this group were males.

Marriage. Only 53 per cent of the females and 50 per cent of the males were married, but if we exclude the age group 15 to 24 we have the following percentages: 67 per cent of the females and

75 per cent of the males were married. Only about one-third of the married patients had children, and few patients had more than two children. The average number of children per marriage was 1.7. This gives them the lowest reproductive record of any group included in this study (except for the patients with cardiac arrhythmia, 1.25). Divorces were infrequent.

Previous Health

Of these patients three-fifths gave no history at all of joint pains. The other two-fifths had vague recollections of growing pains but nothing clearly suggestive of acute rheumatic fever. It is interesting, however, that in terms of the group of serial admissions studied in detail, they rank third from the bottom from the point of view of health record prior to admission. The only groups with a worse record for illness prior to the discovery of the illness in question are patients with anginal syndrome. After correction for age and sex their previous illness record is three times that of the fracture group.

In terms of types of illness only about one-third had major operations as compared with 40 per cent of the coronary patients and 70 per cent of the patients with anginal syndrome. But a greater percentage of these patients had minor operations than in any other group studied. The minor operations were, however, primarily for removal of tonsils and adenoids. Among the major operations there was great diversity: pelvic operations slightly predominated. Again, this group was slightly better than the two groups just mentioned from the point of view of major illness; on the other hand, they had a particularly high percentage of minor illnesses. The most characteristic illnesses were upper respiratory infection, gastro-intestinal disorders, migraine and allergies; although among the women, pelvic disorders were more frequent than in any other group studied with the exception of patients with diabetes.

Tendency to Hypertension. Fifteen per cent of these patients suffered from hypertension; that is, exactly the same percentage as was found in the diabetic and accident groups, and a lower percentage than was found in the anginal and coronary groups.

Statistics Concerning Previous Injury

Twenty per cent of these patients had accidents but only one had had more than one accident. This one patient had seven acci-

dents, and a well-established accident habit, hence she will be discussed separately under the heading of overlapping syndromes (page
605). The type of accident most frequent in these patients was a
cut of some kind or other, but these accidents were all minor and
non-incapacitating except for one of the accidents suffered by the
accident-prone patient which resulted in a fractured arm.

Early Influences and Traumatic Experiences

Traumatic experiences were important in the histories of one-
third of these patients, but in the majority of cases there were severe
frights—not traumatic deaths. Often the patient was frightened by
an older person (e.g., Case No. RF 118, page 380). The majority of
these patients, however, were exposed very early in life to cardiovascular symptomatology and severe nervous upsets in parents or
others to whom they had strong emotional attachments.

As compared with the patients with acute rheumatic fever, the
general background of these patients was better; that is, they came
from a slightly higher economic group and were subjected to less
environmental wear and tear in their early years. Half of them were
born and grew up in New York City, and the others did relatively
little moving about from place to place.

OUTSTANDING POINTS IN THE PERSONALITY HISTORY

General Adjustment

*Vocation—Education.** In spite of the relatively good family
background both economically and educationally, these patients
did not have a very high educational average. They were definitely
below the group of rheumatic fever patients. In this they resembled
patients with hypertension more than any other group studied. Apparently, like the patients with hypertension, they left school relatively early in order to attempt to make something of themselves,
and then, like the former, never quite made the grade. Patients
whose first attacks occurred after grammar school were nearer
average in educational achievement and showed a greater tendency to
complete the units undertaken.

---

* It will be remembered that statements under starred headings are based only on patients
over 21, in order to make them comparable to national statistics.

Income.* Their income average also was low, although there were fewer among them on relief or with WPA jobs than among patients with accidents and hypertension. If this figure were corrected for sex distribution, however, the percentage would become about the same. In the bracket called "marginal" and "comfortable" they were again lower than any other group studied except patients with hypertension.

Occupation.* Their occupational record gives only a partial explanation for this, since aside from 16 per cent who were retired, invalids, or housewives, the remainder of this group was equally divided between group III (clerks, salesmen, and stenographers) and group V (unskilled workers). Even though a larger series probably would show some individuals in groups I, II, and IV, their relative absence among these patients is consistent with the low educational and income level as well as with certain personality characteristics which will be discussed later in more detail. These patients were waitresses, post office employees, mill hands and factory workers, clerical workers, shipping clerks, secretaries and stenographers, and housewives. Slightly less than a quarter of these patients had made a very satisfactory vocational adjustment.

Social Adjustment. These patients were in general good story-tellers, inclined to exaggeration and telling whoppers for effect. They were lovers of adventure and interested mainly in making themselves liked, and they generally succeeded. With increasing illness they became more and more childish but generally in a distinctly appealing way.

Sexual Adjustment. The sex lives of these patients were marked by a masochistic attitude. While there was some homosexual tendency it was less than in the rheumatic fever group, and much less than was found among patients with diabetes. Typical statements made by the females relative to their sex lives were similar to their comments concerning their illness: "I guess I can take it." As already noted, an exaggerated fear relative to menstruation and pregnancy was characteristic. Pelvic disorders and abortions were more frequent than in any other group studied except patients with anginal syndrome.

* It will be remembered that statements under starred headings are based only on patients over 21, in order to make them comparable with national statistics.

Attitude Toward Parents and Children. About forty per cent of our patients lost either father or mother before they were 16 years old, hence step-parents were frequent. But very few lost both parents at an early age, and in 50 per cent of the cases the mother was living at the time of the patient's admission.

These patients, however, did not tend to carry forward their dependence on their parents into adult life, and unlike the patients both with cardiac arrhythmia and rheumatic fever, rebellion and resentment against the parents was very likely to be replaced with fear.

Not infrequently this fear appeared to be almost hypnotic, and on closer analysis revealed the most fundamental difference between this group and all other groups, including the patients with rheumatic fever types A and B, which, as would be expected, they most nearly resembled. The following case is illustrative of this fear attitude.

Case No. RHD 150. A large muscular Irishman, who, like his father, weighed well over 200 lbs. He stated that he was very fond of both parents. His father was good-natured and lethargic. He was the heavy-weight boxing champion of his district. The patient emulated his father all through his schooling, boxing, wrestling, lifting weights, and even spent his evenings listening to various health experts. But while the parental influence was increasing the size of his biceps inch by inch, his mother was giving him daily beatings to improve his mind, for he was not much interested in school work. He stated that his mother was "unbearable," and yet he "loved her very much." When he was 18, he decided not to let his mother strike him, and ran away from her when she began to beat him. But, as he added, she always caught up and hit him just the same. While beating him, the mother yelled so loudly that all the boys in the neighborhood came around later to find out what had happened. He admitted that he was always terrified by his mother, but was "consumed with love for her," adding that "your mother is your best friend, and there is no one in the world like a mother." •

Children when they had them were drawn into the pattern of martyrdom.

General Behavior. In general these patients were agreeable, talkative, ambitious in a vague way, and inclined to overdo. Paradoxically enough they had a love of adventure and an interest in athletics which led them to overtax themselves apparently for no very good reason.

It is possible that their relative lack of success in other fields, plus the restrictions imposed upon them because of their illness focuses their attention on physical prowess.

Characteristic Behavior Pattern: Realization of Ambition in Fantasy

These patients, like those with diabetes, appeared to have a deeply-lying sense of inadequacy, but instead of admitting it they tended to compensate for it by sociability, making themselves liked, overdoing in various ways, and when these measures failed, as generally happened, to make up the rest in fantasy. They were good at bluffing and often pretended to be more "fierce" than was actually the case.

Neurotic Traits—Early and Present

Childhood phobias, frights, nightmares, and tics were regularly reported by these patients. Other early neurotic traits such as exaggerated lying, stealing, enuresis, and so on, were not particularly prominent, although the lying was relatively marked.

The neurotic symptoms shown by these patients at the time of admission were mainly reaction formations against a sense of inadequacy and thwarting. Fears and phobias persisted, especially claustrophobia and agoraphobia. Even these were reacted against to the extent of the development of a deep admiration for the people that frightened or abused them.

Addictions and Interests

With these patients addictions and interests also followed the pattern of reaction formation. Athletics, adventure, accumulation of friends have been mentioned already. There was also the tendency to "buck themselves up" by way of stimulants, particularly coffee.

The fact that so large a percentage of them chose active jobs in the sphere of the unskilled laborer is interesting. There were many instances where a patient was offered a choice between a sedentary job and an active one, such as truck driver or laundry worker, and preferred the latter.

Like the patients in the rheumatic fever group, there was in this group a higher percentage of Roman Catholics than in any other group studied except the group of patients with fracture: Roman Catholics, 44 per cent; Jews, 24 per cent; Protestants, 32 per cent.

There were twice as many Jews among the males as among the fe-males. These patients, however, although tending, like the rheu-matic fever group, to be disillusioned toward religion, were inclined to continue to be governed by its regulations, particularly those that disturbed them most, such as the ban against contraceptives, keep-ing of fast days, and so on. They were very much inclined to use the demands of religion as an excuse for overexertion, long walks to church and other practices which were contrary to doctors' orders. They were also particularly likely to have anxiety attacks and claus-trophobia while in church.

Life Situation Immediately Prior to the Onset

Admissions to the hospital were usually occasioned by unusual ex-ertion in one of the compensatory spheres, or occasionally by a fright, playing into the hands of their earlier phobias or their deep-lying anxiety. As has been noted, the parents of these patients usually did not die of heart disease but instead as a result of an accident, suicide, operation or some illness of an entirely different nature. To such events these patients reacted with an intense and often long-continued fright.

Reaction to Illness

The reaction of these patients to their illness followed the pattern previously noted as characteristic of cardiac patients; namely, an at-tempt to deny or make light of it. They had little sense of reality about the seriousness of their disease, and unlike the patients with rheumatic fever or rheumatoid arthritis they were sure that they would soon be all right again.

IV. DYNAMIC FORMULATION

AREA OF FOCAL CONFLICT AND CHARACTERISTIC REACTION: AUTHORITY—EMULATION OF SUPERIOR ESPECIALLY IN FANTASY; SEXUAL ROLE—TENDENCY TO CURRY FAVOR WITH THE OPPOSITE SEX

The major sphere of conflict for these patients then was that of authority, as we have found with all groups reported so far except the rheumatic fever group in which conflict over the sexual role was pushed into the foreground. In their early lives it was a matter of conflict between authorities—inability to decide whose part to take as between father and mother. Their reaction to this conflict was an attempt to imitate and curry favor with one or the other parent. Their sense of inadequacy and fear prevented rivalry with anyone thought to be superior, and hence the attitude adopted was markedly infantile.

In general the parents were strict, particularly the mothers. Whereas most groups of patients studied preferred the parent who was gentle and understanding, these patients preferred the parent that "beat them up." Characteristic statements were: "We had to go straight and come straight, but I guess it was all for the best," or "Gee, she was strict. We certainly had a lot of beatings but I guess it was good for us" (Case No. RF 304 and Case No. RHD 65, pages 600 and 605).

While having points in common with both the rheumatic fever and diabetic attitudes, the attitude of patients with rheumatic heart disease was essentially different in that they neither sought to conform nor to preserve or increase their ego freedom. The patients of this group were unique in that they derived their compensation through exploitation of their abnormalities and their own ability to suffer, deriving perhaps a certain vicarious pleasure in seeing themselves suffer, or in thwarting their own freedom, and certainly deriving pleasure by attempting to win the admiration and esteem of others for their ability to take this punishment. Unlike the group of patients with hypertensive cardiovascular disease, there was very little sadism involved. They were much more interested in showing others what a whipping they could take than in seeing others get a whipping like theirs. In this respect their masochism approached that of the patients with coronary occlusion, but differed in that they had little or no interest in whipping themselves into shape, but a purely masochistic joy in being whipped.

PROFILE *

Rheumatic Heart Disease

1. *Family History.* Cardiovascular disease in parents and siblings, 44 per cent. Accident history for parents and siblings, 8 per cent. Diabetes, 20 per

* In order to evaluate the distinctive features in this profile, reference should be made to Chapter IX.

cent. Extreme nervousness, 36 per cent (12 per cent institutional or suicide). Exposure to cardiovascular disease or sudden death, about 70 per cent.

2. *Personal Data.* Loss of one or both parents prior to adolescence as a result of accident, suicide, or serious illness, frequently operation. Average economic background. Low marriage rate, few children per marriage, few divorces.

3. *Health Record.* Poor health record with upper respiratory infections, gastro-intestinal disorders, allergies, minor operations and pelvic disorders predominating.

4. *Injuries.* Rarely more than one injury, rate for one accident above average and accidents were mainly minor and of the cardiac type.

5. *General Adjustment. Education:* Relatively low, partly influenced by the illness and medical advice given in early childhood. Patients whose first attacks occurred after grammar school near average in educational achievement with some tendency to complete units undertaken. *Work record:* Variable, with some tendency to stick to the same job, especially when there was an attachment to the superior. *Income and vocational level:* Low, but characteristically classes III and V (stenographers and unskilled workers). High percentage in class VI (dependent). *Social relationships:* Generally liked because of desire to please and childish appeal (particularly true of females), interest in adventure and tendency to be good story tellers. Generally responsive and submissive. *Sexual adjustment:* Fear of sex and marriage and a martyr tendency. Average venereal disease history, high abortion rate, both spontaneous and artificial. *Attitude toward family:* Fear of both parents with a fearfully dependent reaction, usually toward the parent who seemed to be the more terrifying, except that the trend is often changed by the early death of one parent or the other. Role of martyr in relation to parents, spouse, children.

6. *Characteristic Behavior Pattern.* In general agreeable, talkative, vaguely ambitious with a tendency to overdo in an inconsistent way. Emphasis on social and pleasure ambitions which are frequently impossible of fulfillment and never persistently strived for. Otherwise their sociability follows the pattern of the rheumatic fever group, except that they seem to want to be liked by more people and have a tendency to bluff and curry favor.

7. *Neurotic Traits.* Childhood phobias, exaggerated fright reactions, nightmares. In adult life a continuation of these same traits with marked claustrophobia or agoraphobia, and a tendency to develop deep admiration for people that frighten or abuse them. Infantile fixation.

8. *Addictions and Interests.* A tendency to deny themselves (martyrdom —especially females) or to over-indulge in stimulants (rebellion and group

identification—especially males). Wish for adventure and action. Especially among the males a tendency to ride hobbies and to become religious zealots.

9. *Life Situation Immediately Prior to Onset.* Unusual exertion in one of the compensatory spheres, a severe fright or a traumatic death.

10. *Reaction To Illness.* Attempt to deny it but enjoy sympathy and unconsciously increase their suffering. Little insight.

11. *Area of Focal Conflict and Characteristic Reaction.* Authority—emulation of superior especially in fantasy; secondarily, conflict over sexual role together with a tendency to curry favor with the opposite sex. Extreme dominance of passive tendency discernible before illness.

CASE ILLUSTRATIONS

Case No. RHD 287. An unmarried man, aged 20, was admitted to the hospital with the diagnosis of rheumatic heart disease, mitral stenosis and insufficiency, aortic insufficiency, auricular fibrillation. Onset of symptoms: (four months prior to admission) "One day everything I ate seemed to come up. There was green bile. It was like the trouble that Mother was always having. I had a temperature of 101, my heart was going 90 miles an hour. I spent two and a half months in bed. The first thing I did when I got up was to see 'Naughty Marietta' in the movies. It upset me and I got sick again."

Family History. "Father and all his family have stomach trouble, especially gas. I think from nervousness. Mother had it, too, as well as jaundice. Father had heart trouble, too, and a nervous breakdown when I was 12. He used to drop down in the street so that he was afraid to go out alone."

Personal Data. The patient was of linear build and very thin. He was born in New York City. Birth and early development were normal but he soon became a feeding problem and grew so frail that his mother had to carry him around on a pillow. He was the third child, first boy, in a family of five. The next younger sibling was also a boy.

Previous Health. Severe attacks of nausea and vomiting beginning at the age of 12. The physician seen at this time told him that he had ptomaine poisoning from eating fish and milk and that he had a bad heart. Although he had had no previous cardiac symptoms, he had suffered from attacks of palpitation since that time. At the age of 19 he had a tonsillectomy and adenoidectomy.

Previous Injuries. At the age of 5 he fell out of a tree and cut his thumb so that he had to have two or three stitches. No other injuries or tendency to accident.

General Adjustment. Vocation—education: "I liked school but was just about to graduate from grammar school when I got sick. After three years I went back again and I felt kind of funny." At the time of admission the patient was completing the third year of high school. *Occupation:* He took up singing during the period out of school and in the last two or three years has made money singing over the radio. "I always wanted to start a restaurant. I think with my name I would go far." *Social adjustment:* Externally the patient had a pleasing sociable personality. He said: "I like to be jolly with a crowd, but never with people who are angry or cross. I like fellows better than girls but I never have any intimate friends." *Sexual adjustment:* This patient had little to say about sex except as something to stay away from. He had no interest in girls or marriage and pictured himself as taking care of his mother after his father died. He "overcame masturbation long ago."

Attitude toward parents: "Father and Mother are both terribly strict. We are all scared of them. I have learned how to get Mother on my side sometimes. Even now they won't let my grown up sisters (aged 23 and 24) go out alone or have any boy friends. As a family we have awful fights, but we all have clean lives and stay away from sex."

Characteristic Behavior Pattern. "I'm always on the go wanting to make a living and help my mother. That's what gave father his breakdown. I guess I'm going the same way. I'm the worrying type. But that's better than the way I used to be just sitting around holding my heart."

Neurotic Traits. Early: The patient was a feeding problem, had a tendency to attacks of nausea and vomiting like his mother. "I always used to be scared. I don't know of what. I had nightmares." *Present:* The patient remained very fussy about his food. "I only feel well when Father buys delmonico steak and lettuce." Nightmares continued. "Ever since I was little I have eaten fast and the doctor said I always swallowed air with my food."

Addictions and Interests. Delmonico steaks and "things to make me sleep." "What I like to do best is fish and hunt rabbits." As a child he disliked ball games but won a medal for running. This he continued contrary to advice after the onset of his illness, but with the inconsistency character- istic of these patients, he added, "But I never danced or anything like that because I knew it was too much of a strain on me." He was brought up a Roman Catholic and continued to follow the precepts of his church but had little religious conviction.

Life Situation Immediately Prior to Onset. The onset of illness in this patient occurred probably during the first ten years of his life, during which time he was exposed to the constant conflict between his parents, but suc- ceeded in becoming his mother's favorite because he became a feeding prob- lem. During this period he was exposed to the gastro-intestinal symptom- atology of mother, father, and all his father's family and the cardiovascular symptomatology of his father. In any case his first attack of serious illness when the doctor told him he had heart trouble and the first heart symptom developed, was preceded by his father's nervous breakdown which was accompanied by a flare-up of heart attacks; and the second attack, which led to his first hospital admission, by another siege of illness on the part of both father and mother. The preceding months had been a period of strenuous exertion in the endeavor to please his family by finishing high school and to prove himself an adequate breadwinner by singing over the radio.

Reaction to Illness. "I was very scared to come to the hospital. I was afraid they would operate on my stomach, but everybody here is nice. I guess suffering will improve my character." The patient's only gastro-intestinal upset in the hospital occurred immediately following a visit from his mother. He commented: "I feel better when Mother and Father come to see me together." Except for this one occasion they always did.

Area of Focal Conflict. This history shows a child in early conflict with strict and quarreling parents, and his attempt to solve this conflict by becoming like his father: "I see myself taking care of Mother after Father dies. It was too much worry and overdoing that got him down, and I'm going the same way," etc. The parallel conflict in the realm of sex is indicated in his preference for boys, fear of girls, repression of sexual impulses in general, and his adoption of the ideal of chastity, and devotion to his mother whose favorite he succeeded in becoming. He shows clearly the anxiety and the tendency to hysterical mechanisms so characteristic of patients with rheumatic heart disease.

Case No. RHD 69. A widow, aged 40, was admitted to the hospital with diagnosis of inactive rheumatic heart disease, mitral stenosis and insufficiency, cardiac hypertrophy and insufficiency, chronic auricular fibrillation, chronic passive congestion of liver, bronchiectasis of left lower lobe, varicose veins, dental caries, and chronic cholecystitis. Her first cardiac symptoms occurred four years prior to admission, and beginning with dyspnea and palpitation during the year prior to admission, she became increasingly restless, unable to sleep, and lost 14 pounds. The patient was in the hospital about ten weeks.

On the second admission two months after discharge the diagnosis was: inactive rheumatic heart disease, with mitral stenosis and insufficiency, chronic auricular fibrillation. Cardiac hypertrophy and insufficiency, chronic passive congestion of liver. Fibrosis of left lower lobe due to previous respiratory infection. Organized pneumonia with thickened pleura? Basal acid-fast? Bronchiectasis? Varicose veins, dental caries, chronic cholecystitis? After ten weeks in which thyroid oblation was considered and rejected because of her pulmonary infection, the patient was again discharged.

The discharge diagnosis was: Inactive rheumatic heart disease, mitral stenosis and insufficiency, cardiac hypertrophy and insufficiency, chronic auricular fibrillation, chronic passive congestion of liver, bronchiectasis of left lower lobe, varicose veins, dental caries, chronic cholecystitis.

Family History. The patient's father died at the age of 40 of cause unknown, suicide suspected, the patient was then 6 years old. Her mother died at 38 of a ruptured appendix when the patient was 7.

Personal Data. The patient was born in New York City, the youngest of four siblings and the only girl. She was of linear type and very thin. One brother died of pneumonia when the patient was 20 years old. She had five children, three daughters and two sons.

Health Record. Tonsillitis, colds throughout life, also headaches, constipation and gastric upsets, double pneumonia at 18 and chronic bronchitis since then. She suffered also from hay fever, epistaxis, varicose veins, and cholecystitis. She had had two miscarriages.

Previous Injuries. None.

General Adjustment. Vocation—education: The patient completed grade school and went to work at the age of 14, first in a candy factory and then as a janitress. Both before and after her marriage she made extra money nights addressing envelopes, working until 1 or 2 o'clock in the morning. *Social relationships:* The patient generally liked women and was liked by them but her husband's continued drunkenness interfered with her social interests so much that they were gradually given up. *Sexual adjustment:* She was always afraid of sex and "never knew much about it." After her marriage there were seven pregnancies unwanted, two of which were terminated by abortion. *Attitude toward parents:* The patient had few memories of her parents both of whom died before she was 7. She was brought up by an extremely strict grandmother to whom she submitted "out of respect." When the grandmother became feeble they went to live with a married brother, and his wife was so unkind to the patient that "I was forced into marriage before I really wanted to."

Characteristic Behavior Pattern. This patient was generally agreeable and talkative but extremely thin and nervous. As a child she had felt rebellious and wished she had been a boy. There was a general attempt to please and win sympathy.

Neurotic Traits. "As a child I was always afraid of the dark and of being alone. I am ashamed to say that I get scared sometimes even now." The social worker noted that the patient was naturally "very conscientious" being a typical German housewife who must have everything spick and span.

Addictions and Interests. This patient was very much dependent on her five to twelve cups of tea a day but "denied herself" other stimulants. As a girl she was athletic and particularly enjoyed skating and jumping. She still went to church.

Life Situation Immediately Prior to Onset. During the year after her husband hung himself this patient's heart trouble developed.

Reaction to Illness. The patient's illness interfered with her taking a job but she nevertheless worked hard "taking care of my five children." This work was most of it unnecessary because the youngest child was 15, but it fitted in well with the increasing idea of herself as a martyr. "I can't do the work I am supposed to do. I never go out. I do too much about the home. The neighbors say I'm trying to kill myself. I've given up amusement."

Area of Focal Conflict and Characteristic Reaction. Emulation of the strict grandmother was obvious in the patient's story, together with conflict over her sexual role so characteristic of these patients. "I always wanted to be a boy. My brothers never had so much trouble as I did." Her passive tendencies prior to the onset of the illness were obvious as well as their marked reinforcement through the illness itself.

DEGREE AND NATURE OF SOMATIC EXPRESSION OF CONFLICTS

If these patients be compared with the patients discussed in the preceding section—sufferers from rheumatic fever and polyarthritis with more or less cardiac involvement—it becomes clear that in those with the greater cardiac involvement, rheumatic fever type B, there is found a greater limitation of freedom and the passive masochistic traits that are so distinctive of the group here discussed.*

Tension, Aggression, and Resentment

In these patients tension is not marked in either striated or smooth musculature. This seems to be consistent with a greatly decreased tendency to express aggression or resentment. They seem to have little or no characterological armor. Following the analogy of tension driven inward (page 14 ff.), one could almost say that in conjunction with their characteristic regression the physiological equilibrium has been diffusely undermined. Disturbances of breathing, hysterical conversion symptoms, palpitation, on the other hand, are prominent and seem to have been present in childhood. In several instances in which early medical histories were available, it was possible to demonstrate the presence of these physiological disturbances long before any cardiac damage had occurred, and before there had been any evidence of rheumatic disease. To these observations is added

---

* The interplay of these traits and the burden placed on the heart is illustrated particularly in the following case: Case No. HP 1, page 40 and Case No. RHDP 4, page 473. See also Cases No. RHD 65 and No. RF 304, page 605 and page 600.

the fact that such manifestations of disequilibrium tend to be more prominent in the interim between attacks when the heart is relatively well compensated. Hence the disequilibrium cannot be understood solely in terms of organic damage.

Activity, Verbalization, Dreams and Fantasies

In addition to strong tendencies toward self-neglect and overexertion, there was in these patients a considerable urge to *activity*, usually without much directive ability. Patient No. RHD 287, a man, aged 20, had very little idea of what to do with himself despite numerous interests, but as he put it, could not stand just "to sit around holding my heart."

In addition to a restless, exhibitionistic type of activity, these patients were inclined to be *talkative* but not articulate regarding their emotional problems. In other words, they seemed incapable of making satisfactory use of either of these channels for the discharge of emotional tension. Incidentally, as was noted in the discussion of rheumatic fever patients, the greater the patient's limitation in these two respects and the more he was thwarted, the greater was likely to be the cardiac involvement. The *dreams* and infantile *fantasy* life are likely to become more prominent in these patients as other outlets are blocked.

SUMMARY OF CHARACTEROLOGICAL DEFENSES AND THEIR RELATIVE SUCCESS OR FAILURE

The majority of these patients are so similar both psychologically and somatically to the rheumatic fever patients, type B, that they seem to represent a more malignant form of the same psychosomatic process. An interesting question is raised by the fact that these patients are usually first admitted with considerable valvular damage but report no episodes of acute rheumatic fever. Their defenses are very similar but the higher incidence of sudden traumatic experiences seems to lead to a greater crystallization of both defences and organic damage.

Light on the differences between the rheumatic disease personality and other personality types, as well as on the differences among the forms of rheumatic disease itself, seems to be thrown by the various patterns of behavior which are used as defenses against the conflicts mentioned. Those suffering from rheumatic fever and rheumatoid arthritis in the group which we have called type A, seem to begin with a tendency to action, as do the fracture patients. They have not, however, so good a superficial adjustment to the external world in the matter of social contacts. They are far more retiring in disposition. Most important of all, they show a marked tendency to fixate their guilt on a part or parts of the body, such as arms, joints or legs. This latter trait is far less noticeable among accident patients, who consequently are not so likely to develop a somatic short circuit and have a much better previous health record.

Type B among the rheumatic fever patients who are not prone to accidents, have personality traits similar to type A, except that they omit the partial outlet in action, rather keeping their troubles entirely to themselves, so have no outlet except the somatic short circuit.

Patients who suffer from rheumatic heart disease differ from the other two types in that they find less difficulty in making social contacts and make spasmodic efforts to work out their troubles in an adjustment with reality which involves a better imitation of adult behavior and more assumption of responsibility in relation both to job and to family life. However, they seldom succeed in these endeavors and are projected into somatic attacks by their failures.

All varieties of patients with rheumatic heart disease without joint involvement or history of such involvement show a relative inability to accept a heterosexual role, to marry and have children. All three types respond to their illness with regression to an infantile desire to exploit their illness and be taken care of. This trait is thrown into dramatic relief by their tendency to do those things that they like even when contrary to the doctors' orders, and in the case of patients with rheumatic heart disease, by masochistic enjoyment of their suffering.

In conclusion, it may be said, however, that quite apart from the relatively minor personality differences which seem to be associated with these differences in the symptomatology and course of the rheumatic process, we are dealing with one disease and one general personality type which can be distinguished readily from other personality types discussed in this volume. The personalities discussed in this chapter are in sharp contrast with those discussed in the preceding chapter, where again the differences between patients with hypertensive cardiovascular disease, coronary disease, and anginal syndrome seem to be relatively minor, and to suggest, likewise, that in these syndromes we are dealing with different manifestations of one disease process. It is noteworthy also that we find frequent overlapping or progression from one syndrome to another in patients suffering from the illnesses discussed in both this chapter and that preceding, but very infrequently (Chapter X) do we find patients shifting from the hypertensive or coronary groups to the rheumatic group and vice versa.

V. Therapeutic Implications *

Since this illness is considered incurable in terms of our present knowledge, and is characterized by a relatively short life span, the question may arise as to the value of such descriptive material. If the disease is far advanced (see Case No. HP 1, pages 40 and 44) little therapeutic use can be made of such information except by way of palliation.

If, however, the valvular damage is not too severe (see Case No. RHDP 4, page 473) the physician may rescue his patient from continued invalidism and may make possible a fairly healthy and constructive life by judicious management or recourse to psychotherapy. In any case great care must be exercised not to play into the hands of the patient's passive masochistic tendencies.

CONCLUSIONS

(1) Patients with rheumatic disease differ from all other groups studied.

(2) These patients stand out in certain respects from the population as a whole. They show a strikingly uniform ecological background, belong mainly to the lower middle class with a distinctive standard of living and cultural milieu. Like most patients with cardiovascular disease their previous health record is relatively poor. They show in their family history a particularly high incidence of exposure to nervousness, cardiovascular disease, or sudden death.

In view of our lack of information concerning the etiology of rheumatic disease, there is little value in speculation concerning the relationship of personality factors and physiological mechanisms. It

* See Chapter XI, section V.

is interesting to note, however (see Chapter IX for fuller discussion), that although we do find this illness concentrated in certain families as well as in geographical and social groups, the possible hereditary factor seems no greater and no less than that for other types of cardiovascular disease studied. We find rheumatic disease in the family history of one out of four of these patients, whereas for diabetic patients we find diabetes in the family of one out of three. If we look not for rheumatic disease but for cardiovascular disease in general, we find cardiovascular heredity in slightly more than half of the cases, which is approximately the same percentage found for patients with coronary occlusion, hypertensive cardiovascular disease and anginal syndrome.

(3) Although patients suffering from rheumatic disease are more homogeneous than the fracture group, nevertheless three fairly distinctive types may be delineated on the basis of both personality factors and organic damage.

(a) *Rheumatic fever patients, type A,* those who recover without permanent cardiac damage, and also those with well-established rheumatoid arthritis, tend to be somewhat more spontaneous and aggressive than the two following groups. Some of them have in addition to their illness history an accident-proneness and some have hypertension.

(b) *Rheumatic fever patients, type B,* may or may not recover from the first attack of rheumatic fever without cardiac damage; those with damage are potential cardiacs. They are predominantly extratensive and passive. There is a much higher percentage of females in this group.

(c) *Rheumatic heart disease patients,* those admitted with well-established rheumatic heart disease but without a definite history of acute rheumatic fever, are usually repressed, passive and submissive, with dominant extratensive tendencies and little creative inner life.

(4) The following individual characteristics are significant:

(a) They have smooth, untroubled faces with a childish, often cherubic, quality. This is especially marked in patients with rheumatic fever, type B, and with rheumatic heart disease. There are few overt neurotic symptoms but definite signs of anxiety just beneath the surface. This is sometimes indicated by a spasm in the throat, for example, or in a hysterical trend which gradually becomes more obvious.

(b) They show little superficial skeletal tension but tend to convey the impression that there is no danger of an aggressive outburst and that they will avoid argument or a scene at all costs. This generalization should be qualified by the statement that sometimes patients with rheumatic fever, type A, show some resistance resembling that of fracture patients.

(c) These patients appear timid, propitiatory and lacking in self-reliance. They aim to please and appeal for sympathy. In type A these traits are often concealed in the role of being a good sport.

In all types lurking just beneath the surface is a nostalgia for childhood, even though the facts of their lives indicate that there has been some attempt to establish independence. This nostalgia may be revealed in some such remark as "I never got married because I couldn't find anybody who would take as good care of me as my mother," or even more directly in the statement, "The happiest time of my life was when I was a kid." This is so in spite of the fact that childhood years were usually unstable and full of conflict.

(d) There is little striving toward integration and autonomy. There is usually a fairly clear identification with the more passive parent and a masochistic attachment to the authoritarian figure who has hurt the most. Not only do they not make up their minds quickly, but they rarely feel the need of making up their minds at all. There seems to be a vague threat in intellectual values as if these represent a world that is not meant for them. They like to talk about the things they "might have done if —."

(e) Exacerbations of the illness are likely to occur whenever their already limited range of freedom and contact is further reduced. These are likely to be particularly severe if precipitated by a traumatic situation.

(f) Their initial reaction to their illness is markedly colored by guilt which they do all in their power to conceal. Later they compensate by the development of a messianic or martyr role.

(5) It seems likely that, regardless of any external physical agents, there is a psychosomatic predisposition to this disease. The noxious agents which have become suspect are widely present in the population, and it is necessary to account in some way for the differences in immunity shown by different individuals.

Chapter VII

CARDIAC ARRHYTHMIAS AND RECURRENT DECOMPENSATION

Quand on est malade, c'est une dispute entre le malade et la maladie.—GATTI, *Histories Medicales.*

CARDIAC ARRHYTHMIAS WITHOUT DEMONSTRABLE ORGANIC DAMAGE

I. NATURE AND MAGNITUDE OF THE PROBLEM

Under this heading we have included cases of (a) paroxysmal tachycardia; (b) that vague medical entity variously called effort syndrome or neurocirculatory asthenia; and (c) episodic attacks of dyspnea, palpitation with or without precordial pain, usually diagnosed as cardiac neurosis. Although this is an unsatisfactory grouping, particularly because among these patients are some that during the period of observation went on to develop actual heart disease, and also because similar syndromes with exaggerated dyspnea and palpitation are found in the presence of organic heart disease, these patients had some traits in common which seemed worthy of comment.

OTHER STUDIES

Sidney Schnur,[371] after studying 172 patients, reached the interesting conclusion that cardiac neurosis is a distinct entity with characteristic findings recognizable even in the presence of organic heart disease. The criteria for diagnosis are: an inherited or acquired predisposition to neurosis; a definite precipitating factor; symptoms such as inframammary tenderness and hyperalgesia; relief by simple procedures such as the therapeutic test used by Schnur, which consists of the intradermal injection of small quantities of 2 per cent novocain, together with suitable suggestion, the latter being the more important factor. Patients with organic heart disease may have symptoms and signs similar to those described, which can be proved to be of neurotic origin. When precordial pain is accompanied by superficial hyperalgesia and deep tenderness, it is more likely to be of neurotic than of organic origin; thus, deep tenderness was elicited in the inframammary area in 5 per cent of patients having organic heart disease and in 80 per cent of those suffering from neurosis alone.

For a review of literature covering this general field, reference should be made to Caughey.[76]

II. ONSET OF SYMPTOMS

The average age of these patients at time of admission was 30 years which makes them the youngest of all the cardiovascular groups studied, with the exception of patients with rheumatic fever type A. The age at time of onset, however, was more difficult to determine than in the case of any other group studied. They seemed to have suffered from this syndrome more or less all their lives, although the symptoms are likely to subside during adolescence (see *Life Situation Immediately Prior to Onset*, page 443).

III. PREDISPOSITION TO ILLNESS—FACTORS TO BE EVALUATED

ORGAN CONDITIONING—PHYSIOLOGICAL AND PSYCHOLOGICAL

Heredity—Actual and Pseudo

Cardiovascular heredity for the group (44 per cent) was in the same general range as for patients with rheumatic heart disease or coronary occlusion. It should be noted, however, that there are no statistically significant differences in the figures for cardiovascular heredity among the groups studied, even including the fracture group. If we look for trends we find the fracture, coronary, rheumatic heart, and cardiac arrhythmia groups slightly lower; and the hypertensive, anginal, and rheumatic fever groups slightly higher. But both higher and lower groups include patients with syndromes involving cardiac damage as well as those with syndromes in which cardiac damage is absent. There was no important difference in the percentage of the disease in the maternal as opposed to the paternal side of the family, or in the affliction of males as opposed to females. Patients with cardiac arrhythmia differ from most of the other cardiovascular groups in the incidence of exposure to cardiovascular disease rather than in the incidence of cardiac heredity. The figure for heredity is relatively low (heredity plus exposure 65 per cent) as compared with the figures in the hypertensive and coronary occlusion groups (90 per cent or over). This emphasizes again the importance of the pseudohereditary factor in the psychosomatic picture of patients with different types of cardiac dysfunction. Exposure is a much more constant finding among patients with severe organic damage than among those with cardiac arrhythmia or anginal syndrome. It may be added that with the fracture patients there was very little evidence of exposure to cardiovascular disease, in spite of a cardiac heredity of about the same incidence as in the other groups.

Accidents occurred in the families of 19 per cent of these patients. There was a family history of *diabetes* in only a few cases.

Nervousness was reported in the families of 56 per cent of these cases, including 6 per cent institutional.

There was a history of traumatic death in the families of 19 per cent of these patients.

Constitution—Age Range, Sex, and Marriage

These patients were mostly of the *linear* or *mixed type*.

The *age range* was 19 to 50 years. Twenty-five per cent of these patients were in the decade 15 to 24, and 62 per cent in the decade 25 to 34.

The *sex* distribution in this group was about two females to one male.

Of these patients 50 per cent were *married* (60 per cent of the males and 45 per cent of the females). Again taking patients 25 years old and over, this percentage becomes 67 per cent (75 per cent of the males and 62.5 per cent of the females). No divorces were reported. Of those married only 62.5 per cent had children. The average size of the family was one and one-quarter children per marriage.

In 50 per cent of the cases the patient was the first child in the family (including 20 per cent in which the patient was the only child). Only one-third of these patients came from small families; one patient was the twenty-first child in a family of twenty-one. In this respect, however, there was a marked difference between males and females; 60 per cent of the males versus 18 per cent of the females came from small families.

Previous Health

Exactly one-quarter of these patients had major operations, but the majority of these were among the females. The typical operations were the following: appendectomy, cholecystectomy, ovariectomy, abortion with sterilization, and thyroidectomy.

Minor operations were reported by 50 per cent of these patients, but only 37.5 per cent reported more than one such operation.

Major illnesses, prior to the onset of the present illness, were reported by 50 per cent of these patients, and, as in other cardiovascular groups, pneumonia, pleurisy, influenza and bronchitis predominated.

There was a history of well-defined minor illness in 37 per cent of these patients, and all the patients reported symptomatology related to the vegetative system, such as susceptibility to colds, allergy, migraine, gastro-intestinal upsets, disturbances of circulation. Allergy alone was present in 31 per cent of the group, gastro-intestinal upsets in 44 per cent, and 25 per cent suffered from severe pyorrhea and bad teeth. This group was relatively free from pelvic disorders except for self-induced abortion. The venereal disease rate was average (6 per cent).

None of these patients had hypertension although two of the patients discussed under the heading "Hypertensive Cardiovascular Disease" had marked dyspnea and palpitation in addition.

Statistics Concerning Previous Injury

This group resembles the rheumatic fever type A group in its high accident history. Twenty-five per cent of these patients reported injury, and 12.5 per cent reported more than one injury. The accidents occurred just prior to the onset, not in childhood.

Early Influences and Traumatic Experiences

Traumatic experiences were frequent in the histories of these patients, as will be seen from the previous statistical material, but as a rule these experiences were not blamed by the patients for their illness.

From the point of view of geographical distribution this represented rather a heterogeneous group, but sudden changes in environment, moving from place to place, were not strikingly frequent. Although these patients came from homes in which there was a great deal of friction, they had not been subjected to privation to a degree comparable with that of some of the patients in other groups reported. In general, they belonged to the middle class and were in moderately comfortable circumstances.

OUTSTANDING POINTS IN THE PERSONALITY HISTORY

General Adjustment

Vocation—education.* These patients were second only to the patients with diabetes from the point of view of the small percentage in the grammar school category, and outranked all other groups studied in the college category. There was a tendency to complete the educational unit undertaken except for the falling off in college. Unlike the patients with diabetes the men in this group excelled the women in academic achievement.

Income.* Although these patients did not attain the income level of patients with coronary occlusion, like patients with fracture, they ranked close.

Occupation.* Although their work record was somewhat unstable, over 40 per cent of these patients were in groups II (proprietors, managers, officials) and III (clerks, salesmen, stenographers). In this respect their choice of occupation resembled that of patients with coronary occlusion and with anginal syndrome, but there were very few skilled workers among them and relatively more housewives.

General Behavior. These patients were superficially gay, flighty, eager for popularity, and inclined to hair-trigger mood swings. They often appeared nervous and panicky. When alone, or in occasional

---

* It will be remembered that statements under starred headings are based only on patients over 21, in order to make them comparable to national statistics.

more intimate moments, they showed a marked tendency to self-depreciation and depression.

Social Adjustment. These patients usually reported a good social adjustment and many friends. Consistent, however, with their tendencies to play to the gallery and their exhibitionism, they had a feeling that their friends were not very trustworthy or sincere.

Sexual Adjustment. A fear of pregnancy was marked among the females, as well as disgust or timorousness about sexual experience. This was not a matter of sexual drive but in one way or another their sexual relationships were never quite satisfactory, and the sexual partner was generally blamed. Among the males there was a marked interest in sex; they believed that they might be too highly sexed, a trait which they feared might result in impotence, and to which they often ascribed their symptoms. The oedipus conflict is more readily recognized and more elaborated in this group than in any of the others.

Attitude Toward Parents and Children. In these patients the emotional relationship to parents was inadequate. There was no consistent preference for one parent or the other, and confusion about identification was marked. Nevertheless there was a tendency to take sides in family disputes, and as was the case in patients with rheumatic heart disease, the side chosen was usually that of the stricter of the two parents. The majority of the parents of these patients were strict but not so much in the sphere of everyday living as in relation to the patient's sexual and social life. Most parents were excessively nervous, and the majority of them had temper tantrums. The patients themselves, however, were not addicted to temper tantrums, probably because they were too much frightened. As is evidenced by the frequent self-induced abortions and fear of impotence, the attitude toward spouse and children of their own was generally fearful; being doubtful about their ability to bring them up they preferred not to have children, or if they had them, they were troubled and insecure in their relationship to them.

Characteristic Behavior Pattern: Playing to the Gallery and Self-Depreciation

More than any other group of patients studied, these patients indulged in playing to the gallery, but their accompanying tendencies toward self-depreciation, supersensitiveness and emotional instability revealed their deep-lying insecurity.

Whereas a compulsive character is a general finding among patients with hypertension and some develop compulsion-neurotic symptoms in the course of treatment, patients with marked symptoms of dyspnea and palpitation are characterized by phobias and prominent conversion mechanisms. In both groups there is a tendency to competition. The hypertensive patient actually competed but was thwarted because of his unconscious passive-submissive trend, whereas patients in the present group were not quite able to compete because of their fear of a break-through of hostility and their strong reaction formation in the direction of making themselves liked. With them the mechanism is sometimes genital, as in hysteria; more often it is pregenital, ranging toward that which is characteristic of the asthmatic. But there seems not to be such a marked prominence of anal material and oral character organization on the one hand, and of the tendency to act out aggression on the other, as is found in asthmatics.

Neurotic Traits—Early and Present

From the point of view of childhood phobias, exaggerated fright reactions and nightmares, these patients surpassed those of all the other groups reported. Among the males sleep-walking was also common. Enuresis continuing into adolescence was the only other early neurotic trait of any prominence.

From the point of view of neurotic symptoms these patients showed little change from childhood to the time of admission, except for a quantitative increase in the tendency to be afraid of everything and to worry about their physical well-being. Fear and anger were both very prominent in their dreams and nightmares. Claustrophobia was a regular finding, and most of the patients were addicted to patent medicines, usually trying out a considerable variety.

For example, patient No. CA 159, a married woman, aged 30, reported recurrent dreams that her daughter was being killed or that she herself was being beaten by her father. With such dreams she would awaken with tingling and pain in the buttocks. Other characteristic dreams were an inability to solve problems, particularly problems such as she had had at school. A particularly disturbing dream was the following: "My arm was being slashed with a knife.

I can see the skin gaping but no blood coming out. I awaken and feel my arm quickly. It takes a long time to be sure it is really all right."

Addictions and Interests

Addiction to coffee was prominent in this group. It was found in the majority of the males, but in only about one-third of the females. Excessive smoking was found in 80 per cent of the males, although in only about 20 per cent of the females. While all these patients made alcohol a part of the daily routine, none of them was definitely alcoholic.

Like the patients with fractures and unlike any other group studied, these patients showed a marked interest in gambling. A characteristic story is the following:

Patient No. CA 349, a man, aged 37, had broken an arm at the age of 17, and a hand at the age of 18. He stuttered from the age of 12 to 15. At the age of 21 he began to suffer from sudden attacks of anxiety, characterized by difficulty in breathing, by choking and gasping. (He was afraid to swim because he was afraid he would choke.) These attacks came on particularly in the subway, and also sometimes when the patient was at work. They became so severe that he was unable to go to work alone. He carried a bottle of elixir alurate in his pocket so that he could take a teaspoonful every time he became upset.

The onset of these attacks was definitely related to reverses in his financial situation. He had left high school to work in the stock exchange and was relatively successful, earning $150 a week, and gambling on the side; then his gambling debts began to accumulate and his income to drop. (At least half of his week's earning he regularly lost in gambling.) At the time of admission he was earning only $30 a week. At this time he broke his engagement to a girl he had wanted to marry. The reasons for this are not exactly clear, he merely stated that he was unsure of himself. He had just become engaged and broke the engagement before the admission to the hospital.

Unlike the patients with fractures, however, this group showed very little interest in athletics. In general their interests were diverse, mainly social in character, and such as to contain an element of excitement and to bring them into the limelight.

The religious tendency in this group showed a definite cardiac trend. It was very similar to that found in the group of patients with anginal syndrome. Among these patients 30 per cent were Roman

Catholic; 25 per cent were Jewish; 37 per cent, Protestant; in 69 per cent there was no particular change in religious practice between childhood and adult life. There were more than twice as many Roman Catholic females as Roman Catholic males, and more than twice as many Jewish males as Jewish females.

Religion was largely a matter of principle, though occasionally there was an obscure emotional involvement. Thus, patient No. CA 315, a married man, aged 42, and a Catholic, was not at all upset by his wife's use of contraceptives, although he was tortured by a conflict between rational thinking (the doctors could not find anything wrong with him) and superstition (he was one of three close friends, two of whom had died: ergo his wife must not invest any money for him because he must die very soon). So also, patient No. CA 324, a woman, whose father was a lax Catholic and whose mother was Protestant, joined the Presbyterian church, and enjoyed going to church for a number of years, but had had to give up attendance during the last five years because sitting in church increased salivation to such an extent that it choked her.

Life Situation Immediately Prior to Onset

Admission to the hospital usually followed a period of gradual failure in adjustment, accompanied by increasing attacks of dyspnea and palpitation. The onset of symptoms regularly followed some traumatic experience in the sphere of personal relationships over which the patient continued to brood while his fear and anxiety accumulated. There was usually a period of a number of years during which the patient consulted doctors, experimented with self-medication and faith cures, before he arrived at the hospital. The final decision to come to the hospital usually occurred when some person on whom the patient had depended seemed likely to let him down. For example, one patient lived in constant fear that his mother, who was perfectly well, might die so that there would be no one to cook his meals for him and take him to and from work. In the majority of cases there was also a gradual period of restriction of activity, increasing fear of people, and of going anywhere alone. Another patient was afraid to travel because there were so few good doctors in the world and he felt it was necessary to know one that was reliable everywhere he went.

Reaction to Illness

It was usually extremely difficult for these patients to come to terms with their illness. In the first place, most of them had been told that there was nothing physically wrong, and yet they were subject to symptoms of an alarming nature. Hence they were likely to feel that they were beyond the reach of help by a physician or that they had had bad luck in not being able to find a physician who had been able to help them. As a result they were often distrustful and full of resentment.

IV. Dynamic Formulation

AREA OF FOCAL CONFLICT AND CHARACTERISTIC REACTION: CONTACT WITH OUTSIDE WORLD (NARCISSISTIC WITH-DRAWAL VERSUS DESIRE TO BE EFFECTUAL OR ADMIRED)

In all cases one or both parents lived well into the patient's adolescence, and usually well on into the patient's adult life. In only 25 per cent of these patients was there a loss of either parent. In this respect these patients resemble the patients with fractures more than any other group studied. It will be remembered that, except for the fracture group, their accident record exceeds that of all other groups studied, patients with rheumatic disease coming second. As might be expected from the similarity of symptoms themselves—that is, a syndrome characterized by palpitation and dyspnea—these patients showed many personality resemblances to patients with rheumatic heart disease.

Mention has been made already of the inadequate and frightened relationship of these patients to their parents. Patient No. CA 159, for example, said: "All my life I've lived in terror of my father. It was not only that he used to beat me so that I would have welts for weeks afterwards, but it seemed as if he was always trying to find excuses for beating me, or to fool me into doing something he could beat me for. He would hang up his trousers at night and shake them, showing us children that the pockets were full of change. In the morning he would count the change hoping to find we'd taken some. Once I did, to buy some candy for a friend who told on me and I got the worst beating I'd ever had in my life. It seemed as if he was disappointed if he found the change all there, and sometimes I think he counted wrong and beat us even if we hadn't taken any."

The fear and distrust of doctors, so characteristic of these patients, seemed to have an important background in childhood experiences with parents, and occasionally in some such experience as the following which itself was probably colored by the atmosphere of fear in the home. For example:

Patient No. CA 315, a married man, aged 42, whose admission diagnosis was tachycardia, expressed at length his disgust with doctors who told him that nothing was wrong with him. "Either they want to fool me or they don't know their job. I was fooled enough by my father and I simply won't take it any more. They [doctors] killed my grandfather when I was a child." The grandfather died at the age of 65 from obstruction of the kidneys. "They killed my mother too." The mother died in childbirth. "My older brother was an M.D. and promised to help me financially so I could finish my course in engineering, but he never kept his promise."

It is easy to see how such childhood experiences could lead to difficulty and conflict in the patient's contacts with the outside world. Their reaction to such difficulties in terms of narcissistic withdrawal on the one hand, and the desire to win prestige on the other is also understandable. The intensity of the traumatic element throws light on the tendency to keep resentment pent up and on the periodic panics together with the reaction formation in the direction of verbalism and exhibitionism.

PROFILE

Cardiac Arrhythmia *

1. *Family History*. Cardiovascular disease in parents and siblings, 44 per cent. Accident history for parents and siblings, about 18 per cent. Extreme nervousness, about 56 per cent; highest for any group studied. Exposure to cardiovascular disease or to sudden death in 65 per cent of the cases.

2. *Personal Data*. Both parents lived well into the patient's adolescence, and were generally limiting to the patient's activities, especially in the sphere of sex. Middle-class moderately comfortable background. Tendency to be first child. Low marriage rate. Few children, few divorces.

3. *Health Record*. Poor previous health record, closely paralleling that for

* See Chapter XI, and also page 585 ff., in order to evaluate the distinctive features in this profile.

coronary patients except for relative freedom from hypertensive cardio-vascular disease and pelvic disorders.

4. *Injuries.* Highest of any group studied for more than one accident except for the fracture group. Low record for single injury. Accidents just prior to onset of illness, not in childhood.

5. *General Adjustment. Education:* High educational record especially among males but no marked tendency to complete educational unit. *Work record:* Somewhat unstable. *Income and vocational level:* Next to coronaries, highest of all groups studied. Characteristically class II (proprietors, executives, and officials) and class III (clerks, salesmen and stenographers). *Social relationships:* Pleasing, adaptive manner. Generally liked. When most insecure tend to be flighty and alternate between shyness and exhibitionism. *Sexual adjustment:* Considerable confusion about sex combined with fear and disgust. High frequency of self-induced abortion. Average venereal disease. *Attitude toward family:* Emotional relationship inadequate but continued. No consistent preference for one parent or the other. Confused identification. Tendency to exaggerate family disputes in which the patient took sides usually with the stricter of the two. Fearful toward spouse and children.

6. *Characteristic Behavior Pattern.* Hysterically inconsistent action. Fearful of expressing hostility. Often morose when alone and with close friends but cheerful with strangers or in large groups. Rather free use of activity, verbalization and fantasy. Articulate about feelings. Most spontaneous emotionally when incorporating fantasies in responses to others. Work well with adequate external inducement.

7. *Neurotic Traits.* Childhood phobias, exaggerated fright reactions, nightmares, enuresis often continued well into adolescence, and nailbiting. Some tendency to sleep-walking, especially among males. In adult life, continuation of phobias, especially claustrophobia. Much overt anxiety and overactive fantasy life.

8. *Addictions and Interests.* Excessive smoking and addiction to coffee, especially in the males for social reasons or for the fun of being "bad." Lack of interest in athletics but much interest in gambling. Diverse social interests, especially in activities which would bring them into the limelight. Considerable interest in religion, especially religious or moral principles.

9. *Life Situation Immediately Prior to Onset.* Gradual sense of failure with precipitation of symptoms by some traumatic experience in the sphere of personal relationships.

10. *Reaction to Illness.* Fear and discouragement.

11. *Area of Focal Conflict and Characteristic Reaction.* Problem of finding themselves in the outside world, of determining their role in life. React with characteristics wavering between withdrawal and attempt to be effectual.

CASE ILLUSTRATIONS

Case No. CA 315. A married man, aged 42, was admitted with a diagnosis of paroxysmal tachycardia of three years' duration. One night after midnight the patient, while studying, suddenly developed a severe pain in the head, and this was followed by palpitation and weakness. He thought that he was going to die, and was very much frightened. He made his wife have him taken to the nearest hospital. After taking two aspirins his symptoms slowly disappeared. He has had attacks of palpitation and weakness with a great deal of fear of impending death on the average of about once a month ever since. He has seen numerous physicians, but has always been reassured and told that there was nothing really the matter with his heart.

Family History. The father, a physical giant, was a mechanical engineer (unlicensed) in charge of a big sugar mill in Cuba. He died at the age of 34 in an accident. The mother died at 36 in giving birth to twins. The patient blamed the doctors for his mother's untimely death as well as for the prior death of his grandfather from kidney obstruction. There was no family history of cardiovascular disease or diabetes.

(*Note:* This patient represents the 50 per cent of this group who had no cardiovascular heredity or pseudo-heredity, but among whom traumatic deaths in his early years, together with distrust of doctors, are prominent.)

Personal Data. The patient was born in Cuba, the youngest of three sons. Both parents died prior to his adolescence. The family had planned that the oldest boy should be a doctor, the second a dentist or a chemist, and that the patient himself should go into a related profession so that the three "could be a triumvirate." The patient was married at the age of 36 and never had any children "for financial reasons."

(*Note:* The patient is typical of this group in his comfortable economic background, and although atypical in that his parents died relatively early, he was still typical in that all three sons were sufficiently limited by their parents' ambitions for them so that they followed out the vocational pattern laid down for them.)

Previous Health. The patient's health was above the average for this group but nonetheless characterized by frequent colds and vegetative symptomatology. He had a tonsillectomy and adenoidectomy at the age of 34, and had suffered for ten years from urinary frequency and nocturia.

Previous Injuries. Three and a half years prior to admission the patient cut his head in diving, but was not rendered unconscious.

General Adjustment. Vocation—education: His school record was good through high school and part of an engineering course which for financial reasons he was unable to complete. At the age of 19 he left Havana, disillusioned because his doctor brother had let him down by not seeing him through financially. In this country he went to college and obtained his degree of pharmaceutical chemistry, working at the same time as an engineer. A year prior to admission he obtained the degree of bachelor of science. *Social adjustment:* "I have very high ideals and am sensitive and proud. I am careful not to hurt other people's feelings because I am so easily hurt. This makes me prefer to stay away from people. Lately I have felt people were reproaching me because I couldn't make my castles in the air come true." *Sexual adjustment:* "I always thought I was highly sexed. My wife and I used to have intercourse six times a night. She always used contraceptives because we didn't want children until we were better set up. Since I've been sick I've been practically impotent and lately I haven't even had erections. When I think about sex I get palpitation and pain."

Characteristic Behavior Pattern. The material under vocational and social adjustment shows clearly this patient's need for admiration together with the strong tendency to self-depreciation and depression. When, however, he received a letter from his brother inviting him to come to Cuba to recuperate the patient said: "A kind word from a relative makes you feel like living again." In his conversation the patient seemed under constant pressure to agree with and please anyone with whom he was talking.

Neurotic Traits. Early: Nightmares. *Present:* Depression, suicidal ideas, fear of contamination. He spent a great deal of time in the washroom. He was taking baths all the time, and washing his hands a great deal, allegedly because he was afraid of contamination from the patients who happened to have skin lesions, and who were on the same ward with him. One of the nurses made the statement that whenever anybody wanted the patient, they always knew where to look for him, namely, in the washroom.

Addictions and Interests. This patient's ideals for himself required moderation in the use of tea, coffee, alcohol, and tobacco, and he lived up to these ideals. He had no important interests outside of what he called his "castles in the air," becoming the type of person he wanted to be, and winning recognition from his more successful brothers. Although he had been brought up a Catholic he felt that he did not need the church to tell him what to do.

Life Situation Immediately Prior to Onset. Four factors assumed prominence just prior to the onset of this patient's illness. First, the death of two friends. Second, he had been married for three years and felt that he was "not making good." For this he blamed his brother whom he had never forgiven for not assisting him to complete his engineering and pharmaceutical studies. The first attack, it will be noted, came on at midnight while the patient was working. Third, two or three months previously he had had his first and only accident, a blow on the head. Fourth, he felt that he was becoming impotent and had lost interest in sexual relations with his wife which caused him great anxiety in terms of its effect on her.

(*Note:* It is interesting that the medical admission note, after describing the onset of the patient's illness, states: there have been no precipitating factors.)

Reaction to Illness. As has been noted already, the patient reacted to his illness with an increase in his life-long distrust of physicians. On the ward whenever he talked about his illness he would start to cry: "I just can't go on. Whatever you say to me I know I'm going to die. I'm not worth treating. I won't let my wife waste money on me. My two best friends have died and it's my turn."

Area of Major Conflict and Characteristic Reaction. It is clear from the above that this patient's major conflicts were in the sphere of personal contacts. His reaction showed both elements noted as important in this group: narcissistic withdrawal and a strong urge to be effectual and admired. During the course of his illness the narcissistic withdrawal had gained the upper hand but he responded gradually to consistent kindness and interest on the part of his physicians, and the friendly gesture from his brother toward whom he had cherished a life-long bitterness, made him willing to live again and brought out his desire to please and to work.

Case No. CA 313. An unmarried man, aged 23, was admitted for dyspnea and palpitation of six weeks' duration. The admission note read as follows: Patient's present illness began six weeks ago, with attacks of palpitation and dyspnea, a sick panicky feeling, occasional extra systoles, weakness in legs, hot flushes, and cold clammy hands and feet, and bitemporal "pressure sensations." These symptoms would occur six to eight times a day and last from a few minutes to an hour. For the past two weeks the patient has had these attacks at night. During them he becomes panic-stricken, calling his mother, who comes and sits with him until the attack passes off. One week ago and again last night, the patient had very bad attacks with palpitation off and on all the night. Discharge diagnosis: Neurocirculatory asthenia.

Family History. The patient's father had died suddenly four years previously at the age of 63, on the patient's birthday, of coronary disease and his mother had always been very nervous.

Personal Data. The patient was an only child, born and had always lived in New York City.

Previous Health. The patient had always suffered from colds, hay fever, and stomach upsets, especially from eating chocolate. He had had two attacks of pneumothorax.

Previous Injuries. The patient had had one accident two weeks prior to the onset of the illness: the oxygen tank he was trundling along the sidewalk got out of hand and in an effort to right it the tank fell on his toe. He sustained a fracture and open reduction of his right big toe.

General Adjustment. Vocation—education: The patient did particularly well through grammar school and high school but managed to get himself expelled during his fourth year at college. He was studying mechanical engineering. Since that time he had worked as a shipping clerk and assistant head of an importing department at only $18 a week. Failing to get a raise he quit, did odd jobs, and then got a position in an oxygen therapy service at $30 a week. He ascribed his two periods of pneumothorax to the exposure to pneumonia involved in this job.

Social adjustment: The patient claimed that his social adjustment was good and stated that he enjoyed people that were gay and cut a figure. He liked to organize things like golf and parties. It made him feel surer that he was really liked.

Sexual adjustment: Patient knew little about sex and although he had heard of masturbation he was not very clear what it was until a friend of his, a medical student, explained to him how girls masturbated. This was immediately prior to his first pneumothorax. Thereafter he had sexual intercourse on three occasions and suffered from ejaculatio praecox. These experiences were not with the girl he had planned to marry. He had gone with this girl for three years and just prior to the onset of the present illness gave her up because of his mother's objections. His mother objected to the girl because she considered that it was up to her son to support her in the way his father had done, and that he was not earning enough to support both her and a wife. Furthermore, the girl was a Catholic.

Attitude toward parents and children. The patient was both dependent on his mother and resentful of her. He lived with his mother and grandmother in a five-room apartment and felt under obligation to support them; hence a family of his own was impossible. The patient stated that both parents expected a great deal of him, but his father really made more sacrifices for him than his mother. His father's death made him feel guilty about his tendency to gamble and his lack of responsibility about money.

Characteristic Behavior Pattern. The patient was tense, anxious and panicky, showing a desire to please, and a preoccupation with his symptoms and achievements. This behavior alternated with feelings of unworthiness and a sense of impending doom.

Neurotic Traits. Early: Nightmares, sleep-walking (at the age of 10), and enuresis. *Present:* Urinary frequency, nocturia, nightmares, anxiety attacks.

Addictions and Interests. This patient said he was crazy about golf and organized the first golf team in college. Aside from this he was addicted to cigarettes, milk, and sedatives, and was interested in gambling.

Life Situation Immediately Prior to Onset. Following his father's death three years before the onset of illness, the patient became increasingly tense and anxious. It was about this time that he got himself expelled from college. Paralleling the conflict of whether or not to marry his girl he developed an increasing fear that his mother might leave him, and an inability to be comfortable anywhere without her. With his first sexual experiences and the work with oxygen tents came the two attacks of pneumothorax and a tendency to claustrophobia. The first attack of actual palpitation was precipitated by his decision not to marry. Accompanying the attacks of palpitation the patient had olfactory and visual hallucinations, together with panicky feelings, and a fear of death.

Reaction to Illness. The patient reacted to his illness with an increase of fear, feelings of weakness and unworthiness, and a terror of being alone. He had furthermore, serious doubts as to whether anyone could help him.

Area of Major Conflict and Characteristic Reaction. It is clear that this patient's major conflict lay in the sphere of personal contacts, and his reaction was characterized by the attempt to win approval combined with increased preoccupation with himself, depression, and narcissistic withdrawal.

Case No. CA 336. A 23-year-old, single, Jewish girl was admitted for symptoms of dyspnea and palpitation. There was a question of hyperthyroidism which was ruled out. Physical examination was negative except for a short apical systolic murmur. Blood pressure was 120/70.

Family History. The patient's mother was living and well but excessively nervous. "She is always thinking of some catastrophe—always thinking something is going to happen." The father was also living and well, calmer, but very strict. There was no family history of cardiovascular disease, diabetes, or accident. (See note under this heading in Case No. 313.)

Personal Data. The patient was born in New York City, the oldest of three children. A sister 20 and a brother 16 are living and well.

Previous Health. Subject to colds, digestive upsets, and eructations. Menses regular, some dysmenorrhea.

Previous Injuries. Just prior to the onset of her present illness the patient agreed to go out in a canoe with her boy friend on the Hudson River. "I of water. The canoe capsized and he had to knock me out to rescue me." thought that I could trust him although I have always been scared to death

General Adjustment. Vocation—education: The patient's school record was excellent. She graduated from high school at the age of 16 and won a medal for her work in French. Since this time she had done secretarial work.

Social adjustment: She stated that she got along with both men and women. "Just the same I am always wondering whether people like me or not. I think the trouble is my nose. If I could get a doctor to make it shorter I would be more attractive like my sister." She talked much about the way she would like to be changed physically to be more perfect, i.e., taller, slimmer, ankles thinner, etc. "Still I have had many friends and many love affairs. They all come and go. As soon as I feel someone likes me I am up in the air. But I can't be satisfied with just one person." Her attitude toward the outside world was pictured in a dream she had during treatment of herself as a beautiful woman lying in the bottom of a goldfish bowl.

Sexual adjustment: She had been going with a boy friend for seven years and during the last year had begun to have intercourse with him, practicing coitus interruptus. Concerning this she said that occasionally it disgusted her. She was afraid of becoming pregnant and she would have much preferred just to have him hold her hand. She felt that marriage was impossible because of her fear of having children and her inability to stand pain.

Attitude toward parents. The patient was brought up by her maternal grandmother until she was 17 although her parents lived next door. "It was the nurses and doctors who killed Grandmother, she had gall stones, got delirious and died. Grandmother used to give me enemas and it scared me to have all that water inside me. Grandfather was laid on ice when he died and I could hear the water dripping as the ice melted." Her relationship to her parents was inadequate, characterized by fear. There was marked rivalry with her attractive younger sister who used to steal her clothes. When this occurred the patient would burst into hysterical weeping. "There's just nothing to do about it," the patient complained. (Had this patient had a diabetic personality she probably would have hidden her clothes. Rheumatic fever patients confronted by the same problem react by telling tales or resorting to men's clothes.)

Characteristic Behavior Pattern. The patient was panicky, fearful, exhibitionistic, and demanding of affection. "When somebody likes me I am walking on air. When I don't think somebody likes me it's like drowning. I go off by myself and cry and think I'm going to die."

Neurotic Traits. Early: Phobias, particularly fear of water and animals continuing to the present. She was also afraid of the dark and had fantasies of people hiding to jump out at her when she goes to the bathroom at night. Nightmares of deep water rising higher and higher. Frequent dreams of getting married, then having a baby and dying. "When I'm frightened I start to notice how I breathe, then I think I'm going to die. Since the canoe accident I won't ever go on a ferry. It makes me nauseous."

Addictions and Interests. Addictions to cathartics and sedatives. Her only important interest was in clothes.

Life Situation Immediately Prior to Onset. (1) The first symptoms of dyspnea and palpitation followed the death of the patient's grandmother "who was killed by nurses and doctors." The grandmother had represented her only moderately adequate personal contact. (2) Then followed the period of conflict about marriage, culminating in the canoe accident after which these attacks became increasingly frequent and severe, especially at night. She saw several doctors, who told her there was nothing wrong with her, and became increasingly depressed and discouraged.

Reaction to Illness. During treatment her major reaction was a demand for reassurance and affection, her constant preoccupation was with the question of how much her doctor liked her.

Area of Focal Conflict. Here again we have a patient whose major conflicts are in relation to personal contacts. Her reactions were characterized by an alternation between narcissistic withdrawal and attempts to gain admiration and affection. She was unable to live without love and unable to enter into any human relationship that was more than superficial.

Case No. CA 296. A 44-year-old, widowed seamstress was admitted to the hospital with paroxysmal auricular tachycardia. The first symptoms occurred about a year ago with palpitation on slight exertion. Three weeks prior to admission she had developed precordial pain without radiation and more palpitation.

Family History. The patient's mother was living and well at 77, but exceedingly nervous; the father, aged 85, was blind and cranky as well as strict and nervous. There was no history of diabetes, cardiovascular disease, or accident.

Personal Data. The patient was born in Ireland, the third of eleven children —nine girls and two boys. She was married at the age of 27, and her husband died of transverse myelitis contracted during the war, four years prior to her admission.

Previous Health. The patient suffered from head and chest colds and there was some question of tuberculosis. She had had one attack of pneumonia and a mastectomy; and at the age of 27 and again at 29 minor gynecological operations to overcome sterility.

Previous Injuries. None.

General Adjustment. Vocation—education: The patient completed elementary school education in Ireland and then came to this country with her aunt and supported herself as a seamstress for thirteen years, until she was married. After her husband came back from the war, ill, her time was absorbed in caring for him. They lived on money previously saved plus $150 a month he was getting from the Government. After his death she again worked as a seamstress.

Social adjustment: The patient stated that she got along well with both men and women, only not with her relatives. She showed great concern over being liked: "If I think somebody doesn't like me I get in the dumps. Then I wonder why people should like people like me anyway." Details of her appearance such as rose nail polish, were of great importance to her.

Sexual adjustment: The patient knew little about sex till she was married at the age of 27. She stated that she never masturbated and thought the idea disgusting. Nevertheless she enjoyed intercourse with her husband. She was not, however, much disturbed by her sterility (for which she had two operations), because she had always been a little afraid of having children.

Attitude toward parents and children. The patient described both of her parents as strict, "but too busy with so many children to pay much attention to me." She felt that her sisters tended to pick on her and could not be relied on to help her when she was in trouble. There was marked resentment and distrust of them for their attitude. (See also *Sexual adjustment* above.)

Characteristic Behavior Pattern. This patient's general behavior was characterized by an external charm and attempt to please, combined with a marked tendency toward self-depreciation.

Neurotic Traits. Nightmares as a child. Palpitation and panic at night. Sense of impending doom and fear of death.

Addictions and Interests. Coffee, alcohol in moderation, and two packages of cigarettes a day. The patient had been brought up a Catholic but showed little interest in religion. Like several other patients in this group she said: "The church tells you what to do, but doesn't help you understand. They tell you what they expect, what you must do. But they don't help you."

Life Situation Immediately Prior to Onset. (1) Her husband's death four years previously. (2) Constant quarreling with two sisters in this country. She had thought it would be better to live with one of them instead of living alone but was unable to make any satisfactory arrangement. (3) The most severe attack occurred three months prior to admission when she was on a train going to her sister's home. She had a smothered feeling on the train and that night woke from a sound sleep with severe palpitation and dyspnea. A doctor was called who said she had a bad heart and gave her some green medicine, a few drops every ten minutes. Following this she developed a severe pain in the precordial region. After this she resigned herself to living with her landlady and the latter's family, whom she liked, "except they are not the kind of people you can depend on to take care of you."

Reaction to Illness. The patient termed herself a poor old lady all alone, with lots of relatives and no help. She was much upset because the city was paying her hospital bills: "I've never accepted charity before. When you have kin they should take care of you."

Area of Focal Conflict. This patient's preoccupation with the problem of personal relationships was clear, as well as her conflict between narcissistic withdrawal and her desire for affection combined with the fear of being alone.

(*Note:* This patient died at home of pneumonia three months after discharge.)

DEGREE AND NATURE OF SOMATIC EXPRESSION OF CONFLICTS

Review of the preceding material indicates that these patients are more nearly aware of the area in which their major conflicts lie than are patients in some of the other groups studied. Physical symptoms seem most likely to develop when the pendulum is half way between symptoms of anxiety and feelings of resentful distrust of the outside world. Attention should be called to the extremely close relationship between these patients' dreams and their physical symptoms.

Several generalizations can be made which apply to patients with an exaggerated syndrome of dyspnea and palpitation with or without organic damage. In no group of patients with actual structural damage is what we have called the pseudo-hereditary factors so important. Even where the dyspnea and palpitation have as their basis rheumatic heart disease and myocardial damage, this symptomatology is much more marked in those who have been exposed to parents or friends with such symptomatology. Attacks may be precipitated by such exposure, whereas it is unusual to find that an accident to a fracture patient has been precipitated as a reaction to an accident on the part of a friend.

Diseases of childhood play an important role, seeming, similarly, to give psychological prominence to certain types of symptoms as well as physiological preparation for them. These may serve as predromata of the cardiovascular symptomatology. This element is particularly marked if the symptoms are out of proportion to the structural change. Attention has been called to the fact that in asthmatics (F. Deutsch, Dunbar, and others) there is usually a history of repeated croup and pertussis and sometimes bronchitis. We find this in these patients also.

The symptom complex has a definite significance to these patients, usually in terms of the oedipus situation and of the tendency to identify with the mother, together with the need to break away and

take revenge. Dreams of smothering and a tendency to claustrophobia
are characteristic. The group of patients with cardiac pain either in
addition to or apart from dyspnea and palpitation, however, seem to
show a still greater tendency to anxiety hysteria.[152, 153] It may be noted
in passing that although these patients may have either agoraphobia
or claustrophobia the great majority of them have claustrophobia.
However, they tend to translate these phobias into somatic symptoms to avoid acting out of their fantasies. Fracture patients, on the
other hand, tend to defy their agoraphobia and their fears of falling,
they have many accidents on the street and falls from high or low
places.

Comparison of these patients with the fracture group, however,
brought out marked differences both in reaction type and in history.
Nearly all of the fracture patients gave a history of parental sternness,
frequently in both father and mother. Of this group of cardiacs, on
the other hand, parental sternness was reported in less than half the
cases and only 2 per cent reported strictness on the part of both
father and mother. Interestingly enough, in only three more cases
was the mother strict or violent with the children; in one of these
three the mother had cerebral syphilis and in another the mother was
alcoholic. Although usually the relationship to neither parent was
very intimate and neither parent was consciously preferred, there
was a dependent relationship to the mother on the part of both males
and females, accompanied by fear of the father, or absence of the
father as a result of death or divorce. Also, in contrast with the
fracture patients, relatively few of the patients with cardiac arrhythmia had retained a definite religious "fixation." [153]

Tension, Aggression, and Resentment

The disturbances in the muscular armor of these patients are more
of the nature of localized spasms which are likely to have a psychic
meaning and there is a general tendency toward jerky, hysterical behavior. It is probably important to note that the heart itself is an
organ poorly suited for concrete symbolization or vector analysis
(page 646) and is usually involved in more direct expression of
anxiety. This may be one reason for the frequent involvement of
the gastro-intestinal or other systems in this group of cardiacs. Their
gastro-intestinal disorders often assume a symbolic meaning in con-

trast with hypertensive patients in whom these disorders seem to be rather a part of the generally exaggerated tension of both smooth and striated musculature in relation to inhibition of hostile impulses.

Dilation of spontaneous emotional and creative experience is more prominent in this group than in any other group studied. Other patients most closely resembling them in this respect are some fracture patients and patients with anginal syndrome. It is interesting to note again that the patients with anginal syndrome who are the most dilated are less likely to have organic damage.

Although the patients with cardiac arrhythmia resemble patients with hypertensive cardiovascular disease in that their tension cloaks their aggression and resentment, physiologically considered, their tension is less generalized and there is more recourse to neurotic symptom formation. Since they are less preoccupied with the active-passive conflict their resentment is more externalized, more projected. They are more concerned with controlling their hostility in relationships with other people than with an aggressive assertion of their individuality. They are much more emotionally reactive to their environment than the predominantly introversive patients with hypertensive cardiovascular disease, and accordingly have more capacity for feeling and for enjoyment.

Although these patients are generally on guard against making mistakes which might arouse social disapproval, there is nothing they enjoy more than a friend who will encourage them in minor infractions of rules or conventions. They get a childish relish through mischief and in being "just a little bad."

Activity, Verbalization, Dreams and Fantasies

These patients have a strong urge to *activity,* but this is expressed not constantly but intermittently in fits and starts depending on mood swings and inducements for creative outlet.

They are extremely *articulate* when they think they have a sympathetic listener, and they will talk at considerable length about feelings and personal problems. Also, they show an unusual synchronization of what they are saying with feelings and tensions which are clearly registered in facial expression and posture.

They report frequent *dreams* in which their feelings and conflicts are dramatized. There is considerable tendency toward imaginative development and *fantasy,* which, however, they find difficult to integrate into any meaningful system.

In reviewing this material from the point of view of somatic expression of conflict, it is evident that there is less binding of energy in symptoms of skeletal or smooth muscle tension than in any of the other groups so far discussed with the exception of some of the fracture patients. They make freer and more evenly distributed use of the three channels of emotional discharge—activity, verbalization, dreams and fantasies. This is reflected in the fact that their physiological dysfunction continues over a long period of time without crystallizing in somatic damage. The cardiac arrhythmia is a direct expression of the anxiety about the outcome of their conflicts rather than a defense against or a crystallization of these conflicts. This syndrome more than any of the others studied illustrates the degree to which the symptoms may represent a *"dispute entre le malade et la maladie."* The die is usually cast by external factors among which the therapeutic management is not the least important.

SUMMARY OF CHARACTEROLOGICAL DEFENSES AND THEIR RELATIVE SUCCESS OR FAILURE

The most obvious characteristic of the patients just discussed is the prominence of psychic symptomatology. This fact in itself, taken in combination with the absence of organic damage, is one of the reasons why physicians tend to treat them less seriously than patients in other groups and to work out less adequate therapeutic programs.

The psychic symptomatology, the characterological defenses, follow very closely the pattern of anxiety hysteria, of which of course cardiovascular symptomatology is one of the most frequent symptoms in the physical sphere. These patients usually have a considerable phobic façade which serves the purpose of avoiding their deep-lying anxiety. When this façade is in danger of becoming inadequate the cardiovascular disturbance serves to reinforce it. As these patients say: "Anyone whose heart skips beats, races, or threatens to stop, has a real reason for anxiety and fear of death." Generally in patients suffering from anxiety hysteria the phobias begin very early in life. There are few children who have not at one time or another been afraid of the dark or of animals, or of being left alone. The question is why this childhood neurosis persists in the group of patients

under discussion. Of course in the present state of our knowledge
this question cannot be answered, but the following observations on
the life histories of this group of patients are worth reviewing in this
connection.

As has been noted already these patients have had an inadequate
emotional relationship with both parents, but instead of running away
have reacted to anxiety by the utilization of other channels of emotional discharge and by the exercise of considerable ingenuity in the
desire to please and win approval. A combination of traumatic deaths
in the patient's early life and scenes of hostility between the parents
heightens the fear of being alone, and, as it were, holds them trans-
fixed by terror. Careful investigation often reveals the fact that the
psyche in these patients has served as an amplifier for a relatively
minor quarrel. The fear of being beaten and even the idea that their
parents might be beating each other has its effect also in the solution
of the oedipus problem. They show confusion about identification
with both parents and never seem to find themselves or to determine
just what their role should be. These patients, furthermore, belong
to the subgroup of anxiety hysterics in whom a sadistic impulse
justly roused by an object is turned from it toward the ego so that
fear of death appears under circumstances which in ordinary persons would lead to an attack of rage (Fenichel,[179] page 59). This
may have a bearing on the frequency with which the onset of cardiovascular symptomatology in these patients is preceded by an accident.
This was the case in 40 per cent of the patients in our group, and
it will be remembered that more than one accident was the exception.

Freud, in discussing another aspect of this problem, says in effect:
"The child can perceive his birth subjectively only as an increase in
tensions corresponding to an increase in his needs. His reaction to
this, his 'first anxiety' must have served a useful purpose: 'stimulation of the neural pathways leading to the respiratory system pre-
pares the lungs for their activity,' and 'the acceleration of the heart-
beat combats the toxicity of the blood.'" (Fenichel,[179] page 51).
Whatever we comment as to these suggestions, we find generally in
these patients another reason for the prominent role played by cardiovascular symptomatology: Their tendency to fear and suppression
of sexual impulses. The frequency of inadequate discharge of strong
sexual excitation results in cardiovascular symptomatology and serves

to focus both attention and feelings of guilt and fear of punishment on such symptomatology.

Finally, if we realize that in the adult the anxiety we find in phobias is an ego anxiety, fear of losing love or fear of mutilation, it is clear that if the unconscious danger can be turned into a perceptual danger, relief is experienced and a certain equilibrium may be established. As we have seen, these patients reassure themselves continually through playing to the gallery and the attempt to win approval in diverse external ways, rather than in active competition as in patients with hypertensive cardiovascular disease or coronary occlusion. When through some traumatic experience in the sphere of personal relationships this defense is threatened there occurs a breaking through of the hostility which the patient has attempted all his life to subdue in the interests of being liked, and therefore turns against himself in self-depreciation, self-injury, and fear of death. On such occasions cardiovascular symptomatology helps to externalize this fear or to give a valid reason for it. It is usually interpreted, furthermore, as a reason for sexual inadequacy or as a barrier to sexual expression, thus relieving the threat always involved for these patients in the sexual experience.

In general, these patients, in spite of utilizing numerous channels of discharge are particularly relieved by talking or by getting others to talk. The characterological defenses developed by these patients remind one of a child who was afraid of the dark, quoted by Freud as saying, "if someone talks it gets lighter."

V. THERAPEUTIC IMPLICATIONS *

Once the defenses of these patients have broken down and severe somatic symptoms have been added to the characteristic neurotic symptomatology, the majority of them become life-long invalids, and too many of them, having been told that there was nothing physically wrong, die with disconcerting unexpectedness of some somatic disorder. Of course, in the presence of severe organic involvement, relief of this symptom complex may be of importance to life, and it is always important in the prevention of invalidism.

In most patients in this group, as with hypertensives, symptomatic relief is sometimes readily produced by superficial psychotherapy.

* See Chapter XI, section V.

Furthermore, anxiety neurosis (especially if an important aspect is poor sexual hygiene) is a complicating factor of great physiological importance and is often readily eliminated. Finally, if any reader of the foregoing pages be inclined to question the usefulness and application of the descriptive material given, let him turn his attention to the all too numerous mixed syndromes which present difficult diagnostic problems. The following case history is illustrative of the point:

Case No. OCA 154. A married woman, aged 28, was admitted to the hospital three times in quick succession with cardiac failure, on the basis of unknown etiology. At first it was thought that the problem was rheumatic; then gonorrhea was excluded; and then it was decided that she might be suffering from the rare condition known as lupus erythematosus disseminatus. This patient's response to treatment was poor and it looked as though she would have to be kept constantly in bed in view of a very likely fatal outcome. During all three hospital admissions she was on the danger list, and part of the time in an oxygen tent.

Study of this patient showed that there was little in her personality suggestive of the patients with organic heart disease and much suggestive of the patient with cardiac arrhythmia as here discussed.

The following events in the patient's life proved to bear a relationship to her illness. Her first memory of her father was when she was 6 years old and he was brought home on Christmas Eve with a broken leg. What had happened was the following: Both parents had strict religious convictions, but the father had nonetheless begun to be unfaithful to his wife. On Christmas Eve when the tree was to be decorated, which to both of them was a sacred religious rite, he had invited a chorus girl to help him decorate the tree, while the mother sat upstairs and wept. By the time the tree was decorated both father and chorus girl were relatively tight and he felt it necessary to take her home. On the way home, as the story goes, he slipped on the ice, and fell; she managed to land on his leg and break it. She then had to get him back to his home. The mother, shocked by the incident, explained to the children that God had punished their father for his sins.

This patient had a strong father identification, and the father was interested in sports. At the age of 12 she was playing baseball contrary to maternal decree, but with great approval from the father, and she broke her ankle. Just prior to this she had started to masturbate, which she considered a serious sin. She decided that God had punished her just as He had previously punished her father.

Three days after this patient's marriage at the age of 22, she woke up one night to discover her husband in bed masturbating, and talking lovingly. as it were, to some other woman. He then confessed that he had done it all his life and asked her to help him get over it. After about six weeks of morning confessions of a promise broken, the patient decided she could bear it no longer. She consulted her doctor who told her to forget about it, that most men masturbated and all women did. She was incensed at this because she had not masturbated since God had punished her for playing baseball ten years ago. Also, she had just discovered she was pregnant. One morning she decided to rearrange their bedroom and in moving her husband's bed strained her back. After some weeks of pain her physician suggested a lumbosacral fusion and a therapeutic abortion, telling her that she would have to spend well on to a year in the hospital and in bed. She said: "Can it be that I welcomed the idea? I don't believe that I really needed the operation, but I couldn't get divorced, and this seemed a heaven-sent opportunity to get away from my husband's masturbation."

The patient then had a child, hoping that things would be better. But the situation merely became more complicated. Her mother-in-law, who had always opposed the marriage became incensed when she knew the child was expected and became a constant visitor in the household giving orders and advice. The patient's own mother followed suit, and neither one could tolerate the presence of the other. The husband became worried about the effect of two or three months of sexual abstinence on his health and business efficiency and the masturbation problem combined with constant reproaches to his wife became increasingly acute. Although his income was large and that of his family placed them among the upper two or three thousand in the population, he became disturbed about the additional expense and responsibility of a child in the family, and insisted that his wife keep house on fifteen dollars a week, including dinner parties and liquor. He insisted, moreover, on moving into a smaller apartment so that it was frequently necessary for the then 2-year-old son to sleep in the same room with his parents. This greatly worried the patient because of the possible effect on the child of being exposed to the frequent nocturnal conflicts between them.

The patient then fell in love with a mutual friend, a married man, and started an affair with him. After this she spent two months in the country repenting and trying to persuade herself not to see him again, nonetheless she made an appointment for the day of her return to town. The night before, at a gay farewell party she got herself knocked down and thought she had a broken rib. She said this gave her a great sense of relief because now it would be unnecessary to sleep with either her husband or her lover for quite a while. But the rib turned out not to be broken though the symptoms continued, and the next day she was sent to the hospital with cardiac decompensation and pulmonary edema. She said, "I was reading a book, the Lord strikes knives into the hearts of his children that err. I guess that's what happened to me." The patient spent one month in the hospital and then remained in bed at home for two months until a few days before Christmas when she got up for a party. Her lover and his wife were guests at the party; the old conflict returned and six days later, on Christmas Day, she was readmitted to the hospital with cardiac decompensation. She stayed in the hospital for two months, then returned home but stayed in bed.

In early May the patient was again allowed out of bed with strict limitation of activity, and because she found things so difficult at home it was arranged that she visit her aunt in the country. As soon as she arrived she had another attack and was readmitted to the hospital for the third time. A month later when she was ready to leave the hospital psychiatric advice was sought by the patient herself against the recommendation of the attending physician and her husband. The foregoing history was elicited at the time. The medical notes relative to these three admissions are as follows:

First admission note:

On the day of admission the patient gave the following history: She had been perfectly well until 9:30 the evening before. At that time, while returning from a summer in the country, she developed an insistent pain in the epigastrium and lower end of the sternum, which increased in intensity, gradually spreading to both shoulders and the neck. The pain was aggravated by swallowing, coughing, sneezing, and breathing. She was unable to take a deep breath. She had also discovered that she was unable to turn from either side during the night and was more comfortable flat on her back. She had a slight headache. No sweats or actual chill. No visual disturbance, sore throat, stiffness or palpitation. There was slight dyspnea on moving. No edema. She stated that late in the afternoon of the day she developed pain, she had done gymnastics, and thought it likely that she had pulled a muscle. She had also fallen, landing on her right shoulder, but had thought nothing of the pain.

[*Note:* The patient's statement that she was doing gymnastics was a euphemism for the rather wild party in the course of which she had fallen as noted above.]

Past History. She denies all illness except occasional sore throats (frequent in childhood). Quinsy had been present. She had growing pains as a child. She had had a fusion of her lower spine for spondylolisthesis. She had had a pregnancy two years ago.

Positive Physical Findings. A young white female, appearing acutely ill, not flushed. Temperature 99.6° F. Her tongue was coated; her neck slightly tender, suprasternally. The chest examination was unsatisfactory because of her respiratory pain. The lungs were resonant throughout. Her breath sound diminished posteriorly and in the axilla, but there was no true consolidation. Her heart was possibly slightly enlarged. The sounds were of fair quality. There was exquisite and marked tenderness along the chondrosternal margins of the third, fourth, and fifth ribs, and slight tenderness in the lower portion of the sternum. Her abdomen was held tightly. There was an old scar of a previous fusion along the lower aspect of the spine.

Impression. In view of the past history of frequent sore throats and growing pains (pains in the joints) the present episode was interpreted as an acute rheumatic pericarditis.

Two weeks later the patient had a pain under the lower portion of the sternum for half an hour, spreading to the entire anterior chest, which was aggravated by breathing; this was identical with that of the onset of the present illness. Physical examination showed tenderness over the entire anterior chest. Her respirations were short and jerky, not dyspneic. Her blood pressure was 110/80. The patient was upset, and not relieved by aspirin and codeine. Magendie, 0/4 mg. was prescribed.

The following day the patient was seen at the request of her physician. The electrocardiographic findings and precordial pain indicated disease in the myocardium. It was recommended that the patient be treated as having rheumatic carditis. The atypical features of the pictures were: (1) absence of any past history, (2) her age, (3) the season of the year, (4) a normal sedimentation rate and antistreptolysin titer in the presence of active disease, (5) no evidence of valvulitis. It was recommended that the salicylates be stopped for a few days.

Laboratory Findings. The antistreptolysin titer was 62 units. A throat culture showed no hemolytic organisms. Both abortus and melitensis agglutinations were negative. Red blood count and platelets appeared normal. The total white blood count and percentage of polys. were normal. No parasites were seen. The chest x-rays showed a slight enlargement of the heart to the left; the electrocardiograph records showed myocardial involvement in the pericarditis and some disturbance in the heart muscle.

Discharge Diagnosis. Acute rheumatic carditis. Active rheumatic pericarditis.

Second admission note (two months after discharge):

Readmission of a woman, aged 27, complaining of shortness of breath and precordial pain. She had been discharged home after her last admission, and did very well until about a week ago, when fever and precordial pain recurred. During the past week her temperature has run to 101.8° F. and signs of consolidation have developed over both lower lobes, and further evidence of pericardial involvement. Urine showed albumin 2 to 3 plus, red blood cells and very numerous casts. Her dyspnea has been progressive, and is now the presenting symptom.

Physical Examination. The patient was acutely ill. Her heart was markedly overactive and rapid. There was a to-and-fro pericardial friction rub. There was also a precordial rub, synchronous with respiration; and rubs laterally over the left chest synchronous with respiration. Over the right lower chest anteriorly and laterally there was bronchial breathing and a few scattered râles. Her abdomen was negative. The patient was far too ill for a complete examination to be made on admission.

Laboratory Findings. Hemoglobin 12.3; red blood count 4,490,000; white blood count 16,750; platelets 70. Urine: 3 plus albumin and 3 plus acetone on admission; later these disappeared. The electrocardiogram showed some changes, but most of the alterations from the last admission were in the direction of normal. Chest x-ray: There was an increase in hilar markings of both sides, and some density in the left lung field as compared with the right, as well as a heart contour suggesting left ventricular hypertrophy. The sedimentation rate was 61. The stool was negative.

Course. The patient was placed in an oxygen tent and was given considerable sedation in the form of pantopon, also codeine and salicylates. She showed some signs of decompensation as evidenced by pulmonary congestion and elevation of venous pressure to 145. The lung signs and pericardial friction rub persisted. The patient appeared to be extremely ill and required oxygen for several days. She suddenly became better. Concomitantly with this improvement the friction rub disappeared. Her heart seemed to be enlarged to percussion more than it had been before. It was a question as to whether she was developing pericardial effusion. However, if this was so it never reached the point of coronary tamponade for she did not again develop signs of decompensation. The sedimentation rate fell rather rapidly to normal. The electrocardiogram, which again had shown some change in the direction of abnormal, remained static. Her antistreptolysin titer did not rise. She was kept on salicylates throughout her stay. In spite of this, from time to time she had pains in her joints, chiefly in her fingers, wrists, elbows, and knees. During the last two weeks in the hospital, however, she was completely symptom-free and there were no significant physical findings. Her diagnosis was extremely obscure. The possibility of disseminated lupus erythematosis was a good one. Rheumatic fever was also a possibility in spite of the absence of a high antistreptolysin titer. She was discharged very much improved after seven weeks in the hospital.

Discharge Diagnosis. Active rheumatic pericarditis? Arthritis of rheumatic fever?

Third admission note (three months later):

Another bout for this patient started one week ago, and seemed to be extremely mild, but in the first two days her temperature rose to 102° F. Signs of dullness, but not flatness, appeared in her left lower lobe. Râles were never present. She had friction yesterday in her left axilla. By percussion it appeared her heart had increased in size, hyperesthesia of her entire left chest anterior, and suprasternally appeared at the onset.

She had been free from joint pain and chest pain ever since her preceding admission, and was beginning to get on her feet once more. An electrocardiogram about two weeks ago showed marked clearing. As the illness continued, it appeared that she had rheumatic fever. Lupus became a strong possibility.

The patient's lungs were clear. The sounds at the apex were still slightly distant. There were no skin lesions after exposure to the sun and no joint discomfort.

Laboratory Findings. Hemoglobin was 13.1; red blood count 4,370,000; white blood count 8,300; polys. 63. The sedimentation rate was 61 mm., 23 mm. Her stool was bile-positive. Guaiac was negative. The electrocardiogram showed quite marked changes since a month ago. The present electrocardiogram suggested increase in the degree of myocardial damage. This was shown by partial inversion of T in lead 1 and a sharp inversion in lead 2.

Discharge Diagnosis (4 weeks later). Pericarditis, etiology unknown.

In working out this patient's personality profile it became clear that this resembled closely that given for patients with cardiac arrhythmia as here defined, but not that found characteristic for any of the groups with organic damage including the rheumatic fever group. Altogether there were some resemblances to the latter. The outline was as follows:

Family History. Both parents were living and well but extremely nervous. The mother was supposed to have high blood pressure. There was no family history of diabetes or accident. One brother had tuberculosis. Three sisters were living. All of them suffered from hay fever and asthma.

Personal Data. The patient was the fourth child, third girl in a family of five. Her general background was middle class, moderately comfortable. From the day of her birth she was exposed to constant conflicts between her parents, sometimes taking the side of her mother whom she regarded as the more virtuous of the two, and sometimes with her father whom she was inclined to prefer although he was constantly disillusioning her.

Previous Health. Her general health record was characterized by a tendency to colds and vegetative disorders. Operations were tonsillectomy and appendectomy. Her menstrual history was normal.

Previous Injuries. The patient had had three previous injuries, all of which were followed by symptomatology referred to the heart; the third was a precipitating factor in her illness.

General Adjustment. The patient did well in grammar school and high school. For financial reasons she was unable to go to college so took a teacher's training course. She was married before this course was completed. *Social adjustment:* Socially this patient was shy with a marked tendency to self-depreciation for which she was inclined to overcompensate in dramatic behavior and dress. Since she was unusually attractive this tendency to exhibitionistic behavior frequently got her into trouble by arousing jealousy in her women friends. *Sexual adjustment:* See foregoing material. *Attitude toward parents and children:* This patient tried very hard to be a good mother but was constantly thwarted and frustrated by her husband, and inclined to be supersensitive about her child's shortcomings, as possibly indicating inadequacy on her part. (See also foregoing material.)

Characteristic Behavior Pattern. The patient was extremely tense and inclined to be inconsistent and flighty in her behavior. She was bothered by feelings of guilt, depression, and unworthiness when alone.

Neurotic Traits. Nightmares, fear of the dark and nail-biting as a child, all of which persisted into adult life. Mild tendency to claustrophobia, guilt and fear relative to sex.

Addictions and Interests. Excessive smoking and drinking of both coffee and alcohol. All her life she had been interested in dramatics and this was her major hobby in adult life. Her ambition was to support herself in some related field.

Onset of Illness. See foregoing material. In general gradual sense of failure in her marriage, with precipitation of symptoms by traumatic experience and failure in the sphere of personal relationships.

Reaction to Illness. Discouragement and distrust of physicians.

Area of Focal Conflict. In this patient the area of focal conflict was in her contacts with the outside world to which she reacted by playing to the gallery, self-depreciation and narcissistic withdrawal. There was marked pent-up resentment which she rarely expressed because "I think the trouble must be with me; I haven't any right to feel that way."

Course and Therapy. This patient was seen once a week for the five weeks between her third discharge from the hospital and her next attack. The patient and her husband were both told that every effort should be made to make more intensive treatment possible but this was not feasible at the time because she was taken from the hospital in an ambulance to her summer home at a considerable distance from New York. During this period she was seen two or three times by her internist who had taken care of her through the duration of her illness. She had remained in bed and the only visitors allowed were her mother and mother-in-law, the two people of whom she was most afraid. During the fifth week she was allowed to get up for dinner and her husband invited his business associate (alias her lover) and the latter's wife to join them. The following day the patient woke up gasping for breath and with a return of all her old symptoms. She insisted on seeing her psychiatrist although her attending physician and her husband felt this unnecessary because arrangements had been made for her return to the hospital. When the psychiatrist arrived the husband and the trained nurse were agitated, the former pacing the floor the latter asking whether the patient would live through the night. They apologized for having occasioned the psychiatrist a useless trip and said there was not much point of anyone seeing the patient at all because she was disoriented as a result of the medication she had received, conscious only for a few moments at a time, and even then unable to speak.

When the psychiatrist walked into the room the patient opened her eyes, which were full of terror and said in a hoarse whisper between gasps for breath, "Well, you were almost too late. I am going to die but I wanted so much to wait till you came." She was propped up in bed and her whole body was rigid. She said in a few minutes:

PATIENT: "I wanted to confess. I'm no good. I guess I'm done for." Then after a pause, "I can't help being attracted to A———. I hate my husband. I'm being punished."

PYSCHIATRIST: "I think you're very angry. Look at your fists." (Both fists were tightly clenched.)

PATIENT: "That's the pain . . . knife in my heart." Then after a pause, "You think I want to sock someone. Nice girls don't do that." And for the first time her face relaxed in a wry smile, and as it were in spite of herself, she took a deeper breath.

PYSCHIATRIST: "What about a long slow breath?" (The patient's pulse rate had gone down from 150 to 90 during the preceding discussion.)

PATIENT: "I couldn't, the pain would be terrible."

PYSCHIATRIST: "You just did, and it didn't hurt, did it?" The patient tried, looked amazed, and began to speak in her normal voice.

PATIENT: "Do you really think they can do anything for me? They haven't yet."

PYSCHIATRIST: "Perhaps not, but you can."

PATIENT: (in astonishment). "What?"

PYSCHIATRIST: "You might begin by unclenching your fists, at least till the right person comes along to sock, and then breathe naturally."

PATIENT: (after a pause). "My toes are all clenched too. I guess I was mad. Why won't the doctors let me see my friends? People I like. Instead of keeping me in prison, tied to my bed to be tortured by my husband and mother-in-law and mother?"

PYSCHIATRIST: "We'll see about changing that tomorrow. Now what about taking away those pillows and having a good sleep?"

PATIENT: (doubtfully). "I didn't think I could breathe lying down."

PYSCHIATRIST: "Let's try it."

PATIENT: (relaxing). "I feel better. You don't think I'm no good the way the others do?"

PYSCHIATRIST: "Quite the contrary. We'll talk about that in the morning."

PATIENT: "Then I'm not going to die tonight?"

PYSCHIATRIST: "Why should you? Your pulse is normal. You can breathe, and there isn't any more pain, is there?"

(The patient sighed deeply and went to sleep almost immediately. The psychiatrist left the room to be greeted with dark looks from nurse and husband.)

HUSBAND: "Well it's all over this time, isn't it? I was going to have the ambulance if she was alive in the morning."

NURSE: "You stayed quite a long time. (It had been about a half hour.) Can I give her her next injection now?" (Morphine.)

PYSCHIATRIST: "She's sleeping peacefully so I wouldn't disturb her. I think she'll be all right in the morning."

The patient was so much better the next morning that the physician in charge decided it was unnecessary to take her to the hospital. Shortly thereafter arrangements were made for the patient to return to her town apartment where she could have more adequate psychiatric treatment. In about a month she was able to be up around her household and take care of her child. Four months later she was managing a job in addition. There have been no further attacks in a period of four years, although there has been no limitation of activity of any kind.* Concerning her illness this patient said: "Until you made me face what was really bothering me, and showed

---

* Since it became necessary for her to take a full time job treatment was not completed. In such cases relapses may often be prevented if the patient is instructed to call annually, or oftener if there are any signs of slipping.

me I could do something about it, life was impossible except when I was sick. It may sound funny to you, but it used to be a relief to have a real pain to fight, instead of my husband, and all the people I hated and felt despised me. What I used to call the knife in my heart hurt so much that it blotted out everything else, everything that bothered me. It was like being drunk but even more potent."

In brief then, this patient illustrates both the diagnostic value of the personality profile, and the value of psychotherapy in preventing invalidism, as well as possible fatal outcome.

For the physician who recognizes the importance of treating sufferers from cardiac arrhythmia seriously, not merely as neurotic nuisances, the following suggestions are offered.

(1) As should be clear from the profile, the nature of the physician-patient relationship established is of the utmost importance. This alone may determine whether the outcome is to be complete interruption of the syndrome, life-long incapacitation by it, or crystallization into organic damage. In many cases it may even serve as a buffer between the patient and adventitious circumstances in the environment.

(2) The establishment of a favorable physician-patient relationship with these patients demands of the physician an emotional flexibility which naturally leads to the appropriate light touch. They need to be handled with a light rein. A formal, serious, or ponderous manner puts them more on guard. With patients having coronary occlusion or hypertensive cardiovascular disease, on the other hand, such a manner may cause no difficulty because they have a more systematized attitude toward authority and because they lack the extreme sensitivity to nuances of behavior as indices of feeling in the other person. (See Chaps. I, II, XI for discussion of role played by transference.)

(3) Many patients (Chapter XI, section V) in this group, instead of being nuisances, are extremely gratifying therapeutically when handled with appropriate understanding. After a potentially therapeutic milieu has been established in the physician-patient relationship, attention must be paid to the creative outlets.

VI. Conclusions

(1) The group of patients with cardiac arrhythmia has important similarities within itself and differs from the other groups studied.

Superficially, however, they present a more diverse picture because of their more extensive use of neurotic symptom formation and of the various channels of emotional discharge.

(2) The statistical study of this group reveals certain divergencies from the population as a whole. As in all cardiac patients, there is a high incidence of previous illnesses. Family history of cardiovascular disease is even more frequent in these patients than it is in patients suffering from hypertensive cardiovascular disease, coronary occlusion, or anginal syndrome. In the history of exposure, also, extreme nervousness in the family is more prominent than in the preceding three groups. They have a higher record for two or more accidents than any other group studied except the fracture patients, but these accidents occur mostly after 15 years of age.

They are usually very intelligent. From the point of view of education, a greater percentage of them are in the college category, although they have a somewhat lesser tendency to graduate than do the patients with coronary occlusion. An extremely high percentage of them achieve a comfortable income level. Occupationally they exceed even the concentration of coronary patients in classifications I and II (professional and official).

(3) Diverse individual personality pictures are presented by patients in this group. The Rorschach review indicates that they are the most consistently dilated.

(4) The following individual characteristics are significant:

(a) They are generally sensitive and reactive with considerable manifest anxiety.

(b) They show an intermittent variable tension and an urge toward activity.

(c) There is considerable insecurity and groping, which is partially concealed by their adaptive efforts to please. They fear any manifestation of hostility. Given the feeling that the physician is a sympathetic listener, they talk readily.

(d) As a rule there is an interest in intellectual as well as affective values and a consistent effort to find themselves.

(e) Attacks are likely to occur when hostility is aroused, or their sense of helplessness is aggravated by external events.

(f) Marked fear accompanies exacerbations of their cardiac dysfunction.

(5) This personality pattern plays an important role in the illness syndrome. The general physician more readily admits emotional factors and personality traits as etiological in syndromes of this type where no organic damage is demonstrable. Quite apart from any deductions as to etiology, however, this material is descriptive of the type of personality in which such disorders may be expected and has important therapeutic implications.

COMMENTS ON RECURRENT DECOMPENSATION

I. NATURE OF THE PROBLEM

Decompensation, or failure, is of course always the result of some other cardiovascular condition. These patients nevertheless present extremely interesting and difficult therapeutic problems. Instead of following the usual outline in giving our statistical material relative to patients from all groups who showed a marked tendency to recurrent decompensation, concreteness and clarity may be served by stating simply that decompensation occurred in all groups among patients whose profiles indicated a combination of traits characteristic for their specific group with those just outlined for patients with cardiac arrhythmia.*

In our series, decompensation occurred in 38 per cent of those with hypertensive cardiovascular disease, in 9 per cent of those with coronary occlusion, in 64 per cent of those with rheumatic heart disease, in 28 per cent of those with rheumatic fever type A, in 57 per cent of those with rheumatic fever type B, and in 6 per cent of those with cardiac arrhythmia. It was not found in any other group. Attacks of decompensation were precipitated in all these cases by self-neglect and/or overactivity. This was found most frequently in personalities which showed a large masochistic component. It is interesting to note that decompensation was particularly frequent in patients with hypertensive cardiovascular disease or rheumatic disease.

The patients with recurrent decompensation in our series were

---

* Dynamic analysis of the personality produced by these combinations is one of the most important problems for future research. After further study a report will be made under separate cover.

particularly satisfactory in their therapeutic response except when, as in Case No. HP 1 (page 40), the organic damage was so serious as to make any attempt at more than superficial psychotherapy too dangerous from the point of view of the somatic reaction. Such cases, however, were the exception. The majority of the patients with decompensation in our series responded well to treatment very much after the pattern of the last case cited (No. OCA 154) (page 461).

The following case illustrates the effect of the cardiac arrhythmia personality in a patient with an actually damaged heart.

Case No. RHDP 4. A married woman, aged 28, came for treatment in the psychiatric clinic in the spring of 1932, referred from the medical service. She was suffering from serious organic heart disease although not decompensated (diagnosis: cardiac hypertrophy, mitral stenosis and insufficiency, aortic insufficiency and myocarditis). In addition, she was subject to severe attacks of palpitation and dyspnea, very often accompanied by fainting spells. She was nervous, excitable, and had difficulty in sleeping.

Personal Data. The patient was a housewife of average intelligence, married eight years to a taxicab driver. She had worked previous to her marriage in her father's store.

Family History. The patient's father died of "heart trouble" at the age of 63 years, when the patient was 18 years old. The mother was living and well at the age of 65 years, except for "rheumatism" and "a little high blood pressure." The patient was the second of five children. Two younger sisters and a younger brother were living and well. The other brother died of peritonitis at the age of 37 years, when the patient was 17 years old. There was no other history of important illness in direct or collateral lines. No nervous breakdowns or cardiovascular disease. The family were religious, of German Jewish stock, the father a keeper of a small grocery store. Both the father and mother were very sociably minded and the house was always full of friends.

Personal History. The mother reported normal pregnancy and that the child was wanted. The delivery was easy, the doctor not arriving until after the infant was born. She was breast fed; weaned at three weeks because the mother developed a breast abscess. There were no difficulties with weaning or feeding. Sphincter control was established normally, no bed-wetting after 2 years of age. The patient was obedient and "somewhat spoiled," jealous of the other siblings, and subject to temper tantrums.

The patient made average progress at school although she was very much given to dreaming. She was seclusive and timid, having only one close friend. She had had one year of high school, and left because of a dislike of French, a feeling of timidity, and in order to work in her father's store. This was something the patient regretted. Except for one attempt "to get a job on her own," which was terminated by a serious cold at the end of two weeks, she had worked there until she was 18 years old, never receiving any wages but being given clothes and pin money. She was strong, and her major interests were reading (mostly fairy stories and love stories) and dancing, but she mixed very little with others of her own age except for the one girl friend and one boy friend. In April 1921, while she was helping her mother to prepare a meal, the news was brought that an uncle had died. The mother was so much upset that she dropped a pan containing hot fat and was severely burned. One month later the patient's brother's sudden death occurred, following an appendectomy. Fifteen months later when the patient was 18 years old, her father died of angina pectoris. The patient was with her father during many attacks preceding his death in which he shook and gasped for breath and became blue, and he died in her arms. Her mother came into the room, realized what had happened, and began to scream. The patient began to shake and had an attack of palpitation lasting several hours. The girl friend and the boy friend "came to her rescue," and stayed with her constantly during the next few days and the next week the patient announced her engagement to the "boy," who was ten years her senior.

The patient was married two years later and the first five years of her married life were very happy. Her husband made their life a romance, and she felt as if she were living in a fairy-tale world. In 1930–31 he began to stay out late at night and his attitude toward her seemed to change. At this time also she heard from her sister-in-law of the unfaithfulness of her husband (the patient's brother). This was a great shock and she imagined many things concerning her husband. At the same time a break occurred between her life-long girl friend and this girl's husband.

Late in 1931 and 1932 the patient began to suffer from dyspnea and palpitation, following which she would shake for hours, as had happened when her father died suddenly in her arms. On one occasion, sitting at home alone and waiting for her husband who had promised to return at 2 A.M., an attack of palpitation occurred and she felt as if she were suffocating, she gasped for breath and felt as though the walls of the room were closing in on her. She felt as though she were being crushed. She dressed and ran to her mother's house which was a few blocks away, where her husband, who came home at 5 A.M. found her. During the next two months the patient lost 16 lbs. (her weight having been constant at 130 lbs. until then), was very much depressed, and had many attacks of dyspnea and palpitation. She was terrified of something but had no idea of what. At this point she went to the medical clinic, coming to psychiatric service a few months later.

The patient suffered from measles, mumps, whooping cough, and a severe otitis media lasting three years before the age of 5 years. Tonsillectomy had been performed at the age of 13 years, immediately following her first menstrual period; otherwise she had had no other operations, injuries, or illnesses. Although the patient had growing pains from the age of 13 to 18 years, there was no history of rheumatic fever. Nevertheless, when she entered the medical clinic in 1932 there was a definite cardiac lesion, mitral and aortic, with enlarged heart and indication of endocardial damage. Other important elements in her history will be covered in relation to her treatment.

Personality. The patient was of average intelligence but given to day-dreaming, especially in libraries where she went to read love stories. She was not active and was always absent-minded and socially aloof. On the other hand, when forced to be with people she was vivacious and elated. There had always been marked mood swings from elation to depression.

Physical Examination. The patient was of pyknic type, with large bones and short arms and legs. There were no pathological findings with the exception of enlargement of the heart, diastolic and presystolic aortic murmurs transmitted to the left border of the sternum, soft diastolic and presystolic mitral murmurs with a systolic transmitted to the axilla. Blood pressure 112/85. Chest expansion free and equal.

Treatment. The patient was treated in the psychiatric clinic on the average of once every one to three weeks for four months in 1932, and for four weeks in 1934–35, having been followed in between at intervals of three to six months. Treatment elicited the following facts.

Preparation for Illness and Its Course. Physiological: There is a possible hereditary and constitutional predisposition in the direction of disease of the cardiovascular system, although the only such disease in the family appears to have been on the part of the patient's father. This being true, and in view of the patient's close association with him in his attacks, a "pseudo-hereditary" factor has to be considered also. The growing pains following the tonsillectomy may have been the only symptoms of an actual rheumatic fever. This is the only physiological basis on which to explain the rather extensive cardiac involvement present when the patient first came to the clinic.

Psychological: As developed during the course of the treatment, this patient had been prepared psychologically for some type of illness. The fact that the cardiovascular system was selected may have been the result of an inherent weakness or of a certain psychological constellation, or both.

In discussing her symptoms, the patient revealed the fact that the attacks of palpitation and dyspnea and sense of being smothered occurred only when she was waiting for her husband to come home, or when she saw a pregnant woman. (She had several such attacks in the elevator in the clinic.) In associating on the subject, the patient told of her terror when menstruation began. She thought she was bleeding to death and dared tell no one about it, but the boy friend to whom reference has been made. He explained to her the significance of menstruation and "was both a mother and a father to her." The tonsillectomy, however, occurred immediately thereafter, and she was again afraid she would bleed to death (a hemorrhage occurred). Furthermore, she fought violently against going under ether and associated her present attacks of dyspnea accompanied by a feeling of the walls closing in on her, with this experience. She then remembered the only spanking from her mother which occurred when she was 5 years old, as a punishment for masturbation. The patient did not remember further masturbation but did remember reading mystery stories and love stories in the bathroom from the time she was first able to read until the time of her marriage. On one of these early occasions her mother cried out in her sleep and the patient had an attack of trembling and intense fear, expecting something terrible to happen. She was not quite sure what.

In association with a dream the patient recalled a pregnancy fantasy associated with sexual stimulation from a cousin who used to dance her on his knee. She had a vague idea that mothers were likely to bleed to death when children were born. She dared talk none of these things over with her mother, however, for fear of losing her indulgent affection. In discussing the episode of the spanking and that of the tonsillectomy the patient experienced an overwhelming sense of terror accompanied by attacks of dyspnea and palpitation, her lips became blue. In discussing the former episode she said later: "Mother had just had my baby brother and I thought 'how awful if she would die.' He was the only member of the family she liked better than me, but after awhile she didn't do that any more."

The patient's resentment against her mother and the fear of loss of her mother's affection were discussed. In this connection she recalled her first cardiac attack associated with her father's death, and the fact that she had immediately replaced her father by her one life-long boy friend who had been "both father and mother" to her, and that now she was about to lose him. She felt he could not really leave her when she was so sick. She ascribed her fear of having a child to the economic situation. This was discussed on a somewhat deeper level. After going over this material the patient became symptom-free and remained so for two years.

Late in 1933 the patient came in saying that she had decided that she would like to have a child and wanted to know whether it would be safe for her. She said: "It's funny, I want one now when we have less money than we had before. when I thought we couldn't have one because of lack of money." Before there was time to go into this question in detail she became pregnant accidentally in January 1934. She began to dream of her father and to contrast him in her mind with her husband who still neglected her. She spent most of her time sitting at home alone and reading love stories. At the end of the second month of pregnancy the father of the patient's best friend died. The patient went to the cemetery. She became very nervous when the body was lowered into the grave. All through the next day she felt nauseated and dyspneic. She had the old sense of walls closing in. All of a sudden she hated being pregnant. At the end of the next month, following an automobile ride an abortion took place, which really relieved her very much, although she had the same old shaking spells accompanied by dyspnea and palpitation.

The patient returned to the psychiatric clinic and the situation was discussed against the background of the earlier material, in association with her feeling for her mother and father. She was then examined in the cardiac and gynecological clinics and told that she could go ahead with a pregnancy if she so desired, and if she were willing to spend two to six months in bed. In October 1934 she became pregnant again, and again began to dream of her father. The fear of seeing pregnant women returned and there were some mild attacks of dyspnea, none of these symptoms being of anything like the previous intensity.

After six weeks these symptoms disappeared in spite of the pregnancy which from a purely physiological point of view might have been expected to increase her symptoms. She was active (doing all her own work) and free of dyspnea and palpitation throughout her pregnancy, and the spontaneous term delivery of a normal boy was without complications. This is the more significant in that her husband's attitude toward her did not change. She herself, however, had become much less dependent on him, and incidentally no longer ran to her mother at the slightest provocation.

This case indicates, among other things, that it is possible to change the patient's attitude toward an unpleasant situation even where the situation itself cannot be changed. The bringing about of such a change in the patient of course has distinct advantage over the attitude which says, "well anyone would be worried, or would be nervous, living in such a situation. We will see that she gets enough sedative to keep her quiet." It is important to realize that the degree to which "perfectly normal" worries react disastrously, or produce symptoms in the physical sphere, can be definitely decreased with careful handling of the underlying emotional problem. This is particularly important of course when an actual organic lesion is present.

Summary: It will be seen that in this patient there was a *family history* of cardiovascular disease which is more characteristic of patients with cardiac arrhythmia than of patients with rheumatic heart disease. As to *personal data*: The patient came from a middle class, moderately comfortable background and both parents lived well into her adolescence limiting her social activities. There was a strong identification with the father whose traumatic death in her arms brought on her first actual attack. This history also is more suggestive of the cardiac arrhythmia group.

Her *previous health* record might be characteristic of either group and there was no *accident* history.

The same can be said of her *educational, occupational,* and *income* record, and of her general *social* adjustment except that she was less ambitious than is usually the case in patients with cardiac arrhythmia. Her *sexual* adjustment and her fear of pregnancy also would be consistent with both groups except that there was less of a martyr tendency than is usually found in the group with rheumatic heart disease.

The history of early and later *neurotic traits,* exaggerated fright reactions, and a tendency to claustrophobia also is characteristic of patients in both groups.

This patient was *addicted* to coffee and had no interest in athletics but much in social activities which would bring her into the limelight which again relates her more closely to the cardiac arrhythmia group.

The *life situation immediately prior to onset,* marked by unusual exertion in her father's store, and the experience of traumatic death suggests the patient with rheumatic heart disease but the subsequent traumatic experience in her personal relationship to her husband suggests the patient with cardiac arrhythmia.

In her *reaction to illness* we see the characteristics of both groups combined, and similarly in the *area of focal conflict and her reaction* to it.

In this patient, then, the two profiles are almost completely superimposed as indeed were the two syndromes. The response to therapy directed toward the area of major conflict and the patient's reaction to it, was nevertheless just as satisfactory as was usually the case when we were dealing with either of the syndromes separately, and illustrates the degree to which invalidism can be reduced even in the presence of organic damage.

II. THERAPEUTIC IMPLICATIONS

In making plans for a cardiac invalid who has suffered repeated breaks (or periods of decompensation), few question the necessity of provision for special care, relief from responsibility. Yet experience has demonstrated again and again that these may be the very last things the patient really needs. A study was made of serial admissions of patients with severe non-luetic cardiovascular disease who had been hospitalized for the specific illness from one to fifteen times, totaling among them nearly three hundred periods of hospitalization. Attention was given to the emotional factor in the illness of these patients and brief psychotherapy was instituted. Only three of them have been hospitalized since (for the illness in question) and they have been followed from three to twelve years (average five years). Although this observation may not be considered very significant until these patients have been followed considerably longer, it is none the less noteworthy that ten of them had been hospitalized from two to four times during the year immediately preceding the treatment. It is further noteworthy: First, that many of them had been unable to walk more than two or three blocks, to do their own housework, or to hold any type of job, and that all of them are sufficiently improved to walk twenty or more blocks, to walk upstairs, and to engage in some occupation. Furthermore, no one of these patients had attracted the attention of the attending physician from the point of view of the psychic component in the illness. They were discovered in the course of a routine psychiatric study of hospital admissions.

If the physician bears in mind the combination of profiles to which we have called attention, plus a strong masochistic component in the personality, he can readily pick out from among the patients who come to him with decompensation those who are likely to have many recurrences, and institute the type of psychotherapy suggested in connection with the first period of treatment. In our experience the personality pattern to which attention has been called is even more important than the degree of organic damage in determining the course of the disease and the degree of invalidism. Too few hospitals have provided for routine psychiatric interviewing of all patients admitted, although the advisability of such a measure is coming to be recognized. With some disease groups little headway can be made without it.

III. CONCLUSIONS

(1) Some observations relative to recurrent decompensation as a syndrome in itself found in conjunction with several of the syndromes covered in this study have been given.

(2) It seems that a combination of the personality profile char-

acteristic of the fundamental syndrome with that characteristic of the cardiac arrhythmic group, in patients with strong masochistic personality trends, is characteristic of the patient with recurrent decompensation.

(3) Attention has been called to the extreme therapeutic importance of psychotherapy in patients with these characteristics when they are first admitted either with decompensation or with a cardiac condition which would make this likely during the course of the disease.

(4) Although the material here given is less detailed than that given for the eight groups studied in detail, further study of this problem would seem to be of fundamental importance in the management of convalescence or the prevention of invalidism.

Chapter VIII

DIABETES *

Diabetics are thought provoking. No sooner is one goal of treatment achieved than new vistas open up to other and higher levels.—JOSLIN.

I. GENERAL NATURE AND MAGNITUDE OF THE PROBLEM

STATISTICS

The incidence of diabetes is 2.52 per thousand, or very nearly twice that for as common a condition as german measles, and one-fifth greater than that of hay fever. In the decade 45 to 54 it reaches 4.5; for 55 to 64 it is 8.8; and in the age group 65 and over, 10 per thousand.

Those disabled by diabetes [286] on any given day number 660,000 and the annual number of days lost as a result of this disease is 19,200,000. In terms of number of invalids disabled by a given disease it ranks sixth (nervous and mental disease first, then rheumatism, heart disease,† tuberculosis in all forms, and arteriosclerosis and high blood pressure).

"The death rate from diabetes is rising 'at an alarming rate' and so of the number of cases, in spite of efforts being made to fight this disease, Dr. Cecil Striker, of Cincinnati, president of the new association (American Diabetes Association), declared in outlining methods by which the association hopes to aid the three quarters of a million diabetics in the nation.

---

* This was the most confusing personality picture of all the disease syndromes studied and the only one not checked at least roughly by our recent Rorschach research. There is some reason to expect that the Rorschach would be of particular value in further definition of this personality picture. We hope to publish in the near future a critical review of this chapter together with a revised profile of patients with diabetes, incorporating current Rorschach findings.

† Were the third and fifth of these illnesses lumped together as cardiovascular disease, their number would place them second, and diabetes would of course become fifth.

481

"A means of diagnosing diabetes in its early stages is badly needed, according to Dr. Best, who pointed out that at present doctors do not see diabetic patients until most of the insulin-producing cells in the patient's pancreas are destroyed." [160]

OTHER STUDIES

The literature relative to diabetes has been more systematically reviewed from the psychological point of view than has that relative to any other syndrome covered in this study, with the possible exception of hypertensive cardiovascular disease. Daniels' [108] review for *Psychosomatic Medicine* covers the general period 1934–1939, and attention should be called to two articles by Menninger [300, 301] published in 1935. The literature prior to this time is reviewed by Dunbar. [149] In this context, therefore, it remains only to call attention to one or two salient problems in this field.

First of all there is increasing insistence in the literature that diabetes mellitus, even when considered purely from the point of view of physiology, is not a single clear-cut disease entity. This problem is discussed in a recent article by Draper and others [128] on the differentiation that may be made by constitutional methods between pancreatic diabetes and diabetes of pituitary origin. Using clinical methods and constitutional studies on the basis of the Martin and Sheldon techniques, a correlation of 88 was found between clinical groups and morphological findings in 125 sufferers from diabetes. In group I, they found a preponderance of muscular development correlating with sensitiveness to insulin and severe diabetes. In group II, the fat component was preponderant and there was a correlation between resistance to insulin and milder disease.

Second, the role played by the hypothalamus in diabetes has received increasing attention. Grinker [212] in closing his excellent review of literature relative to the hypothalamus, to which reference was made earlier in this volume, makes the following statement relative to hypothalamic discharge of anxiety:

In anxiety . . . the danger is not real, it is unknown, internal, and results from an increase in instinctual tension demanding expression. As Freud points out, it is a conditioned signal within the ego, conscious within the personality as a warning of impending danger. There are specific unpleasurable feelings, efferent discharges and their perception. The result may not be fight or flight, as to a real danger, but a paralysis of certain higher ego functions. Anxiety is then the first sign of an autonomic influence on the cortex or ego, which has been learned by previous testing to indicate danger for the organism. It is a feeling which accompanies autonomic forces sufficiently strong to overcome cortical inhibition and force the cortex into activity, movement resulting in an attempt at solving the situation which has evoked the internal tension. Psychological fight or flight or compromise are attempted. Often successful solutions are not possible and the cortex or ego "gives up," allowing regressive and infantile modes of exteriorization of emotional expression, for the sake of avoiding more prolonged or greater emotional feelings. The result is visceral expression or organ dysfunction, which we term organ neuroses, that constitute the first step toward organic disease.

Grinker calls attention both to the key position of the hypothalamus in the autonomic system, using as a parallel the pituitary in the endocrine system, and also to the close relationship between the two. The reader is referred to Pincus and White [255] for this point. Mention should be made also of recent studies of the role of the gonads in this illness (see page 515).

Finally, there is considerable confusion relative to the personality picture of sufferers from diabetes. Some authors stress manic and especially depressive reactions; others schizophrenic as well as hysterical trends. Only negative evidence on this point, however, has resulted from the attempt to study reactions to changes in blood sugar level in normal individuals.

II. Onset of Symptoms

The period between the onset of the diabetes and the patient's admission to the hospital varied from three months to eleven years, but nonetheless fairly complete histories were obtained for the year or two preceding the discovery of the illness as well as for the patient's whole life span. In all cases there was a history of a long period of wear and tear with too little sleep and many aggravations, general depression, and a feeling of hopelessness culminating in irritability, easy fatigability, and general lack of drive. One of these patients described himself as suffering from "severe voluntary inertia." The fact that these patients led urban lives with little or no tendency to travel, places them in marked contrast with the rheumatic fever group.

In addition to the foregoing, in roughly half the cases there were concrete experiences such as financial difficulty or death in the family, involving the assumption by the patient of more responsibility. To such situations these patients reacted with anxiety, feelings of insecurity and very frequently overindulgence in food, especially in sweets, "to keep up their strength," and they or their physicians often ascribed the onset of diabetes to such dietary indescretion.

III. Predisposition to Illness—Factors to be Evaluated

ORGAN CONDITIONING—PHYSIOLOGICAL AND PSYCHOLOGICAL

Heredity—Actual and Pseudo

Nearly one-third (31.5 per cent) of these patients gave a *history of diabetes* in the family, including grandparents, parents, and parents' siblings; if the patient's own siblings are included, the percentage was 35.2; in one instance diabetes in a cousin was reported.* The diabetic heredity for the males was only 19 per cent (25 per cent including patients' siblings) as compared with 43 per cent (46 per cent including patients' siblings) for the females. Excluding patients for whom the only diabetic history was among their own siblings, we found that in 69 per cent of the cases with diabetic heredity this heredity was limited to the *maternal* side of the family. The ratio of paternal to maternal ancestry for both males and females was one to two and one-quarter; in the males one to one; and in the females one to two and two-thirds.

About 22 per cent of these patients gave a *history of cardiovascular disease* (26 per cent including patients' siblings), but interestingly enough, in a high majority of cases the afflicted relative or relatives were male.

Nervousness was reported in the ancestry of the patients in 24 per cent of the cases (including patients' siblings 28 per cent). Seven per cent of these patients were closely exposed to nervousness in friend or spouse. Furthermore, nearly one-tenth of these patients reported insanity in the family, and the family history of alcoholism was high (5.6 per cent).

* Rabinowitch has reported that 30 per cent of all cases have an hereditary basis, and of the juvenile diabetics 50 per cent.

History of accidental injury was reported in 7 per cent of the families of these patients (including patients' siblings, 13 per cent), and exposure outside the family or to spouse, 2 per cent. In the total group there were only five family histories that were negative for one of the disease designations under consideration, and three of these histories are noted as being incomplete. These patients all had either actual or pseudo-heredity of one or more of the diseases covered in the study. Alexander and Wilson [18] have stressed this point in their quantitative dream analysis.

Constitution—Age Range, Sex, and Marriage

Build. Our patients with diabetes were mainly dysplastic in type; a few were pyknic or linear. Unfortunately our facilities did not permit us to check the observations recorded by Draper and others.[128]

Age Range. The age range was from 15 to 55 years, with nearly one-third in the decade 15 to 24. The distribution was as follows:

Age Group	Per Cent
15-24	31.5
25-34	28.0
35-44	20.5
45-55	20.0

Sex. Forty-eight per cent were male and 52 per cent female.

Only one-half of these patients were *married,* but more than two-thirds of the patients in the age range 25 to 55 were married. Marriage was more than two and one-half times as frequent among the females as among the males. In this age range 25 to 55, 47 per cent of the males were unmarried, as compared with 17 per cent of the females.

Of the patients who were married, only three-fifths had *children,* and only one-third had more than two children; the maximum number was six. (The fact that the patients with larger families in all but three instances were female, is evidence that restriction of family was not primarily a result of the disease itself.) This point is of some interest since the majority of these patients came from large families, 69 per cent of the males and 82 per cent of the females. There was no disease group studied in which so great a percentage of patients came from large families (3 to 20 siblings). Male patients were only children about three times as frequently as were female patients. At the time of this study none of the children of these patients had developed diabetes.

Previous Health

About one-third of these patients gave a history of serious illness or operation prior to the discovery of the diabetes. The most usual were: pneumonia, jaundice, appendectomy, cholecystectomy. Cardiac neurosis was quite frequently reported. But only 15 per cent including only one male had actual cardiovascular disease; in all instances of the hypertensive type. Among these there was one patient with coronary thrombosis, and two with general arteriosclerosis (ages 33 and 49); however, in each instance the cardiac disease developed subsequent to the diabetes.

About 90 per cent of these patients reported one or more minor illness or minor operation. The most frequent were respiratory diseases and pelvic disorders. All but two of the females suffered from the latter. Only 4 per cent of these patients reported having had venereal disease. This is the best record of any group studied, but is of course insignificantly better than the fracture record of 1.9. Thus, in general, the health record of this group resembles that of the fracture group more closely than that of any other group studied.

Statistics Concerning Previous Injury

Slightly more than one-third of these patients reported injuries (52 per cent of the male patients, and 25 per cent of the female patients), but only 3 per cent reported more than one injury. Of the patients reporting injuries, however, only one-half (i.e., one-sixth, or 17 per cent of the total group) reported injuries prior to the discovery of the diabetes, and none reported more than one injury prior to the discovery of the diabetes. In view of our other statistics this suggests that diabetes is a factor predisposing to accident.

As to the type of accident, the distribution follows that for the accident group rather than that for the coronary group. There is one additional point, however: a number of accidents, particularly among those reported by the males, were the result of practical jokes played on them by others, and there is evidence in the personality histories that these patients are particularly alluring subjects for such jokes. For example:

Case No. D 56. A man, aged 24, reported that he was always being teased by his co-workers, and was actually hospitalized for a third degree burn, which he stated occurred because an associate had put some burning matches in his right shoe. At the time of hospitalization he had third degree burns on both feet, the second having occurred from the use of an electric pad while he was in bed for treatment for the first.

Case No. D 90. A 21-year-old filing clerk, as a small child was cut when some other children pushed him through a glass window.

Early Influences and Traumatic Experiences

These patients showed resemblances to both the group of patients with fracture and the group with rheumatic fever in terms of early influences and obvious traumatic experiences. Although exposure to death in the family was a factor in 44 per cent of the cases, such occurrences were taken as a matter of course in about half of the instances, and usually had not occurred in childhood. The patients had suffered, however, considerably from the nervousness of their parents and the friction between them (e.g., Case No. D 62, page 509).

The males were most of them in financial difficulty and the females complained of vocational or financial inadequacy on the part of the husband, but it remained for the more detailed personality histories (page 502 ff.) to throw light on the significances of these statements.

OUTSTANDING POINTS IN THE PERSONALITY HISTORY

General Adjustment

*Vocation—Education.** In no group of patients studied was there so small a percentage who stopped their academic education at the grammar school level, and in only two other groups studied was there nearly so high a percentage in the college and postgraduate category.

*Income.** The income level of these patients is not quite parallel to their educational history. Their income average was close to the average of the total groups studied, in terms of the percentage with incomes over $1500. Coronary patients, and patients with dyspnea

---

* It will be remembered that statements under starred headings are based only on patients over 21, in order to make them comparable to national statistics.

and palpitation were above them, but all the other groups studied fell below.

*Occupation.** The occupational distribution of these patients is more general and diverse (with a marked positive deviation as compared with the general population in groups II and III) than that of any group studied except that of fracture patients. Aside from the 20 per cent who were retired, invalids, or housewives, the percentage in group II ranks them fourth among the groups studied. Otherwise the majority of patients were in groups II and V, as were the patients with rheumatic disease.

Characteristic occupations for these patients were, for example, teacher, commercial artist, nurse, veterinary, bookkeeper, clerk, stenographer, postoffice clerk, furrier, butler, maid, chauffeur, taxi driver, boiler maker, factory worker, delivery boy, and there were several who called themselves "jack of all trades."

General Behavior. These patients were superficially agreeable, and looked and acted younger than their years. This was often a first point mentioned by the patient himself, either as his own opinion or as the opinion of his friends.

Anxiety and indecision stood out in the personality histories. There were no very specific fears, rather a sense of uncertainty and depression. Even as children they showed a tendency to complain and at the same time to submit to considerable wear and tear, accepting what they called their "hard lot" with a feeling of hopelessness as to being able to do anything about it.

Social Adjustment. This inability to cope with external difficulties was reflected also in their personal relationships, which were "good" only if they met the other person more than half way. This they seemed to do for a while in a reluctant spirit and then to cease doing; hence they complained of a general inability to keep friends. It was not unusual for a man to lose his job because of his inability to manage a problem in personal relationships. For example:

Case No. D 41. A man, aged 34, who had had diabetes for three months, reported that his employer "went with" women other than his wife and tried to make the patient an accomplice, at least to the extent of concealing

---

* It will be remembered that statements under starred headings are based only on patients over 21, in order to make them comparable with national statistics.

his behavior from the wife. The patient being unable to figure out how to behave in such a situation got himself fired and, furthermore, ascribed the onset of his diabetes to this trying situation.

These patients, particularly the men, seemed unable to take the initia tive in important matters, although they liked "to do things for people" when no responsibility was involved, especially for theiɪ inferiors. In general they were inclined to give little and make very considerable demands.

Sexual Adjustment. Dislike of menstruation (which was usually irregular), sex, and children was very prominent in diabetic pa‐ tients. The lack of initiative was particularly marked in sexual and domestic adjustments. These patients, generally unhappily married, would threaten or talk about divorce for years without being able to make up their minds to do anything about it. In the whole group there was only one divorce, although nearly half of those who were married were living separately without legalization of the agreement. The majority of these patients had tried living apart at least once and some of them several times. The women, who were for the most part frigid, complained that their husbands made exaggerated sexual demands. Patients of both sexes took out their general dissatisfaction on their children and scolded them or worried about them exces‐ sively.

These facts probably have a bearing on the tendency of the males to remain unmarried, and the tendency of the females to pelvic dis‐ orders of various types.

Attitudes Toward Parents and Children. The general family background of these patients, when they are reviewed as a group, is striking in several respects. First, both parents had usually lived well into the patient's adult life, and in 35 per cent of the cases both parents were living at the time of the patient's admission. Further‐ more, 54 per cent of all the patients had a father living and 67 per cent a mother living. In spite of the fact that a number of the mothers had diabetes there was very little difference in the time of death of the mother and father. The average age of these patients at the time of death of both father and mother was 20 years. In only 1.9 per cent of these cases was there death of both father and mother before the patient was 16. Second, unlike the group of patients with fracture, for example, there were relatively few step-fathers and stepmothers, but a high percentage of parents were separated or divorced and in nearly all cases there was a high degree of friction in the home. In accordance with the tendency of these patients not to be frank in their first statements, friction in the home was occasionally denied at first and later asserted with considerable bitterness.

In this group, there was a striking difference in males and females with respect to their attitude toward their parents. While over three-quarters of the males preferred, and were dominated by, their mothers, only slightly more than one-third of the females had this attitude. On the other hand, with the possible exception of one female (Case No. D 33) whose affection for, and domination by her father was subject to question, there were no cases among either males or females of a patient who preferred and was dominated by the father. This point should be related to the sexual behavior of these patients.

There was a strong homosexual tendency in the group, and practically no satisfactory marriages. But as in the group of patients with rheumatic fever, two types appeared, the active and passive. Unlike the patients with rheumatic fever, these two homosexual trends did not group the patients into two distinct classes, each having a separate mean relative to frequency. Any separation into two classes seemed arbitrary, inasmuch as the greatest number of patients were grouped around the common mean: a theoretical 50 per cent active—50 per cent passive homosexual. If, however, the patients were divided, rather arbitrarily, into two classes, one being over 50 per cent active, the other less than 50 per cent active, an interesting correlation was found:

Among the males, there were 65 per cent passive homosexuals, ranging from the "neutral" mean to extreme passive types having overt relationships with other men. All of these preferred, and were dominated by their mothers. There were about 27 per cent active homosexual types, and of these, less than one-half preferred and were dominated by their mothers, the larger portion showing various degrees of divergence, such as preferring the father, but admitting that the mother bossed them, or liking both parents equally, and stating that neither one was dominant in the home.

Among the females, the situation was even more striking: only 32 per cent were of the passive homosexual type, and of these, all preferred and were dominated by their mothers. Fifty-seven per cent were active homosexuals, of whom only 3.6 per cent preferred and were dominated by their mothers; the remaining 53 per cent preferred neither parent above the other, showed slight preference for father though admitting domination by the mother, or vice versa.

In the females, about 10 per cent of the cases could not be considered either definitely active or definitely passive homosexuals on the character basis, but it may be noted that half of these preferred and were dominated by the mother, and the other half were not. Similarly in the males, about 8 per cent could not be divided, and half of these preferred and were dominated by the mother, the other half were not.

Hence the difference in attitude between males and females of this group toward their parents correlates with the fact that there was a preponderance (57 per cent) of active female homosexuals not preferring or being dominated by their mothers (very much the "tomboy" type), while in the males there was found a still larger preponderance (65 per cent) of passive homosexual types very

TABLE XI

ACTIVE AND PASSIVE HOMOSEXUAL TRAITS AS RELATED TO
PARENTAL INFLUENCE

	NUMBER OF CASES	MOTHER DOMINANT AND PREFERRED	NEITHER MOTHER NOR FATHER DOMINANT AND PREFERRED	FATHER DOMINANT OR PREFERRED
	Per Cent	Per Cent	Per Cent	Per Cent
Active homosexuals:				
Males....................	27	43	57	—
Females..................	57	6.25	87.5	6.25
Males and females..........	42	17.4	78.3	4.3
Passive homosexuals:				
Males....................	65	100	—	—
Females..................	32	100	—	—
Males and females	48	100	—	—

closely associated with their mothers in affection and dominance.

It should be noted that the preceding paragraphs are purely descriptive, not an attempt to correlate preference of the female parent with active or passive homosexual tendencies. Also no causative relationship is asserted. It is suggested that the reader interested in this aspect of the problem compare relevant case histories here with those reported by Henry.[238]

Characteristic Behavior Pattern

Inability to follow any consistent course of action was characteristic of these patients. Changes were not made quickly as with the accident group, but only after a long period of worry and shifting back and forth. More than any other group of patients studied, diabetic patients considered themselves the victims of their surroundings. This behavior was just as marked in childhood and prior to the onset of the diabetes as it was later, although of course the effect of the diabetes was to aggravate this behavior pattern.

The diabetes provided an excellent alibi for their inadequacy, indecisiveness, and lack of success, and it was exploited to the full by the majority of these patients. This appeared to be a factor in their general inability to follow their diet and to co-operate with the medical regime laid down for them, which often resulted in an impression on the part of the physician that they were actually stupid (Case No DP 4). Reference to the educational chart for these patients (page 145) as well as study of their histories, will make clear that they were not lacking in intelligence. A smaller percentage than in any other group studied had terminated their education with grammar school. They ranked high among the groups studied from the point of view of college education, which was often undertaken as a means of compensating for their general feeling of inadequacy. A large number of them wanted to go into a profession, feeling that in professional life there would be less competition than in other spheres, but the majority of them were unable to work consistently toward such a goal. Their difficulty lay more along the line of inviting suffering and a general lack of control. This manifested itself in a tendency to postpone decisions, to diffuse energy rather than to direct it along any one constructive line (for example, a number of patients who, when they felt they ought to get a job, were inclined to keep themselves so busy with little odd jobs for other people that they could never quite get to it), and especially with the men, a tendency to remain inactive.

Neurotic Traits—Early and Present

Most of these patients were feeding problems as children, but otherwise they were considered normal and tractable. Temper tantrums were relatively infrequent, enuresis, lying, stealing and sleep-walking rare or nonexistent. But childhood phobias and nightmares were regularly reported and sleep-talking was frequent (e.g., Case No. D 59, page 504; Case No. D 62, page 509). Long-continued thumb sucking was relatively more prominent than in other groups, and nail-biting usually persisted into adult life. Tics were relatively more prominent in this group than in any other group studied, except the patients with rheumatic fever.

It is more difficult to describe these patients in terms of present neurotic traits because of the effect of the disease itself. In general, they were nervous and inaccessible, with a tendency to hysteria or depression. In addition, there was a marked fear of venereal disease and a compulsive cleanliness. There was a marked paranoid tendency and a considerable difference between the patient's first statements about himself and his family, and those made later after rapport with the physician was established. All the members of our research group who worked with diabetics agreed that they were the most difficult of the groups studied from the point of view of obtaining an adequate history and personality picture. Frequently there was a rather clear-cut self-destructive drive: "I hate myself. I might as well die."

Addictions and Interests

The characteristic behavior pattern just outlined is well reflected in the addictions and interests of these patients. First of all their interests were few and scattered, tending to be intellectual rather than in the field of sports. They had some interest in individual sports, but they avoided competition in this sphere as well as in the vocational sphere. Athletic interest was particularly strong in the active homosexual females. They had a marked fondness for animals combined with a tendency to enjoy their suffering.

There was little addiction to coffee, alcohol, or smoking, as compared with the other groups, but of course a considerable interest in food. Unlike accident patients, however, who also showed an interest in food, these patients took very poor care of themselves from the point of view of general hygiene, and tended to overindulge. A characteristic statement was:

Patient No. D 32: "When you've had a lot of trouble you learn to neglect yourself." (A woman, aged 46, who had diabetes for three years.)

Patient No. D 46, a woman, aged 32, who had had diabetes for five years, said: "And then I stopped caring. After you have trouble you neglect yourself. Food is your only comfort."

In our group 33.33 per cent were Roman Catholic (19 per cent of the males, 46 per cent of the females); 41 per cent, Jewish (37 per cent of the males, 43 per cent of the females); and 26 per cent were Protestant (42 per cent of the males, 11 per cent of the females); but few of them showed any very consistent interest in religion. The general tendency was to become lax or skeptical, except for the group that was consciously worried about homosexuality; these patients were inclined to seek refuge in religion and there were reformers and fanatics among them.

Of the males, 77 per cent became lax in their religious attitude, but were found to have done this without any definite reason; they just did not bother with religion. The most extreme of the active homosexual type males liked to go to church on Feast days, but "don't take it too seriously"; they showed a slight resemblance to the religious attitude of the patients with hypertension (Case No. D 71, a patient with diabetes, fracture overlap, whose accidents were of the cardiac type).

Of the remaining 23 per cent of the males, all were of the extreme passive homosexual type, and all were very religious, tending to become religious fanatics, as for example, patient No. D 59, who had gone from Baptist to high Anglican to Occultist to Yogi science—the latter to make himself "clean inside and outside"; or patient No. D 53, a pious Lutheran, who disliked "boys who used vulgar language" because he was a "communicant of the Church."

It may be noted that there was a close connection between religious fanaticism in these passive homosexual types (patient No. D 59 who had had overt homosexual relations as the "victim") and their urge to cleanliness, as shown by patient No. D 59 and the Yogi disciple, or by patient No. D 53, who said of girls: "If I *have* to kiss them, I go home and wash myself with the strongest antiseptic possible."

In the 23 per cent of religious zealots among males, there was a similarity to the patients with fracture. An example is patient No. D 40, a Jewish boy who called himself a male virgin; he was fond of athletics and inclined to accidents which were typical fracture accidents.

Of the females, 71 per cent became lax in their religious attitude, and of the remaining 29 per cent who continued to take an active interest, none carried religion to the point of fanaticism, nor did any depart from their childhood faith. Furthermore, those with a continued religious interest were not, as in the case of the males of this group, limited to the passive homosexual class. In general, it may be said that the female patients with diabetes showed a slightly stronger religious interest: on the one hand, a slightly smaller percentage (71 per cent) became lax; there was a distinctly greater number of Catholics; and on the other hand, there were no cases found of religous fanatics. Though slightly more religious as a whole, there was less tendency to associate religion with their sexual peculiarities.

Life Situation Immediately Prior to the Onset

Of all the patients studied, the diabetes patients are the most difficult when it comes to describing the life situation immediately prior to onset. In the first place, with diabetics there is no such thing as a first attack in the strict sense of the word; rather a slow insidious onset. Often an emotional crisis, exaggerating symptoms, leads to the first discovery of diabetes. After this, these patients, unlike accident and coronary patients, seem to indulge in fantasies about what brought the scourge upon them, and the reasons invented are diverse and bizarre.* For example:

Case No. D 71. A man, aged 37, who had had diabetes for sixteen months, ascribed his diabetes to a sudden character reform; specifically, going on the water wagon.

* Daniels' [108] discussion of the question as to whether or not diabetes can result from shock.

Case No. D 4. A man, aged 42, who had had diabetes for twenty years, ascribed his diabetes to having fallen off a kiddy-car five months prior to the onset of the diabetes.

Case No. D 53. A boy of 16 years, stated that he was hit across the heart by a Jewish boy for being a Hitlerite. He commented: "You know I am weak, not as robust as other boys. Who knows, I might have fallen into the lathes and been killed. This is what started the diabetes."

Case No. D 69. A 46-year-old Jewish woman, who had had diabetes for three years, ascribed her diabetes to the fact that her husband, who was suffering from shell-shock, attempted to strangle her one evening. "I stayed up all night to protect myself and the children. I sat all night in my chair without moving so that I felt stiff all over. And doctor, it was that excitement that made me sick." She had the usual symptoms of polyphagia, polydipsia, and weight loss, but had never been in shock or had acidosis. Although the first symptoms of diabetes appeared immediately after the birth of her fourth child, and a long time after the strangling episode, she was certain that the latter was responsible for her illness. And although she focused her attention on the choking experience there had been a long period of dissatisfaction with her husband because "he wanted to have intercourse in the Park Avenue fashion" (by which she meant cunnilingus) so that she had been absorbed in finding ways of avoiding intercourse with him and at the same time in attempting to convict him of adultery.

She maintained, furthermore, that he was an opium addict because of the fact that his urinary sediment was orange-colored which, she said, meant opium and nothing else. There was no evidence that either of her suspicions were justified. She had wanted for a long time to divorce her husband but could never quite bring herself to do it.

This history brings out again the element of a long period of emotional strain together with an inability to act which was characteristic of these patients. As already noted, this inability to act kept them in jobs where they were unhappy as well as in marital situations where they were unhappy, and the men were usually in financial difficulty while the women complained of the inadequacy of their husbands. For example:

Case No. D 87. A woman, aged 49, who had had diabetes for ten months, discoursing on her husband's lack of luck in the number of jobs he had lost, said: "It was worry about him that made me sick."

Daniels [108] comments on a patient in our serial admission group studied by him, as follows:

A girl of 17 said that her parents attributed her diabetes to a childhood fright from a dog. Although she had no memory of the event, she still had an active dog phobia. Her mother confirmed the story that a neighborhood puppy had jumped on the child and that she had run screaming into the house. Such a fright presumably would not have caused a lasting phobia if an infantile conflict situation had not been raging at the time.

In general, although these patients often gave bizarre reasons for the onset of the diabetes, and loss of a love object, parent, husband or child, was occasionally noted, sexual maladjustment resulting in alienation of husband or wife seemed to have had much greater significance than death. Furthermore, any situation necessitating the assumption of greater responsibility by the patient readily became a focus of emotional turmoil.

Reaction to Illness

These patients' reactions to their illness was characterized by depression (Harris,[224] Baker, Fazekas and Himwich [29]) alternating with a feeling of relief because they had an alibi for their inadequacies, and a tendency to project, especially to be suspicious of others. In the depressed periods they blamed themselves for poor judgment, lack of control, and wrong dietary habits, but they were more inclined to project their difficulties on to others, and they showed a marked paranoid trend (Menninger [300, 301] and Katz [262]). Sometimes patients were conscious of their tendency to project, as for example:

Patient No. D 68. A boy, aged 15, who had diabetes for four years, said: "When something happens it is usually my fault but I always blame someone else."

Patient No. D 4. A man, aged 42, who had diabetes for twenty years, said: "At first the diabetes was a nuisance, but not so much so now. It has cut my pleasure down a lot though so that I can't go to night clubs and have a few drinks. Your friends appear obnoxious to you if you go and don't drink with them. You forget that you used to be the same. . . . I will drive home late at night rather than stay in a hotel. I can sleep and relax much better at home. I am about one night a week in a hotel, and don't sleep as well then. I feel that I should stay down there as I would work better but

I still don't do it. . . . Now I am getting so that I don't think anything bothers me. My wife does all the worrying about the bills, and that sort of thing. I can go to bed, and am asleep in fifteen minutes. I sleep well until the next morning. When it is light I wake up."

(*Note:* See also Case No. D 34, page 500.)

IV. DYNAMIC FORMULATION

AREA OF FOCAL CONFLICT AND CHARACTERISTIC REACTION

Patients with diabetes find their major difficulty in areas of adjustment involving assumption of responsibility. This difficulty seems to begin in early childhood and long before the disease. They seem not to develop a very strong reaction against their need to be dependent, but rather to vacillate from one attitude to the other. The impulse toward independence is asserted mainly in words and very little in action. Their difficulties in this sphere are paralleled on a deeper level by their inability to attain a mature sexual adjustment. Here again there is no adequate development of either masculine or feminine components in the personality, but instead a vacillation between what they regard as male and female attributes with an accompanying regression to a state where sexual interest is more or less completely denied and oral and anal traits come into prominence as defining their character and behavior.

As a group they are more passive than active, and more masochistic than sadistic. The integrating function of their personality, the ego, is weak in the extreme and their characterological defenses correspondingly feeble. They suffer therefore from intense anxiety until the disease itself appears to give them an alibi, again on a pretty unsatisfactory level.

Most of these patients reported a long-drawn-out indeterminate and subacute conflict with one or both parents. With the men there was a tendency to seek a dependent relationship to the mother, which they could never quite accomplish, and with the women the same tendency with a slight favoring of the father. In this statement there is no implication of revolt against parents because of their strictness, but rather a feeling of malaise and overprotection with a regular assertion that discipline in the household was lax. In the majority of the cases there was positive information that the patient was the oldest, youngest, or favorite child, of which distinction they were inclined to be extremely jealous.

The family situation was complicated by the fact that except for the only children (15 per cent), of whom there were three times as many among males as females, these patients came from large families and had difficulty in adjusting to the presence of siblings. In the case of 81 per cent of the females and 70 per cent of the males both parents lived beyond the patients' adolescence.

Their difficulty from childhood on with any kind of situation involving responsibility, and their indecisiveness, have apparently kept them in painful situations and subjected them to a life of wear and tear where their only satisfaction lay in eating and in suffering.

Patient No. D 68. A boy, aged 15, who had had diabetes for four years, characteristically described his conflict in these terms: "All my life I tried to be independent but mother kept drumming it into me that I couldn't get along by myself. Of course I like to be looked out for but I would have gotten farther in the world if mother hadn't pampered me. But then, as I've told you already, I'm always blaming someone else. It might be my fault after all. Anyway what does it matter?"

Patient No. D 22. A woman, aged 28, who had had diabetes for twelve years, said: "I make it a point not to be dependent. But I have to have people love me and take care of me. Who doesn't?"

Patient No. D 39. A man, aged 31, who had had diabetes for ten years: "I was always dependent. Mother made me that way but I hated it. But now since I'm sick I can't even remember my troubles. They say diabetes takes away your memory."

Patient No. D 78. A woman, aged 31, who had had diabetes for twelve years, said: "Little things at home bother me more than in the office. I wish I was more independent. Not to get hurt too quickly when people say something. That's my weak point. That's from Mother. She was always kind to me. I was unprepared for the world."

It is striking that phrases relative to dependence and responsibility were numerically as prominent in the spontaneous statements of these patients as were phrases relative to authority, being bossed, in the spontaneous conversation of accident patients. The fear of being made dependent or weakened was used as an excuse for avoiding sexual relationships and the awakening of sexual anxiety, before the development of the disease, and then the disease itself was used in the same way as an alibi. The attitude toward suffering is indicated in such comments as the following:

Patient No. D 34. A girl, aged 19, who had had diabetes for five years, said especially characteristically: "As if I hadn't had enough trouble in my life. I found I had diabetes and that took the last bit of hope out of me. I prayed that God would either *take it from me or make me take it willingly.* My only comfort all my life when I was in trouble had been to go off by myself and eat candy. Now even that is taken from me."

Patient No. D 37. A man, aged 42, who had had diabetes for two years: "I try to act like a man all day but I cry like a baby at night. Either the world is against me or I was born the martyr type."

Patient No. D 36. A woman, aged 46, who had had diabetes for a year, said: "I've had so much trouble it would break down a wall. But I won't give in. I do my work carrying a hot water bag and at night I'm so exhausted that the children have to take turns rubbing my head to make me sleep."

Patient No. D 87. A woman, aged 49, who had had diabetes for ten months, said: "I nearly dropped dead when they told me I had diabetes. It must have worried me a little. I made up my mind to stick it out. It is a terrible sickness."

Patient No. D 92. A man, aged 24, who had had diabetes six months, said: "When I was little I could never fight back. In my town people talk behind your back and are nice in front of you. I always used to cry at every little thing and I still do. I get blue when I think of home where people would be nice to you if you cried."

Patient No. D 90. A man, aged 21, who had had diabetes eight years, said: "If you're going to worry about yourself you'll drive yourself nuts. It's only myself that's got to help me. I had to have something pretty bad the matter with me to be able to come to the clinic otherwise they would say I was a baby."

The oral preoccupation of these patients is clear, as well as their tendency toward masochism. These two trends are equally obvious in these patients in their reaction to members of the opposite sex and to the sexual experience itself.

Patient No. D 42 (quoted page 501), said again: "I have always kept my miseries to myself. I couldn't even tell doctors about them, at least men doctors. You can't tell a man doctor anything when it comes to your sex life. But the truth is I always cry when I have intercourse."

Patient No. D 63. A man, aged 33, who had had diabetes for nine years, said: "At first I felt downhearted, especially the needle disgusted me. Now it's like brushing your teeth. Wasn't there some book about a girl who said that about intercourse?"

This is a fairly regular association. The deep-lying sexual anxiety together with the sexual symbolization associated with the necessary treatment for their diabetes is of great importance in understanding these patients, as well as in their treatment (page 489 ff.).

Their homosexual trend is of course consistent with their oral pre-occupation and their conflict relative to dependence. As has been noted already, there is a marked tendency to projection of this particular conflict to the spouse and to suppression of it or projection to parent or friend in the unmarried diabetic. Also consistent with this behavior pattern is the tendency to make excessive demands on the spouse in terms of parental care: "My wife does all the worrying, my wife pays all the bills." Or "My husband is as good to me as a mother." Or "My husband doesn't give me the kind of care I need." This behavior is often marked in relation to children also.

Patient No. D 42. A woman, aged 50, who had had diabetes for three years, said: "Life would be simpler if you didn't have children. But still I'd like to have more, especially girls, because girls always look up to their mothers and take care of you."

PROFILE

Diabetes *

1. *Family History*. Diabetes, about 35 per cent, especially in maternal ancestry. Also cardiovascular disease, about 26 per cent, especially among the males of the family. Accidents, 9 per cent. Nervousness and insanity, about 35 per cent. And exposure to one or more of these illnesses, 100 per cent.

2. *Personal Data*. At least one parent living well into patient's adult life. The subacute struggle with parents usually continued throughout life. A tendency, especially among the males to remain unmarried, and a tendency on the part of both males and females to have few children and few actual divorces although many periods of living apart from marital partner.

* In order to evaluate the distinctive features in this profile, reference should be made to page 585 ff. and Chapter IX.

3. *Health Record.* Good previous record—best of any group except fracture, but differing from fracture pattern in being higher with patients in whom the onset was late. Women poor pelvic histories.

4. *Injuries.* Low accident record prior to onset of diabetes, but relatively high record subsequent to onset. Childhood accidents average.

5. *General Adjustment. Education:* High level with marked interest in advancement but a frequent incidence of nervous breakdown in college. *Work record:* Disinclination to assume responsibility. Unable to take initiative in important matters. Inability to manage personal relationships often cause of loss of job. *Income and vocation level:* Somewhat lower than educational level even prior to the onset of the illness. Diverse occupational distribution with positive deviation from general population in class II (proprietors) and class III (clerks, stenographers). *Social relationships:* Marked social anxiety. Superficially agreeable but self-conscious and inaccessible. *Sexual adjustment:* Marked by anxiety and inadequacy with homosexual trend. Marriage more frequent in passive than in active types. Low venereal disease rate. *Attitude toward family:* Marked conflict between hatred of parents and submission. Same attitude repeated toward spouse.

6. *Characteristic Behavior Pattern.* Inability to follow any consistent course of action, vacillation, and indecisiveness. Conversation to win sympathy. Focusing of emotion on suffering.

7. *Neurotic Traits.* Temper tantrums, phobias, and nightmares. In adult life nervousness, depression, suspicion with a tendency to paranoid ideas.

8. *Addictions and Interests.* Interest in food. Preoccupation with innumerable odd jobs diverting energy from major tasks. Avoidance of competitive sports, interest in animals. Little interest in religion, except when awareness of homosexuality led to religious experiment, usually with ascetic or fanatic trend.

9. *Life Situation Immediately Prior to Onset.* Long period of wear and tear, including hard work, homosexual conflict, struggle with family and spouse. Often dietary indiscretion.

10. *Reaction to Illness.* Depression alternating with a feeling of relief at having an alibi for inadequacy. Suspiciousness of others with a marked tendency to project.

11. *Area of Focal Conflict and Characteristic Reaction.* Responsibility (dependence versus independence—vacillation). Sexual role (ambivalence).

CASE ILLUSTRATIONS

Case No. D 92. A 24-year-old married woman was admitted for symptoms of polyplegia, polyuria, polydipsia, fatigue and weight loss of six months duration. The diagnosis was diabetes mellitus and acidosis.

Family History. No heart trouble, diabetes or accidents in the family, but all of them nervous.

Personal Data. The patient was born in a small town in Pennsylvania. Normal delivery; breast fed; first girl in a family of six. Her father and mother were living and well at the time of admission.

Previous Health. Excellent.

Previous Injuries. None.

General Adjustment. Vocation—education: The patient stopped school at the end of the sixth grade because she had to help support the family. *Income:* Marginal. *Occupation:* Various jobs as a waitress in restaurants and in private families. *Social adjustment:* "I could never get along with people. Both at home and outside they are nice in front of you and mean behind your back. If you buy anything they are suspicious about where you get the money." *Sexual adjustment:* Like most female diabetics the periods of this patient were always irregular (every 20–30 days). "I knew my husband for a year before I married him but I never knew any other men. I didn't like the idea of sex but I wanted to get out of the home and I thought he would take care of me. I never had any satisfaction in sex and was disillusioned when I had to have the baby. . . . I think I'm the type that was meant never to marry. I keep thinking about leaving my husband but he sort of has me caught. I would be afraid of being left alone with the child." *Attitude toward parents and children of her own:* "I've always been mother's favorite. If I swallow my feelings and listen to her she'll give me anything I want. That's the way I learned to get my own way. Father is no good but he has to listen to her too." (See attitude toward child under *Characteristic Behavior Pattern.*)

Characteristic Behavior Pattern. "When I would get disgusted with the work I would go to my room and cry. I would never fight back. Then I would think about getting another job then I'd be afraid I couldn't get one, and try to stick it out. After I changed my mind a good many times I usually did get another job. I didn't realize how lucky I was working. There's nothing I'd like better than to work now and let someone else take care of the child, but my husband won't let me. I'd much rather put in a day's work than take care of a child. She gets me aggravated all the time. She's afraid of me. I get so nervous I don't care what I do to her."

Neurotic Traits. Early: Thumb sucking until the age of 4. Her mother used to wrap up her thumb in salt and pepper to make her stop. Talking and screaming in her sleep but no nightmares remembered. *Present:* Marked tendency to self-neglect blamed on her husband who was not sufficiently careful about withdrawal which resulted in the birth of an unwanted child.

"You can't take care of yourself when you have a child." Violent temper outbursts.

Addictions and Interests. Eight or ten cups of coffee a day "to quiet my nerves. What I really like best is food and now that's taken away from me. . . . I used to like to skate, but since I've been married I haven't liked to do anything. Mother brought me up to go to church but since I've been married I stay as far away from it as possible. The priest would scold me about not wanting to have more babies."

Life Situation Immediately Prior to Onset. This is sufficiently explained under other headings.

Reaction to Illness. "I am very angry about my illness. It seems like the last insult. My husband gave it to me by making me have the baby. Now I don't care what happens to me. I don't care whether I get well or die. I can't follow my diet because I don't want to give up the only pleasure that's left in life, eating what you please."

Area of Focal Conflict and Characteristic Reaction. In discussing further her occupational history and her accidental child, this patient frequently used the expression characteristic of the diabetic patient: "I'm afraid of responsibility. . . . I resented having to have responsibility about supporting the family. . . . I didn't realize that responsibility wasn't half so bad as having to have the responsibility of having to have a child," etc. Her conflict over her sexual role is equally obvious from the above: "I guess I am the kind that shouldn't get married. I never found any good in sex. I like girls better than men. It's easier to make them do what you want."

Case No. D 59. A boy, aged 16 years, was admitted for the second time because of difficulty in control of his diabetes. The diabetes had been discovered three years previously and was characterized by polyuria, polydipsia and severe cramps in the calves of his legs.

Family History. Diabetes was reported in a maternal aunt and uncle.

Personal Data. This patient was an exception in the diabetics studied in that his father had died during his childhood and that the patient had never seen him (lieutenant in the U. S. Army) because his mother had left him. The mother, however, married again when the patient was 7 years old, and her second husband played the role in the patient's life usually played by the father. That is, he was aloof, partially liked and partially disliked by the patient.

Previous Health. At the age of 3 the patient had lobar pneumonia, at the ages of 5 and 9, bilateral and unilateral pneumonia. He had two tonsillectomies, and at the age of 15 after the onset of his diabetes, dysentery.

Previous Injuries. None.

General Adjustment. Vocation—education: The patient did not care much for school but at the time of admission was completing his third year of high school. *Occupation:* He had no ideas about what he wanted to do after school or anything that he would like to do instead of going to school. *Income:* The patient was perfectly willing to let his mother support him.

Social adjustment: He was very slow in making acquaintances but maintained that he had a few good friends of his own sex. It turned out that these were the men with whom he had had homosexual affairs in the passive role. He commented: "There's probably something about me that draws men to me. I'm always being approached. In the swimming pool, in restaurants, on the street and most anywhere. One reason I don't like to be with people is that they can always tell that about you, and mostly they don't approve. Animals are best, but I don't like goldfishes. They're so dull they don't talk, just look up out of the water with a silly expression on their faces, and cats are too clever. You never can tell what they will do to you. But dogs and horses are real friends." He commented further that the only men he liked were militarists, which was hard "because I am a confirmed pacifist."

Sexual adjustment: His mother had given him books to read about sex and allowed him complete freedom, but the patient said he could never find anything in it. Because of the books he tried masturbation between the ages of 12 and 13 but gave it up because "there was no fun in it." He then experimented with mutual masturbation with boys at school and this "wasn't any fun either." He then experimented with a prostitute "who was very good to me and didn't charge me anything"; but he commented: "I was quite disappointed. Sex just isn't what it's cracked up to be. That experience was an awful let-down, although the girl was very nice. So I just decided to have nothing to do with it." In discussing his homosexual experiences, he said: "If you have to have sex at all that's probably the best way." He said further: "Of course I was always the 'victim' but that's all right because the other fellers were better than me." One of these experiences was with a counselor at camp. His mother got wind of it and his final break with her was because of her objection to this relationship.

Attitude toward parents: The patient had no contact with his father and little with his stepfather; his maternal grandmother and aunt he hated "because they talked too much and always wanted sympathy"; and he could never get along with his mother. He stated: "I look just like her and act like her, she is tall and slim with long hands. Her eyes are very far apart from each other and dark like her hair. I have the same tastes, I guess we're too much alike."

Characteristic Behavior Pattern. Submission and dependence relative to mother and male friends, with occasional feeble attempts to break away. The patient showed in general the vacillation and inability to think things through which was a regular trait among our patients with diabetes.

Neurotic Traits. The patient still talked in his sleep, and often woke himself shouting but could remember no dreams or nightmares. He suffered from enuresis until the age of 10, and used to be ragged about it in summer camp. When he began to talk he started by lisping and then became a stammerer (he had particular difficulty with the sounds of m and n). At the age of 13 after leaving his mother and stepfather to live with an aunt and uncle in Virginia he developed a tic involving motions of the jaw and ending in a jerk of his head. Like his mother, he suffered from temper tantrums in which, in spite of the fact that he was usually quiet and placid, he would become very tense, tears would roll down his face, and then he would throw things and smash them. On several occasions when he and his mother were indulging in simultaneous temper tantrums and throwing things at each other he threatened to leave her and she said "go ahead." "But I could never bring myself to it because I love her too much."

Addictions and Interests. The patient found alcohol a sort of relief but preferred good food to coffee and cigarettes. He became an ardent Baptist at the age of 12, then shifted to Presbyterian, Congregational and finally to high Anglican. At the age of 14 he had reached the conclusion that "there was nothing in ordinary religion and took up the science of Yogi to make myself clean inside and outside." At the time of admission he was interested in occultism.

In commenting on his inability to find anything he would really like to do he said he planned to become a psychiatrist but he was afraid people would laugh at him if he told them. When the point was brought up that in that case he would have had to go to college and medical school, he said he had never thought of that, he guessed he would "just be a lay psychiatrist." He then said: "What's a schizophrenic anyway?" When asked the reason for his question he said he had seen Mary Petty's cartoon, "Why don't you go out and mingle with other schizophrenics?" He had been thinking about doing this but wondered where to find them. He had read "The House That Freud Built" and wanted further reading in this field.

The patient had some interest in non-competitive sports, especially horseback riding. He also enjoyed fencing.

Life Situation Immediately Prior to Onset. After years of turmoil, including many threats to leave home, the patient reached a compromise solution and decided to live with his maternal aunt and uncle in Virginia. (While he was away the mother separated from her second husband.) After the patient had been with them for four months the tic developed and the diabetes followed. It is of some interest that the maternal aunt with whom he went to live had diabetes. Characteristically, the patient ascribed the onset of his diabetes to the tic.

He had lived with this same aunt from the age of 6 to 7, just prior to his mother's second marriage, and said: "She came down to Virginia to see me so that we could get married—I mean, so that they could get married."

Subsequent to the last break with his mother, at the age of 13, the patient had seen little of her, he had "sort of visited around among the relatives."

Reaction to Illness. The patient ascribed the pains preceding his first hospital admission to some dietary indiscretion and interpreted his discomfort as a kind of atonement. He showed little anxiety on learning of his diabetes but simply wanted to get well.

Area of Major Conflict and Characteristic Reaction. This patient's reluctance to assume any responsibility for himself is obvious from the foregoing. But his difficulty in the sphere of sex is equally obvious.

Although psychotherapy was recommended for this patient and he showed considerable interest in it, he returned to the clinic very irregularly, saying that he preferred the Yogi system of relaxation.

Case No. D 88. A 50-year-old, unmarried man, was admitted to the hospital for the first time with symptoms of increasing fatigability, weakness, loss of 23 pounds in two to three months, and polydipsia and polyuria of two months' duration. Blood sugar on admission was 400 mg. per cent.

Family History. No diabetes on either side.

Personal Data. The patient was born in Philadelphia, a normal delivery. He was an only child. He had lived all his life with his mother. His father died of pneumonia just prior to the patient's adolescence; his mother was living and well at the time of admission.

Previous Health. Excellent except for typhoid fever at the age of 12.

Previous Injuries. Several weeks before admission the patient slipped in the bathroom and fell against the tub, hurting his spine.

General Adjustment. Vocation—education: The patient completed grammar school and high school and wanted to study medicine. After one year in college, however, he was told that his astigmatism was so severe he should give up schooling. (There seems to have been no basis for this since he has had no further difficulty with his eyes and his vision was good at the time of admission.) *Income:* Always relatively good, although at the time of admission he was about to go on a WPA job. *Occupation:* After leaving college he went on the stage for five years. Then he taught dancing, experimented with the hotel business, and became a traveling salesman. *Social adjustment:* The patient preferred not to see too much of people, got along better with men than with women. He had always lived with his mother and was still living with her at the time of admission. *Sexual adjustment:* The patient stated that he "had forgotten all about sex years ago." He never married because he never knew any married people that were happy, besides which he and his mother were like brother and sister "although she is twenty-five years older than I am I get as much kick out of dancing with her as with any girl. She's really the only one I like to dance with." *Attitude toward parents:* The patient disliked and had an almost complete amnesia for his father, and was devoted to his mother.

Characteristic Behavior Pattern. The patient described his adjustment to life in these terms: "I believe in getting the most money and the most fun with the least trouble. I have always managed to get jobs that were easy. For a while I couldn't make up my mind whether I ought to go out with girls to be like other people; then I decided it wasn't worth the trouble. It's hard for me to make decisions, but the way my life has been I haven't had to make any."

Neurotic Traits. All early neurotic traits were denied. The patient could remember only that his mother said that he used to cry out in his sleep as a child.

Addictions and Interests. The patient was a moderate coffee drinker, but smoked and drank somewhat to excess. No interest in religion.

Life Situation Immediately Prior to Onset. There had been financial worries terminating in loss of his job when the company with which he was working closed its offices. After seeking in vain for employment he finally lost his $17,000 house just prior to the development of the first diabetic symptoms. These he blamed at first on his teeth, eight of which he had had extracted, and then on worry on having to "drive his mother out of house and home." It was a great blow to his pride that he and she had to become just ordinary boarders. The day before admission he came back to New York to see his dentist, "had a breakfast of griddle cakes and a pitcher of syrup and felt so tired that I consulted a doctor who found that my urine was full of sugar."

Reaction to Illness. The patient accepted his illness philosophically, saying that with the loss of his house he had lost all he had to lose, and that after all he was better than some because he had a mother to look after him.

Area of Focal Conflict and Characteristic Reaction. Throughout his life this patient had sought jobs involving little responsibility. He said of his father: "He was the great so and so, but where does that get you? My system is better. Get your pay with as little responsibility as possible then you have no worries. That's another reason I didn't marry. A wife is always a responsibility and if you have children it makes it worse. Living with

Mother's fine. She had a little money of her own and is a much better house-keeper than any girl I've seen. When it comes to having fun give me Mother or the boys."

It is interesting that this patient had no conscious conflict about his sexual adjustment, but as he put it, "had just forgotten about sex because it gets you into trouble." Although his impulses followed the homosexual pattern there were no overt experiences after his early manhood, and incidentally he lacked the interest in religion char-acteristic of these patients who become worried about their sexuality, as, for example, patient No. D 59.

Case No. D 62. An unmarried boy, 22 years old, was admitted to the hospital for the second time for diabetes discovered when he was 14 years old. The symptoms were polyphagia, polyuria, polydipsia, weight loss, acidosis, and coma.

Personal Data. The patient was an only child, born in New York City. His birth and early development were said to have been normal. Both his parents were living at the time of admission.

Family History. No history of diabetes, but the maternal grandfather died of stroke.

Previous Health. Excellent.

Previous Injuries. The patient had had two injuries: fracture of the left wrist shortly after discovery of his diabetes (the circumstances of the acci-dent were not clear), and slightly later fracture of his left ankle.

General Adjustment. Vocation—education: The patient stopped high school at the age of 17 because he disliked it so much. He went to commercial art school, and then made feeble attempts at self-support, although he was actually *supported* by his parents. *Social adjustment:* "I prefer to be alone. One reason I would rather be an artist than anything else is because that keeps you alone a lot. I don't like either boys or girls. My only real friend is a German shepherd dog. Ever since I can remember I used to bring home stray cats and dogs." *Sexual adjustment:* "I discovered masturbation by accident. Father never told me anything about sex, but it isn't much fun anyway. I've never wanted anything of the kind myself. Even masturbation has no lure." The patient stated that he never had nocturnal emissions and rarely got an erection. *Attitude toward parents:* The patient had been estranged from his father as far back as he could remember. His father was a salesman for stocks and bonds and a philanderer. "He neglected Mother and never had intercourse with her. I guess Mother is happier that way. Father lives a very raucous life."

"Mother is a disappointed woman. But I try to make it up to her. I never could understand why Father wouldn't get a divorce. He's never at home. Mother wants it. But Mother and I don't talk back to him. Mother said to pay no attention, otherwise I probably would have gotten into many a fistic battle with him."

Characteristic Behavior Pattern. His inconsistent action, vacillation and indecisiveness were apparent in his quitting school, his dilatory efforts to support himself, the lack of any plans for the future. He kept waiting to be "given a chance" to become an artist instead of trying to give himself a chance.

Neurotic Traits. The patient could remember no *early* neurotic traits except that his mother told him he used to have nightmares. *Present:* The patient had considerable tendency to projection. He stated that the reason he couldn't get along in school was that the teachers used to call on him first which wasn't fair, his father didn't give him enough money which wasn't fair, and he said: "My doctors have never understood my case so how can I be expected to get well? One of them asked me if I wouldn't like to be a doctor. Of course I wouldn't because I can't stand to see misery. I have to put myself in the place of everyone that suffers."

Addictions and Interests. The patient was interested in swimming and enjoyed watching baseball and football, otherwise his only interests were art, animals, and candy. He always had a ten cent ice cream, cake, candy, bread and jam between meals as well as with meals. He had no interest in religion.

Life Situation Immediately Prior to Onset. "I worried a good deal because my family thought I ought to support myself. But after all that shouldn't be expected of an artist. They didn't give me much money so I spent it all on candy instead of food. Maybe that's what gave me the diabetes."

Case No. D 89. A 26-year-old, unmarried girl, was admitted to the hospital for the sixth time with diabetes discovered at the age of 14. The symptoms were polyuria, polydipsia and polyphagia, with loss of weight and fatigability.

Family History. No family history of diabetes or cardiovascular disease.

Personal Data. The patient was the older of two sisters. Her birth and early development were said to be normal. Both parents were living and well at the time of admission.

Previous Health. Excellent except for scarlet fever.

Previous Injuries. The patient fell off the banister at the age of 10 and struck her head.

General Adjustment. Vocation—education: The patient stopped school at the end of her second year in high school because she was tired of it. *Occupation:* She then became a stenographer and after that had several jobs, her present job was in a bank. This again is the characteristic occupation for the diabetic. Her *income* was average. *Social adjustment:* The patient was resentful and suspicious in her attitude toward people. *Sexual adjustment:* "Mother never told me anything about sex. It was probably the beginning of my monthlies and a scare that caused the diabetes —unless it was falling off the banisters." The patient's periods were never regular. She was engaged for three years but broke it off. She was unwilling to discuss the reason but stated that the only time she had ever been in a coma was at this time. She was a virgin and said she "intended to remain so."

Attitude toward parents: "Mother runs the household. Father is a sergeant in the police force. They are both all right but I don't have much to do with them."

Characteristic Behavior Pattern. This patient's behavior was indecisive. She attempted to avoid responsibility, to demonstrate her superiority, and at the same time to be liked and taken care of. "I always do things my way and nobody can make me change" was a characteristic statement. On the other hand in many situations she submitted to other people's wishes although she refused to admit it. Her means of dealing with her conflicts and her anxiety was simply to deny them.

Neurotic Traits. Nail-biting throughout life and enuresis between the ages of 12 and 14.

Addictions and Interests. "My sister always played with dolls, but I've been the boy of the family. I liked football, baseball and swimming." No interest in religion.

Life Situation Immediately Prior to Onset. This patient, like other patients with diabetes, reported a subacute struggle with both her parents. She attempted to outdo her younger sister by showing that she was more capable, and by concentrating her interests in the field of sports and job, but she admitted a sense of failure, commenting: "You see I have never really liked myself." The onset of the diabetes followed her first period and she ascribed it either to this or to falling off the banisters.

Reaction to Illness. "I just forget about it. I've learned to put things out of my mind if they make me unhappy."

Area of Major Conflict and Characteristic Reaction. The patient's dissatisfaction with her sexual role is more obvious in this history than her conflict over dependence and responsibility; this latter was equally prominent, however, although better covered up.

Case No. D 65. A 26-year-old, single woman, was admitted for regulation of diabetes, first discovered when she was 15 years old. Three years prior to admission, after a life-time of constipation, she developed watery diarrhea of such severity that she frequently soiled her clothes. The last year and nine months prior to admission she spent mostly in bed.

Family History. The patient's older brother, the first child in the family, was in a hospital for mental illnesses.

Personal Data. The patient was born in Brooklyn, the fourth in a family of five. Her birth and early development were normal. The patient's father and mother were living and well at the time of admission.

Previous Health. Good.

Previous Injuries. None reported.

General Adjustment. Vocation—education: The patient went through grammar school and three years of high school. She gave up school when the diabetes was discovered. *Occupation:* Stenographer. *Social adjustment:* "I've always liked best to be alone, only sometimes I'm lonely. I used to like to be with my sister, she used to take me under her wing. Except for her I like boys best, but not in a sexual way. I like to advise them about their love affairs. I've married off a lot of my brother's boy friends." *Sexual adjustment:* The patient learned about sex from her sister and was not disturbed by the beginning of menstruation. "I used to be worried because I had no sexual feelings. When I was 20 I had intercourse once in a while but it was never any good." She said: "I was so tight that it hurt. I noticed sensations of tightness there even before I had intercourse."

Attitude toward parents: "I never cared much about them although I was their favorite until my brother was born. Mother was so nervous and always having headaches that father did most of the housework. He took care of the children too and used to give us all our baths. He kept on giving us our baths until we were quite big."

Characteristic Behavior Pattern. "I've never liked anything very much or else I haven't known what I liked. I didn't like school. I did stenography because I had to do something but I've never liked it. I thought of nursing but that's too dirty. . . . I hate housework. I never help mother because I won't be ordered around like father. I like it better in the hospital because I don't have any responsibilities. They just take care of you and don't expect you to do anything."

Neurotic Traits. She suffered from enuresis which stopped with the beginning of menstruation. She bit her nails until she was 18 years old when she had to give it up because of her job. *Present:* "Once I wanted to be a nurse but I couldn't face having to handle bed pans. I've never been able to do housework either because I don't like to get myself dirtied up."

Addictions and Interests. The patient was not particularly interested in coffee or smoking, but was proud of her ability to tolerate a good deal of alcohol without showing it. She had no interest in religion.

Life Situation Immediately Prior to Onset. Although this patient complained that discipline in the family was lax, there had been a life-long conflict with her mother "over petty things. . . . It was all right though, because I was the favorite until my little brother was born when I was 10 years old. I thought mother shouldn't have any more children. She was pretty silly about him. My oldest sister was my only comfort. About that time my oldest brother went crazy. It's not good to have so much worry when you're just beginning to become a woman, only I never wanted to be a woman anyway."

It will be remembered that the diabetes was discovered when this younger brother was 4 years old and very shortly after the patient's first menstrual period.

Reaction to Illness. "It doesn't bother me except that I always wanted to be like my older sister because she had so much poise. She can do everything better than a man. That may be why she never married. Now I have to give up that ambition but I guess it's all right. I probably couldn't have been that good anyway."

"I don't like the way they take care of me, always changing doctors. I suppose it doesn't matter. I've had a hundred and one doctors so what's one more?" The patient never followed instructions relative to diet and was constantly developing abscesses because she "couldn't remember to boil the needle or use alcohol." She said: "I never test my urine because the colors might worry mother." When she was changed to protamin insulin she was unable to follow directions about that either.

Area of Major Conflict and Characteristic Reaction. This patient's tendency to avoid responsibility and her dislike of the feminine role are clear from the above.

DEGREE AND NATURE OF SOMATIC EXPRESSION OF CONFLICTS

Tension, Aggression and Resentment

Much of the aggression and resentment in these patients seems to have been driven inward in a manner which suggests patients with rheumatic heart disease, but they have not given in so much to the passive masochistic role. In addition to being expressed in tension of striated and smooth musculature, it gnaws at their vitals, and probably because of their infantile regression and extreme ambivalence brings about what might be called a somatic psychosis. They are extremely irritable but expression of aggression leads too often in the direction of psychic disorientation or of diabetic coma. The psychosomatic disintegration which accompanies this disease constitutes one of the major problems for the physician.

Activity, Verbalization, Dreams and Fantasies

The relative poverty of these patients from the point of view of any one of the normal channels of discharge of emotional tension is obvious. They were defeated in the sphere of *action*. They were even denied normal vegetative discharge in the sphere of sex. They had little outlet in *speech* because of their difficulty in the sphere of social intercourse, and their *dream* and *fantasy* life was too frightening to them to have offered the opportunity for much compensatory elaboration.

The few dreams remembered reflected their social and sexual anxiety. Ninety per cent of the remembered dreams were either of being chased or laughed at by large numbers of noisy, unidentified persons, or of being stabbed or gored by unidentified persons or monsters. For example, patient No. D 70, an unmarried, 29-year-old, taxicab driver, had horrible nightmares of demons and monsters. "I could swear that one came down and started to bore into my stomach once." Dreams were remembered more frequently by those patients who suffered also from hypertension and by the passive homosexual type without outspoken neurotic symptoms. In general the patients seemed to deny their emotional conflicts and to forget their dreams. They were inclined to wake up in the middle of the night shouting or in terror, but with no memory of what they had dreamed, and even to talk in their sleep, again awakening with a complete amnesia. After the onset of diabetes such forgotten nightmares were likely to be associated with going into shock on the following day.

If we are to speak in terms of our figure, "somatic short circuit," it would seem almost better in the case of these patients to speak in terms of "a leak" with a gradual accumulation of anxiety over a long period of time (see the literature already cited on this subject, pages 11–16, especially Grinker [212] relative to hypothalamic discharge of anxiety). Reference to their illness histories indicates that in terms of general health, aside from the illness under consideration, the records of these patients were relatively good. Their weakest point seems to be various pelvic disorders for the females and gastrointestinal complaints for the males. As might be expected, since these patients vacillated between action and passivity, a few shifted a little in the direction of impulsive action and had accidents, and a few others overdid the matter of keeping their troubles to themselves. These latter, as, for example, patient No. D 42, a woman, aged 42, who had had diabetes for three years, had hypertension.

An interesting question for further investigation would be the hormonal deficiency of patients with diabetes, to which attention has been called in recent literature.[108] The question arises as to what role may have been played by this deficiency in their inability to accomplish any type of sexual adjustment, and whether their characterological difficulty in the sphere of sex may have played a role in bringing about the hormonal deficiency, thus possibly supplying a physiological connecting link with the development of the diabetes. From both physiological and characterological points of view it is interesting how frequently the onset of diabetes coincides with critical periods in sexual development.

Psychotic Trends

In these patients somatic dysfunction or psychosis is rather frequently accompanied by general psychotic trends or episodes. This is probably in part because of the infantile regression prior to the disease and of the psychosomatic disintegration favored by the disease.

Because of the many character traits in these patients suggestive of the schizophrenic with cyclothymic tendencies (page 502) it may be useful to give in full the history of a patient analyzed ten years ago and followed ever since at intervals of four or five times a year, who developed diabetes subsequent to an apparent "cure" of schizophrenia.*

Furthermore, the question naturally arises as to whether the particular constellation of personality traits which we have called the diabetic profile has any significance from the point of view of predisposing an individual to diabetes.

While we were thinking about the somatic expression of conflicts

---

* So far as I know this is the first patient with diabetes recorded in the literature who had had psychoanalytic treatment before the onset of diabetes.

in patients with diabetes, the patient whose history follows, who had had an extensive though incomplete psychoanalysis with me eight years previously, turned up with diabetes. On rereading his record I was impressed and startled to discover that in my final notes relative to status of this patient at the time treatment had to be interrupted, I had stressed exactly the points which now appear in our outline of the personality constellation characteristic of patients with diabetes.

In order to avoid the question of hindsight it may be well to begin with an abstract of this patient's history based on a paper presented before the New York Psychoanalytic Society in 1933. At this time the patient's treatment was interrupted because the illness of his father made it necessary for him to take a job in a different city. About five years later he developed diabetes. A thorough physical examination including urine and blood analyses prior to a hernia repair one year before the discovery of his diabetes gives a fair degree of assurance that he was not suffering from diabetes then.

Family Background. The patient * was an unmarried man of 29, the younger of two sons of Protestant parents who had been happily married for thirty-three years, their children being the central interest of their lives. The father was a journalist of moderate distinction, and the older brother held professional rank in a university. The patient's paternal grandfather died in a mental institution. (*Note:* Seven years later his father died of stroke.)

Physical Status and Previous Illnesses. The patient was of average height, asthenic physique, and distinctively above average intelligence. He had had no serious illnesses, and no physical defects had been discovered, although he had been frequently examined in the hope of finding some organic basis for impotence, from which he had suffered since the age of 16, and for palpitation, of which he complained.

Present Illness. He came for analytic treatment of his own accord, stating that he had to call on his father for funds. At first he said he had decided

---

* The case of this patient was first presented in an unpublished paper in October, 1933, under the title, "Problems in a case of Social Anxiety." The patient at that time had not developed diabetes, but had been hospitalized nearly a year for mental disorder, diagnosed as schizophrenia. Analysis after his release, during a period of some sixteen months, spread over a period of two years, had resulted in alleviation of psychotic symptoms and a better adjustment to the life situation, but was interrupted before completion. The summary of this case here presented (up to the point of onset of the diabetes) is derived from the above paper, which was written at a time when there was no suspicion of somatic disease. Nothing has been added to this part of the case history from subsequent "hindsight."

to come because of a tragic love affair, and because he was in danger of losing his job, but later that his reason was a desire to convince himself of the validity of a religious mission. Though he had "read almost everything written by any analyst" and thought it was all "bunk" except for Adler's theory of the "will to power," he felt that he owed it to the world to put himself through this last discipline before setting himself up as a prophet. He intended either to commit suicide now (or on the death of his parents) or to become a religious leader greater than Buddha or Christ, preaching a religion of suicide.

In addition to impotence and palpitation, he complained of a compulsion to pluck out his eyebrows and of general social maladjustment. He considered himself an unrecognized literary genius and chose as companions other eccentrics and unrecognized geniuses. He rejected his father's strict ethical standards and classed himself with the social rebels and malcontents. He had a job in a store with a small salary and lived in a dark, poorly furnished room, spending the week ends in his parents' rather sumptuous residence. His only complaint about his room was that the door did not lock and so his writing was frequently disturbed by the landlady or the cat.

So much for the situation at the beginning of the analysis. The following material came out during the analytic process:

SKETCH OF LIFE HISTORY, "MACROSCOPY"

First Decade

Family Adjustment. The patient began the analysis by declaring that he and his brother were both treated with absolute fairness by both parents and thoroughly spoiled. His parents were perfect, only a little stupid, and never spoke an unkind word to him or punished him. On questioning his mother, however, at the end of two months of analysis, he was amazed to learn that before the age of 5 years he used to have "terrible tempers" and was several times locked up in a closet by his father, where he kicked and screamed to the point of exhaustion, which his mother claimed was never reached in less than half a day.

His first actual memory is that of coming suddenly to consciousness, with his mother and a woman doctor bending over him. He had fallen and been kicked in the temple by a horse. He was then 5 years old. The existence of a horse phobia prior to this time became clear in the course of the analysis, and was confirmed by the patient's mother, although the patient had a rather stubborn amnesia for this period of his life.

Sexual Adjustment. This same year a little girl in a family where he was visiting with his parents, led him and his brother to the nursery and for their combined enlightenment inserted an enema tube into her vagina. The two boys were proceeding to an anatomical investigation when they were interrupted by their father's footsteps on the stairs. What happened afterward is a complete blank in the patient's mind, although the patient often returns to the subject with a feeling of horror. During the first months of the analysis the patient spoke consistently of his father as the *kindest* of men, but gradually, first in dreams, he began to fear that his father might become intoxicated or in some way lose control of himself. This the patient regarded as a stupid idea, inasmuch as his father never drank.

It developed that the patient's father had always displayed great interest in the patient's genitalia, examining and washing them frequently. The patient obtained the idea that there must be something the matter, probably they were too small. He observed a support that his father wore for a rupture in addition to the usual jock strap, and tried to rig up something similar for himself, being sure it would develop his testicles and make his penis grow. This strap reminded him of the rubber bandage he wore on his knee after the accident with the horse and of the harness horses wear, and he used to meditate on the subject with combined pleasure and fear, picturing his father as a horse. As he said later in the analysis, maleness for him was equivalent to horsiness.

At the age of 7 years the patient surprised his father and mother lying together with the door shut. They were both dressed but he felt sure they were doing something wicked that they wanted to hide from him. This was association with an earlier occasion on which the patient having waked up from a nightmare, got up and ran to his father's and mother's room. He heard what sounded like a struggle and his mother said: "Henry you're wild. If you keep on you'll go crazy like your father!" Whereupon the patient had crept back to bed in terror. His mother's reference was to the paternal grandfather who lived with the family and was later committed to a mental institution. The grandfather had had the idea that he had committed the unpardonable sin, bringing on the world war and so on, had violent tempers and a habit of pulling out his hair.

During the period in the analysis when the patient began to speak of a fear that his father might lose control of himself he began to dream of being crushed by heavy animals, either struggling with them, or that a horse fell on him. Earlier he had dreamed of collisions of fire engines, Zeppelins, etc., and of being crushed by them, and had dreamed also of bruised hips and vaginas. His sadistic conception of intercourse was further elaborated in the analysis.

Neurotic Traits. Christmas Day at the age of 5 is one of the patient's most vivid memories. The day was ruined because his brother had stolen from him a brass button that he had come to consider essential to himself and to have always with him. There followed then a succession of trinkets which he called "fetishes necessary to the completion of my personality." Everything in his room had its own special place, he could not go to bed if a thing were out of order. Later, a school book became imperfect and unworthy of use, if the cover became inadvertently spotted or a page blotted. This persisted through the age of 16 years, and to some degree until the beginning of the analysis.

Educational Development. Also in his fifth year, what the patient terms the "first great tragedy of my life" occurred. He and his brother were in kindergarten together, but the brother, two years older, was promoted to the first grade, and he was kept in kindergarten for another year. He developed an intense jealousy of his brother, and an even more intense hatred of his teachers and all those in authority, together with a grievance against his parents for sending him out of the happy home into this environment of obedience and competition. He wondered if his father had done it to keep him away from his mother. From this time on he knew that his parents did not understand him, and consistently withheld from them all confidence. He and his brother grew up as "perfect strangers."

The patient studied desperately, and failing to surpass his brother, became proficient in athletics. His mother characterized him as having been gay and active, whereas the brother, being more serious minded, stayed at home with his books. The patient described this period in the following words:

"I remember my terror that I might not get enough gold stars when I was 5 in kindergarten. 'Twas a terrible emotional strain. I had to be first or I had this horrible suffering. I think the strain and the fear were so horrible that it made me unconscious when I did my home work. Father said I used to sit up late into the night doing my home work even when I was very little. I remember nothing about it. I always thought I never did any home work. . . . It probably tortured me so that I was unconscious; I probably worked at such white heat to get it perfect. I remember saying that I would kill my teacher with an ax if she wasn't nice to me. . . . And *then there were people to witness my failure* and then something would happen. That's what makes a person go schizophrenic, the *continual strain to be first,* or something excruciatingly horrible will happen. It's like a man's garter, the rubber is stretched and strained year after year until the rubber is worn out. There is no elasticity left in it. It is dead, it can't react to anything more. It has to be thrown away."

Summary. We have here then a patient who already at the age of 5 had a very definite compulsion neurosis. Previous to this time he had had the horse phobia and had been aggressive, defiant and unmanageable. With the development of the compulsion neurosis he became docile, his **extreme** conscientiousness in school, his interest in athletics and his success in taking little girls away from other boys apparently helped to take care of the aggressive tendencies. During that period it was a life and death matter to him that he should excel, that he should be perfect, that people should think well of him. His most frightful type of nightmare was dreams of school: being called on to recite, making a mistake, "and all those people there to witness my failure."

Age 10 to 30

Social Development. What the patient calls the "second great tragedy of my life," occurred at the age of 10 years, when through having to put on glasses he was "forced to give up athletics" (he became afraid of having his glasses broken), and, because "my face was not perfect any more," lost the affection of a little girl.

In other words, as became clear in the course of the analysis, the episode of the glasses reactivated anxiety and, as he felt, defeated him in the spheres of his two overcompensations, athletics and popularity with little girls. During the course of the analysis his reaction to social situations presenting possibilities of loss or injury, as well as minor slights or rebuffs, both actual and symbolic, became clear. If he lost a piece of paper on which he had written or drawn something he developed a violent anxiety, shut himself up in his room and brooded, refusing to eat or see anyone for hours or days. He felt himself an exile from society, and cut himself off from all his friends because he was so afraid someone would laugh at him. He began to do less well in school, to pluck out his eyebrows and set himself up as a rebel against God and all authority.

Here we see the reaction against the anxiety in the form of hate. At the same time he developed an extreme tenderness for all little animals and for little children. [Incidentally, in discussing this period in the analysis he recalled fantasies going back to the age of 6 years, and possibly to the age of 3 (i.e., the period of his horse phobia) in which he pictured himself as a horse carrying around all sorts of helpless and injured little animals inside him.] The anxiety manifested itself more and more in the form of inhibitions accompanied by the feeling that he must either bring about the destruction of the world or go crazy like his grandfather.

Sexual Development. About this time he discovered anal masturbation in the practice of which he usually used a pencil. In boarding school, at the age of 15 years, meditating on the mechanism of intercourse he decided to try substituting a hot water bottle for the vagina, lying on his stomach on the floor. From this time forth till the age of 20 years, he masturbated arranging pillows in the form of a woman's body, at first with the addition of the hot water bottle. He always began by examining photographs of nude women which he had been collecting since the age of 10 years, when he had (so he said) "given up ladies in the life." Through this practice as well as because of the glasses he now felt himself unfitted for even the ordinary required school athletics and for association with other boys.

During the succeeding summer he was seduced by a married woman twice his age, was impotent and disgusted, although he got some satisfaction out of cunnilingus, which she suggested afterward. At this time he was "really in love" with the lady's 5-year-old daughter because "she was so pure and perfect."

Educational Development. He entered college but was unable to stand it for more than a few months, being dictated to by professors who had no insight or understanding, and given no time or sympathy for the development of his poetic genius. He determined to leave college and set up a university of his own in a secluded countryside with plenty of books and himself as the sole student and instructor. He continued in this university of his own making, taking the usual scheduled vacations, reading until late into the night, leading "an ascetic life" for *two and a half years,* i.e., to the age of 22. He wrote a Dadaistic epic which was to be the masterpiece of his life; then it suddenly occurred to him that this was mental masturbation (he having succeeded in practically suppressing physical masturbation), and one night in an ecstasy he consigned it to the flames. He became a classicist and wrote constrained challenges to God and hymns of hate.

A poem dating from this period is the following called "Little Voices." I can give only excerpts:

> Wrapped in black night where the wan earth would stumble
> He sings His song;
> Sings of His might where no one else can grumble
> Against a wrong.
>
> •   •   •
>
> O, for a storm to tear God's dome in tatters
> and wreck the moon.
>
> (and later)
>
> •   •   •
>
> Christ in a vision and sneering traitor God heads—
> I'll fight them all.
>
> •   •   •
>
> Let them roll o'er me, God's grinning lurid oceans,
> For what care I?
> Rather than yield—for I have other notions—
> I'd sooner die.

Onset of Psychosis. The next summer he had the "greatest love affair of his life" with the wife of his best friend, who had given his consent. Under these circumstances he attempted intercourse and succeeded in penetration, although he remained orgastically impotent. To this lady, as well as to the lady of the preceding summer, he afterward proposed double suicide.

This friend and his father finally prevailed on him to continue his university work formally, which he considered a great humiliation because he knew more than any of the professors. He returned in the sophomore class, and during the year had two more unsuccessful love affairs. When one of these ladies married another friend the patient tried to throw himself in front of an automobile. Visiting this friend the following summer, on one occasion he became excited, threw a bottle at the friend's head and broke a window in the cottage. He returned to college very much depressed. He again proposed double suicide. He kept his father waiting in a hotel all day, spending the time with the girl as a proof of his love for her. During the analysis, however, commenting on this behavior, he said, "I think the real reason was that if I had seen father just then I would have killed him."

A little later the patient received a letter from this girl refusing the double suicide and stating that his letters were distasteful to her husband. Removing from his clothes all marks of identification with the exception of this letter, he walked out in the street at midnight, and accosted a policeman with the words: "Who are you? Are you God?" This behavior he explained later, saying that for a long time he had been interested in mental diseases and he decided he would like to spend a week end in a mental hospital in order to get material first hand. He was transferred however, to another mental hospital where he remained for nearly a year, and the following is an abstract from the hospital history:

"*Diagnostic Impressions:* Although there are many features suggesting an obsessional neurosis his tenacious adherence to his ideals of perfection, his belief in a special fate and his antisocial acts and tendencies give signs of an early dissociating process.

"*Prognosis.* Because of the patient's uncompromising attitude and early suggestions of dissociation, the outlook is poor. Further development of paranoid ideas and very slow deterioration is to be expected.

"*Diagnosis.* Schizophrenia."

Age 26 to 27

Mental Hospital Period. This period, the patient described as the happiest of his life. While there he wrote to a friend: "There is a quiet struggle here between Father—doctor—society and me, a struggle between the purposes. The solution is the double act, final synthesis of word and action, by which

God is revealed in (MS) unity. I am the slayer and the slain." This he discussed later in terms of the Damocles sword and the *lex talionis*.

Interval Between Discharge and Beginning of Treatment. Six months following his discharge he obtained through his father the job which he now has. He devoted all his spare time to writing what was to be the great book of his life, containing his system. The one question which remained undecided was the exact role which he was to play in the promulgation of his religious suicide. Should he become a Catholic monk, or a great religious leader, subject to no man, not even to God himself?

At this time he was living a life of somewhat monastic isolation, always very punctual and conscientious about his job during the exact number of hours required. He had accepted this job, because, although the pay was inadequate, and his family had financially to help him out, it required no effort and "did not distract him from more serious things." He lived on a definite schedule including the hour at which he must arise, the jobs to be accomplished before work, the amount of time to be allowed for eating, for clearing up his room, for creative writing, for reading. He had deprived himself of friends (except for an occasional derelict "who needed" him) of the movies, of all light reading, of cigarettes, and of masturbation, although he was having difficulty in living up to his ideal with regard to this latter. All this was required in order that no time be lost in his preparation for his mission. Thus he had justified his avoidance of all social and sexual relationships and the whole responsibility of self-support.

Summary. From this material it is clear that there was a well-established compulsion neurosis at the age of 5, which developed increasingly in the direction of schizophrenic psychosis. The impotence accompanied a strong homosexual tendency, which was strongly repressed. But what was chiefly notable was the social anxiety. Concerning this the following observations may be made.

Retracing some of the steps which led to the life situation in which he came to analysis, we find that probably the patient's first assumption of a passive attitude toward his parents occurred at the age of 5. We have here the factor of inconsistency in his up-bringing—on the one hand, his parents spoiled him; on the other hand, drastic measures had been used in his early training, all recollection of which the patient had repressed. In the analysis he referred also to this period his first disillusionment and fear in discovering that his parents were not omnipotent. (One is reminded of the fact that social anxiety arises where the child begins to realize that the parents who forbid are not all-powerful, but only executors of general social demands.)

He then hated his teachers and his brother whom he tried to surpass, and at the same time was somewhat successful with girls and in athletics. During this period he was being forced more and more into the passive feminine role by his father, especially by the latter's preoccupation with his genitals. Incidentally, his mother had wanted him to be a girl. To this was added a definite castration threat, his father stating that there were certain things little boys might do to their genitals which would keep them small and make it impossible for them to become fathers. About this time the patient was masturbating on the beach and cut his penis with a shell. This he associated with his father's threat, and, during the analysis, with a basin containing menstrual blood which he had seen in his mother's room. This was of course associated with his sadistic idea of intercourse and increased castration fear. Then came the glasses, and the fear of injury which occasioned his first actual withdrawal from the situations which caused him anxiety.

Any relationship with the outer world became intolerable. Finally he isolated himself completely in his own "university" where he himself was the sole authority. There he became disturbed by the problem of his relationship to God. There seemed to be a God who demanded certain things of him. Were these demands just, and was he to submit entirely to this God, living a life of perfection and self-castigation in a monastery completely apart from the world? Or were these the demands of an unjust God who had made him imperfect and injured him, who therefore should be fought? The only way he could see to fight this God was to destroy his creations, preaching a religion of suicide, and finally killing himself in defiance. Then God would have no creatures left to torture any more.

In connection with these things he said in analysis: "For me life is terribly dangerous. The only escape is to do absolutely nothing. The less you move the less chance you have of being struck. You crouch into as small a space as possible. You don't even breathe. If one's not to go psychotic one must have a religion—there must be some compensation for all this pain. But the only religion which is satisfactory is death, a state of painlessness. . . . All activity, every act, hurts me like actual pain. Life is a curse. If I can't be free from it I must find a philosophy of life to justify it. *I must find out which is the greatest role, offensive or submissive.* The best 'solution' is to preach suicide actively for twenty-five years, and then I will have my peace in suicide. I am the Law. I am God. No one who comes after me can do anything that is greater than I because they will have to imitate me. The weakness in the Catholic way of thinking is that the Christian isn't allowed to imitate Jesus, who called Himself God, made Himself the Law for Himself and others, and set Himself up as an authority. If one knows one is a Messiah within it is an unspeakable ecstasy. I suppose I was spoiled at the hospital. I had so many followers. I want to consume the world. I won't ever admit an equal . . ." Incidentally, such outbursts as this were embedded, during the early part of the analysis in a rather suggestive schizophrenic *"Wortsalat"* full of neologisms and rhymes.

Here we see clearly the constant conflict between withdrawal and rebellion. The possibility of becoming a monk in the Catholic tradition the patient cannot quite accept because he would have to acknowledge authority and because it allows him no revenge. He withdraws from the situation he fears, building up a system which is at once his excuse and his protection. The ultimate object of his system is both complete submission and revenge.

The ultimate object of this revenge was God but immediately prior to the psychotic episode, when the patient's still uncompleted system was subjected to considerable strain by the love affairs with the married women, and circumstances which reactivated much of the oedipus conflict, the aggression actually burst forth, first in the attack on the father imago, and then in fantasy on his father. On at least one occasion the aggressive impulse against his father became so strong that he avoided seeing him. Finally we have the sublimation in the psychotic episode, under the cover of which, as he said later, he gained time to reinforce his system, being protected against himself and society in the hospital, saved from slaying and being slain.

COURSE OF TREATMENT

From one point of view the whole analytic process could be discussed in terms of de-deification of the father. In other words, the patient in his life had at least partially accomplished a deification of him which the analysis had to carry out in reverse order. This was done to a large extent in terms of the fear and hate of horses and of animals of brute strength and no intelligence, then the grandfather, teachers, and all those in authority, then especially of doctors and the capitalistic social order, and finally of God.

The first dreams were of aged tyrants and demigods, placed in a more or less mythical setting, in relation to whom he himself played the part of the beloved son and victim, atoning for their sins. An example is the following: The patient saw himself in a dream as a deformed and mutilated dwarf on whose ear was a drawing depicting the crime of his forefather for which he was doing penance, like the maidens who are thrown to the minotaur, or the sentenced Son of God. Here the patient, as victim, satisfied his need of absolution behind which the fear of punishment gradually became clear.

Then came a series of dreams about a huge, brutal, red-headed murderer with broad shoulders. And in these dreams the patient was alternately victim and avenger, or instrument of justice. It was only after more than six months of analysis that he began to dream of his boss and of his father, developing at the same time a marked fear of both. Up to this time he had insisted that no one could be afraid of his father because he was such a kind man. A prominent theme during this period was also the passive homosexuality. He became afraid to be in any small space with a man, especially in elevators.

Then the patient became preoccupied with the material relating to the horse, to which reference has been made. He was afraid of being crushed by a horse, but at the same time he was interested in the various possible ways of torturing a horse. The working through of this material occupied a period of several months and was accompanied by marked anxiety attacks, and nightmares. The patient woke up every morning for a considerable period breathless and having a violent attack of palpitation. It was in connection with this material that a large part of the castration anxiety was dealt with. Both father and mother appeared as castrators. In this connection he talked at length about his ideal type of feminine beauty, the woman with large, low, hanging breasts, and the straps that horses wear that interested him so much were associated not only with jock straps but also with brassieres. There was the identification of milk and semen. It became clear that he was interested in women only as a reassurance against castration, that is in the woman with a penis. The following dream is typical of this period: "I was indulging myself in a orgiastic embrace of a naked woman whom I don't recognize. I remember feeling for her breasts." Later—"Well, this was supposed to be a woman, but I was sucking a penis. At first she didn't give me her penis but a finger and seemed to be enjoying the joke at my expense." There were dreams about horses and wolves biting off his arm or his head, and fantasies about the *vagina dentata*. Here the fear of being bitten (castration anxiety) and of being outlawed and attacked (social anxiety) are brought into dynamic association.

His anxiety and his rage against the cruelty of doctors and the world in general became very intense; he joined the antivivisection society and became a vegetarian. A characteristic utterance of this period was the following: "When I was at home with my parents yesterday, I felt more than ever beneath my love for them this burning resentment. They didn't know any better. I should learn to forgive them and blame God, but I hated them yesterday."

It was the horse material also which led up to the reliving of the fantasies relative to murder of his parents, and of the psychotic episode itself. He recalled the murder described by Dostoievsky in "Crime and Punishment," stressing particularly the murderer's dream of the horse beaten to death by its drunken master with a crowbar because it could not gallop with the load. He said: "The mental condition of the murderer reminds me of the dream-state in which I accosted the policeman. I couldn't do it as I am now. The kind of terrible concentration of mind that led up to my accosting him is like the concentration that led up to the murder. It's a terribly compelling morbid state from which fear has been excluded." After the working through of this material the patient's dreams assumed a very different character.

His father became a ridiculous, ineffectual, little man with broad shoulders. His boss in a dream lost his temper and was shouting at the top of his lungs about how the store should be run. "He was a little man no higher than a dwarf and had to stand on the table to make himself heard, and even then he was no taller than the little page; I had to laugh he was making such a fool of himself."

This period of the analysis coincided with a difficult time in the patient's external situation. For the first time pressure was being brought to bear on him and his protective system seemed to be failing. More than two-thirds of his fellow employees were discharged, those who remained kept their jobs on an open basis of competition, then the pay of the remaining employees was cut in half, and then his father lost all his money, so that the inheritance on which the patient had depended was taken away. There was mutiny in the store, various groups of the employees threatening to strike, or to go to court about the situation. One night the patient gathered all the employees of the store together for a meeting, addressed them sensibly though a bit dramatically, telling them they would achieve nothing unless they stood together. Then he wrote for them a petition which he got all to sign, and presented it to the management. As a result their original pay was restored.

During this same week for the first time in the period of a year and a half covered by the analysis, the patient attempted to have intercourse. He picked up a streetwalker, and although the affair ended in mutual masturbation, it was, for him, a considerable achievement. This attempt was followed by several more unsuccessful attempts, until the patient finally achieved intercourse at first with a Negress, then with white prostitutes. Throughout the course of these activities it was clear from the analytic material that the patient was being propelled by a *vis a tergo* and that intercourse was finally achieved only in the attempt to demonstrate to himself his potency.

It is interesting, however, that the patient no longer consorted with social derelicts, radicals, and unrecognized geniuses. He was cultivating friends of his own social level, and went on week ends to house parties given by girls who, in his present situation, would be considered his social superiors.

Having had occasion to consult a doctor following his first unsuccessful attempt at intercourse because he feared that he might have contracted an infection, he was surprised to find himself liking a man whom he had always hated. The physician he consulted was, as he himself recognized, an old father imago who had treated him several years previously by prostatic massage for his impotence. The patient had been particularly revolted by his broad shoulders and powerful, brutal physique, which on the occasion of his recent visit he described as exhilarating. They sat down together and discussed the stock market. He has developed a friendly relationship with his boss with whom he often discusses the management of the store, and has just demanded and obtained a raise in his salary. He has given up his system and is beginning to write articles for periodicals. He has assumed financial responsibility for the analysis. In other words his social anxiety seemed markedly diminished.

To summarize briefly, we have here general inhibition and avoidance, gradually developing in such a way that activity breaks through essentially only in a series of psychiatric pictures, including obsessional symptoms, a psychotic episode, and the preparation for the assumption of a Messianic role. This behavior becomes intelligible in terms fundamentally of castration anxiety and a superego anomaly, bringing to the foreground a marked social anxiety.

HISTORY SUBSEQUENT TO INTERRUPTION OF TREATMENT

Prior to the Discovery of Diabetes

About a month after the point at which this earlier paper terminates the patient was given an opportunity to take full charge of a business venture in another city together with a very considerable increase in salary. Although it was agreed that his analysis was not complete, the illness of his father, together with business reverses, made it necessary for him to accept this opportunity in order to help his parents financially. His treatment was therefore interrupted but he was seen at intervals of six months to a year from that time to date.

For a while things went well with this patient. There were no incidents of importance till his father's death nearly three years later, when the patient was 34 years old. This further increased the patient's sense of responsibility and he began to give up his friends, particularly a girl friend in whom he was much interested and had planned to marry, on the ground that he no longer had time for such things. "Prostitutes require less emotional energy and attention." The patient, however, began to have disturbing dreams involving attacks of monsters and genital mutilation. Then all of a sudden he developed a hernia concerning which he commented: "I seem to be getting all of father's weaknesses." He was very anxious that this be repaired at once. While in the hospital he wrote the following note:

The Operation

"Arrive 3 P.M., Sunday. Love of hospitals, curiosity, 'vacation,' no anxiety. Ward—pale green, restful, neat, efficiency, sunlight. Must have bed-lamp—

two weeks of reading—I finally got it fixed. Shaving pubic hair, legs—distasteful.

"Monday 8 A.M., my brother—Dr. ——, a quick examination. I am wheeled upstairs into a small ante-room cluttered with surgical apparatus—nurses flitting casually—one tall, beautiful, with gauze mask—no fear, quiet happiness, security—the 'intra-uterine' situation, wrapped in warm blankets, helpless, trusting. Rectal anesthetic—at once a rapidly increasing exhiliration. During the next 2 minutes (?) I feel—2 sidecars on an empty stomach. I ask, 'Would you like to hear some poetry?'—Not waiting for an answer, I commence softly, and as I drift into the darkness I am in the middle of some resounding rhetoric by E. E. Cummings (?)—Harmony of dying.

· · · · · · ·

"I waken some time in the afternoon, 'without memory or desire,' or consciousness of pain—asleep, awake, asleep—I still feel 'high'—I glow—I am hungry—I yell for a piece of steak (!) when supper comes—insipid tea and gingerale—I can't urinate—some doctor says 'try—or we'll have to use a catheter'—hot poultice, rectal tube, and later that night the urine comes, balkedly. My brother arrives—I am glad to see him—I smile and talk and drowse and I sleep fitfully—every four hours I am stabbed with a long needle—water, drink more water—and so the morning shines. Two days later a nurse tells me I came down from the operating room (still) reciting poetry, and that I called her 'Gwendolyn.' Also, Dr. —— reported that I was muttering something on the table, but he didn't listen. 'A psychiatrist ought to listen——' "

His dreams while in the hospital were of himself with an enormous penis above a gaping wound. He reverted in a mild way to earlier thoughts about his mission, reported as a fantastic idea a feeling that his father's death might have been a punishment for his failure to fulfill his mission at the age of 33 as Christ had done, and noted that he would have avoided the further physical insult, the hernia and the operation, had he carried out his early intention to commit suicide when his father died. Nevertheless, he returned to his job and continued to win distinction, although at the expense of constant emotional conflict because he disliked the responsibility and the long hours made it impossible for him to gratify his urge to write.

Shortly after he left the hospital, his father's estate being settled, the patient's mother decided to give up her own establishment and go to live with the patient.

This further restricted the patient's social life because he felt it incumbent upon him to spend all his spare time making his mother happy. His sexual life was denied all overt expression. After nine months of this existence because he was "becoming obsessed with masturbation and cigarettes" he visited a prostitute—forgetting prophylactic precautions which had been habitual with him—and acquired a gonorrheal infection. Gonorrheal arthritis developed and he went to the hospital, where his diabetes was discovered. It is interesting to note that in the year between the operation, at which time blood and urine tests showed no abnormality (i.e. there was still no clinical evidence of diabetes), and the gonorrheal infection, the stresses and strains which are particularly prominent in the life history and character of our series of patients with diabetes were all greatly increased: hard work, greatly resented cutting off of social relationships, increase of responsibility, increase of sexual anxiety, with of course reactivation of his inadequately resolved oedipus struggle.

Reaction to Diabetes

While the patient was in the hospital with the arthritis and the diabetes—a period of four months—he was again "completely happy and serene." He had a goal to work for: recovery of physical perfection, and the ideas relative to his Messianic mission returned in full force.

He made a trip to New York to discuss these things with his analyst. Again in a few sessions he recovered some equilibrium and went back to work. Three months later he visited his analyst again in a state of anxiety and recounted the following dreams:

"There was a beautiful girl corresponding to my ideal of female beauty (Fig. 1). But she had a third hand growing out of her stomach. I was terribly sorry for her. Then I saw an enormous ape coming to attack her."

"The only way to fulfill my religious mission was to suffer. Something made me get up in the middle of the night to go out into the woods to a group of disciples who had made a pact to die the most awful death as penance. They had locked themselves in a cage filled with straw, poured on kerosene and set it on fire. I saw their writhing shapes. They were being burned to charcoal. I felt guilty not to be dying with them. Then I was in the cage myself fighting desperately to get out with everyone accusing me. It was the way I used to feel, both victim and victor."

Although the patient insisted that he had no diabetic symptoms and that he had been following his diet carefully, it was suggested that he have a physical check-up. His blood sugar was 430.

When the patient reported this he said: "Those must have been bodily injury dreams. I have had fantasies about being burned up inside and purified by fire."

In the course of reviewing possible reasons for the exacerbation of his condition, he stressed the embarrassment of having to walk with a cane, nightmares of being crushed by monsters, and said he thought

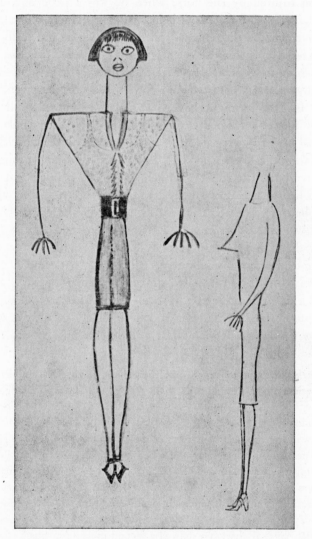

FIG. 1

it was strange that the gonorrhea should have settled in the same knee which was injured by the horse when he was a little boy. He said that his lameness interfered with his dancing, which was one of his few achievements in the physical sphere of which he was really proud, and interfered with his life with girls. When asked whether it had bothered him to give up his vegetarian diet as had been required by the physician who treated him for his diabetes, he said: "No, as a matter of fact it might have, had anyone known about it, but I did not mention it to my physician and kept the whole matter entirely to myself." He said, furthermore, that he had decided that the vegetarian diet was rather silly, he had had to accept insulin which was discovered as the result of much torture to animals and so why draw the line at eating meat. When asked whether he thought the diet had had anything to do with bringing on the diabetes, he said No, that was impossible because it had been very carefully planned and he had not indulged in carbohydrates. He added, however, "It did occur to me that I might have injured my pancreas in the days when I was studying in my own university. Then I used to eat only one meal a day and otherwise lived on sugar because I thought that was the purest food in the world next to air. I was always working to achieve enough perfection to be able to live on air with no food at all."

Six months later during which time the patient had become stabilized again on a diabetic regime, he returned with very similar dreams asking whether the analyst thought he should have another blood sugar test. The dreams were as follows:

"I was walking through the streets of a beautiful city. Big white buildings. A city of perfection. Then there was a conflagration. I felt myself in a white heat of rapture and exaltation. Even this pure city was being made more pure. It was being reduced to a nothingness, which is the only unity and the only perfection. Then a ravenous red wolf came out of the wilds and was about to devour me. I woke up in terror." The other dreams were overtly homosexual. Physical check-up showed a second increase in blood sugar level. The specialist in this field will be able to say much more about these dreams in terms of their relationship both to the patient's schizophrenia and to his diabetes.

After three sessions in which his personality development, his neurosis and its relationship to his physical symptoms were reviewed in detail, the patient gradually improved, and for nearly a year to date he has remained stabilized on a carefully regulated diet, for the last nine months without insulin. (During the two years since this case was presented there have been some fluctuations but no event of major importance.)

An incidental point of some interest was the following. This patient, in spite of his habitual meticulousness, had shown himself to be highly unreliable in his use of insulin. He often forgot it entirely and generally succeeded in infecting himself when he used it. He had strong homosexual and masturbatory fantasies relative to the needle, and often dreamed about it with combined feelings of sexual enjoyment and guilt. It was not until the needle was discontinued in favor of oral insulin that he became stabilized without relapses, and finally free from the necessity of using insulin. This is just one example among many of the importance of the symbolism attributed by patients to some of our routine medical procedures.

To review then: Sufferers from diabetes had marked social anxiety, and this case was presented in the original unpublished paper under the title, A Case of Social Anxiety. They had sexual anxiety and inadequacy, with prominent homosexual conflict and frequent impotence. In childhood they had temper tantrums, phobias, and nightmares in quantitative prominence as compared with other groups studied, and in adult life depression and suspicion with a tendency to paranoid ideas. The hospital diabetic group usually had a relatively high educational level with a marked interest in academic advancement, but a frequent incidence of nervous breakdowns in college traceable to the conflict between their ambition and their inability to compete. Similarly there was a discrepancy between their educational and their income level. Their previous health record was the best of any group studied with the exception of the patients with fracture, but a very high percentage of them suffered in earlier life from what was diagnosed as cardiac neurosis; and it will be remembered that this was the only physical symptom of which the patient complained when he was first seen. They avoided competitive sports and other forms of competition. They were much preoccupied with the sufferings of animals. Although they had little or no early interest in religion, they often attempted to create a religion of their own under the tension of awareness of homosexuality. The life situation immediately prior to the onset of diabetes in our total group exhibited long periods of wear and tear, hard work (not voluntarily undertaken and constantly resented), homosexual conflict, struggle with family and especially conflict about the assumption of responsibility. It will be remembered that this was exactly the situation of this patient after his father's death when his mother went to live with him, and he was especially worried about his sexual role. The patients with diabetes also showed a tendency, especially among the males, to remain unmarried. The reaction of the diabetic group to their illness was strikingly similar to that of this patient. It was characterized by depression alternating with a feeling of relief in having an alibi for their inadequacy. It will be remembered that this patient spoke of the three periods of hospitalization as the happiest period in his life. His reiterated ideal of happiness was to spend his life in a mental hospital away from the world.

In one respect the family history of this patient is unlike the current idea of the typical patient with diabetes, though not contrary to our own observations. Careful check-up showed no diabetes in his sibling, in his parents or their siblings, his grandparents or their siblings, concerning all of whom there was adequate information. Our study of the diabetic group at the hospital, however, revealed the incidence of diabetes in the family in one case out of three. It did indicate that in the other two-thirds, cardiovascular disease and insanity were prevalent, and that the patient was exposed, usually at a very early age, to one or more of these illnesses in all cases. The patient here under consideration was exposed both to insanity and to cardiovascular disease. We found also that among the patients with diabetes both parents usually lived well into the patient's adult life and that the subacute struggle with them usually continued as long as they lived.

It will have occurred to the reader that each of these traits taken separately is very widely distributed in the population and therefore that no one of them accounts for any special type of syndrome. What does seem significant, however, is the constellation. Our study indicates that the constellation is specific for particular syndromes in regard to the combination of (1) the nature of the focal conflict, (2) the reaction to the conflict, especially the patient's defenses, and (3) the environmental pressures including the moments in the development of (1) and (2) at which they are intensified or diminished.

In this constellation quantitative factors are as important as qualitative. Alexander has stressed this point in his quantitative dream analysis.

Shift from Schizophrenic to Diabetic Symptomatology

The most arresting aspect of this case is the prior known schizophrenia followed by the onset of diabetes. How can we account in dynamic terms for these two types of illness in the same individual?

First of all, it may be said that the type of conflict usually associated with schizophrenia is sufficiently obvious in the early history of the case. The psychic symptoms may be regarded as a typical form of defense against this intense conflict. The analysis, however, deprived the patient of this defense, at least in his contact with reality, but was not continued long enough to resolve the basic conflict itself. We may then infer that when the life situation created additional pressures, reactivating the unresolved conflicts, the patient utilized somatic short circuits as a means of escape. In quick succession he developed palpitation, hernia, gonorrheal infection with gonorrheal arthritis, and diabetes. While under treatment for these somatic symptoms he showed a tendency to revert to schizophrenia in his fantasy life, thus trying out his former defense while he was getting rid of the somatic means of escape. Renewed consultation with the analyst, however, helped him to reject both the psychic and the somatic forms of defense and so have enabled him at least for a time to alleviate both types of symptoms.

It will be remembered that general practitioners have often commented on the frequent appearance of schizophrenic symptoms in patients with diabetes, and have attributed the psychic symptoms to the somatic illness. On the basis of this case, however, one may be justified in asking whether the schizophrenic symptoms do not have a deeper root in the personality, and whether the diabetes may not be traceable to the same constellation as the psychic symptoms. If this should be true, we might conclude that a given constellation could lead either to a given psychic symptomatology or to a given somatic symptomatology, and that the two may be in some degree reciprocals of each other.

It is clear from the foregoing that this patient followed the diabetic pattern in all points selected as important (see Profile, page 501).

(1) *Family History.* Although there was no family history of diabetes there was cardiovascular disease in his father, and extreme nervousness in both parents. The patient's grandfather was psychotic. [Nearly one-third of the patients studied gave a family history of diabetes, usually among the females of the family, or of cardiovascular disease usually among the males; and many gave a family history of nervousness, often (i.e., 10 per cent) actual insanity.]

(2) *Personal Data.* Both parents lived beyond his adolescence, as was our usual observation with diabetics, and the subacute struggle with them continued well into adult life. Avoidance of marriage.

(3) His general *health record* was relatively good. (It will be remembered that next to the accident patients those with diabetes had the best previous health record of any group studied.)

(4) *Previous Injuries.* At the age of 5 he had fallen and been kicked on the temple by a horse.

(5) *General Adjustment.* He showed the characteristic discrepancy between educational and income level. His occupational grouping was class III (clerks, salesmen, stenographers), improving to class II (proprietors, managers, officials). It will be remembered that the patients with diabetes showed a diverse *occupational* distribution with a marked positive deviation as compared with the general population in groups II and III. His general behavior was agreeable, and his social anxiety was marked even though this was definitely improved by treatment. There was a relapse in this respect immediately prior to the development of the diabetes.

(6) *Characteristic Behavior Pattern.* He had the characteristic difficulty in making definite decisions but with treatment accomplished consistency in vocation.

(7) *Neurotic Traits.* As a child he had temper tantrums, phobias, and nightmares; as an adult the tendency characteristic of patients with diabetes to nervousness and depression together with paranoid ideas.

(8) *Addictions and Interests.* There was the avoidance of competitive sports, the interest in animals, and like the typical diabetic no interest in religion until the patient became aware of his homosexuality and attempted to create a religion of his own.

(9) *Life Situation Immediately Prior to the Onset.* Again this

patient's history reveals the usual period of wear and tear, in this instance characterized by a struggle with homosexual tendencies and an episode with a prostitute which resulted in a gonorrheal infection. The patient himself believed it was the gonorrhea that gave him diabetes, unless possibly the fact that he had been forced to assume the responsibility of caring for his mother after his father's death "had been gradually undermining him." (The diabetics' dislike of responsibility has been noted already.)

(10) *Reaction to Illness.* Like the typical diabetic, his reaction to illness was characterized by depression, alternating with a feeling of relief because now he had time to himself to devote to his writing. During this period, for the first time since the interruption of the analysis, he became preoccupied with his mission, although on a much more modest scale. He became suspicious of the specialist in diabetes who was taking care of him and fled to his psychiatrist for reassurance, insisting that all the details of his treatment be reviewed and approved by the latter.

(11) *Area of Focal Conflict and Characteristic Reaction to It.* There was the usual assertion that he had been spoiled by his parents and handicapped by their lax discipline which proved to be a cover for marked hostility and repressed hatred. The conflict over responsibility and the ambivalence toward his sexual role are of course prominent.

(12) As to the *somatic short circuit*, it is interesting that while this patient had his highly developed psychoneurotic symptoms, his only somatic disorder was occasional palpitation connected with the breaking through of anxiety. After these had been eliminated and his external adjustment had become fairly satisfactory by his partial analysis the diabetes developed.

To summarize, the above traits represent the basic neurotic character which the patient had both before development of the psychosis and after the psychosis and the psychoneurotic symptoms had been removed. Since these basic neurotic tendencies no longer found their expression psychoneurotically, and with the additional factor of a situational exacerbation of the most fundamental of them (forced assumption of responsibility, and the homosexual component), a somatic short circuit appears to have taken place so that he expressed his neurotic character in organic disease.

SUMMARY OF CHARACTEROLOGICAL DEFENSES AND THEIR
RELATIVE SUCCESS OR FAILURE

This material shows fairly clearly the inadequacy of the defense mechanisms constructed by these diabetic patients. Their only success, to judge in terms of making life tolerable for the patient, seemed to lie in finding an alibi to justify their need for particular care and a relatively dependent relationship. This alibi was used also as an excuse for avoiding social and sexual relationships but provided little relief for their anxiety.

It is of some interest that the two groups included in this study in whom the integrating or ego function was the weakest were, on the one hand, the patients with rheumatic heart disease whose parents were outstandingly strict and brutal; and, on the other hand, patients with diabetes, the only group who complained of their parents in terms of weakness and laxity of discipline. Both groups of parents, however, were strikingly inconsistent in their attitude toward their children, a factor which has been stressed by Alexander, Healy, and others as being worse in terms of the child's ego development than either of the extremes. In these two groups also the somatic damage is likely to begin earlier and to be more crippling over a longer period of time. In patients with diabetes the generalized irreparable somatic damage is often accompanied by what we think of as irreparable psychic damage. Apparently, when the conflicts develop under too much pressure both somatic and psychic symptomatology are brought into play with sufficient intensity to cause severe derangement.

V. THERAPEUTIC IMPLICATIONS *

These patients present a difficult therapeutic problem. There are many discussions of the management of the diabetic patient in the books by specialists in the field. In these, attention is called to the importance of educating the patient relative to his illness, reassuring him and securing his co-operation. The peculiar personality traits of these patients which make it difficult for the physician to secure their co-operation, and actually for them to co-operate even when they are devoted to the physician who is taking care of them, have not been

*See Chapter XI, section V.

analyzed in detail. Some of these should be clear from the foregoing

(1) These patients are inclined to be suspicious of anyone in the parental role and particularly of men, hence, it is difficult to gain more than a superficial co-operation.

(2) The physician, whether male or female, is likely to be identified with the mother (and incidentally these patients often do better with a woman physician). When this happens the characteristic attitude is that frequently expressed by these patients when speaking about their mothers: "You listen carefully to what she says. You agree to do it, and you do what you please. Mothers usually aren't right anyway." Because of their general infantile personalities they find it relatively easy to mislead the physician into playing "mother" in just this way.

(3) These patients are very skillful in concealing from the physician their failure to co-operate by their superficial compliance on the one hand, or by their cleverness in finding reasons to blame either the physician himself or the circumstances of their lives for their failure to follow the regime laid down.

(4) Because the majority of these patients are more passive than active, and because fundamentally they enjoy being taken care of, and because they have a prominent self-destructive drive, it is difficult to arouse in them a desire to get well.

(5) Related to the preceding characteristic is the tendency, more marked in these patients than in any other group studied, to deny their emotional conflicts and worries, to forget their dreams, or to invent reasons for unhappiness that have little to do with reality but are more pleasing to their self-respect.

On the asset side of the ledger, however, are the following points:

(1) They are usually intelligent and exaggeratedly pleased by an appeal to their reason and an attitude of sympathetic respect for their difficulties (e.g., Case No. DP 2, page 87, who said: "You're the only person who has ever treated me like an equal"; and the statements of other patients).

(2) They often get a feeling of a new lease on life when anxiety is relieved by an understanding of their emotional conflicts.

(3) Because of their familiarity with tests for sugar it is fairly easy to demonstrate to them the relationship between their emotional conflicts and exacerbations of their diabetes.

(4) To the extent to which these patients gain such insight, desirable modifications of the environment often become feasible.

In general, at least a brief period of psychotherapy is to be recommended for all patients with diabetes. The length of time required is considerably influenced by the degree to which they are passive in type, and the stubbornness of their tendency to deny anxiety and emotional conflicts. If they can be brought to the point of talking honestly and openly about these things half of the battle is won.

There was a marked improvement (Case No. DP 2, page 87) in those patients with diabetes who were treated. But statistics cannot be given relative to this point, because staff time was so limited that treatment of an adequate number of patients in this group was not possible. It can be stated, however, that even brief psychotherapy often made the difference between life-long invalidism with many returns to the hospital and a relatively comfortable life adjustment, including stabilization of the diabetes, freedom from serious exacerbations, and often from insulin.

VI. CONCLUSIONS

(1) The personality structure of patients with diabetes differs from that of any other group studied. These differences appear to antedate the illness by a good many years although they may be exaggerated by the illness.

(2) Such patients may be differentiated from the total population in terms of characteristics for which general population statistics are available. Their educational level is generally high. They have good health records which distinguishes them from the cardiovascular groups. They differ also from the fracture group in that the incidence of previous illnesses increases from decade to decade. Although their accident rate is relatively high, the majority of the accidents occur subsequent to the onset of the illness. There is a tendency especially among the males to remain unmarried, and when married, to have few children.

(3) This group is distinctly homogeneous and there is no difference according to the profile between the two-thirds of the group without diabetic heredity and the third with it. The few Rorschach tests of these patients support the impression that hysterical traits and often psychotic tendencies are prominent.

(4) In addition the following individual characteristics are note-worthy:

(a) These patients appear distant and reserved, wavering between tentative friendly gestures and suspicious withdrawal.

(b) Their tension is hard to describe because of its diversity and variability. They are generally inhibited and their reaction under emotional stress has the all or none quality of the infant.

(c) These patients show little self-reliance and are inhibited and suspicious in social relationships. When they talk freely, there is disconcerting vagueness and contradictions in their statements about feelings and personal problems.

(d) These patients give the impression of wheels turning within wheels exhausting most of their available energy. The focus of their conflicts is the problem of sexual identification rather than the problem of achieving power or creative independence. Their major characteristic is their indecisiveness.

(e) Exacerbations of the illness occur with minor injuries to their self-esteem or after long periods of wear and tear.

(f) Their initial reaction to illness is one of helplessness, sometimes combined with recrimination.

(5) Even though it is too early to state that the personality traits here set down may actually cause diabetes, it is probably not too early to state that they are an important predisposing factor, and hence correction of them (and where possible the situations that give rise to them) before diabetes has developed may have considerable prophylactic value.

Although it will remain for further studies to clarify the picture given in this chapter, we are under the impression that the points brought out, if evaluated in terms of their quantitative and qualitative prominence, are specific for the patient with diabetes, with the modifications suggested for the different types of diabetic encountered.

Assisting the patient to improve his behavior pattern in this area of conflict leads to a stabilization of the diabetes, and freedom from invalidism.

Chapter IX •

CONTRASTING PROFILES AND THEIR USE IN PSYCHOSOMATIC DIAGNOSIS

Ars medica tota in observationibus —Louis.
The sick should be the doctor's books.—Paracelsus.

I. Introduction

The practical value of the personality profiles in psychosomatic diagnosis is brought out more vividly when they are placed side by side and the points of contrast noted. The practicing physician will find it helpful to view the problems of differential diagnosis and therapy in the light of a clear picture of the personalities in which the disease syndrome is manifested. Such a view will often give him security in making practical decisions where the known evidence is equivocal.

It will remain for other studies to correct or further define the personality profile we have sketched for each group of patients studied. Statistical observations, also, should be derived from other series. We ourselves are in process of revising these profiles and particularly of attempting to work out more clear-cut dynamic pictures. But at this point it may be well to bring into focus the elements in each constellation that are the most significant for each syndrome under consideration.

The first four headings in each profile are of doubtful value for the individual case, but are of interest when one group is compared with another. Nevertheless, it should be noted that the exposure, health, and injury records are often indicative for the individual, as well as being characteristic of the group. The last six headings and the dynamic formulation on the other hand are definitive of the constellation for each individual since each point they cover was true of from 80 to 100 per cent of the individuals in the group they represent, and was characteristic of less than 15 per cent of the individuals in any other group studied. The only qualification here is that in saying definitive we mean definitive in terms of a total constellation of factors observed in the serial admissions of patients suffering from the disease under consideration, over a period of four years in one general hospital.

II. FAMILY HISTORY

HEREDITY—ACTUAL AND PSEUDO

It should be noted first of all that in no group was there a family history of the illness in question in more than 52 per cent of the cases, although in nearly all groups history of exposure to the illness in question, including not only living relatives but friends or spouse, occurred at a much higher percentage. Second, family history of the illness in question was just about as high in the fracture group, where a physical hereditary factor was least likely, as it was in the groups with cardiovascular disease. This was true in spite of the fact that the incidence of accidents in the general population is less than the incidence of cardiovascular disease, and consequently a given person would be more likely to have a cardiovascular than accident heredity, if the distribution were a chance one. Furthermore, apparent heredity of cardiovascular disease was just as high in the cardiac arrhythmia group where no organic basis was found, as it was in the group with coronary occlusion or hypertensive cardiovascular disease. Third, the exposure factor as distinguished from the hereditary was highest in the groups with serious cardiac damage, being well over 90 per cent for the groups with hypertensive cardiovascular and coronary disease, much lower in the anginal and cardiac arrhythmia groups, and particularly absent in the fracture group in spite of their equivalent cardiovascular heredity. If we consider a high incidence in the family history of the syndrome from which a patient suffers as indicative of heredity, fracture would be the most hereditary of all syndromes. Whereas a family history of cardiovascular disease is more or less equally distributed among all the groups, accident history in the family is concentrated in the fracture group. Since we are not inclined to consider accidents as hereditary, we would attempt to explain this apparent heredity in terms of exposure. This point may further emphasize the importance of the exposure factor in the cardio-vascular groups.*

One might infer from these data that the evidence concerning heredity in these diseases was completely inconclusive, tending neither to indicate a hereditary predisposition nor to disprove it. They do strongly suggest, however, that there is a correlation be-tween *exposure* to a specific illness and susceptibility to that illness, except in the case of accidents. This evidence is so strong that if the diseases were of a kind thought to be contagious, we should be justified in looking for a microbe or virus as a causative agent.

A hypothesis that does seem to fit the observed facts might be formulated as follows: The personality constellation may predispose an individual to these functional diseases, as well as to accidents. In the syndromes here discussed pathogenic receptivity to a given type of illness developed at an extremely early age. There is considerable evidence that emotional contagion from parents or other love objects plays an important role.

Given this emotional susceptibility to one or more types of somatic dysfunctions the onset of symptoms may be precipitated by such a traumatic experience as exposure to the death or suffering from a specific disease of a relative or close associate. There are indications also that the effect of the suggestion depends on the individual's stage of characterological development or emotional equilibrium at the time that it is received, but observations of this factor are far from conclusive and need extension. The effect of exposure to a mother who undergoes repeated attacks of heart failure seems to be more severe in persons with a pre-existing anxiety than in those with a freer range of emotional outlets. It is also more severe in those patients suffering from cardiovascular dysfunction, who are known to have strong identifications in the authoritarian hierarchy and to be more than ordinarily suggestible. This, incidentally, is one of the reasons why the doctor who mentions "murmurs" and "high blood pressure" becomes so frequently a pathogenic agent in the illness of such patients.

* In this context attention may be called to the fact that in our discussions of hereditary versus acquired characteristics, the effect of intra-uterine conditions is generally overlooked. Is this factor which involves exposure to different chemical and nervous stimuli *in utero* to be assigned to heredity or to environmental influence?

III. Personal Data

Review of the personality profiles for the eight groups of patients studied indicates:

(1) The patient's pattern of reacting to his family situation tends to be reproduced in his reaction to his marital partner and his children. For example, in the group of patients with *fracture* there was usually poor emotional contact with both parents and spouse and the tendency to run away when things become too unpleasant; in the patients with *diabetes* there was a long-continued indecisive subacute conflict first with parents then with the marital partner.

(2) The smallest families were in the groups (fractures, cardiac arrhythmias) where the illness itself was not such as to limit the size of family. The marriage rate, size of family, and divorce rate therefore bore a relationship to the personality pattern of the patient rather than to the physiological component in his illness.

(3) There was a definite relationship between the characteristic behavior pattern of each group of patients and the statistical observations relative to the family constellation both in childhood and in adulthood.

(4) The time of onset of illness, as well as the form which it assumes, is modified by such factors as the nature of the relationship to parents, the period of intimate exposure to parents, and the circumstances under which separation from parents does or does not occur. When separation from one or both parents has occurred it is important to know whether this took place through the patient's own initiative, for example, and whether there was emotional estrangement or a traumatic death.

The major value of such general remarks and statistical observations lies in the degree to which these facts have influenced and in turn reflect the characterological behavior pattern.

IV. Previous Health

Comparative study of previous health records of the eight groups of patients covered in this report brought out the interesting fact that after correction for age and sex distribution, the group of patients with fracture and the group of patients with diabetes had a very low previous illness record, whereas the group of patients with cardiovascular disease had a very high previous illness history irrespective of the degree of organic damage represented by any one specific syndrome. The good health record was revealed by the accident group in each of the four decades covered by this study, whereas for the diabetic group the previous health record was worse in the older than the younger decades.

V. Accident Record

The accident figures as given in the personality profiles are confusing unless carefully analyzed. The points to be borne in mind are (1) percentage of patients having more than one accident; (2) nature of accidents.

Number of Accidents. Whereas 80 per cent of the patients with fracture had two or more accidents, the corresponding figures for other groups are (see Chart X, page 160):

Group	Per Cent *
Hypertensive cardiovascular disease	6.0
Coronary occlusion	5.5
Anginal syndrome	6.0
Rheumatic fever (type A)	14.0
(type B)	0.0
Rheumatic heart disease	8.0
Cardiac arrhythmia	12.5
Diabetes	11.2

These figures rank the other groups in terms of accident-proneness, and at the same time show that the percentage of patients with fracture having two or more accidents is ten times that of the average for the other groups studied.

In these figures are included some patients who, strictly speaking, should be discussed in the following chapter as having overlapping syndromes, that is, patients suffering from more than one of the syndromes covered in this study. But even when such patients are included in the figures, we find ten times as many patients with fracture having three or more accidents as patients with anginal syndrome,

---

* Because of the greater difficulty of determining the exact time of onset of illness in certain disease syndromes as compared with others, these figures cannot be taken as accurate per cents but merely as indicating a trend. For example, in rheumatic heart disease, the only indication of illness prior to admission may be a vague history of growing pains, or in diabetes, of fatigue, polydipsia, or polyphagia, developing over a considerable period of time.

thirteen times as many as patients with rheumatic heart disease, and fifteen and a half times as many as patients with diabetes.

The reason for including the above accident figures here is that the principle of the study of serial admissions was being followed. The separation of patients with more than one syndrome from the others was done later in order to see to what degree the presence of overlapping syndromes modified the characteristic personality picture (see Chapter X). In terms of the accident history, this influence seems to have been considerable, as is indicated by the figures that follow.

If patients suffering from more than one of the syndromes covered in this study are omitted from all groups, the comparative figures for patients with two or more accidents become

Group	Per Cent
Hypertensive cardiovascular disease	2.2
Coronary occlusion	5.5
Anginal syndrome	0.0
Rheumatic fever (type A)	3.6
(type B)	0.0
Rheumatic heart disease	4.3
Cardiac arrhythmia	12.5
Diabetes	0.0

Also when these patients suffering from two or more syndromes are omitted from all groups, there are no patients with a history of three or more accidents in any group except the fracture group, while more than half of the fracture patients gave this history. This observation may suggest that patients suffering from more than one disease syndrome are more likely to be accident-prone than patients suffering from one syndrome only. The figures for accidents per person in the non-fracture groups are increased by two-thirds if patients suffering from more than one syndrome are included in these groups.

Perhaps the clearest picture of the differences in accident tendency in the fracture group as compared with the other groups is given by the figures for accidents per person. The fracture average is four accidents per person, even including those who were in for the first accident and those whose accidents as far as could be determined were unavoidable, while for the other groups the average is less than three-tenths of an accident per person. Hence the accident tendency in

PERCENTAGE OF PATIENTS REPORTING ONE OR MORE ACCIDENTS

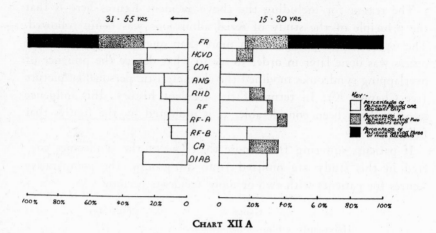

CHART XII A

ACCIDENTS IN CHILDHOOD

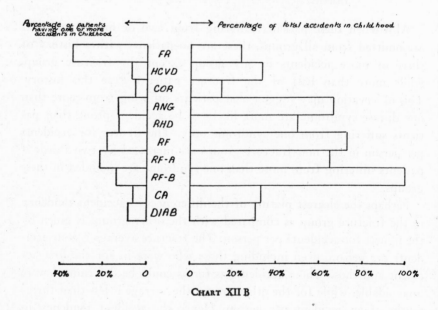

CHART XII B

the fracture patient is about fourteen times that for the other groups studied. Furthermore, a fracture patient who has had one previous accident has about fifteen times the accident tendency of the average patient in the other groups. He is eight times as likely to have other accidents as is the patient with the history of one accident in the other groups studied.

If patients admitted in the age group 15 to 30 are compared with patients admitted in the age group 31 to 55 (Chart XII A) the following points are noteworthy.

(1) Of the fracture patients admitted in the age group 31 to 50, there are about twice as many with only one accident as in the younger age group.

(2) Similarly, in the other disease groups, patients with more than one accident are those under 31 years old. The only exception to this are patients with coronary occlusion, and this is not actually an exception but is accounted for by the fact that no patients were admitted with this illness before the age of 31. This suggests in general that the older an individual is the less significant is the history of one or several accidents as indicating accident-proneness.

Chart XII B indicates the same fact in a different way, in terms of the number of accidents per person.

But the facts presented in Chart XIII relative to accidents occurring in childhood, that is prior to the age of 15, are even more significant:

(1) It is clear (Chart XIII) that the percentage of patients reporting childhood accidents is greater among the fracture patients. But they surpassed patients in the other groups by much less in childhood than in their later accident history.

(2) Less than 24 per cent of the fracture patients' total accident history is accounted for by accidents under the age of 15, whereas 50 to 100 per cent of the accident history for the other groups is accounted for by childhood accidents, with four interesting exceptions as follows:

(a) The patient with coronary occlusion is the only patient among the groups studied who sustained a lower percentage of his total accident history in childhood than did the fracture patient. (This is the more remarkable in that the coronary group had the highest percentage of males of any group studied and both our own statistics and National Public Health Statistics show a greater tendency of males than of females to have accidents in childhood.) Yet patients with coronary occlusion have the highest accident record of any

ACCIDENTS PER PATIENT

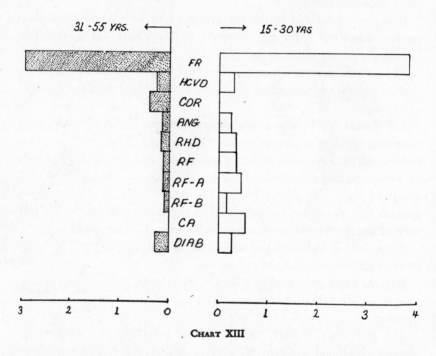

CHART XIII

group except for patients with fracture. They are remarkable also for their very slight tendency to have more than one accident, for the nature of their accidents (cuts—but not fractures) and for their marked tendency to get themselves hurt by someone else. This tendency to get themselves hurt by someone else seems to have developed late in the course of these patients' struggle toward domination.

(b) Patients with hypertensive cardiovascular disease, cardiac arrhythmia, and diabetes sustained about one-third of their accident history in childhood, and this was consistent with our other observations of the accident tendency in patients in these groups.

Types of Accidents. The greatest percentage of patients having only one accident is among patients with coronary occlusion, hypertensive cardiovascular disease, diabetes, and rheumatic fever type A; but in the first three of these groups the accidents are of a specific kind. They are cuts and burns, a type of injury that ranked very

NATURE of INJURY FROM ACCIDENT

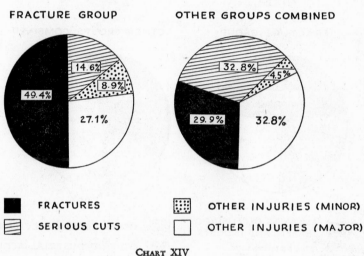

CHART XIV

low in the accident history of patients with fracture. Only the group of patients with rheumatic fever type A show any considerable tendency to sustain fractures; patients with anginal syndrome and cardiac arrhythmias (those with a strong acting out tendency) rank next to them.

Physical Nature of the Accident. (1) Chart XIV shows clearly that the cardiovascular and diabetic groups sustained twice as high a percentage of cuts as did the fracture group.

(2) The percentage of major injuries (excluding serious cuts) in the fracture group is a fifth again as high as the percentage in the accident history of the other seven groups. The percentage of minor injuries in the accident group is twice that of the other groups.

(3) The major accidents in the fracture group characteristically involve injury to body structure. In all the groups with cardiovascular syndromes, major accidents characteristically involve serious injury to body tissue.

Circumstantial Nature of the Accident (Chart XV). Analysis of the accident history of other disease groups as compared with the accident history of the fracture patients indicates the importance of

TYPES OF ACCIDENT
COMPARISON OF FRACTURE WITH OTHER ILLNESS SYNDROMES

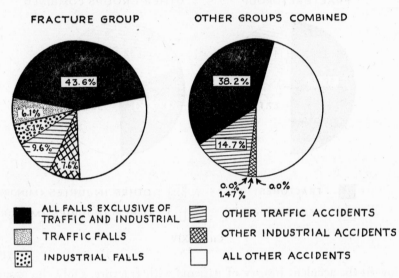

FRACTURE GROUP   OTHER GROUPS COMBINED

■ ALL FALLS EXCLUSIVE OF TRAFFIC AND INDUSTRIAL   ▦ OTHER TRAFFIC ACCIDENTS

▪ TRAFFIC FALLS   ▨ OTHER INDUSTRIAL ACCIDENTS

⦂ INDUSTRIAL FALLS   □ ALL OTHER ACCIDENTS

CHART XV

making certain distinctions. An illustration of this point is provided by comparison of the accident history of fracture patients, patients with cardiac arrhythmia, and patients with hypertensive cardiovascular disease. All three groups were interested in competitive sports. The fracture patient, however, rarely had his accident on the athletic field, although accidents frequently occurred on the way to or from the field. Patients with hypertensive cardiovascular disease and those with cardiac arrhythmia, however, were particularly likely to be injured while *engaged in* athletic sports. It seems likely that in the cardiac arrhythmia group the fear of not succeeding, and in the hypertensive cardiovascular disease group the general fear of expressing anger was the reason for their tendency to get hurt. The accident patient appeared to take fairly good care of himself while he was expressing his aggression in such activity, but to injure himself as a result of what often appeared to be carelessness when he was concentrating on a specific conflict situation for which he had found no solution.

In general:

(1) Of the total number of accidents sustained by fracture patients 55 per cent were the result of falls, including motor vehicle and industrial, as compared with 38 per cent in all the other groups. We can deduce that these patients had a tendency to fall half again as often as the patients who had accidents in the other groups. In comparing the tendency to injure themselves by falling, we find the fracture patient is 15 times more likely to do so, than is a patient in any other group.

(2) The patient with cardiovascular disease or diabetes who has had an accident is more than 50 per cent more likely than the fracture patient to have a motor vehicle accident, in which his role is not that of the pedestrian.

(3) The types of accident occurring in those having cardiovascular syndromes or diabetes, however, do not conform in distribution with figures for the general population. The percentage of these patients having accidents other than falls is roughly one-half again as great. This gives additional confirmation of the suspicion that a great many of the accidents occurring in the general population are the result of accident-proneness, rather than innocent accidents.

(4) Although all types of accident are more frequent in the fracture group, the relative variety as well as prominence of falls is striking (Chart XVI A). Fracture patients have falls at home, on the job, in relation to sports (even though not while actively engaged in sports); and they fall down in the street in front of motor vehicles. Patients with hypertensive cardiovascular disease who have been shown to resemble accident patients in several respects, are the only other group having more than two types of falls. Although in a larger series some other groups might show more than two types of falls, it is probable that patients with hypertensive cardiovascular disease would still lead all but fracture patients in the variety of falls.

(5) It is striking also that patients with coronary occlusion, the most controlled of all the groups studied, and patients with cardiac arrhythmia, who have the most adequate outlet in neurotic symp-

toms, have the lowest records for falls although the highest record for accidents other than falls. But patients with coronary occlusion make up for this by having a relatively higher record for motor

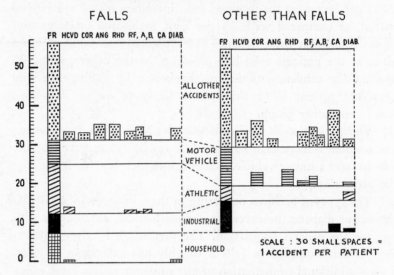

NATURE OF ACCIDENT

ACCIDENTS PER PATIENT

FALLS   OTHER THAN FALLS

FR = FRACTURE ANG = ANGINAL SYNDROME CA = CARDIAC ARRHYTHMIAS
HCVD = HYPERTENSIVE RHD = RHEUMATIC HEART DIAB = DIABETES
   CARDIOVASCULAR DISEASE   DISEASE
COR = CORONARY RF = RHEUMATIC FEVER TYPES A & B

CHART XVI A

vehicle accidents in which they were hit by the car while standing rather than running or falling in front of it. Here their record amounts to more than one-third that of the fracture group, and exceeds that of all other groups, except patients with rheumatic heart disease all of whose motor vehicle accidents occurred while they were passengers or pedestrians.

(6) It is interesting also that this table confirms our impression gained from the personality profiles that the fracture group, patients with cardiac arrhythmia, and patients with diabetes are the greatest industrial risks. Among these, the fracture patient is far in the lead as the greatest risk.

NATURE OF ACCIDENT
PERCENTAGE DISTRIBUTION

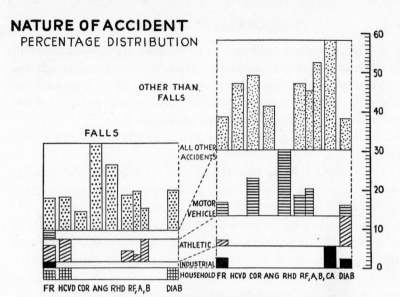

SCALE – 1 SMALL SPACE = 3%

FR = FRACTURE
HCVD = HYPERTENSIVE CARDIOVASCULAR DISEASE
COR = CORONARY

ANG ANGINAL SYNDROME
RHD RHEUMATIC HEART DISEASE
RF RHEUMATIC FEVER TYPES A&B

CA CARDIAC ARRHYTHMIAS
DIAB DIABETES

CHART XVI B

ACCIDENTS SHOWING CARDIAC PATTERN

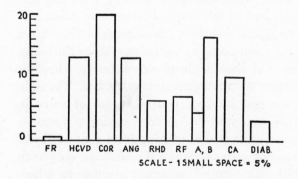

SCALE – 1 SMALL SPACE = 5%

FR = FRACTURE
HCVD = HYPERTENSIVE CARDIOVASCULAR DISEASE
COR = CORONARY

ANG = ANGINAL SYNDROME
RHD = RHEUMATIC HEART DISEASE
RF = RHEUMATIC FEVER TYPES A&B

CA = CARDIAC ARRHYTHMIAS
DIAB = DIABETES

CHART XVI C

555

(7) The percentage distribution of various types of accident in each syndrome is shown in Chart XVI B, section I. Although the fracture group ranks highest for all types of accident per patient, one of the other groups frequently exceeds the fracture group in terms of percentage of one or another type of accident.

Furthermore, each group has its own characteristic accident predilection.

(8) Chart XVI B, section II, (Accidents Showing the Cardiac Pattern), shows the only accident category in which the fracture patients rank lower than any other group, that of accidents resulting from injury by someone else. Next to them come the patients with diabetes. All the cardiovascular groups have a higher percentage of this type of accident. As has been noted in other connections the coronary patients lead, and are closely followed by rheumatic fever type B, anginal, and hypertensive cardiovascular disease.

(9) This table shows also the sharp distinction between rheumatic fever type A and type B. Type A is the lowest of all the cardiac groups for the cardiac type of accident, while type B is the second highest.

VI. Summary of Statistical Headings in Profiles

The four headings in the profiles just summarized are mainly statistical, hence they have a value in the picture of the total group but are relatively useless for prognosis in individual cases. For example, in the case of the patient with cardiovascular heredity, the statistical chances are about equal that he is suffering from any one of the disease entities covered in this study. Furthermore, there was no discernible difference in the course of illness between the 42 per cent of patients suffering from coronary occlusion who had heredity of cardiovascular disease and those without such heredity. Heredity was similarly indeterminate for the other illnesses studied. The only factor covered under our first heading, then, that was of value in terms of the individual case was the pseudo-hereditary factor— early exposure to parent or close friend suffering from a given illness. Of course the significance of such exposure varies also not only with the individual but with the time of exposure, a point to which Deutsch, French, and others called attention also. French's [192] comment relative to the point, I think is worthy of citation here. He gives "a very simple rule by which we may guess in many instances what organ will be chosen in a particular instance for the somatic discharge of an emotional tension. We are familiar (he says) with Stockard's experiments (1921) in which he demonstrated that developing organisms exposed to some more or less indiscriminate toxic agent would be most damaged at precisely those points that were developing most actively at the moment of exposure to the poison. A similar principle would seem also to hold in our problem: symptoms resulting from the frustration of an activity are likely to involve especially the organs which are most active or most under tension at the moment of frustration." There are two factors to consider here: The type of illness to which the patient is exposed, and the stage in his own development at which he was exposed.

The figures relative to time of death of parents also include many individual variations, and their significance in terms of a given case is in relation to later headings in the profile. Nevertheless, it may be significant that for patients in the coronary group the average age of the patient at the time of the father's death was higher than that in any other group studied, with patients in the anginal group coming second. The fact that in the case of patients with hypertensive cardiovascular disease the father tended to die before the patient's majority may be significant in terms of characteristics brought out in the next section.

The previous health and accident record seemed to be most clearly related to the type of serious illness developed. The high accident record for the group of patients with fracture, plus the nature of their accidents, combined with their excellent general health record, singles them out from among the other groups studied. On the other hand, the high incidence of vegetative disturbances characteristic of the cardiovascular groups provides little basis on which to distinguish between the various types of cardiovascular disease, although the past history of vegetative disorders does mark off the cardiovascular groups from the groups with fracture or diabetes. In general, then, these headings have their major interest in terms of the group, or from the point of view of public health, whereas individual variations play a much smaller role than they do under the subsequent headings on our profiles.

The seven headings to follow, and particularly the first two of them, are definitive for each individual in each group studied, with one important proviso: They are definitive provided that the examining physician has had sufficient training and experience and has sufficient opportunity to study the patient in such a way as to make possible a fairly accurate evaluation of his general adjustment and characteristic behavior pattern.

VII. General Adjustment and Characteristic Behavior Pattern

Study of educational, work, and income records taken in conjunction with social, sexual, and family adjustment provides a basis on which to judge the characteristic behavior pattern of the patient.

FRACTURE

The patients with fracture are generally decisive; they focus upon daily pleasures, attaching emotions to people and concrete experience; they show little interest in power or long-range goals. This pattern is manifested in an exaggerated form in the history of type B patients; when the educational record shows interruption, they left school or college before the educational unit undertaken was completed. They had an unstable work record, with good income average, marked by sudden changes and periods of being out of work. There is a cavalier element in their sexual and family relationships. In other words, they evinced a lack of planning and a tendency to be irresponsible which is obvious in one or all of these areas of adjustment. The same behavior which gives them a certain quality of the adventurer results usually in their being generally liked.

The characteristic behavior pattern as manifested in types A and C is less conspicuous but can be detected if the total personality constellation is evaluated.

The only exceptions to this description of the total group were found among occasional patients whose fractures were the result of accidents which, after careful analysis, could not be attributed to any negligence or unconscious impulse of the patients themselves. It is difficult to avoid confusion in discussing this group because if serial admissions to different wards are made the basis of contrast, impressions are distorted by patients who suffer from more than one syndrome. With patients seen on the fracture ward this distortion (see Chapter X) is harder to evaluate because the small percentage of patients without accident habit, or accident-proneness, must be included in this statistical survey. Since this was proved to be a very small percentage, the statistics given in the profiles are relatively useful. It is important, however, to call attention to the fact that accident-proneness and accident habit are not equivalent terms. If the fracture profile had been worked out in terms of the large majority with a well-established accident habit, the general picture would approximate that of type B. Those in type A and type C who have the highest accident record resemble type B in several superficial ways which can be easily detected.

The present tendency to substitute the term accident-proneness for accident habit is an unfortunate one because a given individual may be accident-prone at a particular moment of his life without having been so before and without being so again. Also accident-proneness may exist for a considerable period of time in a person without his having any accident. There is a greater concentration of the accident-prone in groups A and C, and a greater concentration of patients with an accident habit in group B.

HYPERTENSIVE CARDIOVASCULAR DISEASE, CORONARY OCCLUSION AND ANGINAL SYNDROME

Coronary Occlusion

At the opposite poles in personality constellation are patients with fracture and patients with coronary occlusion. The latter persons revealed a compulsion to get to the top through hard work and self-discipline in all the six spheres listed under general adjustment. The educational record showed a tendency to complete the educational unit undertaken and to shift from the academic to the active sphere only when an opportunity for self-advancement was in view. It showed also an unusually stable and persistent work record, and a steadily increasing income level, which on the average surpassed that of all the groups studied except for patients with cardiac arrhythmia. (This exception was not significant in terms of the character pattern under discussion, if we remember that the majority of patients with coronary occlusion started much lower in the social and income scale than did patients with cardiac arrhythmia.) In other words, these patients showed a very high degree of planning and persistence. They were workers, never adventurers.

In family life we found the same pattern: high marriage rate, high record for number of children in the family, and little incidence of separation or divorce, combined with a marked sense of responsibility for their relatives and dependents. Socially, these patients also were well liked, but they were liked because they tried to make themselves liked and knew how to be entertaining as well as dominating in social relationships. They were not thought of as adventurous and irresponsible children, as was the case with many patients with fracture. Personally they had a deep sense of loneliness, but they strove for mastery over themselves and others.

Anginal Syndrome

Differing in only minor respects from the group with actual coronary occlusion, patients with anginal syndrome had similar educational, work and income records, with a slightly greater tendency to choose non-competitive fields for their effort to achieve. Similarly, these patients were less eager to assume responsibility and somewhat less resolute in maintaining responsibilities undertaken. This fact, obvious enough in their behavior, was given statistical confirmation in their lower marriage rate, and their much lower record for number of children in the family as compared with the preceding group, as well as with patients with hypertensive cardiovascular disease.

Socially these patients also were well liked, and they surpassed all the groups studied as entertainers. Being freed to some extent through their individualism from the drive to compete and dominate, their sense of loneliness was slightly less, but this was only a matter of degree, and if circumstances conspired to increase such needs we found not only an identical behavior pattern but also a tendency to actual damage of the coronary arteries.

Hypertensive Cardiovascular Disease

Patients with hypertensive cardiovascular disease were likewise distinguished from the patients with fracture by the pattern of compulsive striving for advancement which they had in common with the two preceding groups. They were distinguished equally from these latter, however, by occasional impulsive interruptions of this compulsive striving. These facts were manifest in their histories and given statistical confirmation by their educational, occupational and work records, which were strikingly inferior. In other words they strove but failed to achieve. Some patients who diverged from this pattern in the direction of more consistent striving, and who did achieve success, later developed coronary occlusion.

These hypertensive patients resembled the two preceding groups in their high marriage rate; and in the average number of children per marriage they were second only to patients with coronary occlusion. Socially they were usually well liked, but in order to relieve tension and reassure themselves took too frequent recourse to wine, women and song. In these ways they sought reassurance also for doubts about their sexual adequacy. Premature ejaculation among the men and other forms of sexual impotence were fairly general in this group, but occurred only as an occasional symptom in the three groups previously reviewed.

Summary

In general adjustment and characteristic behavior pattern, differences among the groups of patients with hypertensive cardiovascular disease, coronary occlusion, and anginal syndrome were not great but seem rather variations in degree, as one might expect through study of what is known as the disease process itself. But all three groups are in marked contrast with the patients studied on the fracture ward. This remains true even though we recognize the fact that a fracture is not a disease entity in the same sense as is coronary occlusion. Had we excluded from the group figures the exceptional patients in whom the accident history was related to bone structure and patients who had "innocent accidents" the contrast in history with these three groups of patients suffering from cardiovascular disease would be clear whichever subdivision of the fracture group was selected for comparison.

RHEUMATIC DISEASE

Patients with rheumatic disease in its different forms show clearcut contrast with the three cardiovascular groups just discussed. The patients designated as rheumatic fever, type A, have a minor degree of accident proneness and a greater resemblance to the fracture group, especially fracture, type B, than patients designated as rheumatic fever, type B, or patients with rheumatic heart disease. This fact may be easier to relate to other facts given if it be remembered that this is the only rheumatic disease group with introversive tendencies. The resemblance of patients with rheumatic fever, type B and rheumatic heart disease to the other cardiovascular disease groups on the one hand and to the diabetic group on the other, is discussed in the following chapter.

Rheumatic Fever and Rheumatoid Arthritis

In the rheumatic fever group, first of all, the educational, occupational, and income level was much more nearly average. Second, closer analysis showed that we were dealing with at least two rather distinctive reaction types, which cancelled each other relative to many statistical points when the group was considered as a whole. For example, although the educational level for the group was average, type A rheumatic fever patients had a tendency to an erratic educational history, like the patients with fracture; and type B patients had a tendency to complete the educational unit undertaken and at the same time had a more regular work record. The rheumatic fever group as a whole was in contrast with the accident, hypertensive, coronary occlusion, and anginal syndrome groups mainly in the averageness of their record.

In general, however, with these patients it was not the educational, occupational and income record which reflected most clearly their characteristic behavior pattern, but rather their social, sexual, and family adjustment. Here we found their behavior characterized by acting a role, often combined with diplomacy and an appeal for sympathy. In the type A group we found impulsive episodes and in the type B group a secondary enjoyment of suffering, but childishness and guilt were prominent in both. Even those in whom the onset of the disease was late were likely to be unmarried although, unlike patients with anginal syndrome, if married they had large families. This point is striking in that the disease itself, particularly among females, would tend to work in the opposite direction. But personality studies indicated that in having large families these patients were acting a role, that of the virile male or the suffering woman, as the case might be. Masturbation combined with dislike of the sexual role, male or female as the case might be, together with unsolved homosexual interests were persistent problems.

Rheumatic Heart Disease

Patients with rheumatic heart disease differed from patients with rheumatic fever only in degree, but the educational, income, and occupational level tended to be lower; the social adjustment was superficially better, that is, there was greater willingness to curry favor and to take recourse to fantasy in realization of ambition. The conflicts relative to sex were similar, but the masochistic component in both males and females was greater. This was indicated, for example, in a much lower record for divorces and also in the willingness of these patients both male and female to use their illness as an excuse for limitation of their families.

Summary

Even this cursory comment on distinctive elements in the personality profiles of patients with rheumatic disease is sufficient to indicate a similarity of patients within the group and important contrast with patients whose major symptom complex places them in a different medical category.

CARDIAC ARRHYTHMIA

Patients with cardiac arrhythmia were outstanding among the groups studied in their educational, occupational, and income level. In these respects they resembled patients with coronary occlusion and anginal syndrome, but with the important difference that their achievement was not so much the result of hard, persistent work as the result of occasional bursts of brilliance combined with lucky breaks or clever manipulation of circumstances.

These patients were nervous, inconsistent and flighty in their social, family and sexual relationships also: alone and with close friends they were morose but in large groups they were cheerful and often brilliant. They were extremely individualistic and had the lowest record for marriage and number of children of any group studied. Fear of sexual relationships was of major importance in both males and females, but without the homosexual coloring characteristic of the rheumatic fever group. Their façade was a combination of playing to the gallery and self-depreciation.

Although patients suffering from various types of cardiac arrhythmia were included in this group they showed a marked similarity.
Even in cases in which exaggerated arrhythmia was superimposed on
a well divided picture of organic damage, these personality characteristics were discernible. No major subdivisions of these patients
are delineated here but further research may result in differentiations
similar to those in the preceding groups.

DIABETES

Review of the general adjustment of patients with diabetes presents a complex picture, and further study will probably result in
differentiation of several types. Unresolved conflict was manifested
overtly in each of the six spheres selected for review. Along with a
relatively high educational level and interest in academic advancement, we found a high incidence of nervous breakdown, especially
in college, which seemed to result from the conflict between ambition and the inability to compete. Their diverse occupational distribution with a deviation in the direction of the higher occupational
groups, and the marked disparity between income and educational
record even before the onset of illness, indicated the same pattern.
Distinctive of these patients also was their social anxiety: superficially
they were agreeable, but they were self-conscious and inaccessible
with a hypersensitiveness which often became a paranoid trend.

Sexually they were anxious, inadequate, and unable to recognize
themselves as either male or female. With their parents and families
there was a continued subacute conflict between hatred and submission.

Their marriage record was as low as that for patients with rheumatic heart disease, and in this respect they were outdone only by
patients with cardiac arrhythmia. The discrepancy here between
males and females placed the marriage record for the males at the
bottom of the list for the groups studied. Yet the record for children on the part of both males and females was the highest for all
groups studied. This seemed to be largely the result of inability to
take a decisive attitude about the desirability of having children.

Similarly, although divorces were relatively infrequent in this group, periods of separation and threatened divorce were higher than in any other group studied. Throughout, their behavior pattern was one of vacillation and indecisiveness.

Those who object to contrasting patients with fracture and patients with coronary occlusion or any one of the other syndromes here discussed on the ground that the fracture is not in the same sense a disease entity, should read carefully (pages 582 ff.) the personality profiles for these syndromes reproduced in parallel columns. Special attention should be paid to the profiles of patients with coronary occlusion and of patients with diabetes which are generally considered as two specific disease entities. Just as the group of patients with coronary occlusion are in sharp contrast with the accident group, both of which have clear-cut pictures, they are also in sharp contrast with patients with diabetes who present the most confusing picture of all the groups studied.

VIII. Area of Focal Conflict and Characteristic Reaction

Although study of the patient's general adjustment as just discussed gives a fair indication of the area of major conflict, study of early and present neurotic traits as well as of each patient's interests and hobbies, his reaction to illness and the life situation prior to the illness, serves to complete the picture.

FRACTURE

Our study of patients with fracture showed that as children a strikingly high percentage had neurotic traits of the active or "asocial type," for example, walking and talking in their sleep, or persistent lying, stealing, and truancy. In later life these tendencies seemed to have been replaced by their accident behavior pattern, hence there was a striking lack of classical neurotic symptomatology except for the small group with agoraphobia or fear of falling.

Their addictions and interests followed the same pattern: coffee and cigarettes for pleasure or to let off steam, absorption in competitive sports, machinery and gambling, that is, a seeking of dangerous situations giving opportunity to challenge fate in a more or less active way. Side by side with these interests was a bondage to religious ritual, which was resented.

The life situation immediately prior to the onset of the illness was found to be characterized by conflict with authority, job, parent, or spouse, which the patient was unable to avoid. In view of these facts it is easy to understand why these patients tended to exploit their illness, to make the authorities pay to the utmost financially or in terms of being sorry and offering additional indulgence, even though many of them preserved their self-respect by making light of it, feeling secretly guilty. Others were exaggerated in their complaints. The realization that conflict with authority could not be permanently removed, may have favored the development of a fatalistic attitude characteristic of many of them.

HYPERTENSIVE CARDIOVASCULAR DISEASE, CORONARY OCCLUSION, AND ANGINAL SYNDROME

Coronary Insufficiency and Occlusion

In sharp contrast with the preceding group, patients with coronary occlusion had few early neurotic traits except for the tendency to brood. They kept their troubles to themselves. This tendency was never replaced by other modes of behavior, but became an inner tension and a tendency to depression rarely admitted to others.

Like accident patients they had a propensity for coffee and cigarettes, but rather as stimulants, to keep themselves alert for longer periods of work, not merely for pleasure or to let off steam. Although many of them were brought up in orthodox religions, many early became skeptics. Their habit of compulsive hard work allowed them little time for hobbies, although many of them had a feeling for music and an interest in philosophy.

In patients with a vegetative nervous system rendered unstable by life-long tension and strain, it is easy to understand why exposure to shock in their careers or business life involving relinquishment of authority * and a thwarting of their life-long striving to be masters of themselves and of others, should be the characteristic finding in the life situation prior to the onset of illness. It is also easy to understand why exploitation of the authorities or revenge does not char-

* In some individuals this included the authority relationship within the family, and an important traumatic element was the disruption through death or otherwise of such relationships.

acterize the reaction of these patients to illness. The struggle must continue; they must get to the top again. Hence they minimize symptoms and place themselves under additional strain which forced quietude can do little to combat. As a matter of fact the effect of this treatment is often that of releasing self-destructive tendencies; they would rather die than submit.

Anginal Syndrome

Patients with anginal syndrome were distinguishable from the preceding group in their childhood history only in that they allowed their feelings more expression, not directly, but usually in artistic channels, and they were more inclined to remember their nightmares and admit their phobias. These patients also evinced the same tendencies throughout life. Those among them who were the most successful in their artistic outlets and the most neurotic in character seemed to remain freest from organic damage. Those in our group who later developed coronary occlusion were either thwarted in the sphere of artistic expression, or because of other pressures followed more closely the coronary pattern.

These patients also were likely to overindulge in stimulants to keep themselves going, had a philosophical and skeptical frame of mind, and, with the modifications just indicated, followed more or less closely the coronary pattern.

The situation immediately prior to onset was the same except that the preliminary experience of shock was more likely to involve accident or death of someone loved in addition to loss of prestige. As a rule they tended to minimize symptoms and go on in spite of them unless the feeling of defeat became so strong that they were willing to be cared for like little children and so to shift their sphere of domination to those on whom they were forced to be dependent. These patients differed from the patients with actual coronary occlusion only to the degree to which they were satisfied to be as good as their superiors rather than to surpass them, and to be boss only of themselves rather than of others.

Hypertensive Cardiovascular Disease

Patients with hypertensive cardiovascular disease had a relatively low percentage of early neurotic traits. Such traits as they had, however, were temper tantrums, nightmares or nail-biting; in other words, impulsive expression of aggression toward others or toward themselves, rather than actual translation of feeling into impulsive action such as the sleep-walking, lying and stealing characteristic of the impulsive behavior of the accident group. Again these same traits, together with perfectionistic inclinations, continued throughout life. Furthermore, in general, passive tendencies were more obvious.

Their use of coffee, cigarettes, and alcohol was not only "to increase their ability to work" but also to give them a sense of social freedom, and help them forget their conflicts.

The life situation prior to the onset of illness was marked by a traumatic separation from someone loved, often by death, or by a setback in the field of the patient's ambition, usually combined with greater indulgence in compensatory gratifications such as food, coffee, and alcohol. In cases where both these factors were involved, as one might expect, the illness picture tended to be more serious. Typical of their reaction to illness was a giving in to passive tendencies which they had done so much to combat. They were more likely to use the illness as an alibi for failure and to insist on being taken care of, although occasionally, like the patients with coronary occlusion, these patients would throw caution to the winds and attempt to keep on in spite of it. Hence, again we have patients whose major conflict was with authority, but patients whose whole life adjustment showed a much greater prominence of the tendency to self-defeat.

RHEUMATIC DISEASE

Patients suffering from different forms of rheumatic disease, like the patients in the three groups just discussed, differed from each other in only relatively minor respects and present sharp contrasts to the groups just discussed. As was clear in the preceding discussion, their conflicts were mainly in the area of their sexual role and only secondarily in relation to authority.

Rheumatic Fever and Rheumatoid Arthritis

Among the groups studied, patients with rheumatic fever were second only to fracture patients in the high percentage giving a history of early neurotic traits. The group that we have called type A were inclined to sleep-walking and sleep-talking, whereas the group that we have called type B were more inclined to temper tantrums and nail-biting. In all these patients tics, finickiness about food, enuresis, conflict over masturbation, and perfectionistic tendencies were common. Whereas the accident patients either masturbated or not, without thinking much about it, and the patients in the three preceding groups soon repressed the tendency or substituted sexual promiscuity, rheumatic patients remained preoccupied with the problem and their attempts to rid themselves of it.

Their interest in self-cure was obvious in their characteristic addictions and interests, which were mainly patent medicines and drugs, and athletic pursuits beyond their strength. They were early disillusioned with religion but found no substitute for it in philosophy or art. The girls were inclined to be tomboys and the boys sensitive and feminine.

In the situation preceding the onset of illness we found disruption of emotional attachment through a change of environment; separation of or from parents; often extreme hardship, and so on. The reaction to illness in the more active group of these patients (type A) was a tendency to overdo and to disregard doctors' orders; in type B the reaction was to get satisfaction out of suffering; but in both types there was an increasing tendency to escape in dreams and fantasy from real situations with which they could not cope.

Rheumatic Heart Disease

Patients who developed rheumatic heart disease with little or no previous rheumatic symptomatology differed from those just described in a lesser diversity of early neurotic traits and in the extreme intensity of their early fright reactions. Often these were occasioned by really frightening experiences. The same neurotic reaction pattern continued throughout life, frequently reinforced by people who frightened or abused them. They overindulged in stimulants to buck themselves up, usually rode their hobbies high and often became religious zealots.

The life situation prior to the onset of the illness was characterized by unusual exertion in one of the compensatory spheres, by a severe fright, or a traumatic death. In their reaction to their illness they showed little insight; they were inclined to deny the illness and enjoy as well as increase their suffering. Their relationship to authority was characterized by emulation of the superior especially in fantasy, and was definitely colored by conflict over their sexual role and the tendency to curry favor with the opposite sex.

CARDIAC ARRHYTHMIA

Patients with cardiac arrhythmia with no demonstrable organic damage are probably the least homogeneous of the groups under discussion. But our study indicates that a larger series and more careful analysis is necessary in order to make an adequate classification.

In the meantime, since so many of these patients at first designated as "purely neurotic" became invalids or developed organic damage or both, they deserve particularly careful study by the general physician. The difficulty in obtaining a group picture, and the probable inaccuracy of such a picture based on a study of serial admissions is to be ascribed not only to the fact that we were dealing with several different reaction types, but also to the fact that each of these patients is highly individualistic.

Nevertheless, we can say in general as to neurotic traits that in childhood, phobias and exaggerated fright reactions were prominent, as they were found to be in patients with rheumatic heart disease. Enuresis and nail-biting were more prominent than in any of the other groups studied, and there seemed to be some tendency to sleep-walking among the males. In adult life these patients continued their phobias, particularly claustrophobia, a marked fear of pregnancy, and a disgust for sexual experience which was in conflict with an equally marked inclination toward it.

Review of interests and addictions revealed coffee and smoking as important, especially among the males, lack of interest in athletics but a tendency to gamble second only to that of the accident group. The most striking factor in this group was the diversity of social interests, but at the same time a predilection for interests that would bring the patient himself into the limelight. Personal relationships were of the utmost importance to these patients, and a traumatic experience in this field, combined with a gradual sense of failure in the prima donna role, was a general finding in the life situation prior to the onset of illness.

The reaction to illness was marked by discouragement, and distrust of and a feeling of hostility toward physicians greater than was found in any other group. Of course this reaction had some justification in their numerous and conflicting experiences with physicians, but was strongly conditioned also by the extreme importance to these patients of all intimate personal relationships. In short, their major conflicts were in the sphere of personal relationships, and their reaction was one of withdrawal, alternating with scouting and raiding expeditions in the effort to evaluate the situation and explore the possibilities of being effectual. In order to visualize similarities and contrasts together with points of diagnostic significance in these various syndromes careful study should be made of the profiles as reproduced in parallel columns on pages 582 ff.

DIABETES

Patients with diabetes were found to be in sharp contrast with fracture patients in the absence of active early neurotic traits. Like some of the patients in the cardiovascular groups, especially patients with hypertensive cardiovascular disease, they had temper tantrums, phobias, and nightmares; but closer analysis showed that these were fussbudgety rather than openly violent in nature. In adult life these neurotic tendencies persisted in the form of nervousness, depression, and a general suspiciousness which often assumed a markedly paranoid trend.

These patients avoided competitive sports, and were markedly interested in the suffering of domestic animals who stand little chance in their life with human beings. They were usually uninterested in religion unless awareness of homosexuality induced an attempt to create or adopt a particular religious ritual, or unless development of paranoid tendencies led them to assume a religious role.

The life situation most closely associated with the onset of their illness seemed to be a long-drawn-out, indeterminate struggle, including wear and tear, hard work, homosexual conflict and conflict with family and spouse. Their reaction to illness was an alternation of depression and feeling of relief at having an alibi for their inadequacy. Suspiciousness of others and a tendency to project were likely to be prominent. Study of this picture taken in combination with their general life adjustment and characteristic behavior pattern brings into sharp relief these patients' conflict relative to responsibility or independence. They seemed unable to decide upon or to adopt any consistent attitude or reaction. They muddled along in their general relations, sexual and otherwise; they were full of anxiety and could not make up their minds.

IX. Summary Relative to Therapy *

Therapeutic suggestions relative to each syndrome covered in this study have been given. An attempt was made to establish criteria for therapy (see Chapter XI), but in reporting therapeutic results it is necessary to be even more tentative than in outlining personality profiles, group statistics, and general principles of psychosomatic diagnosis. The reason for this is that staff time was insufficient to provide the opportunity of treatment for all the patients for whom we thought treatment desirable, or except in a few instances, for any unselected series.

We did treat alternate cases of a small unselected series of patients admitted to the fracture ward, of patients with anginal syndrome, of patients with rheumatic fever, of patients with cardiac arrhythmia, and of patients with recurrent decompensation. Out of the total group of 1600 patients (not limited to the three-year serial admission group on which comparative statistics have been based), about twenty patients suffering from each of the syndromes covered in this study were treated intensively. Our therapeutic results and impressions may be summarized as follows:

(1) In the series of *fracture* patients to which reference has been made, only one of the treated cases had an additional accident over five years of observation, whereas about one-third of the untreated patients returned with subsequent accidents. The patient with a well defined accident habit, however, represents a very difficult therapeutic problem especially if he belongs to the type B classification, because of the relative poverty of his emotional life and insight, and his lack of ability to be articulate particularly with regard to feelings.

(2) In twenty unselected cases with *hypertension* which had been recorded from one to twenty years, it was possible to bring the blood pressure back to normal. This level was maintained for a period of observation of from five to ten years (e.g., Case No. HP 3). It

* See Chapter XI, section V.

should be noted that in these patients there was no evidence of renal disease or severe arterial damage. In several other patients suffering from a more malignant form of the disease, both physical and psychological improvement resulted although the blood pressure remained high. These patients present a much less difficult therapeutic problem than do the patients with the accident habit, because they are relatively articulate, and the nature of the disease is such that it is not difficult to make clear to them the relationship between their emotional problems and their somatic disorder.

(3) For patients with *coronary occlusion* the criteria of cure or relief of symptoms are more difficult to establish because the medical treatment for this illness as we now know it may itself postpone the next attack for from five to ten years. We can speak then only of relief of invalidism and increase of the patient's capacity to return to what for him is a normally active life. This much was accomplished with the patients treated, and it was easy to see in those that were untreated the precipitation of subsequent attacks by such factors as those outlined in Chapter V. These patients are a little more difficult to treat than are patients with hypertensive cardiovascular disease alone because of the strength of their character resistances.

(4) The symptoms of *anginal syndrome* were completely relieved in a series of twenty cases treated, and 20 per cent of the patients in the untreated series went on to the development of coronary occlusion during the period of observation of from five to ten years. Although the therapeutic approach is difficult, as is indicated in Chapter V, these patients, like those with hypertension, are particularly amenable to therapy.

(5) *Rheumatic disease.* (a) Patients with *rheumatic fever*—as we have discussed them here—resemble patients with diabetes (as well as patients with asthma) in being difficult therapeutic problems. Shifts in illness syndrome are particularly likely to occur either spontaneously or in the course of treatment. With type A, shift in the direction of the accident pattern is frequent; with type B, shift in the direction of hypertensive cardiovascular disease (e.g., Case No. RF 304, page 600). In general, from the point of view of personality adjustment, our therapeutic results were good, but as in the case of patients with coronary occlusion we cannot evaluate them from the point of view of the somatic component in the illness because five

or ten years may elapse between attacks even when such patients are treated purely in terms of the ordinary medical routine. (b) Patients with *rheumatic heart disease,* on the other hand, although the organic damage is irreversible, are rewarding subjects for psychotherapy if we think of the therapeutic goal as restoration to a more or less normally active life and prevention of recurrent decompensation (e.g., Case No. RHD 4). Considerable skill, however (probably through psychoanalytic training), is required in handling the marked masochistic component in these patients. This, of course, should never be approached directly.

(6) In our experience, patients with *cardiac arrhythmia* are to be ranked with patients with hypertensive cardiovascular disease and anginal syndrome from the point of view of amenability to treatment, although a little more time may be required. In the cases treated, the immediate results were equally good, although there were 20 per cent of relapses during the period of observation. These relapses were to be ascribed to lack of adequate time, and partly to the relatively lesser stability of the personality, and the greater difficulty in straightening out the life situation in which the patients found themselves at the time they came for treatment. Our therapeutic experience with *recurrent decompensation* is discussed in the concluding section of Chapter VII (page 478).

(7) Therapeutic results in patients with *diabetes* must be evaluated in terms of relief of invalidism since, as in the case of patients with rheumatic heart disease, the organic damage itself, in terms of our present knowledge, is irreversible. With these patients also our results were good (e.g., Case No. DP 2, page 87), but their permanence varied largely with the strength of ego development. It will be remembered that these patients rank lowest of all the groups studied from the point of view of integration, and that their conflicts cause them difficulty in practically all spheres of life adjustment. Hence, much time is required if the aim is to make them really effective human beings, although stabilization on their own level is sometimes relatively easy to achieve.

It may be useful to review here the patients' spontaneous statements relative to their problem and the relationship of thought, speech and action to the nature of their tension, and to their symptoms.

The *accident-prone* patient says: "I always have to keep working. I can't stand around doing nothing. When I get mad, I don't say anything, I do something. I act before I think."

The *hypertensive* patient says: "I always have to say 'yes.' I don't know why. I am always furious afterwards"; or "I'm angry but I never like to fight —I don't know why—something must have happened once. . . . Argument is my long suit. I could argue all day long."

The *coronary* patient says: "I have worked hard all my life. I always have to keep on working. I have to be the boss."

The *anginal* patient says: "I've always been ambitious, trying to succeed. When something happens I feel it in my heart."

The patient with *rheumatic fever* says: "Everything I do hurts, but I have to keep on moving."

The patient with *rheumatic heart disease* says: "I have such terrible dreams." Or "I guess I was born to be a martyr."

The patient with *cardiac arrhythmia* says: "I wanted to amount to something but I guess I am destined to be a failure. I am afraid of people. I am happiest in imagining things."

The patient with *diabetes* says: "Doctor, it's terrible. I don't know what I might do. I'm constantly on the verge of hurting somebody or injuring myself, you've got to help me, I'm not responsible for myself, I can't decide things."

From the point of view of impulsive action, speech and thought, accident-prone patients and coronary occlusion patients represent opposite extremes. The former is inarticulate and prone to action and the latter acts and speaks only in a studied way, and attempts to solve his problems in thought. Patients with hypertensive cardio-vascular disease, anginal syndrome, or rheumatic disease express themselves in all three ways; patients with cardiac arrhythmia mainly in speech and fantasy. The patient with diabetes finds himself blocked in action, speech, thought and fantasy, and has the most complicated personality problems of them all.

In the accident patient attacks of jitters occur when he is discussing problems in the area of his major conflicts, just as attacks of palpitation or increases of blood pressure occur in patients suffering from the relevant syndromes. Much too little attention has been devoted to these, as is revealed in postural attitudes, voice and muscle tension, and their relation to action on the one hand and fantasy on the other. As Freud, Reich, and some others have pointed out, the musculature represents a sort of characterological armor. Hence it should be of special interest to all psychoanalysts and to all students of psychosomatic problems. Muscle tension is a real psychosomatic borderline, a borderline between instinct and outer world, restraining aggressive action toward the latter, and binding vegetative energy. Attention may be called again to the welling-up of emotion that often comes when a patient is asked to relax.

An obvious fact, already emphasized but to which too little attention is generally given, is that all patients are not tense in the same way. Some patients who are tense show this in an appearance of stiffness, jerky movements, or a high strident voice, whereas others give no obvious evidence of tension so that one is surprised to discover in the course of physical examination how tense they really are. The former are usually called jumpy, nervous, hysterical, while the latter often escape notice entirely from this point of view. Among the former are those who tend to be active and get considerable satisfaction from the attention paid to their symptoms. Sometimes they actually get themselves injured and sometimes they merely get sympathy for being such high-strung individuals. In general our patients with certain symptom neuroses, allergies, and those who tended to have accidents, belong to this group. (In some disorders localized spasms are prominent.) Patients with hypertension, gastro-intestinal disease, or some other smooth muscle spasm, on the other hand, are likely to have a generalized tension which often escapes notice because of their appearance of quiet control. This same appearance, however, may be given by the introversive accident patients of group B.

Patients whose tension has been, so to speak, driven inward, tend to give great attention to correct external behavior, and unless there is a marked accompanying symptom neurosis they usually dislike too much attention to their symptoms, and tend to go on in spite of them. They are likely to deny that they are nervous. This seems to be in part because these patients are so afraid of their aggressive impulses. As already noted they are outstanding for the degree of their repressed or pent-up hostility. Hence, they are usually considerate of others and are loath to arouse criticism of any kind so that they try to conceal their tenseness itself. The question arises as to whether the necessity of subjecting to special control the manifestations even of their tension, which itself is serving the purpose of keeping aggressive thoughts and actions in repression, may not have something to do with the development of smooth muscle spasm. The tension seems to be driven inward to involve also the vascular or gastro-intestinal systems. In any case, as patients are relieved psychotherapeutically of their symptoms we often see the process taking place in reverse direction. This point has been discussed or mentioned (pages 9 ff. and 87) but in view of its importance and in view of the fact that some readers will inevitably concentrate on some chapters rather than others, it is repeated here.

Patients with hypertension, for example, as they lose these symptoms, are likely to show an increased nervousness and jerkiness, and often say, "I don't know what makes me feel so funny. I don't know what I might do." These patients may become quarrelsome, show a tendency to get into fights or to have accidents, but in the end they show a poise and general ease involving a change in their breathing also, which is so striking that they themselves or their friends are likely to comment on it, usually in some such words as "why you look years younger."

Finally, the results of such therapy as was possible confirmed and further refined the personality profiles sketched for each group, as well as the suggestions given relative to type and probable success of therapy.

X. Conclusions

Labels are dangerous and inaccurate, but sometimes serve to crystallize a picture. For example, Alvarez' term for the sufferer from stomach ulcer, the *"go-getter"* has been of assistance to many interested in this syndrome. Hence it may be worth while to highlight personality characteristics for the syndromes here discussed.

Patients with the accident habit are to be found among the *hoboes.* Needless to say, all hoboes do not have accidents, just as all go-getters do not have stomach ulcers, but none the less the accident incidence is great in the hobo personality type. Of course, there is the additional qualification that under this heading there is a wide range of variation from the wanderer and gambler in the physical sphere to the irresponsible hobo in the social and intellectual spheres. Also there are persons in whom the hobo traits may not seem at first sight to be the most important characteristics, but if such persons have accidents, this reaction pattern is usually to blame.

Coronary occlusion and hypertensive cardiovascular disease seem to occur particularly frequently among *top-dogs* and *would-be-top-dogs*. Anginal syndrome is a frequent finding among *prima donnas* or *big frogs in small puddles*. Rheumatic fever and rheumatic heart disease occur among *teachers' pets* and *martyrs*. Patients with cardiac arrhythmia, although they have something of the prima donna, give the impression of being *children in the dark*. Patients with diabetes can generally be characterized as *muddlers*.

These labels have at least some cogency in terms of our experience. Much is accomplished when the patient with an accident habit could be sufficiently freed emotionally to face his conflict with authority; when the patient with hypertensive cardiovascular disease, coronary occlusion, or anginal syndrome could be sufficiently freed from the need to be "tops" to be able to co-operate freely with others; when the patient with rheumatic disease could become content with himself apart from acting a role, when the patient with cardiac arrhythmia was freed from confusion about himself, and when the patient with diabetes developed the ability to make up his mind.

In terms of psychodynamics these labels apply really to the patient's defenses. The defenses are significant indicators of the point at which the patient's energy economy is disturbed. To free the patient emotionally, of course, it is necessary to do more than remove the defense. It is dangerous to remove the defense before the patient has been fitted to deal with his emotional conflicts in some more constructive way. When that is done, the defense may not even need to be abandoned altogether as a pattern of action, for it may be useful in dealing with real situations, and no longer dangerous to the patient's health when his energy economy has been sufficiently adjusted so that he does not need it as a defense against inner conflicts. In order to achieve this inner equilibrium, patients in the first four groups must solve their conflict with authority, and patients in the last four groups must learn to be themselves both socially and sexually.

Naturally this is an oversimplification, but nevertheless it may be useful to physicians treating patients who are incapacitated by the illnesses in question. The problem is not so much to make the patient act differently as to *educate him to feel differently*.

In the light of the foregoing it is at least clear why forcing the patient with coronary occlusion to drop out of the race and cut down his work schedule without enabling him to accept the situation emotionally may actually do him more harm than good; or why attempting to force the accident patient with wanderlust to regulate his life and stick to one job is as likely to result in more accidents as in fewer. In this field as in all other fields of medicine, attention must be directed to the root of the difficulty rather than merely to the symptoms, hence the exigency for psychosomatic diagnosis.

These personality profiles are of considerable prognostic importance and also of diagnostic importance especially in anginal syndrome and cardiac arrhythmia, where it is uncertain whether or not the syndrome is likely to progress to actual organic damage. Their major usefulness, however, is in general management and therapy. Finally, careful study of them may be particularly pertinent to the medical treatment of patients who show a marked tendency to two or more illnesses, a matter to which the following chapter is devoted.

PERSONALITY PROFILES

"If I were in search of a man (Martin Hewitt would say) of whom I knew nothing but that he squinted, bore a birthmark on his right hand, and limped, and I observed a man who answered to the first peculiarity, so far the clue would be trivial, because thousands of men squint. Now, if that man moved and exhibited a birthmark on his right hand, the value of that squint and that mark would increase at once a hundred or a thousand fold. Apart they are little; together much. The weight of evidence is not doubled merely; it would be only doubled if half the men who squinted had right-hand birthmarks; whereas the proportion, if it could be ascertained, would be, perhaps, more like one in ten thousand. The two trivialities, pointing in the same direction, become very strong evidence. And, when the man is seen to walk with a limp, that limp (another triviality), reinforcing the others, brings the matter to the rank of a practical certainty. The Bertillon system of identification—what is it but a summary of trivialities? Thousands of men are of the same height, thousands of the same length of foot, thousands of the same girth of head—thousands correspond in any separate measurement you may name. It is when the measurements are taken together that you have your man identified forever."

A patient may have any one or half dozen of the personality traits given in each profile and may be sick or well. The only diagnostic value of the profile lies in its definition of a constellation more or less after the pattern of Martin Hewitt's formula.

Group Statistics

FRACTURE

1. FAMILY HISTORY. Relative frequency of accidents in the family and siblings (about 40 per cent), history of cardiovascular disease, however, not strikingly low (about 38 per cent). Little exposure to disease (about 46 per cent to accidents).

2. PERSONAL DATA. At least one strict parent. Average marriage rate. Few children, relatively many divorces (as compared with general population statistics or baseline for groups studied).

3. HEALTH RECORD. Excellent previous health record, few operations except appendectomy. Women good pelvic histories. Interest in health and vigor.

4. INJURIES. Eighty per cent two or more accidents, majority three or more. Mainly the result of falls. Many childhood accidents.

CORONARY INSUFFICIENCY AND OCCLUSION

1. FAMILY HISTORY. Cardiovascular disease in parents and siblings about average for the groups studied (42 per cent). Accident history for parents and siblings about 9 per cent. Exposure to cardiovascular disease or to sudden death in about 90 per cent of the cases.

2. PERSONAL DATA. Both parents usually lived beyond the patient's majority, the father usually died first. Both parents typically strict. High marriage rate. Many children, few divorces.

3. HEALTH RECORD. Bad previous illness history with predominance of vegetative symptoms and many operations. Anginal symptoms frequent. Tendency to self-neglect. Women poor pelvic histories.

4. INJURIES. Rarely more than one injury. Rate for one accident above average but these accidents were of a specific type: result of action by another person, typically cutting, shooting, or stabbing. Few childhood accidents.

Group Statistics

HYPERTENSIVE CARDIOVASCULAR DISEASE

. FAMILY HISTORY. Cardiovascular disease in parents and siblings, 49 per cent. Accident history for parents and siblings about 10 per cent. Diabetes, 19 per cent. Nervousness in about 75 per cent. Exposure to cardiovascular disease or sudden death, 8 per cent.

. PERSONAL DATA. Both parents usually lived beyond the patient's adolescence, father usually died first and before the patient's majority. Both parents inclined to be strict, mother usually dominant. Average marriage rate. Many children, few divorces.

. HEALTH RECORD. Bad previous illness history, many operations with preponderance of pneumonia, gastro-intestinal upsets, major operations, allergy, and obesity. Women poor pelvic histories.

. INJURIES. Rarely more than one injury. Rate for one accident slightly above average but accidents tend toward fracture type, with many actual fractures. Almost equally divided between childhood and later accidents.

ANGINAL SYNDROME

1. FAMILY HISTORY. Cardiovascular disease in parents and siblings, 65 per cent. Accident history for parents and siblings, about 6 per cent. Nervousness, about 24 per cent. Exposure to cardiovascular disease or to sudden death, 77 per cent.

2. PERSONAL DATA. Both parents usually lived beyond the patient's majority, the father usually died first. Both parents typically strict. Average marriage rate. Few children, few divorces.

3. HEALTH RECORD. Worst previous health history of all groups studied, with preponderance of major illness and major operations. Tendency to self-neglect. Women poor pelvic histories.

4. INJURIES. Rarely more than one injury. Rate for one accident low; accidents about equally divided between coronary type and fractures. Majority of accidents in childhood

Group Statistics

RHEUMATIC FEVER AND RHEU- MATOID ARTHRITIS

1. FAMILY HISTORY. Cardiovascular disease in parents and siblings, 52 per cent (half of this rheumatic disease). Accident history for parents and siblings, 10 per cent. Extreme nervousness, about 35 per cent. Exposure to cardiovascular disease or to sudden death in about 60 per cent.

2. PERSONAL DATA. Many broken homes, poor social and economic background, poor contact with parents, although fairly frequent dependence on mother. Low marriage rate, many children per marriage, few divorces.

3. HEALTH RECORD. Poor previous health record with tendency to minor operations, and minor and major illness and allergy. Women poor pelvic histories. (In type B, marked susceptibility to respiratory infections.)

4. INJURIES. Accident record about average (type A high; type B low). Accidents preponderantly fracture type. Majority of accidents in childhood.

RHEUMATIC HEART DISEASE

1. FAMILY HISTORY. Cardiovascular disease in parents and siblings, 44 per cent. Accident history for parents and siblings, 8 per cent. Diabetes, 20 per cent. Extreme nervousness, 36 per cent (12 per cent institutional or suicide). Exposure to cardiovascular disease or sudden death, about 70 per cent.

2. PERSONAL DATA. Loss of one or both parents prior to adolescence as a result of accident, suicide, or serious illness, frequently operation. Average economic background. Low marriage rate, few children per marriage, few divorces.

3. HEALTH RECORD. Poor health record with upper respiratory infections, gastrointestinal disorders, allergies, minor operations and pelvic disorders predominating.

4. INJURIES. Rarely more than one injury, rate for one accident above average and accidents were mainly minor and of the cardiac type.

Group Statistics

CARDIAC ARRHYTHMIAS

FAMILY HISTORY. Cardiovascular disease in parents and siblings, 44 per cent. Accident history for parents and siblings, about 18 per cent. Extreme nervousness, about 56 per cent; highest for any group studied. Exposure to cardiovascular disease or to sudden death in 65 per cent of the cases.

PERSONAL DATA. Both parents lived well into the patient's adolescence, and were generally limiting to the patient's activities, especially in the sphere of sex. Middle-class moderately comfortable background. Tendency to be first child. Low marriage rate. Few children, few divorces.

HEALTH RECORD. Poor previous health record, closely paralleling that for coronary patients except for relative freedom from hypertensive cardiovascular disease and pelvic disorders.

INJURIES. Highest of any group studied for more than one accident except for fracture. Low record for single injury. Accidents just prior to onset of illness, not in childhood.

DIABETES

1. FAMILY HISTORY. Diabetes, about 35 per cent, especially in maternal ancestry. Also cardiovascular disease, about 26 per cent, especially among the males of the family. Accidents, 9 per cent. Nervousness, and insanity, about 35 per cent. And exposure to one or more of these illnesses, 100 per cent.

2. PERSONAL DATA. At least one parent living well into patient's adult life. The subacute struggle with parents usually continued throughout life. A tendency, especially among the males, to remain unmarried, and a tendency on the part of both males and females to have few children and few actual divorces although many periods of living apart from marital partner.

3. HEALTH RECORD. Good previous record—best of any group except fracture, but differing from fracture pattern in being higher with patients in whom the onset was late. Women poor pelvic histories.

4. INJURIES. Low accident record prior to onset of diabetes, but relatively high record subsequent to onset. Childhood accidents average.

Individual Picture (Part 1)

FRACTURES	CORONARY INSUFFICIENCY AND OCCLUSION

5. GENERAL ADJUSTMENT:

A. *Education.* Some tendency to interrupt in the middle, lack of planning, marked in group B which is predominantly male. Group as a whole nearer to baseline than other groups studied. Generally good intellectual level, especially in group B.

B. *Work Record.* In types A and C tendency to stick to one job but without trying to advance status. Many and diverse jobs in type B.

C. *Income and Vocational Level.* High. Marked by sudden changes in type B. Occupational distribution close to baseline, with concentration in class III (clerks, salesmen, stenographers). Percentage in skilled labor same as coronary.

D. *Social Relationships.* "Good fellow." No marked tendency to dominate or submit. Tendency to aggressive self-reliance. Not likely to curry favor with either sex. Tendency to eccentricity in type B.

E. *Sexual Adjustment.* Superficially good. No tendency to emphasize sexual problems, combined (especially in type B) with lack of real emotional contact. Careful to avoid infection in promiscuous relationships but without exaggerated fear.

F. *Attitude Toward Family.* Dispersion of tendencies among groups A, B, C. Trend toward irresponsibility in group B.

6. CHARACTERISTIC BEHAVIOR PATTERN. Make up their minds definitely and quickly. Focus on immediate values rather than long-range goals. Social rather than power interest. Striving toward integration and autonomy, outside of authoritarian hierarchy. Tendency to attach emotions to people and immediate concrete experience. Little emotional interest in intellectual values and verbalization. Defensive tendency to appear casual about feelings and personal problems. Group B marked adventurous trend and avoidance of responsibility. Living from day to day.

---

5. GENERAL ADJUSTMENT:

A. *Education.* Marked tendency to complete educational unit undertaken Planned career.

B. *Work Record.* Sticking to one job working to the top.

C. *Income and Vocational Level.* Highest of all groups studied. Characteristically class II (executives and officials)

D. *Social Relationships.* Generally respected. Tendency to dominate. Argumentative with men, attentive to women.

E. *Sexual Adjustment.* Role of exemplary husband (and father) combined with frustration and often secret promiscuity; high venereal disease rate Emphasize sexual problems (overt anxiety).

F. *Attitude Toward Family.* Hostile toward father, passive though often hostile and fearful toward mother. With wife and children attempt to be boss and "carry the burden," combined with demand for care and attention.

6. CHARACTERISTIC BEHAVIOR PATTERN Compulsively consistent action. Tendency to work long hours and not take vacations. Tendency to seize authority; dislike of sharing responsibility. Conversation an instrument of domination and aggression Tendency to attach emotions to ideas and goals. Articulate about feelings. Living for future.

Individual Picture (Part 1)

| HYPERTENSIVE CARDIOVASCULAR DISEASE | ANGINAL SYNDROME |

HYPERTENSIVE CARDIOVASCULAR DISEASE

. GENERAL ADJUSTMENT:

A. *Education.* Relatively low educational level. This, however, is not consistent with intellectual capacity which tends to be average or above.

B. *Work Record.* Tendency to work to the top but constantly falling short. Inclined to choose an occupation below their capacity.

C. *Income and Vocational Level.* Low. Represented in all classes but predominantly V and VI (unskilled laborers and WPA).

D. *Social Relationships.* Shy, sensitive, and fearful of not making the grade. Use of wine, women, and song to compensate. Urge to fit conventional pattern. Lack of emotional adaptability in intimate relationships.

E. *Sexual Adjustment.* Attempt to follow cultural pattern as husband and father. Need to demonstrate superiority over wife, secretly and often compulsively promiscuous; insecure and frequently impotent or frigid. High venereal disease record; women many abortions.

F. *Attitude Toward Family.* Ambivalent toward father, passive though often hostile and fearful toward mother. With wife and children attempt to be boss and "carry the burden" combined with demand for care and attention.

5. CHARACTERISTIC BEHAVIOR PATTERN. Urge to keep peace. Alternation between tendency to seek satisfaction within themselves and devotion to achievement of external, long-range goals.

ANGINAL SYNDROME

5. GENERAL ADJUSTMENT:

A. *Education.* Tendency to pursue academic education to high level but less tendency than coronary to finish unit undertaken.

B. *Work Record.* Sticking to one job but usually in a more individualistic field than coronary group.

C. *Income and Vocational Level.* High with leaning toward artistic pursuits.

D. *Social Relationships.* Generally liked. Tendency to dominate indirectly.

E. *Sexual Adjustment.* Similar to coronary with more anxiety and insecurity. Venereal disease rate high but lower than coronary group.

F. *Attitude Toward Family.* Ambivalent toward both parents and toward spouse and children.

6. CHARACTERISTIC BEHAVIOR PATTERN. Similar to that of patients with coronary occlusion, but more outlet in artistic channels, and enjoyment of, as well as a much more vivid, dream and fantasy life; also a greater awareness of anxiety and fear.

Individual Picture (Part 1)

RHEUMATIC FEVER AND RHEUMA-TOID ARTHRITIS	RHEUMATIC HEART DISEASE

5. GENERAL ADJUSTMENT:

A. *Education.* Average record. (Type B tendency to complete units undertaken; type A opposite tendency.)

B. *Work Record.* Variable.

C. *Income and Vocational Level.* Characteristically classes III and V (stenographers and unskilled workers).

D. *Social Relationships.* Shy, childish and not well liked.

E. *Sexual Adjustment.* Fear of sex and marriage. Average venereal disease history.

F. *Attitude Toward Family.* Marked (inadequately expressed) resentment toward both parents with tendency to exploit them. Identification with parent of opposite sex and homosexual trend in later relationships. Resentful of children.

6. CHARACTERISTIC BEHAVIOR PATTERN. Posing as good sport, combined with diplomacy and appeal for sympathy. Quiet, sensitive, a few good friends but uncomfortable in groups, especially type B. Realization of ambitions in dreams and fantasy.

---

5. GENERAL ADJUSTMENT:

A. *Education.* Relatively low, partly influenced by the illness and medical advice given in early childhood. Patients whose first attacks occurred after grammar school near average in educational achievement with some tendency to complete units undertaken.

B. *Work Record.* Variable, with some tendency to stick to the same job especially when there was an attachment to the superior.

C. *Income and Vocational Level.* Low but characteristically classes III and V (stenographers and unskilled workers). High percentage in class VI (dependent).

D. *Social Relationships.* Generally liked because of desire to please and childish appeal (particularly true of females) interest in adventure and tendency to be good story tellers. Generally responsive and submissive.

E. *Sexual Adjustment.* Fear of sex and marriage and a martyr tendency. Average venereal disease history, high abortion rate, both spontaneous and artificial.

F. *Attitude Toward Family.* Fear of both parents with a fearfully dependent reaction, usually toward the parent who seemed to be the more terrifying except that the trend is often changed by the early death of one parent or the other. Role of martyr in relation to parents, spouse, children.

6. CHARACTERISTIC BEHAVIOR PATTERN. In general agreeable, talkative, vaguely ambitious with a tendency to overdo in an inconsistent way. Emphasis on social and pleasure ambitions which are frequently impossible of fulfillment and never persistently strived for. Otherwise their sociability follows the pattern of the rheumatic fever group except that they seem to want to be liked by more people and have a tendency to bluff and curry favor.

Individual Picture (Part 1)

| CARDIAC ARRHYTHMIAS | DIABETES |

CARDIAC ARRHYTHMIAS

. GENERAL ADJUSTMENT:

A. *Education*. High educational record especially among males but no marked tendency to complete educational unit.

B. *Work Record*. Somewhat unstable.

C. *Income and Vocational Level*. Next to coronaries, highest of all groups studied. Characteristically class II (proprietors, executives, and officials) and class III (clerks, salesmen and stenographers).

D. *Social Relationships*. Pleasing, adaptive manner. Generally liked. When most insecure tend to be flighty and alternate between shyness and exhibitionism.

E. *Sexual Adjustment*. Considerable confusion about sex combined with fear and disgust. High frequency of self-induced abortion. Average venereal disease.

F. *Attitude Toward Family*. Emotional relationship inadequate but continued. No consistent preference for one parent or the other. Confused identification. Tendency to exaggerate family disputes in which the patient took sides usually with the stricter of the two. Fearful toward spouse and children.

. CHARACTERISTIC BEHAVIOR PATTERN: Hysterically inconsistent action. Fearful of expressing hostility. Often morose when alone and with close friends but cheerful with strangers or in large groups. Rather free use of activity, verbalization and fantasy. Articulate about feelings. Most spontaneous emotionally when incorporating fantasies in responses to others. Work well with adequate external inducement.

DIABETES

5. GENERAL ADJUSTMENT:

A. *Education*. High level with marked interest in advancement but a frequent incidence of nervous breakdown in college.

B. *Work Record*. Disinclination to assume responsibility. Unable to take initiative in important matters. Inability to manage personal relationships often cause of loss of job.

C. *Income and Vocational Level*. Somewhat lower than educational level even prior to the onset of the illness. Diverse occupational distribution with positive deviation from general population in class II (proprietors) and class III (clerks, stenographers).

D. *Social Relationships*. Marked social anxiety, superficially agreeable but self-conscious and inaccessible.

E. *Sexual Adjustment*. Marked by anxiety and inadequacy with homosexual trend. Marriage more frequent in passive than in active types. Low venereal disease rate.

F. *Attitude Toward Family*. Marked conflict between hatred of parents and submission. Same attitude repeated toward spouse.

6. CHARACTERISTIC BEHAVIOR PATTERN: Inability to follow any consistent course of action, vacillation and indecisiveness. Conversation to win sympathy. Focusing of emotion on suffering.

Individual Picture (Part 2)

<table>
<tr><td align="center">FRACTURES</td><td align="center">CORONARY INSUFFICIENCY
AND OCCLUSION</td></tr>
</table>

7. NEUROTIC TRAITS. High percentage of early neurotic traits, especially lying, stealing and truancy, sleep-walking and sleep-talking. Later life almost no obvious neurotic traits (some infantile trends) except for small group, particularly women, with phobias, especially fear of falling.

8. ADDICTIONS AND INTERESTS. Tendency to use stimulants (coffee, cigarettes, alcohol) for pleasure or to let off steam. Marked interest in competitive sports or gambling (football, baseball, racing, auto-racing), and machinery. Practicing orthodox authoritative religion (institutionalized super-ego).

9. LIFE SITUATION IMMEDIATELY PRIOR TO ONSET. Situations threatening individual autonomy in which direct release of aggression would be too costly. Often connected with actual or contemplated shifts in job.

10. REACTION TO ILLNESS. Bravado or fatalism about specific symptoms, or else exaggerated interest (insecurity) plus poor tolerance of pain; either one frequently combined with tendency to exploit injury for compensations, financial or other.

11. AREA OF FOCAL CONFLICT AND CHARACTERISTIC REACTION. Authority —avoidance. Attempt to establish personal autonomy, to avoid authority relationships (marked passive-active conflict). Little identification with authority figures or concepts.

7. NEUROTIC TRAITS. Few early neurotic traits, tendency to brood and keep their troubles to themselves. In later life inner tension and a tendency to depression which is rarely admitted to others, together with compulsive asceticism and drive to work.

8. ADDICTIONS AND INTERESTS. Tendency to take stimulants to help keep on working (overwork). Little interest in sports, few hobbies. Skepticism about religion. Marked interest in philosophy.

9. LIFE SITUATION IMMEDIATELY PRIOR TO ONSET. Exposure to shock—especially in job or in relinquishment of authority.

10. REACTION TO ILLNESS. Tendency to minimize symptoms and self-neglect.

11. AREA OF FOCAL CONFLICT AND CHARACTERISTIC REACTION. Authority—attempt to be and subdue authority; identification with authority and authority concepts.

Individual Picture (Part 2)

HYPERTENSIVE CARDIOVASCULAR DISEASE	ANGINAL SYNDROME

7. NEUROTIC TRAITS. Low percentage of early neurotic traits, and these in the main nightmares, temper tantrums, nail-biting. Present—obsessive doubts, compulsive traits, particularly perfectionistic inclinaions, and outbursts of rage as a reaction against their passive tendencies. These later come out in their dependence on food, and usually also on someone in a parental role.

7. NEUROTIC TRAITS. Same general type as in patients with coronary occlusion but more phobias and nightmares, and relatively fewer compulsions. In general more outspoken neurotic traits. Tendency to dream about accidents involving death of someone.

8. ADDICTIONS AND INTERESTS. Excessive use of coffee, cigarettes, and alcohol. Some interest in athletics—not competitive sports but rather golf, hunting and riding. Major interest wine, women and song.

8. ADDICTIONS AND INTERESTS. Tendency to take stimulants to help work. Little interest in sports or hobbies. Aesthetic interests. Skepticism about religion. As compared with the coronary group more Roman Catholics and fewer Jews.

9. LIFE SITUATION IMMEDIATELY PRIOR TO ONSET. Death of someone loved or separation from them, or set-back in the field of patient's ambition, usually combined with greater indulgence in compensatory gratifications such as food, coffee, and alcohol.

9. LIFE SITUATION IMMEDIATELY PRIOR TO ONSET. Exposure to shock, death of relative or friend; secondarily, financial reverses or relinquishment of prestige.

10. REACTION TO ILLNESS. Usually a giving in to passive tendencies, using the illness as an alibi for failure and insistence on being taken care of. Occasionally, however, like the coronary, the patient disregards health and attempts to keep on in spite of it.

10. REACTION TO ILLNESS. Tendency either to minimize symptoms and go on in spite of them or to make excessive demands for care.

11. AREA OF FOCAL CONFLICT AND CHARACTERISTIC REACTION. Situations involving aggression and passivity—rivalry and self-defeat.

11. AREA OF FOCAL CONFLICT AND CHARACTERISTIC REACTION. Rivalry with authority but more important to be as good as superior than to surpass him—tendency to imitate rather than outdo father and tendency to be one's own boss rather than the boss of others.

Individual Picture (Part 2)

| RHEUMATIC FEVER AND RHEUMATOID ARTHRITIS | RHEUMATIC HEART DISEASE |

RHEUMATIC FEVER AND RHEUMATOID ARTHRITIS

7. NEUROTIC TRAITS. Second only to fracture group in history of early neurotic traits, particularly temper tantrums, nightmares, sleep-walking, sleep-talking, finickiness about food, nail-biting, tics. As adults, marked mood swings, continuation of nightmares, guilt and depression often related to masturbation, homosexual tendency; absorption in cleanliness, being on time and general perfectionistic trend.

8. ADDICTIONS AND INTERESTS. Addictions not particularly striking, except to patent medicine and drugs. Impulse to athletic activity beyond their strength, especially among girls and small men (especially type A). Early disillusioned with religion.

9. LIFE SITUATION IMMEDIATELY PRIOR TO ONSET. Disruption of emotional attachments through change of environment; separation of parents; extreme hardship, and so on.

10. REACTION TO ILLNESS. Tendency to get satisfaction out of suffering (type A): or to overdo and disregard doctor's orders (type B). Increasing escape from reality in dreams and fantasy.

11. AREA OF FOCAL CONFLICT AND CHARACTERISTIC REACTION. Sexual role— identification with opposite sex; authority —avoidance or submission.

RHEUMATIC HEART DISEASE

7. NEUROTIC TRAITS. Childhood phobias exaggerated fright reactions, nightmares In adult life a continuation of these same traits with marked claustrophobia or ago raphobia, and a tendency to develop deep admiration for people that frighten or abuse them. Infantile fixation.

8. ADDICTIONS AND INTERESTS. A tendency to deny themselves (martyrdom— especially females) or to over-indulge in stimulants (rebellion and group identification—especially males). Wish for adventure and action. Especially among the males a tendency to ride hobbies and to become religious zealots.

9. LIFE SITUATION IMMEDIATELY PRIOR TO ONSET. Unusual exertion in one of the compensatory spheres, a severe fright or a traumatic death.

10. REACTION TO ILLNESS. Attempt to deny it but enjoy sympathy and unconsciously increase their suffering. Little insight.

11. AREA OF FOCAL CONFLICT AND CHARACTERISTIC REACTION. Authority— emulation of superior especially in fantasy; secondarily, conflict over sexual role together with a tendency to curry favor with the opposite sex. Extreme dominance of passive tendency discernible before illness.

Individual Picture (Part 2)

CARDIAC ARRHYTHMIAS

7. NEUROTIC TRAITS. Childhood phobias, exaggerated fright reactions, nightmares, enuresis often continued well into adolescence and nail-biting. Some tendency to sleep-walking, especially among males. In adult life, continuation of phobias, especially claustrophobia. Much overt anxiety and overactive fantasy life.

8. ADDICTIONS AND INTERESTS. Excessive smoking and addiction to coffee, especially in the males for social reasons or for the fun of being "bad." Lack of interest in athletics but much interest in gambling. Diverse social interests, especially in activities which would bring them into the lime light. Considerable interest in religion, especially religious or moral principles.

9. LIFE SITUATION IMMEDIATELY PRIOR TO ONSET. Gradual sense of failure with precipitation of symptoms by some traumatic experience in the sphere of personal relationships.

10. REACTION TO ILLNESS. Fear and discouragement.

11. AREA OF FOCAL CONFLICT AND CHARACTERISTIC REACTION. Problem of finding themselves in the outside world, of determining their role in life. React with characteristics wavering between withdrawal and attempt to be effectual.

DIABETES

7. NEUROTIC TRAITS. Temper trantrums, phobias, and nightmares. In adult life nervousness, depression, suspicion with a tendency to paranoid ideas.

8. ADDICTIONS AND INTERESTS. Interest in food. Preoccupation with innumerable odd jobs, diverting energy from major tasks. Avoidance of competitive sports; interest in animals. Little interest in religion, except when awareness of homosexuality led to religious experiment, usually with ascetic or fanatic trend.

9. LIFE SITUATION IMMEDIATELY PRIOR TO ONSET. Long period of wear and tear, including hard work, homosexual conflict, struggle with family and spouse. Often dietary indiscretion.

10. REACTION TO ILLNESS. Depression alternating with a feeling of relief at having an alibi for inadequacy. Suspiciousness of others with a marked tendency to project.

11. AREA OF FOCAL CONFLICT AND CHARACTERISTIC REACTION. Responsibility (dependence versus independence—vacillation). Sexual role (ambivalence).

Chapter X

PSYCHOSOMATIC DIAGNOSIS IN COMBINED OR OVERLAPPING SYNDROMES

Die Ärzte glauben, ihrem Patienten sehr viel genutzt zu haben, wenn sie seiner Krankheit einen Namen geben.—KANT.

I. GENERAL NATURE AND MAGNITUDE OF THE PROBLEM

The physician who uses the personality profiles as an aid in psychosomatic diagnosis will be puzzled by the question: "What about patients suffering simultaneously or successively from two or more of these illnesses?" Kant has warned against too much satisfaction in a name and the same warning should apply to any arbitrary application of the profiles. Any experienced physician or anyone familiar with Osler's discussion of differential diagnosis knows that some symptoms characteristic of certain diseases may be absent in a given case and that unexpected and complicating symptoms may be present. Osler's general approach to the evaluation of such observations should be followed: It is the total constellation of all symptoms that is pathognomonic; when incongruous symptoms are found, a coexisting illness or an unusual complication may be present. Marked divergence from the personality profiles outlined in the direction either of traits lacking or traits added and inconsistent should be given special diagnostic attention.

Out of the 1600 patients on whom this analysis is based about 20 per cent suffered from two or more of the syndromes here discussed. Interestingly enough less than 1 per cent of these patients had suffered from three of these syndromes. In no instance did a patient have more than three of the eight syndromes considered, except for one patient who on first admission was diagnosed rheumatic fever and on second admission rheumatic heart disease in combination with two other syndromes.

Hypertensive cardiovascular disease was a common factor in all cases with three combined syndromes. In one case the patient had rheumatic fever and coronary occlusion also, in a second case, diabetes and coronary occlusion, in another rheumatic fever and anginal syndrome. In the exceptional case hypertension was combined with rheumatic fever, an accident habit, and rheumatic heart disease. This last combination is probably the least to be expected since it would mean the combination in one person of two distinctly different personality types. Study of this patient, whose history will be discussed later, in detail, does indicate that a personality change took place.

The highest percentages of overlapping syndromes, 32 and 31 per cent, respectively, were found in patients with coronary occlusion and in those with hypertensive cardiovascular disease. Diabetes and anginal syndrome ranked third and fourth, with 30 and 29 per cent, respectively. In a much lower bracket were patients with cardiac arrhythmia (19 per cent), rheumatic heart disease (16 per cent), fractures (15 per cent), and patients with rheumatic fever (14 per cent). It is interesting that these last four groups are the groups with the highest incidence of overt neurotic symptoms. More interesting than these figures, however, is the nature of the combination of illnesses characteristic of each group studied.

An important test of the hypothesis that there is a relationship between personality type and predisposition to a given syndrome may be found in the incidence of the several syndromes among the patients studied. The relative infrequency, in the series, of patients with two or more syndromes and the nature of such combinations as were found provides additional evidence.

If the incidence of the several diseases under discussion was according to a chance distribution, there would be no reason to expect any regularity in the occurrence of two or more of them in single individuals. Or, to put the matter in a different way, one would expect that among those suffering from fracture, let us say, and some other disease as well, the identity of the other disease would be scattered among a large variety of syndromes. Yet the data show such an obvious divergence from scattered or chance distribution that it is not necessary to demonstrate it by statistical calculations.

With nine disease groups (taken from 2 to 9 at a time) there is a mathematical possibility of 502 combinations among the syndromes studied, or if rheumatic fever types A and B are considered as one syndrome, 247 combinations. Yet in this series there were only 22 combinations of syndromes, even including combinations exemplified by only one patient each.

The figures suggest on their face that in the cases having two or

TABLE XII

OCCURRENCE OF OVERLAP COMBINATIONS IN TERMS OF PER CENT
OF TOTAL GROUP

(It may be noted that of a possible 247 combinations or types of overlap — combinations of eight taken from two to eight at a time — only twenty-one were found; and of those found all but four were a combination of two groups only.)

Overlap Type	FR	HCVD	COR	ANG	RF	RHD	CA	DIAB	Percentage Occurrence in Total Combined Groups
FR–HCVD	4	6							2.43
FR–ANG	.8			5					0.68
FR–RF	11				11				5.53
FR–RHD	.8					4			0.65
FR–CA	6						35		5.33
FR–DIAB	6							13	3.85
HCVD–COR		9	27						6.67
HCVD–ANG		5		20					4.04
HCVD–RF		20			13				7.80
HCVD–RHD		4				12			2.86
HCVD–CA		1					4		0.98
HCVD–DIAB		11						16	6.72
COR–RF			12		2				1.97
COR–DIAB			4					2	1.23
ANG–RF				10	2				1.37
ANG–CA				5			4		2.33
RHD–DIAB						4		2	1.23
FR–HCVD–RF	.8	1			.8				.03
HCVD–COR–RF		1	4		.8				0.43
HCVD–COR–DIAB		1	4					2	0.63
HCVD–ANG–RF		1		5	.8				0.44

Explanation: Reading down indicates percentages of a given total group each overlap type constitutes; reading across, percentage of each total group a given overlap type constitutes. A total group is here defined as number of patients having a given syndrome, although some may have one (or sometimes two) syndromes in addition.

It has seemed more logical to consider each of the four double overlaps as two single overlaps as well; hence total percentage overlap for a given total group above is sum of each column minus sum of last four in column, i.e., the double overlaps treated as double overlaps.

more diseases, a factor predisposing to both should be looked for. The nature of the diseases found in combination eliminates the probability that this is an external physical agency such as a microbe or a poison or even a given type of diet, constitution, or heredity. Nor is there reason to suppose, in most cases, that one disease was a result of the other, in the sense of purely somatic etiology. (The only marked exception is in those suffering from coronary occlusion who had previously had hypertension or anginal syndrome, but even here there is necessary an explanation of the difference between those hypertensive or anginal cases which developed coronary disease and those which did not.) The chief remaining possibility of a common factor is in the personality organization of the patient, that is, his focal conflict and characteristic manner of dealing with it.

It may be objected that the neurotic symptoms discovered in the patients may have been an accompaniment of the somatic difficulty rather than a pre-existing factor. It is of course well known that certain diseases emphasize or bring out certain neurotic traits. Yet it is important to note that in every case the study of the patient's personality type is based not simply on observation of his reaction to the given disease, but on a psychosomatic history extending back to his childhood.

The *fracture* group overlapped with patients with rheumatic fever 5.6 per cent, and with patients with cardiac arrhythmia 4.7 per cent. The only other overlap was one of 4.7 per cent with patients with hypertension, but this latter was characteristic of fracture patients without an accident habit. This is particularly striking since the patients in the *rheumatic fever* group had their major overlap with the fracture group (7.5 per cent) and patients with *cardiac arrhythmia* their major overlap with the fracture group (19 per cent). Since the rheumatic fever patients with an accident habit were all in the personality group designated as type A, this gives a tendency to the accident habit of 14 per cent for this characterological type of rheumatic fever patient.

With reference to the study cited earlier suggesting high blood pressure as possibly a predisposing factor to accident, we may note that our material certainly does not tend to confirm this possibility.* Although there were some patients with hypertension in the accident group (4.7 per cent), these were among patients without a well-

* See page 184 and especially Bingham.[38]

developed accident habit; and furthermore, although hypertensive cardiovascular disease is the second major syndrome found in combination with rheumatic fever, the rheumatic fever patients with hypertensive cardiovascular disease were of personality type B and did not have accidents.

Patients with *hypertensive cardiovascular disease*. The major additional syndrome for patients with hypertensive cardiovascular disease was rheumatic fever (slightly over 20 per cent), which is interesting in that, as already noted, the second major overlap of rheumatic fever patients was with the hypertensive group (6 per cent), and the remaining percentage of overlaps for both these groups was with coronary disease and anginal syndrome, except for one patient in the hypertensive group who had a mild diabetes.

Patients with *coronary disease or anginal syndrome*, as would be expected, had as their major associated syndrome hypertensive cardiovascular disease (23 per cent and 9 per cent, respectively). In each case rheumatic fever was second, but only about 4 per cent. From the point of view of combined syndromes, the anginal group showed a greater scattering, having accident habit (5 per cent) and severe cardiac arrhythmia on a neurotic basis (5 per cent).

Patients with *rheumatic heart disease*, like those with rheumatic fever, had their major overlapping with the fracture and hypertensive groups, but among these patients hypertensive cardiovascular disease came first (12 per cent) and the accident habit second (4 per cent).

Patients with *diabetes* had as their major additional syndrome hypertensive cardiovascular disease (15 per cent) as would be expected. But in 14 per cent, the accident habit was well established prior to the onset of the diabetes, a point to which attention has not been called in the literature on diabetes.

In brief then, the nature of the syndromes in combination in each group looks very different from a matter of chance distribution.

Since the greatest variety of types of overlap involves either fracture or hypertensive cardiovascular disease, and since these two syndromes represent widely divergent personality patterns, examples of most of the types of overlapping syndromes found have been given under these two captions, whatever the illness which was primary or dominant at the time of the patient's admission. Under a third caption are illustrated the combinations cardiac arrhythmia-hypertensive cardiovascular disease, cardiac arrhythmia-anginal syndrome, cardiac arrhythmia-fracture, because the cardiac arrhythmia personality is also distinctive. In contrast with the fracture patients who discharge tension in spontaneous activity, and in contrast with the sufferers from hypertensive cardiovascular disease who inhibit spontaneous activity and expressions of aggression, these patients react to difficulties by verbalization and neurotic symptom formation. This arrangement of syndrome combinations recalls Sherrington's three patterns of release of emotional tensions. In each group of overlapping syndromes, however, it has been made clear which syndrome was primary and which secondary.* The pattern suggested by Sherrington has been used because of its appeal to the clinician. It is, however, misleading in several ways (see Chapter XI, section IV).

II. The Accident Habit as Associated with Other Syndromes

Considerable light is thrown on accident-proneness by a study of accident-habit patients found in the several disease groups, including fracture. (It will be noted that not all the fracture patients are accident-prone, and not all the accident-prone patients have a history of fracture.) The figures are: †

Of Patients With	Per Cent Having Accident Habit
Fracture	80
Cardiac arrhythmia	19
Diabetes	14
‡Rheumatic fever type A	14
Anginal syndrome	5
Rheumatic heart disease	4
‡Rheumatic fever type B	0
Coronary occlusion	0
Hypertensive cardiovascular disease	0

* Whereas we found twenty-one syndrome combinations we have illustrated only eleven, because some of the combinations of two were covered by the four examples given of patients in whom three syndromes were combined. The combinations fracture-hypertensive cardiovascular disease, and fracture-rheumatic heart disease, are not illustrated separately because they are both covered by one case in which these syndromes were combined (page 600). Also hypertensive cardiovascular disease-anginal syndrome, hypertensive cardiovascular disease-rheumatic fever, hypertensive cardiovascular disease-rheumatic heart disease, anginal syndrome-rheumatic fever, coronary occlusion-rheumatic fever, coronary occlusion-diabetes, are not illustrated separately because they are all covered by the cases on pages 625, 627, 635.

† The figures given here differ from those in the preceding chapter in that all patients having combined syndromes are listed under the heading of each of the syndromes present.

‡ For discussion of injuries in these two groups see Chapter IX.

An interesting case is that of a patient with rheumatic disease, whose personality type shifted from what we have called rheumatic fever type A (the accident pattern) to type B (the cardiac pattern) together with the development of rheumatic heart disease and hypertension. In reading his history one can note that here, in the same person, one constellation of personality traits was associated with one syndrome, while another constellation was associated with another, overlapping syndrome. In each instance, the personality type conformed with that which we have previously identified with the syndrome in question (page 604).

RHEUMATIC FEVER—ACCIDENTS—RHEUMATIC HEART DISEASE— HYPERTENSION

(Syndromes Consecutive)

Case No. RF 304. A boy, aged 18, was admitted to the hospital with the diagnosis of chronic rheumatic heart disease with mitral and aortic insufficiency, hypertension, anxiety state. He had had an attack of rheumatic fever at the age of 11 which kept him in bed for seven weeks with severe polyarthritis. Although this patient was born in New York City where he lived for six years, he had been for five years in New Jersey and this attack occurred when he moved back to New York.

He had a second attack with marked polyarthritis for which he had had hospital treatment for three months, a year prior to the present admission.

Family History. This patient was among the 25 per cent of our rheumatic fever patients whose family history included rheumatic fever: the mother had had rheumatic fever just before the patient was born, a grandfather had "heart murmur," and both parents were exceedingly nervous.

Personal Data. As in the case of the typical rheumatic fever patient, both parents were living and the subacute conflict had been constant. As the patient himself said: "There is always tension between us. Father is a washout and makes Mother and me mad because he keeps putting on airs. She's very nervous and always sore at Father, but I get on pretty well with her."

Previous Health. This patient suffered from bronchitis at 10 and frequent attacks of grippe, acute sore throat, and rhinitis. He had a tonsillectomy and adenoidectomy at the age of 12 after his first attack of rheumatic fever.

Previous Injury. At the age of 6 when he first moved from the city to his grandfather's farm, the patient fractured his right clavicle. And at the age of 11, when he moved back to the city he fractured his left clavicle.

This happened just after the first attack of rheumatic fever. There were a number of minor injuries in between.

General Adjustment. The patient "quit" high school at 16 because he didn't want to be like his father, "just hanging around the house and doing nothing." He worked for six months as a newspaper boy and then went to work on his grandfather's farm. He didn't like his grandfather so went to work in New York in a restaurant. He gave up this job after three months because that, too, was unpleasant, and he was in danger of being fired anyway because he broke so many dishes on account of nervousness. He then planned to go to a school for dental mechanics but had to give up the idea because he had not completed high school. He became depressed, could not make up his mind what to do, and had his second attack of rheumatic fever.

His *characteristic behavior pattern* was also typical for type A patients with rheumatic fever, especially his appeal for sympathy. In spite of his ability to make friends easily he was uncomfortable in groups and had very few good friends and these of his own sex. He stated that he was too nervous to dance or to be with many people at a time.

Neurotic Traits. Early sleep-walking and sleep-talking (like the accident patient) with a shift in the direction of nightmares (*cf.* later).

Area of Focal Conflict and Characteristic Reaction. This patient's focal conflict was also that of the rheumatic fever patient: difficulty with his sexual role and authority. He admired his mother and wanted to be like her rather than like his father or grandfather. He was unable to get along with girls, preferred boys, although he was uncomfortable with them too because of his girlishness. He was very much worried about masturbation, which he tried to repress. In talking about it he said: "I wouldn't do such a thing. At least if I could help it. Usually I feel it coming and catch myself." He had frequent wet dreams from which he woke up in a panic. His other nightmares were about fighting. "I'm always fighting with my father for no reason at all. I just fight, wrestle and hit him, then run and usually run into somebody."

It is clear that so far this patient followed the pattern that we have called rheumatic fever type A with a tendency to have accidents, a tendency to get into trouble with authority, failure to stick to his job, lack of vocational planning, social anxiety, and choice of friends among members of his own sex. The onset of the second attack of rheumatic fever followed a long period of subacute conflict with his family and employers, plus a change of environment from a farm in the country to a restaurant in New York City.

Then came the change in attitude and in somatic symptoms. While the patient was in the hospital with his second attack of rheumatic fever he did a good deal of thinking about himself. He said: "At first I was so sick I thought I was dead, and *when I became conscious again and began to get better it seemed as if* I was a different person." He decided that he wanted to finish high school and take civil service examinations and then perhaps become a clerk or a stenographer. He decided that he must make up his mind to take a *"responsible position,"* that before *he had been too much like his father.* He *began to admire his brother-in-law,* assistant manager in a cafeteria. *He developed hypertension.*

The medical note when he was in the hospital a year later with *rheumatic heart disease* contains the following interesting statement: "Although this patient seems to have had pericardial effusion a year ago there was no diastolic murmur heard, and the blood pressure was 130/60. It is difficult to see how his cardiac lesion could have progressed to the present point since then." A further statement from the medical record was: "This was an interesting diagnostic problem in a person with known organic heart disease, and presenting symptoms of palpitation and nervousness. The solution lay between an impending cardiac break, hyperthyroidism, or psychic instability. The first two having apparently been ruled out, the latter seems most probable."

On discharge his blood pressure was 146/100. The discharge diagnosis was: rheumatic heart disease, inactive; aortic insufficiency; hypertension; anxiety state. Continued treatment by the consulting psychiatrist was recommended.

A follow-up note for this patient five years later, reads as follows:

(1) *Letter to his psychiatrist.* "I was under your care five years ago and due to your talks with me I improved rapidly. About a year ago I began to notice a change in myself which I did not like. . . . I called you about a month ago to arrange for an appointment. I didn't go through with it because I thought I could help myself. I would appreciate seeing you soon."

(2) *Psychiatrist's note.* This patient held a job as salesman for about three years, after he was last seen, and worked up to the position of manager. This position he could not hold because, as he said: "I just couldn't stand so much responsibility. It made me discouraged with myself because I was failing again, then I thought of going back to dental mechanics but there's too much competition. The only way I might make a living in that field would be if I could open a laboratory of my own. While I was worrying about all this I started to be sick again and decided to take it easy. So I haven't worked for a while but that's no good either."

The patient is a member of a social club and they intend to start a magazine for social clubs. For the moment he has staked his future in that. But together with his failure to carry the responsibility of his job as a manager in which he had achieved the ideal of becoming like his brother-in-law, also a manager, came a fear of social groups.

The patient is bigger and stronger than when last seen. He has matured noticeably but he still cannot break away from his mother: "It would break Mother's heart if I moved out." The conflict is intensified by the fact that he is going regularly with a girl but having no sexual experience. His moral scruples prevent his either marrying her and leaving his mother or allowing himself any premarital sexual life.

Although this patient made considerable progress following his few talks on the ward five years ago, his personality conflicts are still too strong for him and the possibilities of adequate adjustment are slight without extensive treatment which at present is impossible for him.

(3) *A note three months later reads.* The patient has solved the conflict described above by giving up his girl and taking a job as a salesman again, thus freeing himself from the necessity of carrying too much responsibility. He is not happy about these decisions but feels himself not enough of a man to do anything better.

(4) *Final note on the chart at the end of another three months.* The patient came to the hospital with fever of 102° F. and headaches. He is worried about his heart although this appears all right, says he just does not feel well, wants general check-up. The hypertension had disappeared with the resolution of the conflict (as described above). Was referred to his family doctor.

These notes, brief as they are, are significant from two points of view. (1) Very brief psychotherapy helped this patient to make great progress in the way of a normal adjustment in the vocational and social fields. During this time he was symptom-free, but just as he seemed about to achieve his goal—a responsible job and a wife—his earlier neurotic character traits came in to thwart him. (2) Although he put up a good fight, without adequate psychiatric treatment it was a downhill process, and at the end of a year he succumbed to his characteristic illness.

In view of the progress made by this patient as a result of the first period of treatment, one might question the wisdom of the decision to leave him to his own devices since intensive psychotherapy was needed but not feasible. It should be noted, however, that this decision was actually made because at the time of the patient's return, the ten-year study reported in this volume had been terminated temporarily, and the patient's psychiatrist had returned to the outpatient department staff. The patient was then subjected to the unfortunate situations existing in most of our clinics—inadequate staff time to take care of therapeutic needs.

This history suggests that the patient actually did become a "different person," as he said, during his second attack of rheumatic fever. He resembled the fracture patients in his initial manner of dealing with conflicts with authority, particularly his father. He attempted to avoid further conflict by seeking independence without strong identification with any authority figure. He left school and then home, trying out several types of work in a search for some satisfactory job. Like many fracture patients he quit jobs because he did not *like* them and he did not try to put up with a difficult boss or a boring or aggravating job. He resembled rheumatic fever patients more than fracture patients, however, in his fear of his own passivity and inadequacy, his inability to express aggression in minor ways or to focus his attention on immediate pleasures. Unemployment and depression precipitated an attack of rheumatic fever rather than an accident which would have represented outwardly directed hostility.

Hypertension developed when he formed his first strong masculine identification with his successful brother-in-law. He decided to assume an aggressive, responsible role, to work consistently, keeping his hostility in check and putting up with things he did not like. He shifted from the desire to be like his mother and to fight with or avoid authority to the desire to be like his brother-in-law, more masculine and more responsible. During the year while he was attempting to live this "new life" his heart became involved to a degree that was surprising to his physicians.

Like the typical patient with rheumatic heart disease, however, he was relatively unsuccessful in his attempt to emulate authority and become masculine. During the period of his convalescence he tried to get along with his grandfather on the farm and developed increasingly severe attacks of dyspnea and palpitation although no strenuous labor was required of him. He had recourse more and more to the realization of his ambition in fantasy. He attempted to gain favor with one or two social groups and developed a tendency to show off but was dissatisfied with himself in this respect also, feeling that his health made it impossible for him to "keep up." His third attack, at the age of 18, was precipitated as is usual with patients with rheumatic heart disease, by unusual exertion in these compensatory spheres, and a growing sense of failure, accompanied by a severe anxiety neurosis.

It may be interesting to compare with the above history the history of a patient with rheumatic heart disease who, unlike the former case, had had no preliminary attacks of rheumatic fever polyarthritis, but in her earlier years suffered from the accident habit to a marked degree.

ACCIDENTS—RHEUMATIC HEART DISEASE

Case No. RHD 65. A girl, aged 19, was admitted to the hospital with acute rheumatic carditis and early congestive failure. The onset was eight months previously when she was restless and unable to sleep at night. She would try to go to work, faint, and sometimes vomit and spit blood. The doctor told her she ought not to be at work but nevertheless she continued.

Family History. The maternal grandmother died of "heart trouble," the mother was exceedingly nervous, the father died as the result of an accident in a coal mine when the patient was 5 years old. He was nearly smothered and fatally burned.

Personal Data. As was not typical for the history of the patient with rheumatic fever, but was typical for our patients with rheumatic heart disease, this patient lost one parent long before adolescence, and the mother remarried in the middle of the patient's adolescence. Although there was friction with this very strict mother, this patient was equally attached to her, and unlike the typical patient with rheumatic polyarthritis was unable to leave her. Hence there was more repression of hostility.

The patient said of her stepfather: "He is a nice man," but always made a face when talking about him. She said further: "I really don't mind him at all now. He doesn't bother me. My mother likes him so I like him." She then said: "Mother is always having operations. She's had so many things taken out of her insides I don't know what they are. She is good and very strict. But when I see what happens to other girls, the way they're brought up, I guess I should be glad of it. Mother believes you should get up early and work hard. When I was sick she didn't want to have a doctor. She thought if I worked I would be all right. Then I fainted and mother cried."

The patient is the oldest of three children. She said: "My brother (three years younger) is a good boy, neat and clean. He will do anything in the world for me. But he and my half-sister (six years younger) are just two opposites. I think he should treat her nice the way he treats me. But he won't. She is careless and doesn't care about things. She always goes out to have a good time and leaves everything for my mother and me. My grandmother just died a year ago from a heart attack, that's when I began to get sick. She did even more for me than my own mother. I keep thinking if she were living she is the one I would go to for comfort when I was sick. I wonder if it was her dying made me sick."

Here again we find the reaction slightly different from that where polyarthritis rather than cardiac involvement predominates. The attachment to the mother and grandmother was more marked. There was a definite emotional reaction to the death of the latter which was traumatic in its effect.

Previous Injuries. As a youngster the patient fell out of her high chair and broke her nose. "All my life I'm always burning myself or cutting myself." Sometime between the age of 7 and 10 she fell off a ladder and fractured her elbow and wrist. During her first year of high school she was "looking over a railing and for no reason at all fell down six steps onto a cement walk and was knocked unconscious."

General Adjustment. The patient graduated from high school at the age of 17, at the head of her class in English. "I cried when I had to stop school but I had to go to work to help Mother. It was a great disappointment."

"I was the strongest girl. I always challenged the strongest boy to fight and always got the better of him. I was the best at basket ball and was the head of the team as a junior. My last year at high school I had to work as nursemaid in the afternoon to help Mother so I had to give it up. I still love swimming. But I get short of breath and spit up blood afterwards."

"We used to live in Pennsylvania and I had a lot of girl friends. We had a club. But I haven't any friends now. If I could go back to school maybe I would make some friends. I had two boy friends but Mother taught me to keep them at a distance. I like to be liked by boys, but Mother says they are no good as friends so I have given up all that stuff. I am always dreaming about having pretty clothes but I guess it's silly. You can make people like you without them."

This is a definitely different social adjustment from that characteristic of the patient with rheumatic disease characterized mainly by polyarthritis. In other words, the patient does get along with groups, and although she started out as a tomboy there was a shift in the direction of currying favor with the opposite sex along with her sexual inhibition.

Characteristic Behavior Pattern. "I'm always dreaming about places I would like to go, an airplane trip, an ocean voyage. There you would have something to think about afterwards." As is clear from the foregoing, she was in general agreeable and talkative with a tendency to curry favor and show off.

Here we see the characteristic tendency to realize ambitions in fantasy rather than actually to break away.

Neurotic Traits. This patient has always talked in her sleep. Beginning when her father died, she had nightmares of fires, smothering, snakes with fiery eyes coming toward her, rats, spiders in bed, and of her sister and brother dying. She also had a chicken phobia. Throughout her life she was afraid of staying alone at night. If left alone she would sit near the door so she could get out if anyone broke in, or else go to her bedroom, lock the door and lie there in terror. She said: "All my life I seem to have been running away from something and just escaping death." She said further: "The only thing that settles my nerves is chewing gum." This patient also had a tendency to overeat to which she resorted when she was in emotional conflict. She also showed a strong tendency to sadism in her nightmares and fantasies, awful things happening to her brother and sister and helpless animals.

Addictions and Interests. From the point of view of addictions and interests this patient showed a wide spread. She took stimulants to buck herself up (rheumatic heart disease) and she liked adventure and action, like fracture patients and rheumatic fever type A patients, but with the difference from the former that she went swimming even when she knew it would "hurt her health," and from the latter that she rode specific hobbies hard, for example, swimming or clothes. Unlike rheumatic fever type A patients, however, she remained bound to religion which suggests the fracture patient, except for the overt conflict involved: "I believe in the Catholic religion very, very much. I would like to be a super-Catholic (rheumatic heart disease zealot tendency) but I don't believe I could stick to it." She used gum and sedatives to settle her nerves.

Life Situation Prior to Onset. One year previously the patient had just come to realize "how important school was and to enjoy it." She had just been forced to give up pretty clothes and going with boys. She tried to adjust to these deprivations by working hard in order to win her mother's approval.

"But I guess the disappointment and the hard work got to be too much for me." There was also the element of traumatic death which was the usual finding with these patients. "I just lost my grandmother (maternal) a year ago. I felt so terrible. She did even more for me than my own mother. We had everything we wanted. She had a gall bladder and then a heart attack. I kept thinking about it, and thought that if she was living she was the one I could go to for comfort, when I was sick. When my younger sister was sick my grandmother took care of her, and kept her until she was strong and healthy."

Reaction to Illness. Concerning her illness the patient said: "I want to find out what's wrong with me. I can't beat the boys wrestling any more because I get too tired. When I have a pain I never tell anybody. I think it might be imagination." Relative to her constant disobedience she said: "I don't care what the doctors say, I won't give up swimming. It makes me so lonely when I can't do what I want to do that there's no point in living anyway. Probably I won't live very long and I might as well have a good time while I can."

Area of Focal Conflict and Characteristic Reaction. It is clear that this patient had trouble with authority to which she reacted by an attempt to emulate authority. She made herself like the man her mother liked, work hard like her mother and stepfather, and give up her sexual interests according to the ideal her mother set up for her. She had also to a large degree the other conflict—that over sexual role—characteristic of patients with rheumatic fever.

Concerning the onset of menstruation she said: "Nobody ever told me anything, but I visited my cousin and happened to see her. She said: 'don't tell anybody but you will have it some day.' When I did have it, Mother noticed it and said not to worry. The only important thing was to stay away from boys. I always have cramps and often feel dizzy and vomit. I get terribly angry. I don't see why girls should have such trouble. Nobody can speak to me or play the radio when I'm that way. . . . I like children. I say to mother 'why don't you buy a baby for me?' She said wait till I get married and I would have plenty even if I didn't want them. She said I wouldn't want them but I don't believe her. Maybe what I ought to do is to be a nun anyway. I believe in the Catholic religion but I'm sure I'd never be able to stick to it. If I want to do something I do it. You can't talk me out of it. Nothing can change my mind."

The reader who has studied the preceding chapters will recognize this statement as in general characteristic of the patient with heart disease, as is also this patient's reaction to her illness.

To the reader who is not fully conversant with the personality pictures given in the preceding chapters, the differences may seem insignificant between this patient with accident habit and rheumatic heart disease and the patient with rheumatic fever combined with accident-proneness who shifted to rheumatic heart disease and hypertension. The differences are actually slight, as one might expect in view of the fact that as far as we know, both syndromes are manifestations of the same illness.

The picture is further confused because accident-proneness is associated with what we have called rheumatic fever type A (accident pattern), a type which is not predisposed to hypertension, whereas both these patients—the one who developed hypertension as well as the one who did not, had an early history of accidents.

However slight the differences may be, they are highly significant. The personality pictures of these two patients prior to the development of heart disease showed a typical divergence. Whereas both suffered from a focal conflict with authority, the first—until he attempted to become a new person—dealt with it by avoidance; the second dealt with it by emulating the person in authority and submitting. And though both had difficulty with conflict over the sexual role, in the first there was a more marked identification with the opposite sex together with homosexual tendencies, whereas in the second it was more a matter of adolescent competition with the opposite sex and an attempt to curry favor.

The first patient in so far as his early personality picture could be determined seemed to belong to the rheumatic fever type A. Patients in this group do not usually develop hypertension but like the hypertensive group they have introversive tendencies. His history showed that his personality constellation did change as he shifted from one syndrome to another. The necessary period of immobilization after his second attack of rheumatic fever added to his fear of passivity. The resolve to be more aggressive and masculine further aggravated the passive-active conflict which led to the development of hypertension. Both the internal and external difficulties involved in upholding his new role resulted in victory for the passive tendencies, in cardiac damage and the more passive type of adjustment characteristic of patients with rheumatic fever type B.

On the basis of these histories, plus five years of follow-up, there is indication that the tendency to have accidents disappeared after the development of actual cardiac damage—that is, after more active outlets for energy had been corked up.

ANGINAL SYNDROME—ACCIDENTS
(Not the Coronary Type of Accident)

Case No. AS 215. A married man, aged 34, was admitted to the hospital with the diagnosis of coronary disease. Further study showed that this patient did not have coronary disease but merely an anginal syndrome without organic damage. Study of this patient's history led us to predict that there would be none, and in four years of follow-up the patient has had no further attacks.

Family History. As is typical of both anginal and coronary groups, but particularly of patients with anginal syndrome, shortly before the onset of illness the patient had been exposed to his father's death of cardiorenal disease. There was no other family history of cardiovascular disease except for a paternal aunt with heart trouble.

Personal Data. Both parents lived through the patient's adolescence. The mother was the center of the family. The patient was the oldest of five children, one brother and three sisters.

Previous Health. The patient's health was not particularly good. He had had two major and one minor operation, one major and one minor illness, and two allergies.

Previous Injuries. This patient broke both wrists, first one and then the other, playing football in early adolescence. He then broke the toes of his left foot by knocking an iron bar from a table onto his foot. At the age of 18 he fractured his jaw in two places in a fight. He said he was clowning and didn't take it seriously because the other man was smaller, then he "got a swift one in the jaw." At the age of 27 he ran through a fence in a racing car and fractured an arm and a leg. A year and a half prior to admission he fractured his acromium in a fracas with his young son. He had two accidents after his discharge, one an automobile accident and the other the result of a fall in which he injured his knee and then stated that he had had several more accidents which he had forgotten when he was driving buses. Concerning his injuries he said: "I don't mind injuries and I don't mind being hurt."

General Adjustment. After completion of the eighth grade this patient wanted to get away from home and went to work on a ranch. He then drove buses and was an inspector for bus lines for eight years. His father had always wanted him to go into business with him (printer's supply business) but the patient preferred to be his own boss until his father died, after which he stepped into the business and became vice president (this was five years before admission). He was unable to feel comfortable in the job, however, because he "would feel better if he were really president," and was bothered by his competitors, whom he claimed were always underselling him.

Characteristic Behavior Pattern. This patient's behavior pattern is a combination of that characteristic of the accident patient and that characteristic of the anginal patient, but very different from that of the coronary patient. Although he had the latter's dislike of sharing responsibility he had a lesser tendency to work long hours and little ability to control others. He could never get assistants to suit him. He aimed to be his own boss but not the boss of others. He attached emotion to both ideas and action and attempted to impress people by his conversation, but not to use it as an instrument of aggression. He stressed the fact that he was a great reader, commenting that he was sure people realized "I know a lot more than I talk about." When it came to a clash he would resort to impulsive action, either fighting or running away, but still he was unable to get rid of his worries and said: "I have a bad habit of keeping bad news to myself."

Neurotic Traits. He had enuresis, nail-biting and occasional sleep-talking when younger. (It will be remembered that the first two are characteristic of patients with the anginal syndrome, the third of patients with the accident habit, which this patient had also.) He also had dreams of falling through space tremendous distances.

Addictions and Interests. The patient was interested in travel, adventure and racing, like the accident patient, but gave this up when he settled down to take over his father's business. He had always had a tendency to overeat, and smoked excessively. He was skeptical about religion.

Life Situation Immediately Prior to Onset. The anginal syndrome developed as the patient began to feel himself a failure in his identification with his father, and in running his father's business.

His accidents occurred when he first left home after grammar school, during the period when he was resisting his father's entreaties that he come home and help him in his business, at the time when after his father's death he made the decision to take over his father's business, immediately following the first anginal pain, and immediately following his discharge from the hospital after his attack.

Reaction to Illness. This patient had a tendency to minimize his symptoms but at the same time to stress the fact that he could bear pain.

Area of Focal Conflict and Characteristic Reaction. It is clear that this patient, like both the coronary and accident patient, had trouble with authority. He alternated between the attempt to escape from it and the attempt to identify himself with it. He was not equal to working up from the bottom in a business of his own, although he made some attempt in this direction during the period of bus-driving when he worked up to the rank of inspector. Again, when his father died he felt obligated to take over his father's business but was unable to manage his subordinates. This disturbed him because his father had been able to do it and because, as he said he and his father were so much alike that they used to be taken for brothers. He then identified himself with his father in illness.

There was also the strong attachment to his mother. The patient said: "When I was driving buses they always used to laugh at me because I would go home and take my mother for a drive." He was disturbed by the fact that his wife could not get along with his mother although he tried to make their home with her. As is a regular finding with these patients, his wife was frigid, but this did not upset him because he had always been disgusted with sex.

Summary. Here we have a patient who had the fundamental conflict with authority typical of both accident and anginal syndromes, but alternated in his manner of dealing with it between the pattern characteristic of the accident-prone and that typical of those predisposed to the anginal syndrome. Whenever he engaged in activities representing escape and was forced to face situations which he had been trying to avoid, he had accidents—as in playing football, after he left home, when he engaged in a playful fight, when he resisted his father's plea to enter the business, when he left bus-driving after his father's death to enter the business, twice when he was reacting against the discovery of anginal disease. But anginal attacks intervened when he attempted (unsuccessfully) to identify himself with his father and fill his father's role, both in relationship to the business and in attachment to his mother. Finally he did succeed in imitating his father in his illness.

DIABETES—ACCIDENTS

The patients with diabetes who had suffered also from the accident habit were nearly all males (88 per cent). The following histories are typical.

Case No. D 40. An unmarried Jewish man, aged 22, the first boy, second child in a family of six, was admitted to the hospital for the eighth time for diabetes. His diabetes was first discovered when he was 13 years old.

Family History. Although there was no family history of diabetes or cardiovascular disease, his father had asthma and as is usually reported by diabetics, both parents were exceedingly nervous.

Personal Data. As was a regular finding in patients with diabetes, both parents lived through the patient's adolescence, and the patient was engaged in a long-drawn-out subacute conflict with them.

Previous Health. Like the typical diabetic, this patient had a relatively good health record, except for pneumonia at the age of 1, and a mild attack of rheumatism at the age of 7.

Previous Injuries. At 2 years of age the patient was severely burned. He did not remember how. At the age of 5 the patient fractured his leg riding a tricycle, in an attempt to escape from another little boy with whom he was fighting. After the admission to the hospital during which he was studied, he fractured the same leg crossing the road on a rainy dark night. He said: "I knew the car was coming and the driver probably wouldn't see me in time to stop, but something made me want to find out. I was feeling sort of gloomy because I was coming back from a basketball game and wondering why I'd never been as good as the other fellers in sports."

General Adjustment. This patient's educational record followed the diabetic pattern. He finished high school at the age of 18 and had been working since going to City College at night. He wanted to finish college and go to a veterinary medical school. He preferred to study medicine but felt he could not possibly finance it and so decided on becoming a veterinary as a second choice. His income level was characteristically lower than his educational record, but this of course was partly because completing his education was still his major interest. His occupational grouping at the time of admission was group II, but he wished to improve it. Again, like the typical patient with diabetes, this patient had few friends and preferred to "keep to himself."

Characteristic Behavior Pattern. The most outstanding characteristic of this patient was his social anxiety. Although his general behavior was agreeable (but at the same time he was somewhat inarticulate and evasive), he was aware of his marked mood swings and stated that they made it difficult for him to be sure all the time of what he wanted to do. He thought there was no correlation between his mood swings and his physical condition.

Neurotic Traits. In his early years he suffered from nail-biting which still persisted. He used to have nightmares. "Something compels me to worry about all sorts of petty little things."

Addictions and Interests. Again like the typical diabetic, this patient always avoided competitive sports. He was much interested in animals, as is indicated by the fact that during his school years he used to get jobs in a pet shop, and his current ambition was to become a veterinary. Although he had been brought up strictly he had no particular interest in religion. He was an excessive smoker and had food compulsions.

Life Situation Immediately Prior to Onset. Even as a young child this patient had been bothered by his inability to get along with his nervous parents and his siblings. He stated that the parents were somewhat strict, but were very fond of him and tended to let him have his own way more than the other children. Then the patient said spontaneously: "Perhaps i was because of this that I could never get along with my friends. Girls didn't like me and I was always having fights with boys. . . . Just before I got sick, when I was 13, a boy whom I always thought was my only good friend egged me on to a battle. I was badly beaten up and I always thought it was a great injustice. Could that have caused diabetes?"

Here again is evidenced the characteristic attempt made by these patients to pin their illness on to something, no matter how unlikely it may seem.

Reaction to Illness. This patient stated that he tried very hard to take good care of himself but that he had a compulsion to eat lots of bread and sugar. He didn't know why he did it because he really wanted to get well. He even tried to get a civil service job and lied, saying that he had no physical disease but it didn't work. It made him very much embarrassed to have anyone know he was sick.

Area of Focal Conflict and Characteristic Reaction. "My troubles probably come with having been allowed to get away with so much at home. It's hard for me to work with other people or take responsibility and I can't make up my mind whether to keep on living at home or not. I've moved out now and then but somehow or other I always go back. . . . I'm afraid of girls. I guess I think they wouldn't like me because of my sickness. No wife would put up with me. But then even when I was little I didn't like them. I guess I'm destined to be what they call 'a male virgin.' I've read you can live a healthy life by masturbating but somehow or other it makes me uncomfortable. I guess I'm afraid people will know about it or think I'm queer." Another characteristic of this patient frequently found among diabetics was the constant assertion that "something made me do this or that." In other words, a compulsive character and a reluctance to assume responsibility for his own actions and decisions.

Here is the typical diabetic conflict over dependence versus independence, and the characteristic ambivalence relative to his sexual role. His reaction to these conflicts is also characteristically that of narcissistic withdrawal—an inability to decide between avoidance and trying to make something of himself. This was combined with impulsive action which led to accidents.

Case No. D 71. A married man, aged 37, was admitted for diabetes discovered sixteen months previously. The discovery of the diabetes followed a decrease in weight from 162 to 127 lbs. in a period of six weeks. He was born in Rhode Island, the *oldest* of three children, the only boy.

Family History. There was no history of diabetes or cardiovascular disease but both parents were described as extremely nervous, excitable, "worrisome" people.

Personal Data. As we have found regularly with patients with diabetes, both parents lived well on into the patient's life, that is, both were alive at the time of admission. This patient, like others with diabetes, states that he was brought up rather indulgently and was the favorite of the family.

Previous Health. This patient also had a good health record except for pneumonia at the age of 2. He was subject to bad colds.

Previous Injuries. At the age of 10 this patient cut his foot on the neck of a broken bottle as he was running barefoot. He said furthermore that he was always spraining his ankle. But that these experiences "had taught him that you had to be careful and so far he had managed to avoid breaking anything."

General Adjustment. After grammar school this patient had some work in commercial school. After graduation he was offered a good opportunity in his father's hardware company but didn't like it and went into the drug business. As a boy he had always liked to get bottles filled in the drug store and run medical errands. Although he never obtained any pharmaceutical training other than practical experience he found a state in which he could register as a practical pharmacist without training, and he made one hundred dollars a week as a manager for a big pharmacy in New York. This job, however, did not last because he could not get along with his boss, who, he insisted, knew less about drugs than he did. He then spent five years in the "selling and collecting business." This turned out to be selling and collecting clothes. He worked for two years in one city, two years in another, and then attempted to carry on in New York. He was able to just make ends meet, with considerable borrowing from his family. In this way he found it much more satisfactory. During this time he had been separated from his wife who herself was earning eighteen dollars a week.

Characteristic Behavior Pattern. It is clear from the above that this patient attempted to be independent but could not quite make a go of it. On the surface he was affable and co-operative, but concerning himself he was some-what evasive. His spontaneous remarks seemed to be an attempt to indicate satisfaction with himself, but underneath there was a great deal of anxiety concerning what other people might think of him. It is easy to see this patient's vacillation between impulsive behavior and an attempt to behave sensibly and win approval.

Neurotic Traits. Temper tantrums and nightmares.

Addictions and Interests. Aside from the patient's interest in drugs, he had a considerable interest in gambling which we noted as particularly char-acteristic of accident patients, otherwise his major pleasure was night clubs and alcohol. He had been brought up in the Catholic church but says he never took religion seriously; now he goes to church only on Christmas and Easter to smooth things over with his family. In addition to excessive drink-ing he was an excessive smoker.

Life Situation Immediately Prior to Onset. The onset of illness in this patient followed five years in which he had been going steadily downhill from a responsible job at one hundred dollars a week, which he couldn't quite manage, to an irresponsible one, buying and selling old clothes, getting his wife to work to help with the family budget, and finally borrowing from his family. It will be noted, however, that he ascribed the onset of his diabetes to his sudden character reform, specifically, going on the water wagon. He complained that this made him seem queer to his friends, spoiled his enjoy-ment of night clubs and in general cut him off from all social life.

Reaction to Illness. "At the first the diabetes was a nuisance because it interfered with my pleasure, but it helped me to give up my friends because they seemed disgusted with me when they were drunk and I wasn't. Being sick has cured me of all my worries. Nothing bothers me any more. It's all right to take money from the family now. They want to help me because I'm sick. My wife takes care of the bills . . ." etc.

Area of Focal Conflict and Characteristic Reaction. The area of focal con-flict for this patient was dependence versus independence, the desire to be pampered and taken care of. Furthermore, he always got along better with men than with women, and his major social life was in night clubs and bars. It should be noted that he married a masculine type of woman and as time went on forced her to be the man of the family. "My wife does all the worry-ing about the bills and that sort of thing. I can go to bed . . ." Although the patient claimed that his sexual relationship with his wife was satisfactory one had the impression that this was a statement that he wanted to have believed rather than a true picture of the situation. His wife had been told that her pelvis was so small she should never have children. This was shortly after their marriage when she had given birth to a child who died within three days. This child was never really wanted by either parent and was an accident because they had not found a satisfactory contraceptive. In accord with the patient's lack of strictness about religion is the fact that he went to church and even made the two requisite confessions, Christmas and Easter, with no conflict over lying to the priest about his use of contraceptives.

This patient's early character resembled that of the accident patient. The fact that he was treated indulgently by his parents, however, and considered their favorite, kept him from being as aggressive and independent in behavior as is the usual accident patient. His major conflict was over the desire to be independent and the desire to be taken care of. He nearly accomplished his goal of independence, albeit more by bluff than by working up. His boss, however, found him irresponsible and bad tempered, and the patient started the downhill course just described. He stopped drinking, made up his mind to give up what his wife called "his evil companions" and to control his temper. Then came the diabetes.

DIABETES—ACCIDENTS—HYPERTENSION

Case No. D 19. An unmarried boy, aged 25, was admitted to the hospital for the fifteenth time with the diagnosis of diabetes mellitus.

Family History. The patient's mother died of cancer when he was 11 years old; the father was living and well. The patient stated later, however, that his mother had had "trouble" and an uncle "once had sugar."

Personal Data. The patient was born in New York City, the second child, the first boy, in a family of two. "I was the favorite, but we were both brought up very laxly. Mother spoiled us and Father was too busy to care what we did. Now my sister, who is married, lives in the house with us and takes care of things. Her son is a brother to me."

Previous Health. The patient's health was good in general. He had had three minor illnesses.

Previous Injuries. He had had a mild face burn (see below), an infection from having "a pimple squeezed" and several other minor injuries such as cuts and burns for which "somebody else was always to blame."

General Adjustment. The patient stopped high school at the end of the second term in order to work in his father's business. His occupational group was III (as was characteristic of diabetes)--a salesman in his father's business. His *social* adjustment was good with members of his own sex. He was afraid of girls. If he saw them at all he preferred several at a time "because there's safety in numbers." He "wouldn't think of having an affair with one of them," and stated that he would never get married.

Characteristic Behavior Pattern. The patient's behavior resembled that of patients suffering from the three syndromes from which he suffered; that is, superficially he was unable to follow any consistent course of action, but the reason for this was not primarily impulsive action without thought as in the case of patients with fracture, although this occurred now and then, nor was it because of outbursts of hostility, alcoholism or interest in women (like patients with hypertensive cardiovascular disease), which got him into trouble, but rather the inability to pursue any consistent course of action because of a conflict between the desire to do so and the inability to decide.

Neurotic Traits. The patient denied neurotic traits, but there was indication that nail-biting and masturbation had been problems, the latter still continuing. He was sullen, not very talkative, and indecisive.

Addictions and Interests. "My only amusements are fishing, yachting, and going off with the boys. I sometimes play with mechanical contrivances." The patient stated he hadn't the slightest interest in religion and added: "I'm mentally and physically lazy. I do think the doctors should take care of people better. I like to read about socialized medicine."

Life Situation Immediately Prior to Onset. The patient had almost a complete amnesia for the year between his mother's death of cancer and the discovery of his diabetes when he was 12 years old. All he remembered was that he had a few accidents, none of them serious.

Reaction to Illness. The patient found his illness on the whole convenient, because "no one would expect you to go with girls or get married if you have diabetes." But he had the tendency of most patients with diabetes, to blame the doctors. He said: "I was in ———— hospital where they put me into acidosis so I had to be sent here. Even in this hospital they're not so good. A nurse squeezed a pimple on my face and made me sick for six months. . . . It's nice having Sister take care of Father and me. I'm easy going and never worry about anything. The trouble with Father is that he worries."

Area of Focal Conflict and Characteristic Reaction. Sexual role; and homosexual inclinations which this patient accepts.

III. Hypertensive Cardiovascular Disease Combined with Other Diseases

As in the case of the accident habit, light is thrown on the tendency to hypertensive cardiovascular disease by study of the disease combinations in which it was found. The figures are:

PATIENTS	PERCENTAGE HAVING HYPERTENSIVE CARDIOVASCULAR DISEASE
Coronary occlusion	27
Diabetes	15
Rheumatic heart disease	12
Anginal syndrome	12
Rheumatic fever, type B*	6
Fracture	5
Rheumatic fever, type A	0
Cardiac arrhythmia	0

HYPERTENSIVE CARDIOVASCULAR DISEASE—CORONARY OCCLUSION

As has been pointed out earlier, these diseases seem to occur in combination in individuals whose personality shifts from the hypertensive to the coronary pattern, and in those patients who start out with the coronary pattern but lose their grip and shift in the direction of the hypertensive pattern. The following case histories are illustrative.

Case No. H 42. A married man, aged 44, was admitted to the hospital with the diagnosis hypertensive cardiovascular disease of fifteen years' duration, with a question of myocardial infarct. After discharge he was followed two weeks in the clinic and was readmitted to the emergency ward at which time the electrocardiogram showed changes suggestive of coronary occlusion, an irregular coupling of beats.

Family History. No history of heart trouble, or nervousness in the family, and the only exposure was to the sudden death of pneumonia of the patient's father at the age of 40, when the patient was 16 years old.

Personal Data. The patient was the oldest of four brothers. He states: "Mother was a hard-working woman and ran Father's business as well as the house whenever he was away. They were both very strict but I got all the lickings because of being the oldest. I had to be like Father." The patient has three children, a boy 15 in trade school, a daughter 16 of whom he required that she give up her business course in order to get a job to help the family, and a girl aged 9 "the exact picture of me. She sticks to me like my little brother did."

Previous Health. The patient was typical of both hypertensive and coronary groups, with diphtheria, scarlet fever, pneumonia, pleurisy and

---

* The only exception was the rather unusual case like No. RF 304, page 600, where there was the shift from type A to type B which of course is not actually an exception.

bronchitis, and continued colds as a child; kidney trouble and frequent bronchitis in later years. (Bronchitis at least twice a year together with five or six incapacitating colds annually.) Nevertheless the patient stated characteristically that he had always been very healthy.

Previous Injuries. No accidents or injuries, as is characteristic of the hypertensive patient, and to a less degree of the coronary patient.

General Adjustment. The patient was forced to give up high school at the age of 15 when his father came to this country, and to take a job at "slaving wages" in a laundry which he greatly resented. He admitted that he had never got on with his teachers—there was one to whom he was going to give a black eye some day when he could get back. But he had made up his mind to finish his education because "you need it if you are going to amount to anything." He finally quit the laundry work and became an apprentice in a music shop where the proprietor took an interest in him and he learned the trade. He worked up to piano repair man, and then foreman in charge of the inspection department. This was ruined by the war which "hit the piano business hard" so the patient went South and tried to sell real estate. He lost everything in the Florida crash, returned to New York and worked up from janitor to superintendent in an apartment house.

Here we see a patient with the coronary pattern of always working up. He survived three hard blows in the field of his ambition, giving up high school to work in a laundry, failure of the piano business during World War I, and the Florida "crash." To each of these he reacted with extreme resentment, and as he said: "Gradually it became impossible to keep my feelings to myself." He exhibited the constant striving toward occupational group II, characteristic of both hypertensive and coronary patients, and the relatively good work record and income level.

The patient was well liked, made friends easily, was adopted as a "son" by the proprietor of the piano store, and as a "father" by the thirty-six families in the apartment house of which he was superintendent. His marriage, eighteen years ago, at the age of 26 was undertaken with characteristic sense of responsibility. He was engaged to his wife for twenty-one months, waiting until he was sure of his income and until he had prepared a home for them. He said: "My wife and I are the kind that don't give up. We've stuck to each other through thick and thin. She is like my mother and can manage the business when I'm sick." And the patient has been faithful to her in spite of the fact that intercourse is not particularly satisfactory. "I always use a condom because it wouldn't be fair to put the responsibility on her and we can't have any more children because three is all I can *be a good father to*." As is also characteristic, there were no abortions or miscarriages.

Characteristic Behavior Pattern. In the patient's own words: "All my life I've been heart and soul for the job. No slipshod business for me. I may be a little too exact. I guess I inherit it from my father. He always used his fist to convince people he was right. I started out doing that but I found it got you into trouble, and tried to stop. I guess I have the habit anyway."

Neurotic Traits. Except for nail-biting the patient had a good record for early neurotic traits. In later life he shifted between keeping his troubles to himself together with assuming all the responsibility, and occasional out-bursts of anger.

Addictions and Interests. Although the patient was brought up a Catholic he was skeptical about religion, saying characteristically: "That's for people who can't think for themselves." He drank beer regularly and highballs to keep his mind alert when he had to work long hours.

Life Situation Immediately Prior to Onset. This patient's hypertension was discovered one or two years after the ruin of the piano business, the only job he ever really liked, his second traumatic experience in the vocational field, when he had to make a fresh start in real estate. This was particularly disturbing to him because his wife had just given birth to their first child. In addition he had just assumed the responsibility of supporting his mother.

Reaction to Illness. In spite of this patient's illness history, he considered himself a man of good health. Furthermore, he refused an offer of financial assistance from the social service department, although during the period of his hospital stay his wife was paying to a man who was filling in for him the full amount of his salary. He insisted that he and his wife "had everything under control," even though his physician told him that he would never be able to work so hard again. On his discharge, his employer requested a report from his physicians, and he entreated them not to say that he was permanently incapacitated, but merely that he ought to work less hard for two or three weeks. His employer was considerate and said that absolutely nothing would be required of the patient, and if he did any work it was entirely on his own responsibility, but again, characteristically, the patient immediately resumed his full responsibility.

He was readmitted to the hospital two months later with a definite diag-nosis of coronary occlusion, but nothing daunted by this, he again refused help and insisted he was perfectly capable of working. At the end of two weeks he was readmitted for another coronary attack, and this time in a severe depression. He said that he and his wife had agreed that under the circumstances he might as well be dead. Concerning his illness the patient said: "I want to keep on working. I want to get well. But there is something that's eating my strength away. There is a feeling in the back of my head and neck like I would like to step on sugar. You know what I mean, it's like feeling you're slipping and being very mad about it."

Area of Focal Conflict and Characteristic Reaction. As is clear from this patient's statements he set out to outdo his father and be father of the family. His father ran a business of his own and he wanted to do the same, only run a better business. He was so frequently thwarted in this that he felt he had reason to express his anger and resentment once in awhile, which may have had something to do with the early development of hypertension and the relatively late coronary attack. Furthermore, he had the hypertensive sense of not quite making the grade. Nevertheless, he worked long hours under high tension, tried to keep his troubles to himself, and finally succumbed to coronary disease.

CORONARY OCCLUSION—HYPERTENSION

Case No. CD 348. A married man, aged 38, pyknic in build, was admitted to the hospital with coronary occlusion and hypertensive cardiovascular disease. He looked older than his age.

Family History. The patient's father died of heart trouble, his brother had heart trouble, and his mother had a nervous breakdown after the birth of the patient's youngest sister.

Personal Data. As was frequent with coronary patients, the father died just prior to the patient's adolescence. The father was very excitable and the patient said his mother was the only responsible member of the family. The patient was the oldest of three boys and had an older sister to whom he was devoted because she was the artistic type like his mother.

Previous Health. Two major operations and one minor operation; seven minor illnesses, plus a tendency to gastro-intestinal upsets; bad teeth, allergy and chronic colds. This patient also stated that his health was good. His only complaint was "jumpy intestines."

Previous Injuries. One minor injury of the coronary type.

General Adjustment. This patient, like the preceding one, had trouble with his teachers in school but decided to stick it out because he needed an education. He delivered laundry after school hours. "Finally, I raised a rumpus and started out on my own as an office boy. Then I got a job in a post office and have been there ever since—twenty-one years. The trouble is my wife doesn't want me to work hard and get ahead. And I have trouble with my intestines because with my job there isn't time enough to go to the toilet."

As is usual with these patients he stressed sticking to his wife, but said that intercourse was unsatisfactory because he always had to use a condom.

In the year prior to his illness he had been bothered by frequent erections every night and morning, one to three times a day, which he tried to relieve by micturition, and concerning which he consulted his doctor. "But I didn't feel free to bother my wife about it because she was so worried about the priest and contraception." He stated further: "The people next door fight like cats and dogs and we have nothing to fight over."

Characteristic Behavior Pattern. "I never went in for recreation. It was always the job that was important. I can't listen to the radio because there are too many sad stories."

Neurotic Traits. No early neurotic traits. Present: only a few compulsive character traits relative to responsibility and promptness.

Addictions and Interests. The patient refused to let himself drink tea, coffee, or alcohol, and also refused to let himself smoke. He stated that there is not much of anything he liked to do except work. "It might be better if I stepped out more, and sometimes I think it would help me to get ahead if I took more stimulants, but my wife is always trying to keep me from working long hours."

Life Situation Immediately Prior to Onset. As happens frequently with coronary patients, his illness came on suddenly at 8:12 P.M. (note accuracy as to time) as he was walking home from work. He was in a hurry to get home to go to church. "I was bothered because the priest slammed the door in my wife's face and refused to hear her confession until she went back and said she would not use contraceptives. I couldn't see confessing to the priest that you wouldn't go on using them when you knew you would. I don't believe religion is so important anyway, but I have to keep my wife happy."

Reaction to Illness. The social service note states that the patient was a placid, somewhat apathetic male who claimed to have led a quiet exemplary life and was adjusting sensibly to his illness. This was true of the impression given by this patient, but it should be clear from the preceding that the personality beneath was somewhat different. When questioned about sick benefit through the post office, he said, "I didn't really believe I was entitled to it, and didn't want to bother them."

These two cases are remarkably similar to each other, even in details such as quitting school to work and attitude toward use of the condom in intercourse. One problem in considering them is to differentiate them both from (a) the patients who had hypertension without coronary symptoms and (b) the patients who had coronary occlusion without hypertension. It is also important to see if anything can be learned from the minor differences between them.

Both showed the typical coronary picture in most important respects. They had no, or insignificant, previous history of accidents. They worked up in their jobs rather than avoiding difficulty, had ambitions to get to the top, worked long hours and assumed responsibility. They had bad health records, with vegetative trouble. They had few early neurotic habits, and their later ones were those typical of the compulsive character, such as sticking to routine and attention to punctuality and detail. They tended to keep their troubles to themselves, stuck to their wives and did not quarrel with them in spite of circumstances creating tension, such as frigidity or worry about the chance of pregnancy and the use of contraceptives. They were skeptical of religious authority and inclined to use stimulants as an aid in work. The circumstances prior to onset in both cases consisted of a shock in the region of their major conflict—that with authority (in the first case the patient lost his job and later his money; in the second, the patient was worried because the priest had slammed the door in his wife's face because she would not promise not to use contraceptives). Both minimized their symptoms, made light of their illness, and refused to accept compensation. Both tried to rival authority and subdue it rather than submitting or running away—both cases in relation to teachers, one case with father and the other with priest. In view of our previous observations concerning the coronary personality there is therefore no occasion for surprise that these patients developed coronary disease.

There are, however, a few points in which the two cases vary from the typical coronary profile in the direction of the hypertensive. While both patients worked hard and had ambitions to get to the top neither actually did so; the first was compelled by bad fortune to shift jobs several times; and the second remained in the postal service for years without acquiring a position of authority. In both, the attitude toward mother and wife was like that of the hypertensive, more submissive than is usually the case with patients with coronary occlusion. The latter are customarily on good terms with wife and mother, but tend to disregard their influence in career and domestic life rather than being ruled by them. The first allowed his wife to manage his business when he was sick, said she was "like his mother" and was faithful to her in spite of unsatisfactory intercourse. The second refrained from stimulants that he felt he needed, because of his wife's objection, and in spite of unsatisfied sexual impulses he stuck to his wife and did not object to her refusal, because of her respect for the authority of the priest.

The principal difference between the symptoms of the two was that the first developed hypertension some time before the coronary attack, and the second did not suffer from hypertension, so far as is known, before his coronary accident. It therefore becomes pertinent to inquire what significant differences can be found in their histories, personalities or reaction patterns. The first differed from the second —as well as from the typical coronary patient—in that he was not exposed to heart trouble or nervous difficulty in his parents or family; in this he was more like the hypertensive profile. Second, he was more given to verbalizing both his aggression and his attitude toward life in general; he confessed to occasional outbursts of anger alternating with periods of keeping his trouble to himself and talked freely about his personality traits such as being perhaps "too exact." In the case of the second, however, the social service note described him as a quiet, apathetic male who had led a quiet, exemplary life and was adjusted to his illness. The patient gave, on the surface, the same impression to the psychiatrist, though careful examination revealed the hidden conflicts. Finally, the first had had no accidents at all, as is more characteristic of hypertensive than of patients with coronary occlusion, while the second had had an accident of the coronary type—caused by another person, and with a sharp instrument.

RHEUMATIC HEART DISEASE—CORONARY OCCLUSION—HYPERTENSIVE CARDIOVASCULAR DISEASE

(Syndromes successive)

Case No. RHD 60. A married Jewish man was admitted to the hospital for the second time because of shortness of breath on exertion, swelling of ankles, precordial distress, increasing weakness and loss of weight, of which the onset had been two and a half years previously. Medical examination revealed rheumatic heart disease with mitral stenosis and insufficiency, hypertension and coronary sclerosis. There was a suspicion of subacute endocarditis which was later ruled out.

Family History. Probably no history of cardiovascular disease, diabetes or fracture. The patient's father died when the patient was 9 years old, of "consumption," and his mother at the age of 61, when the patient was 21, of pneumonia (?). One sister committed suicide.

Personal Data. The patient was born in New York and at the time of admission was one of two surviving siblings of a family of ten.

Previous Health. Colds, rheumatic fever, excision of tumor of right chest, and another minor operation.

Injury. None.

General Adjustment. Education: The patient completed grammar school and then went to work to help support the family. He *worked* first as a shipping clerk and then in the produce and installment business where he made very good money. For eight years prior to admission he had been in the real estate business *making* nine or ten thousand a year. *Social adjustment:* "I have always had my own way in the world and was never afraid about getting a job because I am such a good talker. People respect me." *Sexual adjustment:* The patient was married at the age of 32. "I never bothered much about sex. My wife and I have a perfect understanding. Sometimes my wife gets caught but I always find a doctor to do something about it. Since I got sick I haven't liked sex any more." *Attitude toward parents and children of his own:* "I never knew my father. I had to be the father of the family and take care of mother." The patient was very much interested in his 11-year-old son, "the apple of my eye." "I just want to live long enough to see that he can paddle his own canoe the way I did. I want him to take up real estate because that's how I made my money."

Characteristic Behavior Pattern. (a) Prior to the death of his mother when he was 21, he was agreeable, talkative, vaguely ambitious, working not very consistently to help support the family and he had a strong desire to be liked. (b) After the age of 21, "I was suddenly alone. I had to make plans for my life. I thought about nothing but work and making money and made up my mind that when I got married we wouldn't be poor."

Neurotic Traits. The patient had a tendency to talk in his sleep, and a marked tendency to work long hours and neglect himself.

Addictions and Interests. The patient was addicted to tea, coffee, and alcohol "to keep myself going," and boasted of smoking ten to twenty cigars a day as well as many cigarettes. Like the group of patients with hypertensive cardiovascular disease, this patient showed a considerable interest in wine, women and song, but as he said he kept this under sufficient control so as not to interfere with his going where he wanted to go in the world. There was no interest in sports or religion.

Life Situation Prior to Onset. (a) Onset of rheumatic fever: As nearly as could be determined the patient's rheumatic fever occurred after his mother's death when he was 21. "After that I had to live alone. It was eleven years before I could find a wife. I decided the only thing for me was work." (See rheumatic fever profile.) (b) Onset of hypertensive cardiovascular disease: This patient's hypertension was discovered four years prior to admission when he had a life insurance examination. This occurred in the midst of financial reverses when his wife was beginning to complain about his being a less good provider than he had been previously, and he had finally decided to give her the security of a good life insurance policy. (c) Onset of coronary disease: This occurred shortly after the patient had lost all financial status and then had had to go on relief.

Reaction to Illness. "It is terrible that I have to draw in my oars. I don't like to go home where my privacy is interfered with. I don't even have a private bathroom. I used to have cars and servants, now even my wife is disappointed in me, but I have decided to be a good patient and get well just the same." Some of the nurses doubted the sincerity of this remark and felt that the patient enjoyed the hospital too much (on third admission this reaction was more clear).

Area of Major Conflict and Characteristic Reaction. In this patient we see a shift following the death of his mother from the rheumatic fever type of personality to that of the patient with hypertensive cardiovascular disease, with emphasis on the traits which suggest progression toward coronary occlusion. Unlike the coronary patients he had not broken the ties with his family and set out on his own but instead had stayed at home attempting to take care of his mother until her death to which he reacted with a turning of all his energy into work and the attempt to climb to the top.

RHEUMATIC FEVER (TYPE B)—HYPERTENSION—ANGINAL SYNDROME

Case No. RF 343. A married woman, aged 42, was admitted to the hospital with a diagnosis of rheumatic heart disease, mitral and aortic stenosis and insufficiency. Her first attack of rheumatic fever accompanied by migratory polyarthritis, occurred twenty years ago; there have been many subsequent mild attacks. Eight years prior to admission she developed hypertension and cardiac symptoms. A year and a half prior to admission she developed anginal pain.

Family History. Her mother died at 38 of heart trouble, when the patient was 7 years old; and her father from "a broken heart grieving," one year later.

Personal Data. The patient had two older brothers and was brought up by her maternal aunt and her husband, who had two younger boys in the family. She had three children of her own, a girl of 21, looking for a job as a stenographer, a boy of 18 still in school, and the youngest a boy who died at the age of 11 of rheumatic heart disease. She also had a fourth child, a girl, who died in infancy.

Previous Health. The patient had had a tonsillectomy, diphtheria, frequent bronchitis, chronic colds, gastro-intestinal disturbances and gall bladder colic.

Previous Injuries. Typical of type B, this patient had had no injuries.

General Adjustment. Although the patient liked school and did well in it she had to stop after the sixth grade to contribute to the family support. She worked as a nursemaid in the same household until her marriage at the age of 17. From the age of 17 until the time of admission she had done no work except for three years when she helped her husband as superintendent of an apartment house. Although in early years she tended to stick to one or two good friends of the same sex, like the rheumatic fever patients, she gradually shifted in the direction of enjoying groups.

The contraceptive problem was solved by a miscarriage, after which the patient was unable to have any more children. When her periods started she was "scared to death"; she could never get anyone to explain it to her, and at the time of admission she was still vague about "why women had them." She was similarly unprepared for the sexual side of marriage, and resented her husband's interest in it. Finally her mother-in-law and the priest explained to her "that was a cross that had to be borne by every married woman, so I must do my duty and think as little about it as possible." The patient lived on this basis for awhile but still didn't understand what was right.

Characteristic Behavior Pattern. "I always keep going if I possibly can. The doctors tell me to rest but when I do I have bad thoughts. You have to do something pretty big to get me angry. I am friends with everybody. When my husband bothers me about sex, even if I feel so sick I can hardly stand it, I just tell him to hurry up and get it over as soon as possible."

Neurotic Traits. None.

Addictions and Interests. The patient was brought up a Roman Catholic and all her life attended church nearly every day. On the other hand, her husband was an Episcopalian and not religious. She said: "We get along very well and never discuss it."

Life Situation Immediately Prior to Onset. Conflict with husband and priest relative to intercourse and child-bearing. She was convinced that that was what gave her her sickness because her first attack of rheumatic fever (migratory bilateral polyarthritis) was immediately after her marriage, and her heart became affected as soon as she started to have intercourse again subsequent to her miscarriage eight years ago. It was at this time also that she developed hypertension. "The priest insists that it is necessary to men and part of my duty to my husband, but I don't understand why the Lord should be so much more interested in men that he requires something so unpleasant for women."

Reaction to Illness. The note appears in the medical history: "This patient constantly abuses her health." In discussing this the patient made the remark noted above that she had bad thoughts if she didn't keep busy, and furthermore, she was convinced that the real abuse of her health was in the matter of submitting to the sexual relation which her religion requires of her. There is also a further note: "Was placed on bed rest and digitalis, however, she refused advice and is up and around." Then later a note by the resident and the attending physician: "I advised this patient to enter the hospital but she would rather be at home. That won't work. She refused to come in and today sends her daughter around to ask our advice as to what she'd better do. Doctors ——— (including the names of the resident and four attendants) have all told her what to do several times. The last time, last week."

Area of Focal Conflict and Characteristic Reaction. It is clear that this patient's focal conflict was in the sphere of her sexual role. She had always thought it would be better to be a boy because women have to suffer too much. As is characteristic of the type B rheumatic fever patient, however, her characteristic reaction pattern was submission in the spheres of both sex and authority.

DIABETES—HYPERTENSION

Of the patients with diabetes combined with hypertension, 80 per cent were female, which is interesting since the other major combination with diabetes was the accident habit, where 86 per cent were male.

Case No. D 85. A married, Jewish housewife, aged 30, was admitted for diabetes of three years' duration and hypertension. Her blood pressure was 225/105.

Family History. The patient had three maternal aunts with diabetes, and an older brother who died of diabetes. Both her parents were nervous.

Personal Data. Characteristically, the patient was the first girl in a family in which there were also two boys. Both parents were living and well but very nervous. The patient stated that although her parents were not the kind to show favoritism they were really nicer to her than to her brothers because she was always submissive "on account of being a girl," and so got a good reputation and was able to get away with things without being punished.

Previous Health. The patient had had only one operation, a minor one, but no illnesses were reported.

Previous Injuries. None.

General Adjustment. The patient completed high school at the age of 16 and then worked as a commercial artist until her marriage. After her marriage she had worked off and on because she often had to support her husband. Her income level was marginal to comfortable, as is characteristic of these patients, but largely through her own efforts. This patient's social life was better than that of the average patient with diabetes and followed the pattern of the patient with hypertension.

Characteristic Behavior Pattern. Like the typical diabetic, this patient was indecisive. She and her husband separated several times but she could never quite make up her mind to divorce him. "I don't know just why I don't do it because it would probably be easier to take care of one than two, and as it is I have to earn a good deal of the money, but I keep thinking if something should happen to me, if I left him there wouldn't be anybody else to count on."

Neurotic Traits. Nail-biting and nightmares throughout life. The nightmares consisted of people chasing her with knives. The patient liked animals and suffering creatures.

Addictions and Interests. The patient had few interests other than her addiction to coffee to relieve tension when she was annoyed. No interest in religion.

Life Situation Immediately Prior to Onset. The patient's illness was discovered about a year after the death of her brother from diabetes. She stated that she was not much upset by his death, she "didn't care much for men anyway," but she was devoted to her mother who had been greatly upset by her brother's death. "I guess it upset me, too, to see her suffer so." The hypertension was discovered only a little later.

Reaction to Illness. The patient enjoyed her illness because it gave her an opportunity to be taken care of, but she was also angry about it because she thought her husband was to blame for it. "Why should he have all the privileges of being a man and still make me take the responsibility of supporting the family? I wondered too, if stopping intercourse brought on the illness. I don't miss it, but people say it's bad to stop when you are used to it. I stopped because I don't like my husband any more. I think he's more interested in other men and women than he is in me."

Area of Focal Conflict and Characteristic Reaction. This patient tried to resign herself to her role as a woman but was constantly rebelling both about this and the necessity of assuming the financial responsibility.

Case No. D 42. A married Irish woman, aged 50, was admitted to the hospital with diabetes mellitus of nine months' duration, elevation of blood pressure and varicose veins of the legs.

Family History. No history of heart disease or diabetes but considerable nervousness.

Personal Data. The patient was the youngest daughter in a family of seven. Both her parents were excessively strict, "but they were easier on me than the others. Just the same I couldn't like them. I never knew which one of them was in the wrong." She had four children and three miscarriages, and one therapeutic abortion. "All the children are sick, the girls with thyroid, the boy with heart trouble."

Previous Health. She had had a major operation (therapeutic abortion) and a minor operation; two minor illnesses, and also bad teeth, besides being subject to colds. At the time of admission she had Laënnee's cirrhosis of the liver.

Previous Injuries. None.

General Adjustment. The patient stopped school at the end of the sixth grade in order to go to work taking care of an invalid. She came to the United States at the age of 18 and worked until her marriage at 23. She had done no work since her marriage. The income level was marginal to comfortable, her husband was a bus driver. The patient had always preferred to be by herself and had never had friends.

Characteristic Behavior Pattern. "I think I've been injured all my life but there's nothing I can do about it. You can't tell anything to men even if they are doctors." "Lots of people have lots of patience but it isn't true, I'm almost always angry, but I get over it quickly. I just go and drink a little coffee."

Neurotic Traits. Early: Nail-biting and nightmares relative to being hurt. *Late:* Nightmares, inadequate control, inability to follow orders. "I don't want to see my doctor because I know he'll holler at me. He isn't nice to me unless I do what he wants. During the holidays I had to eat. You'd think any man ought to know that. There's always candy around and I pick at it. Who wouldn't?"

"The least little thing worries me today. The big ones don't bother me at all. . . . Just before I got my diabetes I had a fight with my husband and he fainted in his chair. I thought he was dead but it didn't bother me at all."

The patient cited this as an illustration of the fact that she always worried about little things and didn't bother about big things. On the other hand if one might judge by her spontaneous conversation one might be justified in suspecting that it actually worried her a great deal but that she repressed her worry. She came back to the subject again and again.

"What would have happened if he had died? The whole family would have been better off. But it's an awful thing to say. It makes me feel diabetic to think about it. Ever since it happened I've had nightmares about my husband's dying or being killed and the worst part of it is I never can tell whether I'm glad or sorry."

Addictions and Interests. The patient overindulged in coffee, she drank ten to fifteen cups a day; had weekly headaches relieved by Epsom salts and aspirin. Characteristically she had a habit of eating irregularly, five breakfasts every morning with different members of the family. When she was particularly low she indulged in alcohol. She had no interest in religion.

Life Situation Immediately Prior to Onset. "Just before I got my diabetes I had a fight with my husband and he fainted in his chair. I thought he was dead but it didn't bother me at all" (see *"Neurotic Traits"*).

Reaction to Illness. The patient enjoyed coming to the hospital because it gave her a rest from all her irritations.

Area of Focal Conflict and Characteristic Reaction. Her focal conflict was characteristic of diabetics, a rebellion against her sexual role with projection of her homosexual tendencies in the direction of her husband. She said: "It's amazing how my husband can act. You would have thought he's the nicest man in the world." She stated further that he was suspicious, easily offended, that she didn't dare cross him in anything because she was sure he would beat her up if she did although she admitted that in twenty-seven years of married life he had never done anything of the sort. "He spends all his time with other men. I'm sure they take up all his sexual attention which is very disgusting. Even his children are disgusted with him. He never does anything to help. . . . I was very angry about having children. Life is much simpler without them. But now I'm glad I have them, at least the girls, because girls always look up to their mother and want to take care of her."

This latter case is a good example of the passive type of diabetic patient. All the overlaps between diabetes and hypertension occurred in the passive type, whereas the overlaps between diabetes and the accident habit occurred in the active type. Both types, however, were homosexually inclined.

If this latter history be compared with the more clear-cut pictures of diabetic patients with a passive trend (see Chapter VIII), it will be obvious that in this patient the aggression is much nearer to the surface (a regular finding in patients with hypertension) and the sadomasochistic conflict more acute.

DIABETES—HYPERTENSIVE CARDIOVASCULAR DISEASE—CORONARY OCCLUSION

(Syndromes apparently simultaneous)

Case No. D 41. An unmarried colored man, aged 34, was admitted to the hospital with hypertensive cardiovascular disease, obesity, and diabetes. Three months prior to the onset he complained of severe epigastric pain, and three days prior to admission he complained of severe pain in the left lumbar region together with faintness.

Family History. The patient's mother died of heart trouble when the patient was 13, his father was living and well. No family history of diabetes or accident.

Personal Data. The patient was born in Baltimore, one of eight siblings. "I came from a fine Baltimore family." His father was first a coachman and then owned a stable of his own. After his mother's death he was brought up by his aunt.

Previous Health. Frequent colds and bronchitis.

Injury. None.

General Adjustment. Education: The patient finished one year of high school and then went on the stage. His family thought that beneath his dignity so he gave it up and at the age of 15 took a *job* as a valet and later butler in a family where he remained until six months prior to the discovery of his illness. He had a good *income* as is evidenced by the fact that after his discharge he invested $3000 in furniture for an apartment which he took with a male friend. *Social adjustment:* "I have always had lots of friends and used to go out a lot. I lived high. I got along better with men than women." *Sexual adjustment:* "I didn't want to marry until I had saved enough money (coronary). But I wasn't sure I wanted to be married at all because my brother and sister and the master all had such unhappy marriages." *Attitude toward parents:* The patient was devoted to his mother until she died. "I didn't get over that for months. . . . Father is a fine man but strict so I wanted to be on my own" (coronary).

Characteristic Behavior Pattern. The patient was good-natured and sensitive with a strong desire to please, and occasionally relieved his feelings of hostility by drinking (hypertensive cardiovascular disease). It will be noted that he persisted in one job with the aim of saving a lot of money and being like his father. He showed the diabetic indecisiveness only in his inability to decide what to do about his job (see below) and about marriage.

Neurotic Traits. The patient remembered no early neurotic traits except for enuresis (diabetes) and temper tantrums (hypertensive cardiovascular disease).

Addictions and Interests. Excessive use of coffee, tobacco, and alcohol and little interest in sports (characteristic of all three groups), and much interest in wine and entertaining but little interest in women. He had a fanatical interest in religion characteristic of a certain group of patients with diabetes.

Life Situation Prior to Onset. His employer "went with other women and tried to make me an accomplice, that is, he wanted me to help keep it secret from the mistress who was a fine Southern woman. I said I couldn't do this but I kept changing back and forth because I couldn't make up my mind. I told him he wasn't behaving right and we had a fight. He gave me a dollar and told me to leave. That was when I had my first fainting spell. I kept thinking about it ever since and that's made me worse. Since then I haven't been able to get a good job again." Here we see thwarting of a life-long ambition for which the patient had worked persistently, nearly twenty years (hypertensive cardiovascular disease—coronary occlusion), and a long period of wear and tear combined with indecision and homosexual conflict (diabetes).

Reaction to Illness. This patient's reaction to illness alternated between that characteristic of diabetes and hypertensive cardiovascular disease, giving in to passive tendencies and the feeling of relief at having found an alibi for his illness, and the coronary occlusion patient's tendency to minimize his symptoms and the desire to make a fresh start.

Area of Major Conflict and Characteristic Reaction. Although hypertensive cardiovascular disease and coronary occlusion are relatively infrequent among Negroes, this patient's profile resembles that of the patient with hypertensive cardiovascular disease progressing in the direction of coronary occlusion, rather than that of the patient with diabetes. The two important exceptions which probably had something to do with the development of his diabetes were his overt homosexual conflict which interfered with any attempt at sexual adjustment and the long period of wear and tear in a situation in which he was incapable of making a decision.

IV. CARDIAC ARRHYTHMIA AS COMPLICATING OTHER SYNDROMES

Although the first two of the cases cited here could have been grouped under the preceding headings, they are discussed in relation to cardiac arrhythmia because the cardiac arrhythmic personality is dominant in both of them.

FRACTURE—CARDIAC ARRHYTHMIA

(Simultaneous Syndromes)

Case No. F 149. An unmarried girl, aged 21, was admitted for fracture of both bones of both legs and malunion after left Colles fracture.

Family History. The mother had had a stroke, and previously had fractured her leg. The patient's father had diabetes, and her paternal grandmother had broken her rib in a fall. There was a third instance of exposure to accident when her best friend broke a rib. (*Note:* Exposure to accident is not prominent in the history of fracture patients although it is likely to be prominent among patients with cardiac syndromes who also had accidents.)

Personal Data. The patient was born in Boston in 1917, normal delivery, the first and only child (as is characteristic with cardiac arrhythmia). Her background was middle class and comfortable. Both parents lived well into the patient's adolescence, and the mother was particularly strict. The patient lived in Boston until she was 11 years old, moved to New York and had her first accident.

Previous Health. Unlike the typical fracture patient, but like the patient with cardiac arrhythmia, even at her early age the patient had had a bad previous illness history including several attacks of measles, as well as scarlet fever, mumps, whooping cough, bronchitis, pneumonia, frequent gastrointestinal upsets and an operation for appendicitis.

Injury. The patient was running, fell over a toy fire engine and broke her arm. At the age of 17 she was running on the sand and cut her foot on a piece of glass necessitating several stitches. At the age of 20 she was running across the street and failed to see a car coming rapidly toward her. She was hit, thrown in the air, and "somehow broke both legs."

General Adjustment. Education: Like the typical accident patient, this girl stopped her academic education in the middle of an academic unit, in the second year of high school "because I never liked discipline." She then *worked* as a sales girl earning a fair income but she had had an irregular work record. *Social adjustment:* "I choose my friends very carefully and never bother with the common herd. My friends like me very much." *Sexual adjustment:* Onset of menstruation at the age of 15, normal history except that all three of her accidents were associated with a menstrual period. "I always planned to get married, and probably will in a year or two, I have a steady boy-friend." *Attitude toward family:* "My parents were all right. I wasn't very sorry when my father died although I wished it had been my mother instead."

Characteristic Behavior Pattern. "I have always been nervous and I like to do crazy things. It makes me feel morbid to be alone but I feel cheerful with lots of people around who like me unless they are mean or suffering" (typical of cardiac arrhythmia).

Neurotic Traits. Early: Nail-biting and temper tantrums (like the patient with cardiac arrhythmia), no nightmares, sleep-walking, or sleep-talking (unlike the accident patient). *Present:* Like the accident patient she liked to think she took good care of herself; she ate irregularly and didn't care what she ate. Unlike the accident patient nail-biting and a quick temper remained a problem. In addition (again unlike the accident patient) diverse neurotic symptoms were manifest, anxiety attacks, paranoid trends, narcissistic withdrawal and evasiveness, which led the examining physician to question the possibility of incipient schizophrenia.

Addictions and Interests. Unlike the accident patient, she had no interest in tea, tobacco or alcohol, nor in religion. Some addiction to coffee to "make me feel strong." Like the accident patient, however, she was very fond of competitive sports, skating, tobogganing, skiing, horseback riding and swimming. But although she took many risks in connection with these sports they never resulted in accidents. Like the patient with cardiac arrhythmia she was inordinately fond of the theatre, dancing, and "high society."

Life Situation Immediately Prior to Onset. The first accident occurred immediately after moving to New York, where she felt "out of it" and wondered whether she could make enough new friends. Her first attack of "palpitation" occurred at this time also. The second accident occurred immediately after the death of her father from diabetes; the third accident immediately after her mother's stroke, while the patient was caring for her. Prior to both of these accidents also, she had suffered from cardiac symptoms. Thus all three attacks (accident plus cardiac arrhythmia) were precipitated by traumatic experiences in the sphere of personal relationships, as is typical of the patient with cardiac arrhythmia. The reason that this patient had to have accidents also is probably to be explained on the basis of her other personality traits.

Reaction to Illness. She recalled sitting up and looking at the bone sticking out of her bleeding legs, but said: "I felt no pain. I felt as strong as ever. I knew it happened. I couldn't help it. It was done already. I didn't see any use in worrying." This reaction of course is typical of the accident patient, but in addition this patient was evasive and very suspicious of her doctors and nurses, complaining that she had not been given the right treatment. She was afraid that the whirlpool bath for her hand would somehow or other result in her losing her hand. She couldn't stand hearing the other patients cry. She said, "By Monday I will be a corpse if I stay in bed on this ward any longer. The wheel chair is no good either because the nurses don't know how to fix it and I am afraid it will tip over and break off my legs again.

I feel as if it would have been better if I had been killed. I cried last night. I never did that before." (This reaction is typical of the patient with cardiac arrhythmia rather than the accident patient.)

Area of Focal Conflict and Characteristic Reaction. It is clear from the above that this patient's sphere of conflict included most of the outside world and that she attempted to withdraw from it and at the same time stand on her own feet. Like the accident patient, she had a very special trouble with authority. She attempted to deal with these difficulties by verbalization, keeping fear and anger pent up, but she also resorted frequently to impulsive behavior.

This patient showed two syndromes in simultaneous combination more clearly than most of the patients studied, and also she showed more diverse neurotic symptom formation than is characteristic of the group of either of the two syndromes with which she suffered. The interesting question remains as to whether or not the suggestibility characteristic of the patient with cardiac arrhythmia plus her unusual exposure to accidents was a determining factor.

HYPERTENSIVE CARDIOVASCULAR DISEASE—FRACTURE—CARDIAC ARRHYTHMIA

The history of patient No. H 351 (page 286) reveals a prominence of neurotic symptom formation unusual in either the typical patient with fracture or the typical patient with hypertensive cardiovascular disease. This prominence is, however, characteristic of those with cardiac arrhythmia.

ANGINAL SYNDROME—CARDIAC ARRHYTHMIA

Case No. AS 153. A married woman, aged 36, was admitted to the hospital with the complaint of dyspnea and palpitation, occasional blood-streaked sputum and precordial pain.

Family History. The patient's father died of pneumonia when the patient was 21. The mother was living and well. No family history of cardiovascular disease, fracture, or diabetes.

Personal Data. The patient was the first child in the family and had a younger brother.

Previous Health. The patient had had one major operation and two minor ones; two attacks of pneumonia, diphtheria and two other major illnesses, various gastro-intestinal upsets, trouble with her teeth, and hay fever. In addition she had had six miscarriages.

Injury. None.

General Adjustment. Education: The patient finished high school and then married. She was intelligent, ambitious and anxious to go on the stage. *Social adjustment:* "I always got along well with people, which is a wonder considering the life I had." *Sexual adjustment:* "Mother was very limited as to sex but gradually I learned about it. I was always frightened about it. I guess I was right, I have had six miscarriages, and one son 7 years old who has never been anything but a trouble to me." *Attitude toward parents:* "I've always hated my mother. She was not my real mother. I am the child of a very beautiful and brilliant artist with whom my father had an affair. I always loved my father and my life was ruined when he died. I was 21 then, just about to go on the stage. I lost my voice then, just as he died with pneumonia."

Characteristic Behavior Pattern. "I have always been nervous and people call me flighty. I feel gloomy when I am alone."

Neurotic Traits. "I used to have nightmares about killing my mother or her killing me. I still have nightmares like that or else about sex."

Addictions and Interests. The patient does not drink coffee or alcohol, and does not smoke. She is not interested in athletics but is much interested in painting and social gatherings.

Life Situation Immediately Prior to Onset. As is typical of the patient with anginal syndrome the onset of illness in this patient followed a disillusionment in the sphere of her ambition. It followed also a traumatic event (her father's death) in the sphere of personal relationships. "After father died the only way to live was to get married and that scared me too."

Reaction to Illness. "I guess my life is ended. I ought to be taken care of but nobody understands me." In this the patient showed a combination of the distrust of her physicians characteristic of the patient with cardiac arrhythmia and the tendency to make excessive demands for care which is one of the reactions characteristic of patients with anginal syndrome.

Area of Major Conflict and Characteristic Reaction. In this patient the area of focal conflict was rivalry with authority but was diffused to include all relationships with the outside world. Her reaction alternated between withdrawal into herself, satisfaction of ambition in fantasy, and the desire to shine in a theatrical way. Verbalization of her conflicts was prominent and the pent-up fear and anxiety was revealed in her persisting nightmares.

On the whole this patient's personality was more characteristic of the cardiac arrhythmia patient, particularly the group with no organic damage, and the anginal syndrome was relatively minor. On this basis one might predict that instead of going on to develop organic damage this patient would probably divert more and more of her energy into neurotic symptom formation. This impression was borne out by a follow-up interview five years later.

SUMMARY

The case illustrations given in this section do not present the classical picture of paroxysmal tachycardia or effort syndrome. (For illustrations of such cases see pages 445, 447, and 453.) But the syndrome of dyspnea and palpitation together with the relevant personality traits are sufficiently marked in these cases to justify treating them separately even though many physicians did call them "cardiac neurotics." In all cases of cardiac arrhythmia the neurotic symptom formation was marked.

Patients with cardiac arrhythmia who had additional syndromes were found among the accident-prone more frequently than is the case with any other group (19 per cent). *Per contra*, of patients hospitalized for fracture, 4.7 per cent also had, or had had, cardiac arrhythmia. There appears to be an indistinct borderline between these two syndromes.

Considered on the basis of somatic phenomena, cardiac arrhythmia is the least disabling of any of the cardiovascular syndromes; it is least frequently associated with organic damage and has a better prognosis. Many patients with dyspnea and palpitation are customarily characterized as "neurotic" by the medical examiner; others with paroxysmal tachycardia or more serious symptoms are frequently found to be without structural damage.

One channel of escape used by these patients, which is far less characteristic of either the accident-prone or those with well-developed cardiovascular disease, is that of classical neurotic symptoms. In other words, that part of their emotional response to conflict which does not find its outlet in speech or physical symptoms is channeled into neurotic behavior patterns. One may infer that if this channel were not employed by them, they would more frequently suffer injury from accidents or organic damage.

V. Discussion and Conclusions

In the introduction to this chapter it was suggested that in a patient suffering from a combination of syndromes, there is evidence of personality factors predisposing him to each syndrome in question, just as there appear to be predisposing personality factors when only one illness syndrome is present. This impression is borne out by the absence of a chance distribution of the overlapping syndromes, and by the prevalence of particular kinds of combinations. In the discussion of the several prevailing combinations illustrated by case histories, an attempt was made to discover just which personality traits led to the combinations in question. It remains to be seen what principles govern the prevalent combinations.

One possibility is that the area of focal conflict may be the same for two diseases found in combination, but that the manner of reacting to the difficulty may differ, and that this difference may be accompanied by a different syndrome. A patient exhibiting both syndromes could suffer from one of them when he reacted in one way and from another when he reacted in the other. The change could occur either chronologically as in patients who in earlier years have one syndrome which later is exchanged for another, or irregularly and alternately as in the case of the patient who shifts back and forth between the syndromes.

This hypothesis seems to fit certain of the more outstanding groups of combinations under discussion. For instance, there is an important overlap among hypertensive cardiovascular disease, anginal syndrome, and coronary occlusion. In the profiles for each of these syndromes the area of focal conflict is that with authority. When more than one of these syndromes is found in the same person, there is a tendency toward change over a period of time, from the less serious to the more serious, rather than an irregular alternation. The differences among the several personality types which have only one of these diseases seem to lie almost entirely in the manner of reacting to the focal conflict. The coronary occlusion patient exhibits a compulsive drive to get to the top and constitute himself the unchallenged authority, whereas the hypertensive cardiovascular disease and anginal syndrome types are a good deal less persistent in this endeavor, or exercise it in a more limited field. When any of the two syndromes are found in combination, however, the type of reaction associated with the syndrome first exhibited changes to the type associated with that eventually discovered.

Another significant observation concerns the nature of the com-

binations found between accident-proneness and the several cardiovascular syndromes. Both seem to be characterized by a focal conflict
in the realm of authority. There are no cases, however, of overlap
between hypertensive cardiovascular disease and accident-habit or
coronary occlusion and accident habit, although patients with both
syndromes have some accidents. The personality types found in both
hypertensive cardiovascular disease and coronary disease differ radi-
cally from that associated with accident-proneness, not in the area
of focal conflict, but in the manner of reacting to it. Patients with
these cardiovascular syndromes are much disturbed by the conflict
and attempt to be victorious in it, whereas the accident-prone try
to minimize and avoid it. Patients with coronary occlusion and hypertensive cardiovascular disease inhibit hostility whereas accident-
prone patients tend to act out their emotional difficulties.

Patients with anginal syndrome, however, in contrast with the
hypertensive and coronary patients show a certain overlapping with
the accident habit (5 per cent). This combination may be accounted
for by the fact that in early years these patients tend to act out their
difficulties; later they adopt a type of reaction more like that characteristic of patients with coronary occlusion.

Some medical authorities believe that hypertensive cardiovascular
disease, anginal syndrome, and coronary occlusion are physiologically
so close as to be different aspects of the same disease process. If this
is true, it would tend to substantiate the personality profiles for
these syndromes because they show more similarities than any of the
other profiles outlined. In turn the personality profiles may be useful
to the internist in helping to explain why this disease process (considered as a single disease process) should become manifest in such
different ways in different people.

It will be noted that the patients having cardiac arrhythmia have
a greater overlap with the accident-prone than does any other group
listed (19 per cent); their overlaps with hypertensive cardiovascular
disease and anginal syndrome are much smaller and they do not overlap at all with coronary occlusion. Here the area of focal conflict is
contact with the outside world, including the realm of authority,
but includes other spheres as well. The typical reaction is much more
like that of the accident-prone than like that of patients having
coronary syndrome. Those with cardiac arrhythmia alternate between

impulsive acting out and talking about their troubles. There is not a chronological development from one syndrome to the other, but rather an irregular alternation between the two. They also exhibit more of the classical neurotic symptoms than any of the other patients with cardiovascular syndromes.

A second hypothesis to explain overlapping syndromes on the basis of personality traits would be that though the focal conflict associated with the syndromes differed, the manner of reacting to conflict was similar. The preceding case histories provide illustration.

The combinations of rheumatic fever and rheumatic heart disease with accident-proneness, fit this hypothesis. The area of focal conflict appears to differ from that of fracture patients, but the type of reaction to it is similar in type A rheumatic fever patients, 14 per cent of whom have an accident habit. In patients with rheumatic heart disease, who have a smaller overlap (4 per cent), and in type B patients with rheumatic fever, who have no overlap with accident-proneness, the habitual reaction is of a different character altogether.

A few of the combinations of syndromes cannot be explained by either of the above hypotheses. Those patients in whom these combinations were found evince a rather complete change both in personality type and in syndrome, the personality type in each case being appropriate to the syndrome found at the time. One of these patients said himself that he "had become a new person."

Among patients with diabetes the greatest overlap is with hypertensive cardiovascular disease and a smaller but still significant overlap is with patients with fracture. These combinations may possibly be accounted for by the physiological disease process of diabetes itself. Many investigators are trying to establish a connection between the often noted coincidence of hypertensive cardiovascular disease and diabetes. It may also be suggested that patients with diabetes, when they are suffering from hypoglycemia, tend to be mentally confused, and this may account for their proneness to accidents. In relation to this suggestion it must be remembered that among patients with diabetes the accident-proneness often developed before the onset of the diabetic syndrome.

In addition to possible physiological explanations, however, we may suggest a psychological hypothesis, which is not necessarily an alternative to them. Psychiatrists have noted that psychoneurotic patients frequently suffer not from a single conflict or type of neurotic disorder but from a combination of them. For instance, hysterical patients sometimes exhibit compulsive traits and vice versa. It is generally remarked that the more serious the mental illness, the greater the variety of neurotic responses and somatic symptoms. The suggestion has been made that patients with diabetes have a schizophrenic personality trend, although some observers stress manic depressive or hysterical symptomatology. All agree, however, that psychotic tendencies are particularly frequent in patients suffering from this degenerative disease. This may account for the fact that diabetic patients not only overlap to a significant extent with cardiovascular syndromes and accident-proneness but also exhibit minor combinations with coronary occlusion and rheumatic heart disease, as well as supplying half of the cases in which there is a triple combination—diabetes being combined at the same time with hypertensive cardiovascular disease and coronary occlusion.

In reviewing such problems in terms of personality profiles it is important to avoid over-simplification. For instance, in the case of the conflict with authority there is a difference between those with whom the conflict is long drawn out and those who escape it in early childhood through death of parents or running away. There also appears to be a difference between those the center of whose early conflict is the father and those who feel the conflict mainly with the mother. There are numerous cases in which the conflict with authority is combined with a conflict over sexual role. In these one or the other is for the time more prominent. But in them one vitally affects the other, as where inability to deal with the conflict with authority creates not only a problem in managing aggressive drives but also a problem in the sexual sphere leading to the desire to assume the opposite sexual role.*

In conclusion two points should be emphasized. (1) Among the patients studied those who had two or more diseases represented the exception rather than the rule. (2) Among the syndromes here discussed the combinations do not exhibit a chance distribution, but rather cluster about a relatively few varieties of possible combinations.

As a corollary, however, it is necessary to emphasize the further

* The well-trained psychoanalyst can fill in the gaps here with his understanding of infantile development and maturation of the oedipus conflict.

fact that a given individual of one general personality type may have different illness syndromes accompanying particular emotional tensions. Hence the same illness syndrome may accompany a specific emotional tension in different personality types. This seems more likely to be the case with syndromes of a minor nature such as gastrointestinal upsets or transitory skin complaints, for example, than with syndromes which lead more or less quickly to serious organic damage like coronary disease. When individuals of the coronary or accident type go on to develop other syndromes there is more likely to be a change in the total behavior pattern.

All this appears to be consistent with the theory that there is a correspondence between personality types and physical symptomatology.

Chapter XI

CONSIDERATIONS OF GENERAL THEORY AND CRITERIA FOR THERAPY

Mankind in its progress passes through three states: The unanimity of the ignorant, the disagreement of the inquiring, and the unanimity of the wise.—H. SPENCER.

I. COMMENT ON SOME EXISTING HYPOTHESES

In understanding illness from the psychosomatic point of view we have been primarily interested in three questions, as follows: (1) What is it in a personality which generates the predisposition to illness? (2) What determines the choice of the specific expression of the illness? (3) What is the precipitating factor which brings on the illness, given the predisposition and the choice of manner of expression? In an earlier book, "Emotions and Bodily Changes" [149] and in subsequent articles, I called attention to specific pieces of research in this field which are helping to answer these questions. In this volume I have reported a general dynamic and statistical study which provides a different kind of material and a different perspective, but in any new field a theoretical framework is of fundamental importance in understanding and applying the results of such research. Hence, we felt it desirable to discuss our own theoretical framework and perspective.

Theoretical hypotheses relative to one or more of our three questions have been suggested by Freud,[194] Ferenczi,[180] and Abraham,[180] Alexander,[10] Kardiner,[260] Deutsch,[123] and French,[192] among others. In this context a few brief comments on suggestions offered by each of the last four of these authors are relevant.

Alexander has supplied one of the few general hypotheses dealing with choice of symptoms. He has suggested that in organ neuroses as well as in organic diseases of psychogenic origin, the symbolism which Freud discovered in conversion hysteria cannot explain the choice of the channel for the repressed conflict, because these internal organs are usually unknown to the child and perhaps are unknown even to the unconscious. Not being parts of the body through which we ordinarily express conscious emotion, they cannot well be vehicles of symbolic action. What they can express is rather the physiological consequence of emotional tension. This part of his theory is thoroughly substantiated by study of the syndromes with which we have been particularly concerned in hospital research; namely, cardiovascular disease, "rheumatism," diabetes, and fractures.

It will be remembered that we have commented on the relative lack in patients in these categories of elaborated symbolism, whether conscious or unconscious, connecting the emotional difficulties with the organ systems involved. There are individual exceptions particularly among fracture cases in which the accident-prone patient seemed habitually to select a certain member for injury, and the patients with rheumatoid arthritis, whose fantasies were symbolized in the members in which pain was felt.

Alexander goes on, however, from organ symbolism to something very like it; namely, what he calls a vector, or "the dynamic direction of impulses." Emotional tendencies, he asserts, can be classified according to whether they embody a wish to incorporate, to eliminate, or to retain. But these are the very physiological functions performed by internal organs, and so the appropriate functions, with the organs exercising them, are chosen to express repressed emotional tendencies of the same vector. Though he pointed out that this vector analysis is particularly appropriate to the gastro-intestinal tract, the respiratory system, the genito-urinary system, and to a certain degree, the skin, he expressed the belief that in the conception we have found "the common denominator of psychological and biological processes."

There is a theoretical difficulty in applying the vector concept to the organic dysfunction of those with cardiovascular or diabetic symptoms. Only in a more indirect and remote sense do persons through these syndromes exert any effect on their environment which could be expressed by such words as incorporation, retention, or elimination. Nor is it easy to find any other words, or any vector concept, which could describe these functions in such a way as to indicate a parallelism with emotional tendencies. What, for instance, would be an emotional state which would bear an obvious and superficial resemblance to the secretion of insulin in the pancreas, or the changes in blood chemistry which accompany hypertension, or the action of the ductless glands?

Alexander's hypothesis has been criticized because it is concentrated mainly on libido phenomena, giving inadequate weight to the rest of the personality. Although the difference may be mainly a matter of focus and emphasis we have found somatic symptoms to be more understandable in terms of the personality's patterns of behavior including necessity for defense, and the choice of the nature of the defense in each case.

Kardiner has approached our problem mainly from the point of view of interaction of ego and environment. In taking the *action syndrome,** as a basic unit, he points out:

The internal environment—the system of organs and systems regulating the internal balance—is related to the activity in the outer world because the conditions for effective functioning are governed by it. The sympathetic and parasympathetic systems are synchronous in function with those of the skeletal system. Since the conditions for action vary, the autonomic system regulates the internal environment so as to be consonant with these conditions by distributing tissue fluids, internal secretions and regulating blood pressure and heart rate. These internal activities thus become an integral part of the action syndrome (Kardiner,[260] pages 170–171).

It is likely that the total personality organization and environmental factors both play a large role in disease.

Deutsch,[123] who has been particularly interested in the choice of the specific expression of illness, finds three factors of importance: the extrinsic organ factor, the personality organization at the time, and the action of the neurosis in the environment. "If these three factors coincide the direction in which the choice of organ tends is definitely laid down. The development of the symptoms depends on the interrelationship of these three factors, so that if all three factors can be known the course can be prophesied."

French, in his excellent paper, "Physiology of Behavior and Choice

* See also David Levy.[279]

of Neurosis," made a comment which I believe is valuable in that it provides a basis for including in one framework these various approaches to our three questions.

Analysts will notice that what I am here proposing is merely an attempt to develop in very explicit form a procedure which analysts have long used in terms of Freud's original libido theory. We have long been accustomed to attempt to explain numerous psychological mechanisms by displacement of libido from one organ of the body to another. My only innovation in this procedure is to *discard as unimportant the old and meaningless controversy as to whether the energy that is shoved about in these displacement processes is of a sexual nature or not. I think it is much more important to recognize that these displacements of energy are really of functional significance.** As a matter of fact every integrated activity involves the functional excitation now of one organ, now of another, according to the particular pattern of the activity. One moment we are looking, another we are thinking, and then there may be motor discharge. I believe it is introducing entirely unnecessary confusion to conceive of these "displacements of energy," when we encounter them in the dream work, as some sort of mysterious displacements of libido (French,[192] page 567).

After giving illustrations from dreams and their physiological accompaniment, he goes on to say:

It will be noted that the physiological mechanism implied in all these instances is one of attempting to distract energy from some conflict involving the need for energetic motor discharge by means of an intense intellectual preoccupation or visual fascination (French,[192] page 570).

French concludes his article with the bridge simile, the physiologist working at one end and the psychologist working at the other, and states:

At the present time an enormous amount of work is being done in the attempt to bridge the gap between the physiologist's detailed knowledge of the mechanisms of isolated reactions and the psychologist's attempts to work out the motivations that determine the larger patterns of behavior viewed as a whole (French,[192] page 571).

It is our hope that the following suggestions may supply at least part of a basic structure for a span which may ultimately tie together the ends of the imagined bridge.

---

* The italics are mine, F.D.

II. Suggested Laws of Emotional Thermodynamics *

The organismal theory provides the fundamental concept, or way of looking at the subject, in what is called psychosomatic medicine. Once we have grasped the idea that the psychic and somatic are not two different universes, but the same one viewed from different approaches, it may be possible to present the scientific problem attacked by our research in somewhat more rigorous and clear-cut terms. The following effort to do so is presented mainly for those readers who have an interest in the philosophy of science; others may omit it with the assurance that the practical bearing of our results is not affected by this excursion into theory.

The basic laws of physics are recognized to be the first and second laws of thermodynamics. The first law of thermodynamics is the familiar law of the conservation of energy. No energy ever ceases to exist; a given quantity of energy has a given amount of effect of some kind, which can be measured and equated with the original mechanical impulse. Energy which does not do mechanical work may be transformed into heat, or vice versa; it may also be transformed into other physical or chemical phenomena.

The second law of thermodynamics has to do with the reversibility of the flow of energy. Ideally, every engine ought to run backward without any loss of energy, active or latent. If we should connect one steam engine with another just like it, except that the valves of the second were so arranged that it would work backward, one could imagine the second engine generating by compression as much heat in its boiler as the first engine took from its boiler to operate the second. As a matter of fact, however, it is impossible to produce such a perfect result. Some energy is always lost during its flow, by being transformed into friction, heat, chemical or electrical phenomena. This lost energy does not cease to exist, but it departs from the engine or other device which we are operating. This dissipation of energy does not controvert the law of the conservation of energy, but is a supplementary observation. It constitutes the second law of thermodynamics, and may be stated in the words: *"In every*

---

* This discussion has been presented in two papers: the first, read before the Family Study Group of the New York Hospital on March 5, 1940; the second, "Motivation in Certain Psychosomatic Syndromes," read before the Association for Research in Psychoanalysis and Experimental Psychodynamics on December 20, 1941.

transformation of energy which occurs of itself, some energy is made unavailable."

Psychiatrists * are thinking more and more (with or without actual formulation) in terms of a concept of vital energy † which is in every way analogous to the first law of thermodynamics, or the conservation of energy. Freud, who was particularly explicit on this subject, postulated as a result of his observations in the hypnotic treatment of hysteria, that emotion has both a *dynamic* factor and an *economic* factor. In discussing the dynamic factor he stated that emotion failing to find its proper or normal outlet in speech or action, but rather dammed up by repression, will not cease to operate, but will find another channel. It may thus appear as a neurotic symptom. In discussing the *economic* factor he said that the quantity of the emotional energy bound up in the outlet or symptom would be equal to that present in the emotional impulse which gave rise to it. Much of his work consists in tracing the various psychic channels through which repressed emotional stimuli may seek their outlet, and the transformations through which they may go. And much of his therapeutic method was to reverse the flow of energy from the symptom back to the original but repressed emotional impulse which, when made conscious, could then be given a less injurious expression or outlet. The basic law of Freud's work, which now is a basic law of general psychiatry as well, may thus be called the "first law of emotional thermodynamics," or conservation of vital energy.

But this law, as expressed in Freud's studies, has implications which have not until recently been fully apprehended, although Freud himself called attention to them. It is often assumed that his dynamic conception of emotion referred only to the transformations of vital energy into various patterns of emotional or mental behavior. Yet many of his cases and observations reveal the transformation of vital energy into physical symptoms, and vice versa. These symptoms

---

* See Sherrington [379] and page 53 of this volume.

† See the many writings of Adolf Meyer and his concept of ergasiology. White [417] speaks of the organism "as an energy system, not a closed system but an open system, which receives, transforms and delivers energy, and under these circumstances it is not a distinct and separate entity but it is a part of a larger whole—society, if you will—which again becomes likewise a part of a still larger whole." An earlier background is given in Meyer.[305]

were, moreover, not always hysterical or difficult to connect with bodily changes, but were often what the general physician would call "genuine" somatic illness. In this respect also the law of the conservation of vital energy is analogous to the physical conservation law, which postulates the transformation of energy not only into crude motion and work but also into heat, electricity and chemical changes. One can regard the bodily symptoms which sometimes retain and bind discharges of vital energy as the counterpart of the heat, or of the electric and chemical changes which embody some of the transformations of physical energy. Indeed, the analogy is extraordinarily close, since recent physiological research has shown us that changes in the body which are associated with emotional stimuli are, in sober fact, basically changes in temperature, electric potential, and chemical composition. So close is the analogy that one is tempted to hazard the guess that future study may reveal that it is not a mere analogy but an identity. Vital energy may some time be revealed as identical with physical energy, and its transformations as identical with physical work, heat, electrical or chemical changes.

Aside from such speculation, research into psychosomatic phenomena such as is described in this report may be regarded as an attempt to test by systematic observation the law of the conservation of vital energy in its broader aspects. The research is directed to indicate answers to certain questions to which this broad postulate gives rise. Can we discover the prevalence of important emotional components in patients suffering from specific types of verified physical disease? Do these components consist of repressed conflicts? Can the physical symptoms be identified as transformations of vital energy? Can the flow of energy be reversed, so that when it is returned to the original emotional form, the physical symptoms tend to disappear? Is there a specific course of the energy transformation in each type of syndrome, or can we discover in a given syndrome a specific mechanism of transformation (in the form of personality structure or method of dealing with emotion)—as it were, a specific kind of engine?

Our approach suggests also an analogy with the second law of thermodynamics. We may regard the human organism as if it were an engine or motor for the transformation of vital energy into work or motion. This work or motion may be conceived as the proper or normal outlet of energy in the functioning of the personality within its environment. Just as the steam engine or electric motor is designed to channel energy into the work desired, so the human personality may be thought of as a mechanism to channel energy into bodily sustenance, self-protection, love, creative activity, and various effects on the environment.

But no engine or motor is perfectly efficient: according to the second law of thermodynamics some of its energy is always dissipated without doing the work for which it is designed. Energy is lost through friction or is dissipated otherwise in undesired heat or electric or chemical effects and so becomes unavailable. Similarly we may think of pathological mental or physical symptoms as paths for the diversion of vital energy; by so much as they exist, they render the human organism less efficient for its inherent goal-directed activities. When such symptoms are so serious as to be associated with structural damage, the flow of vital energy becomes, at least in part, dissipated. Energy has been used up in effecting these changes as if it had been lost. Often little can be done to redirect the energy from the symptoms into more creative channels so that the symptoms may disappear. In this sense we may postulate a second law of emotional thermodynamics. This law might be phrased as follows: *If symptoms representing pathological outlets of vital energy are crystallized in permanent structural damage, the energy is by so much dissipated and becomes unavailable* in terms of both present efficiency and future therapy. The pathology is rendered to this extent irreversible.

As yet we have no accurate line of demarcation for permanent structural damage and many disease processes which were considered irreversible,[149] have proved to be reversible with adequate therapy, or occasionally "spontaneously," that is through a combination of factors not yet understood. Probably we will not begin to understand phenomena of this kind until we have a clearer picture of the organism-environment as a continuum.

This second law of emotional thermodynamics is a postulate also tested in part by our research. As an unformulated assumption, it led us to ask whether a pathological symptom might not be reversible by psychotherapy in the early stages of the disorder, but become irreversible later if psychotherapy was inapplicable because permanent structural damage had by then occurred. For this reason we were particularly interested by cases which came to the hospital showing a typical disease picture, but were dismissed without treatment because no structural damage was found, and later admitted with structural damage from the very disorder which the original picture suggested. *Per contra,* we were interested by cases in which symptoms disappeared through the application of psychotherapy, although surgical intervention would otherwise have been indicated. No rigorous proof of this postulated law is attempted, but many indications of it were found.

Finally, it must be noted that quantitative measurement such as would confirm these postulated laws of emotional thermodynamics awaits experiment in the indefinite future. Carnot deduced the two laws of physical thermodynamics long before they could be established by experiment and measurement; they were subsequently proved by Joule, Kelvin, and others when the necessary techniques had been developed. It may be doubted whether it will ever be possible to measure accurately the quantity of vital energy at its source, and then to balance against that quantity its effect in the various channels through which it may flow. Yet it is not such a far cry to imagine that psychological and biological techniques may some day be devised sufficient to impart a measurable impulse to a human organism, and then to trace and measure all its effects in terms of speech, action, or bodily changes such as tension, electrical discharges detected through such instruments as the electrocardiograph and the electroencephalograph, or changes in chemistry of the fluid media of the cells. If such experiments should become possible, they could be used to test not only the dynamic factor in emotion which Freud postulated and which has been systematically observed in the present research, but the *economic* factor as well. Likewise it would be possible to measure not only the conservation but the dissipation of vital energy.

Of course any reader will realize the danger in attempting to apply thermodynamics to the laws of energy economy in the organism. The problem of entropy needs further analysis. Some light as to a possible resolution of some of these difficulties is obtained by going back to our initial thesis of thinking in terms of an organism-environment equilibrium, not merely an organism in a vacuum.*

---

* In the meantime the reader interested in the suggestion which is here sketched but neither adequately qualified nor elaborated, might study simultaneously Bridgman's [50] recent book on thermodynamics and comments made recently by George Soule [392] discussing the field of psychosomatic medicine. *See also Symposium.*[408]

In conclusion we may come back to our consideration of the theory of motive, particularly in regard to the choice of syndrome in psychosomatic disease, and the precipitating factor. It would appear that in view of all the complications we can derive little light from thinking of motive in terms of concrete wishes, repressed or otherwise, and of its expression in terms merely of bodily symbolism closely related to fantasy life. It seems more pertinent to think of the personality structure as an organization determining the nature of the flow of energy in the individual, and of somatic dysfunction as a waste or dissipation of that energy due to the faulty design of the personality, diverting energy from the goal-directed activities of the type of human beings whom under given circumstances we regard as the norm. Of course there may be many different kinds of faults or inefficiencies in the personality organization and the associated channels for energy, just as there may be in the design or operation of a mechanical motor. The motor obviously is inadequate as an analogy if we realize that we are dealing with organism-environment as a system.

In view of the concrete evidence under discussion, one of the most useful concepts is that of the constellation of factors which make up the emotional and environmental conditions peculiar to any specific syndrome under consideration. The single elements composing any constellation are widespread among the population, but a particular combination of these elements may not be found except in connection with a specific disease syndrome. For instance, conflict with parental discipline is a very general condition, but not all those who experience it develop somatic diseases, and a still smaller number somatic diseases of a particular kind. When we add to the conflict with parents a particular type of conflict, or a particular type of family setting, we somewhat narrow the class under consideration. A further reduction of numbers occurs when we specify a particular manner of dealing with the conflict with authority, such as avoidance, surpassing, emulation, and so forth.

Another factor of great significance in our studies, which applies to all the groups under consideration except the accident-prone, is exposure to the syndrome which the patient later develops. This exposure is significant, not in terms which are usually taken to mean hereditary predisposition, that is, the occurrence of the syndrome in parents or grandparents, their siblings or perhaps the patients' siblings, but its occurrence also among associates having no blood relationship. The guess may be hazarded that while in some cases the exposure constitutes a psychological suggestion of a certain type of syndrome, in others it is really an exposure to a type of action or reaction pattern which leads to the syndrome. Environmental factors of various kinds which affect the conflict or the defenses erected against it form an important part of the constellation.

Finally, we have as a precipitating factor a combination of quantitative increase of the misdirected energy associated with the conflict, and a failure of the non-somatic channels of discharge, or a breakdown of the action syndrome. We might cite as an example the occurrence of coronary occlusion when the predisposed individual suffers a dramatic reversal in his life role of occupational success or supremacy over others. The operation of the precipitating factor differs markedly, however, according to the nature of the personality and the syndrome in question. In diabetes, for instance, it appears to be much more in the nature of a gradual retreat under a long harassment, consequent upon the failure to erect any adequate type of defense or to establish any moderately satisfactory release even for a short time.

Naturally all such discussion is still in the realm of hypothesis and speculation. We are now in a position to infer that if we were able to identify and include all the relevant elements in a given constellation we should have a specific indication of a particular disease syndrome. Nevertheless it is far from certain that we have yet been able to do so. We cannot conclude that everyone with a given personality structure and a given means of reacting to a conflict in a given area is predisposed to a certain syndrome, and will contract it in the presence of the appropriate precipitating factors, without discovering whether there are persons subject to this same constellation who do not develop the syndrome. So far we have found strong evidence only that there are persons subject to the constellations in question who do develop the associated syndromes, and that of those who have the syndrome all, or nearly all, appear to be subject to the appropriate constellation. We are convinced, furthermore, that the quantitative prominence of the constellation, its state of equilibrium or disequilibrium at the moment of the impact, and the quantitative intensity of the precipitating impact, must be considered along with the qualitative factors.

The observation of correlation between specific constellations and specific syndromes in our study is of course purely empirical. Can we hazard any theoretical explanation which might account for this correlation, beyond the general premises underlying the psychosomatic approach? What, in more precise terms, is the psychosomatic process involved in determining which syndrome is associated with a given constellation?

A process of elimination may offer clues. In most cases it is not a matter of symbolism such as exists in conversion hysteria. While the vector concept may be useful in understanding the sort of syndromes studied by Alexander, it appears to throw little light on those included in this study although it could be appropriately modified. No simple ideational formulation seems to cover all the data. Study of the physiological phenomena accompanying emotional states in the peripheral regions of the nervous system, in the circulatory system, or in the ductless glands may give us valuable information concerning the mechanisms by which emotional tensions can become translated into organic terms, but would scarcely account for the occurrence of a total syndrome and its relationship with a specific constellation of emotional factors. In other words, while we learn that emotional tensions are accompanied by biochemical and electrical phenomena which can cause changes in the functioning of various organs, normal as well as abnormal, this information would scarcely tell us why one person suffering from repressed conflicts developed hypertension, whereas another suffered from diabetes, and another developed a psychoneurosis.

What we have to deal with is obviously a problem of organization. In psychological terms, this involves the total personality, its behavior patterns and the relevant environmental factors. In physiological terms, its key must lie in the correlates of what Coghill terms the factor representing the organism as a whole. It has been suggested that the central nervous system and particularly the cortex is the structural representative of the integrating or organizing function, and hence most closely associated with the ego which Freud has termed the organizing and reality-testing function of the personality.

We may find, however, that the physiological correlate of the ego cannot be localized structurally at all, but is more analogous to the dynamic balance of an electrical field.

Recent physiological research has apparently demonstrated that in the human nervous system the cerebral cortex is not only the integrating and inhibiting agent, but is also an essential part of emotional processes. It is not permissible to speak of the thalamus or the hypothalamus as "the seat of the emotions," though they are important mediators. Lower centers, governing autonomic or vegetative processes, are also subject to influence by emotional states in which the cortex may or may not participate. Indeed, one can scarcely pick out any single "seat of the emotion" as if emotion were a function or secretion of a particular organ. Emotion is rather the psychological name for a flow of energy which permeates (though not in equal measure) all parts of the organism. And in the *organization* of emotion, in its direction or misdirection, the central nervous system undoubtedly plays a dominant role.

The significance of this fact for our inquiry is that the very same bodily agent which organizes conscious material and behavior, which exercises control over the voluntary muscles and is the register of associations and behavior patterns, also probably organizes distribution of energy in the involuntary muscles and in the vegetative system. If the cortex is blocked out, the vegetative system will continue to function, but often in extremely unbalanced and abnormal ways whenever external impulses are applied to the system. When a somatic short circuit occurs, it means simply that the cerebral cortex, which normally would have utilized a certain quantum of energy in a certain organization of external behavior, instead has to discharge this energy through the only other channels open to it, that is, through the involuntary and vegetative parts of the organism. It therefore should occasion no surprise to discover that when a person subjected to an unresolved emotional conflict, attempts to discharge energy in action or to develop defenses against it in the form of a certain pattern of behavior, and then this pattern is found to be an insufficient channel of discharge, or is denied by the circumstances of the environment, the resulting short circuit in somatic processes should also occur in a certain pattern, specific in each case to the pattern of impulse and reaction which has become insufficient or is blocked.

III. Classification of Psychosomatic Disorders

We are in the pre-Osler stage relative to psychosomatic nosology. During the period of the writing of this book there have been various attempts to classify psychosomatic disorders. The term is usually limited to disorders of the vegetative nervous system, although recently there has been some realization (Freud,[195] Dunbar,[145] and Kubie[277]) that *psychosomatische Entgegenkommen* including the laws of immunology should be covered in the concept. It probably is inadvisable to attempt any classification at this time. The observations given here lead to the conclusion that instead of a special classification of *psychosomatic disorders* there should be a recognition of *psychosomatic factors in all medical diagnoses* and probably an appropriate change in the classical medical nosology.

It is tempting to present through the dramatic means of an illustrative chart some of the dynamic factors as we have seen them in operation. A few points stand out as providing a frame of reference but further research is required for an accurate development of the hypothetical chart. Nevertheless we submit the following suggestions:

(1) In persons whose ego function (integrating function, physiological and psychological) is weak, there appears to be an impulse toward inconsidered action toward the environment; or an escape from the environment into unreality expressed in speech and fantasy, or sometimes both.

(2) This tendency may be expressed in symptoms which appear mainly in the psychic sphere, or in symptoms which involve somatic damage, or both. This fact could be represented schematically by outer and inner circles. The outer circle would represent behavior symptoms, the inner circle somatic dysfunction or damage. Between these there is both a parallelism and constant interchange, with occasional sudden shifts of energy concentration from one to the other.

(3) These sudden shifts from one type of manifestation to the other seem to be governed by the principles here presented.

(4) The shift may occur across any diameter, if there is enough propulsion, as well as around the circumference or across any radius. For example, in an individual with weak integrating function the shift might take place around the outer circle from "adequate" be-

havior, in the direction of delinquency on the one hand or psychosis on the other. Also the shift might take place along some radius to a somatic manifestation with no marked change in behavior. In persons with a strong integrating function with selective repressions, shifts tend to occur more frequently along the "outer circle" or in the direction of more normal-appearing behavior. But if pressure becomes too great the shifts may occur also in the direction of psychoneurosis or across the radius to somatic symptoms.

What remains is to discover the operational principles governing these observed specificities—operational principles which will account not only for such phenomena as those described as symbolic or vector, but all the others as well. We may, for instance, find an important clue in Cannon's observation that the bodily processes accompanying rage or fear are those which would facilitate the goal-directed activities of the organism in reaction to the situation producing rage or fear, that is, preparation for conflict or flight.* It may be that the influence of the cortex on the distribution of energy throughout the organism can be understood entirely in terms of preparation for goal-directed activities appropriate to the stimuli registered. For example, the emotional situation of the diabetic might possibly be analyzed in such a way as to show that such impulses on a normal scale would lead to preparation for action which would involve intensified activity of the pancreas in secreting insulin, and that continual and exaggerated impulses of this kind exhaust the organ so that it can no longer perform its function. An alternative and perhaps better explanation might be that after repeated stimulations of this sort were followed by insufficient use of the insulin secreted, because of lack of the appropriate discharge in behavioral channels, the cortex over-reacted by inhibiting the secretion altogether.

A large number of variations or complications suggest themselves when one speculates in this field, but there seems some probability that the functioning of the cortex is a primary factor and that all must include a large element, on the psychological side, of ego organization—or disorganization. Certainly our therapeutic experience, which it has not been possible to describe here in any detail, indicates clearly

---

* See studies by Bard [30] which showed expression of rage with removal of the cerebral cortex similar to expressions of rage in normal animals except that the cat clawed the table instead of his tormentor, i.e., they were not adequately goal-directed.

that in somatic disease, just as in abnormal behavior, the chances for successful treatment increase in proportion to the adequacy of ego organization—if one allows for the extent to which irreversible structural damage has occurred.

IV. Contributions of the Rorschach Test to Psychosomatic Diagnosis *

INTRODUCTION

When this study was undertaken (page 105), considerable skepticism was expressed by the hospital staff and Rorschach experts regarding the value of the Rorschach test in psychosomatic research. It was generally agreed that the test was of extreme value in distinguishing severe neurotic and psychotic conditions from syndromes involving injury to the central nervous system. But partly because of a tendency to confine the term "somatic" to syndromes involving organic damage of the nervous system, there was a general feeling that if other types of somatic damage were involved, the test had little to offer. This impression was a symptom of the times and a basis for the skepticism concerning the value of asking the question which gave rise to this study: Were certain types of persons more likely to develop one type of illness than another? Most clinicians agreed that it is more important to know what kind of person has the disease than what kind of disease the person has. But this point of view was applied to the patient's response to treatment and not to the development of the illness itself.

As the clinical research gradually indicated that certain personality types are associated with different disease syndromes, it seemed more and more reasonable that the Rorschach test would be helpful in delineating these types. Recent experience with the test indicates that it is extremely valuable if it is used with the general orientation represented by this study. We have found it useful not only as a source of evidence and as a check on clinical material, but also in the development and clarification of theoretical concepts. Because of this recent experience it seems desirable to include a brief sketch of Rorschach contributions in this chapter.

* Camilla Kemple in consultation with the author.

SOME SPECIFIC CONTRIBUTIONS OF THE RORSCHACH TEST TO
PSYCHOSOMATIC DIAGNOSIS *

The Rorschach inkblot test is a relatively speedy, standardized technique for getting the individual unwittingly to reveal the underlying mental and emotional frame of reference according to which he interprets his environment and reacts to it. It probes beneath the observable behavior, conversation and mannerisms to deep-lying, often unconscious feelings and motives. The psychosomatic examination usually gives more clearly the specific people and situations in a person's life which occupy his attention, arouse his interest, love, anxiety, fear, and so forth. The Rorschach test shows the extent to which his interpretations of this external reality are rational and objective or distorted and erroneous because of past conditioning. The test distinguishes between specific superficial shock reactions and the more deep-seated characteristic reaction patterns. And it gives some indication of *whether a symptom or illness represents a wholesale solution of most of life's problems or just a temporary expedient in dealing with a specific problem.*

Following is an interesting example of a case in which the Rorschach test gave important evidence not obtained in the psychosomatic examination:

Case No. 58 FA. A fracture patient reported to the examining physician that he was an expert dart-thrower and that he earned money selling darts after demonstrating his dart-throwing in clubs and taverns. The strong aggressive sadistic tendencies in this patient which were apparent in the psychosomatic examination were also clearly manifested in the Rorschach test. The test showed in addition a marked oral component which did not come out in the interview. (See Rorschach interpretations: "a snake smashed up," "a wolf—a bull's head," "two Scottie dogs kissing," "two birds with their mouths open waiting for the mother to feed them," "a couple of figures having a fight.")

Later, the patient confessed to the Rorschach examiner that he was expert not only at throwing darts but also at *blowing* them and that his dart-blowing was a special feature of his exhibitions. He challenged others to contests in which he blew the darts while his opponent threw them and he

* See Chapter II, section V.

nearly always won. Here, by chance was obtained the clinical evidence of the oral component in his aggressiveness which was missed by the examining physician but caught by the Rorschach test.

The psychological principle of projection as it is applied in the test is described by Piotrowski in the following passage:

. . . we look upon these inkblot interpretations as being closely parallel to the subject's intellectual and emotional reactions to his personal environment. Response to the inkblots is not a concrete and well defined task as in other attempts at personality measurement where the subject answers logical questions or reacts to a physical stimulus or assumes an attitude toward a practical situation. The flexibility of response to inkblots lies in the multitude of form and color. The subject selects unwittingly those items to which he reacts. These selected areas correspond to those situations of the subject's socio-physical environment to which he has established mental attitudes. Obviously no one reacts mentally to all stimuli in his environment. The freedom which the subject has in the selection of these areas and in the manner of reacting to them assures complete spontaneity in the expression of personality rather than a specific product of the subject's treatment of an objective situation . . . he can freely express his personality insofar as he is in no danger of suffering a conflict with reality . . . (Piotrowski,[334] pages 23-24).

Among the fundamental concepts in Rorschach diagnosis are those of *introversion* and *extratension, constriction* and *dilation*. These concepts have proved extremely useful in further definition of the personality profiles (see, for example, Chapter IV). As has been noted earlier, careful review and checking of the fracture profile on the basis of follow-up examinations led to the impression that several distinct personality types were involved. When the profile was first drawn up disregarding this clinical impression and generalizing about the fracture group as a whole it was stated that fracture does not represent a specific illness syndrome, in the same sense as diabetes or rheumatic fever. It became clear that this composite profile resulted in an overstressing of some characteristics and in understressing of others where opposite personality types tended to cancel each other out. Although intensive psychoanalytic study of a few cases had provided some clues supporting the impression from follow-up examinations, application of the Rorschach test resulted rather quickly in the discovery that the fracture group was divided almost equally among the three types—constricted, introversive, and extratensive.

Some readers may be disturbed by this statement because personalities that could be classified in these terms are pretty well distributed in the general population. But this objection is no more valid than was the objection made ten years ago to Alexander's suggestion that the personality types associated with gastric ulcer have marked dependence-independence conflict. Then, too, it was said that such a conflict was clearly characteristic of our culture. But as has been suggested earlier, any specific personality trend or conflict must be evaluated in terms of its intensity and of the total constellation of personality traits. For example, the particular type of introversive personality which seems to be important in connection with accident-proneness can be clearly distinguished from the introversive personality which has been found to be associated with hypertension.

The Rorschach concepts of *introversion* and *extratension* are only remotely similar to the concepts of *introversion* and *extraversion* which were originally formulated by Jung and are now variously interpreted, usually upon the basis of external, observable behavior. The Rorschach labels are applied with precision at the level of the experiential reaction within the individual. Klopfer explains the Rorschach usage as follows:

. . . it is assumed that the actions and reactions of human beings are stimulated or prompted both from without and from within. . . . One object of Rorschach interpretation is to discover the role which the different areas of stimulation play in the life of a subject, their strength, and their importance in his general life situation. In this sense, and in this sense only, does the Rorschach terminology distinguish between people who are predominantly stimulated from within (introverts) and people who are predominantly stimulated from without (extraverts or extratensives) (Klopfer,[272] page 221).

Promptings from within may range from the lucid quality of original ideas and thoughts, or the colorful products of a brilliant fantasy, to the rather foggy stirrings of instinctive impulses or inner conflicts (Klopfer [272] page 204).

Responsiveness to stimuli from without represents not only the general readiness of the subject to establish a relationship with the world around him, but it seems to involve more specifically the *emotional* qualities of this relationship, especially the intensity and quality of his emotional relationship to other people (Klopfer,[272] page 205).

A person who represses most of his impulses to respond emotionally to the world around him and to develop his inner resources for creative thought and imagination is described as *constricted*. He would usually be described as very much *repressed;* the word "constricted," however, is particularly appropriate in the Rorschach frame of reference because it connotes the *narrowness* of experience, the *stricture* of the personality. The constricted person has not expanded, has not developed his resources for varied and complex experience. He attempts to meet life on a purely rational, intellectual plane. Such reactions are reflected in the Rorschach test by a search for percepts having the most exact resemblance to the objective, factual reality with which the constricted person is characteristically concerned. Everybody reacts in this way part of the time, but the more spontaneous and free from repression a person is, the more free he feels to deal with a broader reality which includes the more subjective factors —instinctive drives, all kinds of feelings, and the creative constructs of spontaneous thought.

This greater freedom and spontaneity is reflected in the test by a freer manipulation of the blot material, by responses to the less "formal" stimuli of color, shading, and appearance of movement, based on associations with feelings and inner promptings. These more spontaneous reactions in the Rorschach test represent a *dilation* of the personality which is contrasted with *constriction*. This dilation goes in the directions of introversion and extratension. The personality is called "dilated" when both introversive and extratensive tendencies are well developed.

The constricted and dilated personalities may be thought of as the poles of an axis with introversive and extratensive experiences increasing on either side from constriction to dilation. The following excerpts from the case histories and Rorschach reports of two butchers are presented as illustrations of these polar extremes.

Constricted Personality

Excerpts from interview:

Case No. 50 RHA. "I always like to keep on the go and keep occupied. When in the butcher shop I was on the go. Customers all the time. As long as it kept me busy I didn't care. . . . I imagine that is in me, cutting and display. Always trying to cheat the customer. Cut it so the bone shows less but is still there. I think, 'Gosh, poor people,' but you can't help it. I used to worry about the place as if it were my own place. . . . I just want a chance to get into something where I can make good. Worked seventy-two to eighty hours a week sometimes. Sometimes half a day on Sunday for no more money. I was interested in trying to learn the trade. . . . Making salami, I look for a way to try to improve it. I found it interesting no matter how hard it was. Sometimes I was just disgusted and didn't care what happened. The boss was never satisfied.

"The only thing I enjoy myself is going out. Out in a crowd, a few drinks or a ride. Not staying idle, it bores me. . . . I try to see myself being more active than the next person and even better than them. . . . I have to get work to keep my mind occupied. . . . At the place of business time passes better and I can sit there and not be so upset. If I don't get a job I will go out and strangle somebody. . . . If I can get a job to occupy my mind, then you don't have time to think. I get too much time to myself. I need to keep on the go. . . . Sometimes I can't even sit through the movies, I'm so restless.

"I love to sing even if it may sound bad to others. I write a few songs. I waste a lot of time. People enjoy them and yet I'm afraid to sell them for fear they will make good and I will get cheated and hear people singing the song I write a year after. Jesus, I'd shoot them and how!

"I work too hard. Don't appreciate anything. . . . I was having everything I wanted (referring to job), even if I went home angry every night. This way I was tired. If the baby would make a noise I would get angry."

Excerpts from Rorschach report:

This is an extremely constricted young man, afraid to give in to any expression of feeling or imaginative impulse. He seems to have average mental capacities, but his productivity is limited and the quality of his thinking impaired by his neurotic inhibitions. He is ambitious, he overgeneralizes, is impractical, extremely stereotyped in his associations. He is very easily disturbed by emotional stimuli, becoming blocked through fear of emotional self-expression.

He is under constant tension; there is some evidence of worry about health, but probably his anxiety is mostly rationalized, expressed in compulsive traits, and physical symptoms. A pervading joylessness is inevitable in so constricted a personality.

Dilated Personality

Excerpts from interview:

Case No. 28 FA. Says he is a butcher by trade, learned in Ireland. Does not like butchering in this country. Here he was an agent for Irish Sweepstakes until the war. What then? "Well, then I went to work" (laughs). He was a labor organizer for a while, and has lately gone back into the butcher business.

"The work I really like is meat, but it isn't a good paying job. I like to work and never feel the day pass. I like to take an animal and cut out the pieces and figure the percentage on each piece. I was once paid by the Union to help run it but I prefer contact with a job."

Asked what he liked about work as Irish Sweepstakes agent, he said it was because it was only three times a year, i.e., easy. "I had a lot of friends." Asked how he liked work as labor organizer. "It was exciting." (Refers later to need for help in labor adding, "That's why I was a labor organizer. . . . My heart's always with the underdog.") Asked why he doesn't like butcher business in this country, he says that it is because of such long hours, poor money—"In Ireland butchers don't have to work hard. Get good money. There's always time to pass the time of day with customers."

Asked why he likes butchering especially, he replied: "Well, I don't know. I like to work with meat . . . to make a nice display. Do you know what I mean, how it looks nice laid out in the window? When I used to finish making a display I'd just stand outside a few minutes and admire my own handiwork. . . . And another thing, it makes you terribly hungry working with meat. You're always as hungry as a wolf."

He is unemployed now but not worried about a job. If he receives a settlement compensating him for his accident, he wants to use the money to open a restaurant of his own. "That's what I'd like to have, a nice restaurant with a bar, a place with good food. I like good food. Good food, good talk, good company—there's nothing better than that."

"Of course, you might say I don't amount to anything, young man 35 years, not doing anything steady. But what about the man who does work steady? What is he working for? Usually turns out to be money. Take (patient on the ward), he's the serious type. I was arguing with him—that's the trouble I get all excited. . . ." Tells case of this man and of others he knows who work very hard for money, planning to enjoy it later; they lose their money or they get sick and die. . . . People who work very hard don't have any time to see their wives and children. They are always worrying. Their wives get mad at them. . . . "I think I have a lot more fun than they have. . . . I live from day to day. Of course I take some thought of the future."

Speaking of a patient on the ward who is much worried about losing his foot, he says, "I wouldn't feel that way about losing my foot. I'd figure it could have been a lot worse—it could have been an eye. . . . I always figure there are so many people a lot worse off than I am."

This patient was very friendly and talkative in interviews, smiling and laughing a good deal. "He's the kind of person with more personality than brains," remarked one of the nursing staff. "He's intelligent enough but he just— All the patients like him, all the doctors and nurses like him, except when he gets noisy. He sings all the time. Every song that comes over the radio he sings to it and he sings even when the radio isn't on. He's just very much in love with life."

Excerpts from Rorschach report:

The personality is dilated with a slight preponderance of extratensive experience. Intelligence is definitely superior. Abstractive and organizing ability is excellent. There is a special gift for combinatorial fantasy—the creative imagination of a "story teller." Attention is efficiently distributed between generalities and obvious practical matters; there is a slight over-emphasis on small details but no pettiness or distraction by the unimportant. Associations are free and varied but slightly more stereotyped than they would be if the subject had had more education. He has a great many interests both abstract and concrete.

He is extremely responsive to emotional stimuli reacting with many nuances of feeling. The dominating, controlled, adapted responses indicate a person who is friendly, spontaneous, and at ease with others, quickly establishing rapport. Lability, excitement, "overreaction," are present but with little loss of control in relations with others. He wonders how to realize his ideals, how to adapt his instinctive drives to them. He has a strong determination to follow his own judgment, to do what he wants to do, to be independent and to express his individuality.

The first patient likes butchering because he likes to keep busy and not have to think, he likes to work with his hands, he likes the tricks of the trade which lead to money and success. He worries about his job, works long and hard—anything "to keep my mind occupied." The picture is that of a constricted, compulsive, anxious personality so seriously lacking in inner resources for pleasure and security that he is continually running away from himself, seeking escape from anxiety in any kind of activity.

He seeks security in external achievement, in public recognition, the popular symbols of success. He wants "to make good" at butchering, to sell his songs for money and recognition. His lack of inner satisfaction or reliance upon his own judgment is reflected in the violence of his defensive reactions to frustration. He will "go out and strangle somebody" if he does not get a job; if he were cheated out of the rewards for his songs, he would "shoot them and how!" He is afraid to take the chance of publishing his songs for fear he will be cheated, projecting onto the world the aggressiveness which he has such trouble controlling in himself. Even when he was doing well and "having everything I wanted," he went home angry every night.

He is certainly right when he says "I don't appreciate anything." He lacks the capacity for appreciation or joy because he has repressed and left undeveloped most of his resources for more varied and satisfying emotional experience. His constant tension, irritability, anger, and pessimism are characteristic of the constricted compulsive neurotic.

The second patient exemplifies the dilated personality, having a richly developed capacity for varieties of experience. For him, life holds many immediate pleasures, both in relation to himself and in relations with others. He enjoys the beauty of his "handiwork," the sensual pleasure of hunger, and he likes "to pass the time of day" with friends and customers. He also likes the game of cutting meat and figuring percentages but does not associate it with cheating the customer and is more concerned with the immediate interest of the task than with the competitive goal of success. Hard work interferes with the immediate pleasures on the job and with the many other pleasures of his life. He wants money but not badly enough to work hard for it. He cares little about being more active or better than the next person, relying for his self-esteem upon his own judgment. He judges the conventional values of society in the light of his own experience, accepting and rejecting on this basis. The power and prestige connected with a position of authority in a labor union did not compensate him for the loss of "contact with a job." He is not interested in power over others because he has little fear of weakness or overdependence in himself.

This subject is a dramatic example of a person striving for self-expression and experience outside of the authoritarian patterns in his culture. He avoids both submissive and dominating roles not because he fears submission or wants power but because both roles interfere with his independence and spontaneous self-expression. He has a characteristic equalitarian attitude toward others, feeling "just as good as anybody" and assessing people according to his own standards and their interest value for him. The good temper, friendliness, optimism, and love of life characteristic of this subject are possible only in such a dilated personality where potentialities for spontaneous emotional and intellectual expansion have been developed.

Although there are a great many differences among individuals falling in the categories of constricted, predominantly introversive, predominantly extratensive, and dilated, the characteristics common to each group are significant enough to offer one valuable basis for a broad typology of personality. Introversive people, being more responsive to the stimuli of inner life than they are to the emotional stimuli of the outer world, are characteristically more individualistic, independent and creative in their thinking, less adaptable to outer reality, less suggestible, more stable in mood. Extratensives, living more through emotional responses to the world around them and less within themselves, are more dependent on the outer world, less creative and imaginative, more adaptable, more suggestible, more liable to affective disturbance through environmental stress. Friendliness, affection, love, and passion are types of extratensive experience. The introversive person with little extratensive development is cold and withdrawn affectively from others; he is excited and inspired mostly by his own imagination. The constricted person, while he is very dependent on the outer world is relatively torpid and feels little fire either in attachments to others or within himself.

The following excerpts from a psychosomatic examination are quickly identifiable as descriptions of a strongly introversive person:

He has five siblings with whom he rarely communicates. He seems quite unconcerned as to their welfare . . . and offers no information concerning them. All he says about his mother is that he sees her at irregular intervals when traveling. His first wife died. He responded regarding her in a very guarded manner; denied any residual emotional attachment. He has a son toward whom he tersely admitted a strong emotional bond.

He belongs to no clubs, is not interested in sports. He reads a good deal; says "I spend a lot of time around used bookstores."

He has special training as a stage mechanic and electrician but has worked very irregularly, has tried independent concessions, is now employed as handiman which he feels is "beneath my dignity."

He seems quite self-satisfied and self-assured. . . . Throughout most of the interview he remained reticent . . . and most responses were brief answers to direct questions.

Excerpts from Rorschach report:

This man has superior intellectual capacities. He is artistic, with a good imagination. He is highly ambitious but at present he is so withdrawn from affective contact with the world, so absorbed in fantasies and preoccupation with himself, that he fails to apply himself productively. He is easily disturbed by affective stimuli to which he is afraid to respond, becoming blocked or reacting with inappropriate behavior. He is usually calm and controlled with little show of feeling. He suffers, however, from much inner tension and depression, because of his repressed affectivity, his lack of satisfactory emotional contact with others. He feels bitter and hopeless about reality, trying to compensate by satirical fantasies. He tries, also, to deny the reality and importance of emotions, to adhere to intellectual and formal aesthetic values.

People as introversive as this man are very often difficult to communicate with and will not reveal much in a first interview with a physician. The Rorschach test shows the superior intellectual capacities which may be concealed by reticence in conversation, and which also are not demonstrated through achievements because the environment holds little stimulus value for action.

An entirely different picture is presented by the following material on a predominantly extratensive subject:

He talks freely and with feeling about his parents and siblings, saying for example, that one sister died of a broken heart. Before he was married he made a living for his parents. He tells a romantic story about meeting his wife— "It was just as though fate had brought her to me." He carried a picture of his wife and child to the operating table with him—"You'll think it's silly, but they are all I have, they are my life." He begged to have his son brought to the hospital and when the child did come he said, "It was a great pleasure to see my boy. He looked like an angel in a little sailor suit."

He belongs to a lodge and tells at length of the good times they have. He enjoys movies, radio concerts, picnics and other activities with his family. He reads very little, has trouble concentrating on reading.

He has had one job for the last fifteen years, likes it very much in spite of the low income because he is his own boss, is physically active, and meets many interesting, "intelligent" people.

He is always friendly and talkative in interviews. He smiles and laughs a good deal, gesticulates freely, expresses irritation at disturbances in the ward, tells of his pains, fears, and worries, and cries several times when most depressed.

Excerpts from Rorschach report:

With good average intelligence, this subject is overambitious intellectually, going in for vague generalizations without precise observation. He has little imaginative capacity, little originality, and stereotyped associations. He tends to be more responsive to the world around him than to stimulation from within himself, is more extratensive than introversive. He is friendly and gets along easily with others. He is sensitive to nuances in his environment, tactful, and very desirous of good social adaptation. He is rather tensely active . . . has occasional depressive moods.

This type of person reveals much more about himself in casual conversation than does the introversive type, showing his sensitivity to the world around him by his very reaction to the physician—his obvious desire to be liked, his fear of offending, or his defensive aggressiveness, showing off, and so forth. The general emotional reactivity may well be apparent, but the quality of these responses and the resources for control within an individual are more likely to be quickly and accurately indicated by the projective test unless the physician has had long experience with the psychosomatic approach.

The patient just described gives controlled, adapted emotional responses expressing empathy with the other person and wish for a genuine, two-way rapport. Such responses are usually manifested by an easy, friendly manner, spontaneous, unaffected "small talk" and tact, adaptive behavior such as listening with interest to the other person, and contributing to the other's comfort in small ways. This patient shows also, according to the Rorschach test, the more egocentric emotional responses which express stronger feeling with less control and concern for adaptation. When such responses are repressed a person gives the impression of being pleasant but superficial and lacking in deep feeling. The Rorschach responses of this patient make it clear that he has great trouble with these strong feelings which he expresses much less often than he would like because of his fear of losing control. And a big reason for this difficulty is the weakness of his inner life. The relationship of inner life to emotional control is described by Klopfer as follows:

> The subject who feels enough at home with himself to take his own outlook and ideas seriously and to enjoy the workings of his imagination has a temporary retreat when emotional contacts with the outer world become too complicated. This offers him an opportunity to "mull it over," to digest the emotional impact, before being forced by his impulses or by circumstances to do something about it (Klopfer,[272] page 231).

Having very little of this inner retreat, this patient expresses his strong feelings every so often in rash, *impulsive* behavior. Against the background of his characteristic activity, excitability and emotional expressiveness, however, such "explosions" are less conspicuous than they are in the more quiet, less expressive, introversive subject.

Impulsive in the Rorschach context is applied to the emotional response in which feeling dominates over thought or reason, and a person is described as characteristically impulsive when such responses play a large role in his total experience. The adventurous, seemingly unplanned behavior of many imaginative subjects is not impulsive in this sense, when it represents a living-out of adventurous fantasies and is consistent with their emphasis upon immediate subjective pleasures rather than external achievement. One patient of this type opened an office but found after two weeks that poor health prevented his doing the work; he closed the office, threw the keys down the sewer, and took a plane for points unknown. "I had heard a lot about these adventurers," he said, "so I decided I would be one." A similar patient, who heard that his friend was going to America, decided "on the spur of the moment" to go with him. Both of these patients simply decided quickly to do something which they had wanted to do and had thought about for a long time; they were not impulsive in the sense of losing rational control over their behavior. In contrast, the patient described above as an extratensive personality is considered impulsive when he becomes angry at his wife for locking him out of the house and climbs a rickety ladder trying to get in one window after another without regard for his safety. He is acting under the sway of emotion without good judgment according to anybody's standards including his own.

Constricted and introversive people are never *characteristically* impulsive in the Rorschach sense, but many of them are likely to act impulsively in situations of extreme emotional stress. The failure to follow a planned career, however, the tendency to live from day to day, to skip from one activity to another, are traits quite different from an impulsive, irrational release of emotion. These traits are especially prominent in introversive individuals with considerable imagination. Their lively imaginations interfere with concentration on mundane tasks and their poor affective contact with outer reality leaves them continually frustrated in their search for emotional satisfaction. One such patient said that he quit school because he "didn't like it." He changed jobs frequently because he "didn't like" them. "Adventure and excitement appeal to me," he remarked. "I can hold a job if I want to. I may get depressed and say 'This isn't the thing for me, this isn't getting me anywhere,' and leave." His behavior is not irrational according to his standards, but is, on the contrary, highly rational. It is also healthy in that each change of activity represents a carrying into action of ideas developed through his busy inner life and adds to the stimulus value of his environment, bringing him into closer contact with it. Were he to inhibit these impulses and passively remain where he is uninterested, he would turn more in upon himself and increase the dissociation between inner and outer experience (see Chapter IV).

The Rorschach test throws some light on the relationship of imagination and fantasy to action. The introversive experiences of creative reflection, imaginative dramatization, and creative fantasy are most active during periods of physical inaction, and are inhibited to the degree that attention is turned toward outer reality. It is not true, however, that people with strong introversive tendencies are generally inactive. They often have a great deal of vitality, strong instinctive drives, and aggressive impulses which lead to much activity.

Sherrington's theory regarding the release of tension through action, speech, and thought makes the assumption that tension-producing stimuli are always such as to require action for the dissolution of the tension, and that, being so, they involve some relationship with the external world. This assumption does not take account of the inner stimuli involving a person's relationship with himself and requiring a response which is the antithesis of physical action, the response of reflective and creative thought, of imagination. Failure to respond to these stimuli results in a failure to assimilate experiences, to integrate thoughts and feelings, to develop the creative resources of the self as an essential basis for emotional maturation.

All persons with introversive development (and most people have some) feel the need for a proportionate amount of time to themselves for inaction or freedom from external stimuli; they feel tension when this time is denied them. People with the habit of responding readily to these inner stimuli feel an increase in tension especially in periods when they are forced into excessive action in response to external stimulation. The more unusual, complex, or concentrated the external stimuli and responsive action have been, the greater the inner need not only to assimilate and integrate the experiences but also to manipulate and interpret them creatively. The longer these introversive impulses are inhibited, the greater the tension. The exact opposite of Sherrington's theory applies to this situation —the greatest release of tension is provided through thought. Thought represents the type of action most appropriate to the goal in question.

This brief discussion of the Rorschach concepts of introversion, extratension, constriction and dilation demonstrates the value of distinguishing between these very broad but significantly different personality types. In addition to clarifying the composite fracture profile, the application of the test points to a confirmation of the impression that the other syndromes studied are more homogeneous in personality. Although one might find all these types among sick and somatically healthy individuals, the predominance of one type in a specific disease group is important. If considered as part of the total personality constellation, it may be significant in differential diagnosis. For example, there is an inclination among clinicians to regard hypertensive cardiovascular disease, coronary disease, and the anginal syndrome as different manifestations of the same disease process. The assumption seems to be that the disease may find one of several outlets depending on factors unknown. But if it is found (as has been indicated in the recent Rorschach study) that patients with hypertensive cardiovascular disease are predominantly introversive, and those with coronary disease are predominantly extratensive, there might be a basis for determining which patients with hypertensive cardiovascular disease are likely to sustain a cardiac accident and which are not.

This point is interesting in terms of the recent controversy as to whether a person with relatively stable hypertension is or is not a better risk (in military service) than a person with extreme vascular lability: Is a person whose systolic blood pressure ranges from 130 to 190, as compared with a person with a stabilized hypertension, more or less likely to succumb to a cardiovascular accident? Use of the personality profiles in conjunction with the Rorschach test would probably help in answering this question.

The Rorschach results tend also to confirm our clinical distinction between patients suffering from different forms of rheumatic disease. Our initial impression was that patients with rheumatic heart disease are predominantly extratensive in the Rorschach sense, whereas those who progress from rheumatic fever with joint involvement to rheumatoid arthritis have more introversive development. In the young patient with rheumatic fever the Rorschach test may, on the basis of the distinction between introversive and extratensive tendencies, indicate those patients who will be likely to develop cardiac involvement. The psychoanalyst who can study patients over a long period of time may be able to make a similar prediction. But in these days when such treatment is available to only a very small percentage of sufferers from rheumatic disease, the use of this test might help in outlining a therapeutic program.

At this time it is impossible to make any more definite statements regarding specific contributions of the Rorschach test but these possibilities seem to deserve further investigation.

ENERGY DISTRIBUTION AND FUNCTIONS OF THE EGO

Empirical recognition of the importance of energy distribution in a patient (the concept that Dr. Meyer expressed as "ergaseology"), illustrated by the observations that something appearing to be a somatic short circuit of energy occurs in different ways in all of the illness syndromes studied, emphasized the necessity for a clear picture of the distribution of psychic energy. Although the experienced physician may develop a ready clinical sense for such a picture, the Rorschach test is especially well adapted to this kind of diagnosis. It offers a concise description of the distribution of psychic energy in various types of experience, of the imbalances and inefficiencies of this distribution according to norms of psychic health. It shows where energy is expended in neurotic defenses and where it is blocked from any expression through psychic experience. It is this energy which is blocked from expression through psychic experience that leads to organic damage.

The pattern assumed by the inhibiting function is important in determining energy distribution. This is quickly and concisely revealed by the Rorschach delineation of types and quality of controls used. When the dominant control is the formal, intellectual type of the constricted person who expresses little emotion and represses his inner creative impulses, the inhibiting function is obviously strong. A person whose inhibiting function follows this pattern may appear to the clinician to have a weak or strong ego depending on his approach. This type of control is precarious because of the tension and limited adaptability resulting from extreme repression. Also, it limits the understanding of reality because the person attempts to eliminate from his concept of reality the feelings and imaginative constructs which he eliminates from his own experience. Constricted compulsive persons may often demonstrate a superior accuracy of perception and logic of thought except regarding matters of feeling and motivation. These aspects of reality may be more accurately perceived by people with much less intellectual talent and much weaker inhibitory power. Thus, the constricted person may be described as strong but not selective in the inhibiting function of the ego, and weak in some aspects of the reality-testing function.

The reality-testing function must be evaluated in addition to the inhibiting function in order to complete the picture of energy distribution in a patient. A subject's interpretations of the blots show the accuracy of his perceptions of reality, the selected aspects of total reality habitually perceived, and the logic of associations. They show how certain associations and certain feelings may influence selection, accuracy, and logic.

Stable control and selective inhibition, as well as a broader conception of reality, are possible only when there is some development of spontaneous inner life and of affective response to the outer world. The relationship of inner development to outer control is described by Klopfer.

One way of controlling one's impulses in emotional contacts with the outer world is an attempt to "channelize" them into "proper" forms of expression. In other words, without attempting to repress the attraction or repulsion or any other emotion which one may feel for anything, one seeks to express it in a form which does not violate the rational implications of a given life situation. . . . In most cases, efforts for outer control of emotional impulses demand some degree of *inner control*, both as a prerequisite and as a support. Only when the attitude toward one's instinctual drives, toward the whole of what may be called the "inner life," is stabilized to some extent, is one able to exercise the outer control just described. The essential property of this inner control seems to be the acceptance of promptings from within as something positive and constructive, and not as an uncontrollable force which is constantly interfering with the security of one's existence (Klopfer,[272] page 227).

When affective responses alone come readily to expression and "promptings from within" are strongly repressed, a person is likely to show inhibitory weakness by expressing emotions in forms which do violate the rational implications of given life situations. He may be overly aggressive, overly passive and upset, hysterical, or in some way unadapted in his behavior.

When a person is predominantly introversive, the inhibiting function concentrates on the expression of feelings, on all affective contact with the outer world. From the clinical point of view, he may appear to be weak in restraining impulses to idle time away, to daydream, to withdraw, or to be eccentric, non-co-operative, asocial, or narcissistic. And in his occasional expression of affect he may explode or go to pieces showing poor inhibitory power in situations of stress.

In every case, the conception of reality is based on the types of experience absorbing psychic energy and is limited just as these experiences are limited. Excessive inhibition in any area of experience distorts the reality picture of this area. All functions of the ego— the inhibiting function, the reality-testing function, and the integrating function—are interrelated and approach the optimum of strength as a person achieves the maximum of inner and outer spontaneity that it is possible to combine with adaptation to the culture. Klopfer makes the following significant comments on the problem of spontaneity and adaptation:

It is true, of course, that cultural factors play an enormous role with regard to . . . [the] distribution of life energy. There seems, for instance, little doubt that pre-depression America set a high premium on an extraversial life. This interplay between cultural values and pressures on the one hand and the individual's personal tendencies on the other creates a whole host of emotional problems for the individual. One could find an appalling number of subjects in the United States who were trying desperately to run away from their basically strong tendency to be prompted from within. . . . These distortions of one's own tendencies create more neurotic tensions than the other solution: namely, being what one is naturally inclined to be, and then dealing from the firm basis of a healthy and fully developed personality with the environment and its values as best one can (Klopfer,[272] page 222).

Underlying this point of view is the assumption that human beings have an innate tendency to expand, to develop their individual potentialities for various emotional and intellectual experiences during the process of interacting with their environment.* A generally repressive, simple, homogeneous culture offers little opportunity for such individualistic development.† Our relatively complex and heterogeneous culture offers the environmental stimulation necessary for this development and is relatively tolerant of individual differences. But it contains many repressive elements which prevent spontaneous self-development in a large proportion of the population and thus prevent a realization of the cultural ideals of happiness, health, and efficiency. The physical ideals of individual health and longevity may be generally realized in a simple, homogeneous, repressive culture where there is little environmental stimulation of complex individualistic impulses, where the problem of conflict between adaptation and self-expression is reduced to a minimum through the cultural mandate

* Erich Fromm [197]: "Life has an inner dynamism of its own; it tends to grow, to be expressed, to be lived" (pages 183–184).

† Recent experimentation with the Rorschach test in different cultures is very promising as to its validity for anthropological research. In the type of simple repressive society just referred to, the test indicates the extreme constriction and lack of individualistic development that is observable in their outward behavior. See Bleuler,[41] Hallowell,[221] and DuBois and Oberholzer.[187]

of just what behavior pattern is expected of everyone. It is the inconsistencies in our culture, the presence of stimulation of spontaneous impulses together with repressive forces, which results in severe neurotic conflict and the deflection of energy into neurotic defenses and organic damage. Physicians during the last century of overspecialization have tended to be oblivious of this aspect of the organism-environment equilibrium (page 5) and the inherent possibilities of injury by the environment in more than chemical and bacteriological terms.

Although spontaneous self-development is essential to psychic health, it is important to point out that the individually healthy spontaneity which "bucks the culture" to any considerable degree will usually be a source of external strain and consequently a breeding ground for internal conflict. While it is difficult to restrain impulses to be one's-self, it is also difficult to be one's-self. In a person who represses most of his spontaneity for the sake of adaptation to the culture much of the disturbing effect of neurotic inhibition may be compensated for by social approval, a sense of group security, and vocational success, if his neurotic defenses "work," and if he is lucky as well as "self" sacrificing. This balance between the disturbing effects of extreme repression and the cultural rewards may be compared to the other type of balance between the disturbing effects of "bucking the culture" and the rewards of spontaneity. The psychological disturbances of each condition are not comparable except in a gross quantitative sense, but the potential or actual organic damage may be.

The Rorschach test shows the relationship of spontaneous self-development to a strong integrating function in the ego. It shows the points at which neurotic inhibition is at work and forbidden impulses are blocked from consciousness as well as blocked or distorted in expression. Of free, spontaneous experiences, a person has clear intellectual awareness; they can be fitted into the *Gestalt* of remembered experience and thus related constructively to future experience. The nearer a person's Rorschach picture approaches the healthy standard of controlled spontaneity, the greater his efficiency in applying his energy, his learned and his creative capacities, toward his goals. Rorschach tests done before and after successful psychotherapy show that a more balanced picture of energy distribution follows the therapeutic release of neurotic inhibition and the increase in integration.

Another factor which is obviously related to the strength of the ego functions and of great prognostic importance is the person's vitality or will to live (page 49). This factor is demonstrable through the Rorschach signs of ambition, of strong instinctive drives, and of some identification with aggressive, "extensor" (reaching out) roles in life as opposed to passive, "flexor" roles. The concept of "ego" in the context of Rorschach diagnosis is most clear and useful when thought of in terms of the several interrelated functions which may work at variance with one another and must be in equilibrium to produce the greatest unified strength.

Energy distribution and the integrating, inhibiting, and reality-testing functions are related to psychosomatic syndromes in that an imbalance tends to favor the development of somatic symptoms, unless sufficiently compensating factors are present. In considering the relationship between the Rorschach contributions to general theory and the foregoing exegesis of psychosomatic diagnosis, the reader might refer to the material on the personality profiles and the somatic short circuit (page 15). An adequate discussion of the Rorschach evidence regarding the particular types of disturbed energy economy which seem to be related to disease syndromes would require too much space here and will be more valuable after further material has been studied.

V. Criteria for Therapy

The practicing physician or psychiatrist, who has followed the discussion of psychosomatic diagnosis and studied the personality profiles for each syndrome, will wonder how to apply this information in his therapeutic management of the patient. Although it is not the purpose here to discuss therapy in detail a few general criteria on the basis of which to determine the procedure of choice may be useful. The suggestions as to general management and therapy given at the conclusion of each chapter are sketchy but may be used by any general practitioner. The most effective use of the following criteria requires some psychosomatic training. They are given because so many physicians have the impression that the alternative to general "common sense" in the management of patients with serious emotional problems is intensive psychotherapy by specialists.

Today when we realize all too well that intensive psychotherapy is available for only the chosen few because of economic limitations and limitations of psychoanalytic service, attention is being directed more and more to a selection of those patients for whom briefer psychotherapy might be indicated. This point was borne in mind throughout this study and except for a small number of cases briefer psychotherapy was all that was possible. On the basis of this experience with the application of briefer psychotherapy, the following illustrations are given of some of the ways in which the special techniques described in Chapter II may be useful.

CRITERIA FOR BRIEFER PSYCHOTHERAPY

Patients with the illness syndromes discussed in this volume are suitable for briefer psychotherapy, as well as patients suffering from gastro-intestinal diseases, allergies, or any illness where psychic factors play a significant role. As our knowledge increases this will probably include patients with any type of illness where the organic damage is not too great, and a good many of the latter also. It is not true, however, that all patients in each category will respond to such treatment. The following are some of the criteria we have used in selection:

1. Our experience has indicated that patients with no readily recognized neurotic symptomatology added to their somatic disorder usually respond most readily to brief psychotherapy. The better crystallized the classical symptom neurotic picture the greater the time required for alleviation of a somatic dysfunction.

2. The better the patient's adjustment prior to the episode that led him to seek treatment the shorter the time required for treatment. This does not mean that patients suffering from acute disturbances are always easier to treat than those chronically ill. In many instances a chronic somatic dysfunction may have existed for twenty or thirty years along with a fairly good adjustment in other respects, and unless physiological dysfunction has resulted in severe structural damage the response to treatment may be good.

Of course there must be careful evaluation of the patient's disorder not only in terms of the duration but also in terms of the degree to which it has penetrated into his general life adjustment.

3. The greater the integrative capacity of the personality or the stronger the ego, the more rapid is the patient's response to treatment. A judgment relative to this point can be based to a considerable degree on the psychosomatic life history but there are two or three additional techniques which we have found useful.

4. The patient who in the first two or three interviews can be brought to recognize the relationships between his somatic disorder and his emotional difficulty seems to be a favorable subject for treatment. There are various methods of doing this, one of which will be illustrated in the following case history, but as long as the goal is clear the specific choice of technique may be left to the ingenuity of the examiner provided he is adequately trained.

5. The more readily a given patient establishes rapport with his physician and the less his tendency to deny "nervousness or emotional difficulties," the more ready is his response to briefer psychotherapy.

This last point is mentioned with the qualification that the better the physician's training, the greater the number of people in whom he will bring out this response. As would be expected from their personality profiles, patients suffering from different syndromes show differences in their readiness to establish emotional rapport. And of course there are differences within each group depending on the extent and quality of habitual emotional responsiveness to other people. In general the physician-patient relationship is established in terms of the patient's characteristic attitude toward authority. Both patients with accident-proneness and patients with cardiovascular disease have extremely intense, although different, problems in this sphere. The former, in his attempt to maintain autonomy, will prefer to avoid a submissive relationship with the physician. The patient with coronary disease readily assumes a submissive attitude provided the physician conforms to his stereotype of a respectable authority figure. With the former the physician should don an informal, good-fellow manner; and with the latter he should wear a gray wig and goatee. In order to make the best therapeutic use of his own personality the physician should be aware of the extent to which it normally diverges from these pictures, and should attempt to make the appropriate adjustments. For example, with the coronary patient if the gray wig is unavailable, a large array of degrees may provide a substitute. A female physician may have an easier time at the start because of the mother-attitude than a male physician who appears too much the callow youth, or arouses a sense of competition. The cardiac arrhythmia patient, for whom the physician is likely to feel the least interest and the least patience, is just the person for whom intuitive adaptability is especially important.

Probably if patients with different types of cardiovascular disease or patients with fracture were rated in terms of this criterion, and arranged on a statistical graph, patients with cardiovascular disease would be concentrated in the part of the graph representing good initial emotional rapport, and patients with fractures at the other end of the graph. Such a rating would be irrespective of the training or personality of the examiner although the total percentage of good rapport in both groups was slightly increased by this factor. It is further emphasized by the fact that the more deeply entrenched the accident habit, or the greater the number of previous accidents, the less is likely to be the patient's awareness of tension or emotional conflict, and the less good his initial rapport with the examiner. Such an observation, however, should not be interpreted as meaning that accident-prone patients are necessarily harder to treat, but only that a different type of relationship has to be established. The kind of relationship required usually demands more of the physician, perhaps because it so often conflicts with his own idea of himself.

What has been said under this heading is of course to be understood by the psychoanalytically trained physician as evaluation of the transference (including the patient's capacity for, as well as the immediate nature and intensity of, the transference), but the term *rapport* has been used because it is more generally familiar.

For the physician who feels insecure or who has had inadequate experience in this field, routine use of the Rorschach test is highly recommended. More experienced physicians are increasingly inclined to use it anyway as an aid in determining the most suitable psychotherapy.

6. Other considerations usually discussed such as diagnostic classification, age, social and financial status, intelligence, and so on, seem to be relatively unimportant with the obvious qualification that full-fledged psychotics, mental defectives, and those whose age precludes any very adequate correction of what has become a bad life situation are not good subjects for such treatment.

APPLICATION OF BRIEFER PSYCHOTHERAPY—CASE HISTORY

The above general remarks as to types of patients suitable for treatment by briefer psychotherapy can be made more concrete by a case history. For purely experimental reasons the method of history-taking applied first with this patient was that current among general physicians and generally necessitated for the selective service examiner. The following information is further evidence of the validity of the contention that special training or a special approach is essential in dealing with such problems:—

Case No. HO 229. A retired naval officer, who had been taken out of retirement as he said "to help the Waves send the boys overseas from the Bowery" consulted me about his son, aged 22, who had been three times rejected for service in the Navy because of hypertension. The father's story was that the boy was 6 feet 2 inches, excellent physique and never sick. Three years ago when he applied for admission to Annapolis he was rejected because of a blood pressure of 150/90, more recently on three examinations for the Navy his blood pressure had been 180/130 to 180/140, which we will all agree is a high blood pressure for a husky boy, 6 feet 2 inches, and 22 years of age. I asked the father, as any physician might, for events in the boy's life three or four or five years ago: Illnesses, shocks, worries, troubles at school, etc., and all his replies were negative. He added, "I can't understand it because he is such a good boy. He never drinks, smokes, or gets mixed up with girls and I thought it was only these things that made high blood pressure." Then a little later I said:

Q. "Is the boy's mother living?"
A. "No."
Q. "When did she die?"
A. "About three and a half years ago."
Q. "Cause of death?"
A. "High blood pressure."
Q. "Was the boy upset?"
A. "You wouldn't believe it. That big strapping youngster went all to pieces. He was like a baby. He couldn't think. He couldn't do anything."
Q. "Was he very fond of her?"
A. "You wouldn't believe it, doctor. He ate with her, slept with her, he could hardly take time off to go to school."

This interview illustrates some of the problems involved in the technique of diagnosis by the questionnaire method in which we are so much interested today, as well as the need for special training. This need for special techniques is further illustrated in the first interview with the boy.

The boy was attractive, healthy looking as his father had said, with apparently not a trouble in the world, except his difficulty with the Navy. I took his blood pressure when he came in and left the cuff on, standing the large floor model hemomanometer in his line of vision but without calling attention to it. I reported that his blood pressure was 180/130, as he had been told. He then discussed in a random way his problems relative to plans for the present year, his interest—he had wanted to study medicine—and his social life, in relation to all of which he was spontaneous and happy-go-lucky. After about twenty minutes I took his blood pressure and it registered 135/90. I told him if he could keep it like that he could probably get into the Navy. We then discussed his mother and her death. He stated that it was probably a good idea she had died, that he had never really liked her as much as he liked his father, and that since he had known for about six months that she would probably die he had not been in the least disturbed by it. While he was talking I took his blood pressure again and called his attention to the fact that the reading was 185/130. This startled him and opened the way to discussing his real feelings about his mother, his ambivalence toward her and his conflict with his father. When he left his blood pressure was again 135/90.

After one more interview, he went up for the examination which represented his last chance for the Navy. He passed the examination with a blood pressure reading of 138/90.

An interesting point is that he came back to say that for the first time he had been able to sleep well at night, and although he had got into the Navy he did not feel that he was completely cured and could he continue treatment for the seven days preceding his actual induction?

In view of the obvious question as to whether this boy, even with reduced blood pressure, would be good for the Navy, a Rorschach test was given between the first and second interviews. The essential points of this test are as follows.

"Intelligence does not seem to be more than average, although it is difficult to estimate sometimes in these very constricted records (only 9 answers).

"He is incapable of becoming genuinely interested in objective matters because of his anxiety and preoccupation with personal problem. He strains his vital energies far out of proportion to his ability to apply independent creative judgment (W:M—6:1; should be 2:1). In an unfamiliar situation he feels helpless and at a loss for clues; he vacillates between a floundering passive co-operation and negativistic blocking.

"Instinctive drives are strongly repressed. There is little sensitivity to emotional nuances in the environment, showing a characteristically adolescent repression of subtle adaptive responses, the effort to be intellectual, the fear of sensual stimuli. He does give some indication of a desire for friendly rapport, but when he expresses such feeling he is so self-conscious and confused that his behavior is inappropriate. Even when his heart is in the right place, he does not know how to show it.

"There is no evidence of free-floating anxiety and little of critical introspection. He is most likely constantly anxious and depressively toned, with compulsive traits.

"The ability to overcome some of his inhibitions after the test proper and to apply concepts suggested by the examiner indicates that the extreme neurotic anxiety state projected at first is rather easily modifiable."

SUMMARY AND CONCLUSIONS

This patient's unusually rapid somatic response to two periods of treatment should receive comment in view of the criteria given. Of course no long-time predictions are made, and the personality pattern associated with his illness had not been corrected.

1. There was no readily recognized symptom-neurosis. The fact that the examining physician recognized a deep-seated neurosis is not contradictory because we have used the phrase "readily recognized" in terms of recognition by the general physician or by the patient himself.

2. The patient's adjustment prior to the onset of his illness had been good in his own terms, and from the point of view of the superficial observer, although even here it is obvious that there was a somewhat neurotic behavior pattern, exaggerated devotion to mother, fear of wine, women and song, and so on.

3. The integrative capacity of this person, as anyone reviewing the sketch just given will realize, was not great, and this is one of the reasons for doubt about the permanency of this "apparent" cure. But on the level he had selected he "got by."

4. The rapidity with which this patient made a connection between the behavior of the hemomanometer and the subject matter under discussion was an important positive factor.

5. Rapport with the examining physician was quickly established partly because "all his doctors had failed" him, and taking "chloral hydrate didn't

lower" his blood pressure; and partly for other reasons which will be clear to the reader from the foregoing discussion. The fact that he belonged to the cardiovascular dysfunction group should not be overlooked.

The fact that this patient passed his final examination for the Navy was to some degree unexpected. It should be remembered that quick relief of somatic symptoms is not always desirable; often the personality constellation favoring the syndrome must be modified beforehand.

The majority of patients suffering from the syndromes mentioned, responded to brief treatment and in most of those whom it has been possible to follow for five years or more there has been no return of symptoms. The results of Alexander, Menninger, Dunn, Ginger, and others who have worked on this problem would not show quite such a high therapeutic average. If this is true it would be because they have seen mainly patients already recognized from superficial observation as having important psychological difficulties in addition to their somatic illness. Study of serial admissions to general hospitals, the majority of whom on superficial examination appear to be perfectly normal, results in a higher average of patients in whom the psychosomatic illness has not become crystallized in the form of a well-recognized symptom neurosis, or in other words a higher percentage of patients in whom the psychosomatic illness is in a very early stage and therefore more easily treated

The method of psychotherapy indicated in connection with this one case is not a universally recommended method for briefer psychotherapy. With other cases suffering from hypertension different methods were followed and the time range was longer, although never shorter. This is the reason for stressing psychosomatic training on the part of the therapist and an experimental approach to the whole problem. By way of conclusion it may be said that, as in all of medicine, the earlier in the disease process treatment is initiated in a patient suffering from psychosomatic illness, the better the result.

Chapter XII

CONCLUSION

Without hypotheses there is no useful observation.—CHARLES DARWIN.

This book represents a trip through the laboratory rather than a series of formulae resulting from the experiments conducted therein. The reason for presenting the material in such extension and detail is to give the reader an opportunity to reach his own conclusions concerning hypotheses that are presented as tentative, as well as those for which there is adequate evidence. Furthermore, it is hoped that the description of the difficulties encountered in psychosomatic research will be useful to those now engaged in extending knowledge in this field.

I. FUTURE RESEARCH IN PSYCHOSOMATIC PROBLEMS

Although relatively few syndromes have been discussed in detail a general pattern for psychosomatic diagnosis has been outlined which might be applied to other disease syndromes. A preliminary exploration with limited objectives has been described and its principal value should be in laying the groundwork for future research. The profiles can be checked and further defined by additional research following the principles here outlined, and the suggestions for diagnosis, prognosis, and therapy can be elaborated and made more precise.

The picture here given is significant in that it is not based on a few scattered cases, or on a selected group in whom emotional factors were already suspected, but on all serial admissions to a large general hospital for the group of important disease syndromes which now account for the greater part of mortality and disability. Although, as previously explained, some of these cases had to be excluded for practical reasons (such as death on admission), the exclusion was not on the basis of the relevance of the material.

The summaries of the statistical material could be made more precise if in another study subgroups were isolated and if more detailed analysis and comparison were made relative to age and sex distribution, as well as to race and nationality distribution. The present impression is, however, that more thorough research would tend to sharpen the pictures given but not contradict them in their major outlines. Evidence favoring this impression is provided by results of the 1942–43 continuation of the research with the inclusion of the Rorschach test.

The methods employed in history-taking and the correlation of psychiatric with general medical data while the patients were under treatment in the hospital are of fundamental importance for psychosomatic diagnosis and have been given too little attention. There is evidence that psychiatric study combined with whatever psychotherapy is feasible should be applied in conjunction with the usual medical treatment for the diseases in question, at the same time and in the uniform environment provided by the hospital. In some cases treatment should be continued subsequently.

In the foregoing material clues are given as to desirable next steps in research relative to psychosomatic problems. For the benefit of those interested in further exploration in this field attention should be called to the following points:

First, as is illustrated by the defects in this presentation, the time of a research staff should not be devoted mainly to history-taking, diagnosis, and analysis of the data, but should be adequate for brief, or when indicated, more intensive therapy. Therapeutic results were noted as a consequence of the mere process of examination, and it was possible to give intensive therapy and adequate follow-up in a random series of cases; study of diagnostic and therapeutic problems should, however, go hand in hand. In this way light is thrown on the therapeutic usefulness of the conclusions and methods developed, and further clarification of the dynamics of the disease processes in question is facilitated.

Second, the clues obtained from the three to twelve year follow-up of patients in this series would acquire added validity from follow-up studies of a larger percentage of the patients initially studied. It was possible to follow nearly half of these patients over a period of years. With a trained social worker assigned to the research staff a better follow-up record could probably be achieved. It is unsatisfactory to rely on the regular hospital follow-up system, which is so managed that only those patients return whom the regular medical staff wishes to re-examine.

Third, further clarification will of course result with the applica-ion of as many as possible of the appropriate physiological tests, as well as of projective psychological tests such as the Rorschach. The experience here reported indicates that routine use of the Rorschach test amply justifies itself and serves as a valuable corrective to some defects in technique on the part of the clinician. It is also a time saver.

Fourth, students of psychosomatic problems interested in checking these observations should make certain that the same degree of training is available for the work and that the same or improved techniques are employed. This is a universal requirement in scientific corroboration. If, as may be expected, future researches of this kind do substantiate these findings, at least in general, it ought to be possible also to modify, elaborate, and refine them.

Fifth, a natural question is whether these basic principles of psychosomatic diagnosis could not be better evaluated if the same type of examination could be applied to a control group of so-called normal persons, selected from a section of the population which has exhibited a good health record in the same decades covered. It would be interesting also to select groups from the general population showing the personality profile described for each syndrome here studied, and to follow their illness histories. Aside from the difficulty of examining persons who are not patients in the hospital, it would be practically impossible to find at random a group essentially comparable to the hospital population in terms of economic status, education, and so on. It was suggested that a control group might be found among patients in the hospital for fracture. As it turned out, however, these patients were not a control group in the sense of being emotionally normal, or without a specific personality bias and illness tendency of their own. Nevertheless they were a valuable *contrast* group.

In the absence of any real control group it would be valuable to study as many cases as possible of non-hospitalized subjects with personality patterns like those of the hospital patients. Questions to be answered are: How often do these subjects develop the syndromes here correlated with specific personality patterns? What environmental factors and emotional changes seem to precipitate and accompany the development of illness? If these subjects do not become ill, why not?

Sixth, at the present stage of knowledge it should not be inferred that anyone with one of the personality pictures identified is sure to suffer a somatic disease or a fracture. Nor, assuming that a given personality predisposes to a given illness, can we be certain what the determining factors are unless persons are discovered with a similar personality who do not develop the disease process in question. A most important clue lies in the quantitative importance in the personality of the traits outlined, plus the quantitative impact of the precipitating factor.

Whereas all the disease groups here discussed are comparable in that they were derived from a study of all serial admissions to a given hospital, in a given period, they are of different sizes. This of course would be expected in any random cross-section of the population. But it may lead to some statistical uncertainty in that the exceptional or aberrant case may be given undue weight in the smaller groups as compared with the larger ones. As was noted earlier, there are other ways in which the statistical method here employed should be improved and refined, but it should be remembered that the statistical method has been used only for the light it may throw on the validity of the conclusions reached from dynamic personality studies and analyses, not as in itself the basic method of study.

If the personality profiles here given are reviewed in the light of this statement, it becomes obvious that the statistical method as it has been applied cross-sectionally for the purpose of comparing illness groups according to various headings may underemphasize or omit significant elements within an individual group. This method which gives information under each heading is of research interest and helps to point up the distinctiveness of each profile. But some headings should be disregarded and others given particular emphasis in order to bring out the salient points in the constellation for a given group if the profiles are to be used in individual practice, as for example in the detection of the accident prone in the army or in industrial plants, or for diagnosis and prognosis in cases of anginal syndrome. Certain environmental and personality factors are important for one illness group but not for another. For example, the addiction to stimulants and the attitude toward their use may be valuable indices of personality for patients with fracture or with coronary occlusion, but relatively insignificant for patients with rheumatic disease. The incidence of cardiac heredity is about equal for patients with fracture or with coronary occlusion, but the incidence of exposure to cardiac illness within the family or among any intimate associates is very much greater among patients with coronary occlusion. Thus, cardiac heredity is relatively unimportant for fracture patients and is important for those with coronary occlusion, when in addition they have been exposed to the illness.

Finally, more than cursory investigation of the psychobiological mechanisms which form the connection between psychic and somatic symptoms would be valuable. At present the most that can be said is that the juxtaposition of certain personality structures and emotional difficulties with certain kinds of syndromes may furnish hints as to the physiological mechanisms involved, and so provide leads for future research in that field. Such research would have to be carried on by collaboration between psychiatrists and physiologists, and would require the invention of new instruments and techniques making possible more exact and continuous measurements of the bodily processes involved.

Experiments with animals will help, but before this line can be carried to definite conclusions new methods of research with human beings must be developed. Better knowledge of the disease processes under consideration would also be necessary, but this may await further contributions from psychosomatic research itself. Illustrations of what is meant here is the type of work carried out recently by Deutsch,[124] and others, correlating capillary behavior both with personality types and with specific emotional reactions; or the work of Hallowell Davis,[113] making similar correlations between encephalographic readings and personality studies; or the direct observations made on a patient with gastrostomy by Harold Wolff.[307]

II. Basic Principles for Psychosomatic Diagnosis

METHODOLOGY

(1) A method of history-taking has been developed which includes a history outline, together with a method of correlating observations of the emotional and physiological aspects of the course of illness

while the patient is under treatment in the hospital, that seems adequate to reveal the area of life adjustment in which the patient's major difficulties have occurred, together with his characteristic patterns of dealing with them.

(2) This method of history-taking in itself not only serves to clarify the personality picture, but also benefits the patient in at least two ways: (a) It releases more or less of the energy which for the patient was bound up in repressing unpleasant experiences, and (b) it almost always reveals to the patient an association between his symptoms and his emotional conflict. He thus comes to understand that what happens to him is not just "hard luck" and that he can do something to prevent it. These two accomplishments in themselves constitute a beginning of psychotherapy and often exert a favorable influence on the course of illness, and particularly on the tendency to relapse during the convalescent period or later.

(3) There is evidence that a patient for whom thorough-going psychoanalysis is impractical or undesirable, may be benefited by a few hours (10 to 20) of psychotherapy directed toward increasing the awareness of the areas in which he is likely to have difficulties, together with the defects in his manner of attempting to meet these difficulties. This is usually sufficient to liberate energy from the disease process and redirect it by making it available to him in everyday living. In such cases as have been studied adequately, this usually results in an elimination of the disease process. In some syndromes, success is particularly frequent, for example, in the accident habit or persisting hypertension. Where irreparable organic damage has taken place, as in patients with diabetes * or rheumatic heart disease,† such therapy decreases invalidism and serves to prevent further acute attacks. In a few cases where fatality resulted from the disease, it was impossible to use this type of psychotherapy because the conflicts were so deep seated, and the organic damage already so great, that any attempt to clear up the emotional difficulties would have aggravated the symptoms to a dangerous extent and so had to be abandoned.‡ In such cases the fault lay not with the method, but rather with lack of opportunity to apply it early enough in the course of the disease.

* Case No. DP 2, page 87.
† Case No. RDHP 4, page 473.
‡ Case No. HP 1, page 40.

(4) The Rorschach method of personality study may prove to be of inestimable help in diagnosis of such disorders. In some cases it offers clues as to the best therapeutic program for the individual patient and for certain groups of individuals (page 674).

RELATION BETWEEN PERSONALITY AND SYNDROME

In a study of 1600 patients hospitalized for eight syndromes (usually termed organic disease), 80 per cent were discovered by the routine psychiatric examination employed to have emotional difficulties which had a bearing on the origin or course of their disease. This does not eliminate the possibility that similar difficulties existed in the other 20 per cent, since such difficulties might have been revealed with more intensive study.*

It was further discovered that among this 80 per cent there was a prevailing correspondence between the type of personality profile in each case and the somatic syndrome from which the patient suffered. These correspondences are set forth in detail in Chapters X and XI.

It should be remembered that many patients whose illness is seriously conditioned by emotional factors when examined by means of the routine medical history and techniques admit no conflict in any of the spheres of adjustment and give no evidence of conflict. They may give superficially the picture of a normal life adjustment with little conflict.

A further complication is the fact that whereas the coronary patient, for example, shows his conflict with authority and his characteristic means of dealing with it mainly in the vocational sphere, sometimes the same conflict may show more clearly in the sphere of family adjustments, as illustrated in the person who wants to be the patriarch in a family including all his sisters, his cousins, and his aunts; or again the patient with rheumatic fever may in one case express his fundamental conflict in his fantasy life, and in another case in his overt relationships. From this point of view the statistical tables giving a picture of the total group may be misleading, in leaving the reader unprepared for such variations through creating the expectation of uniformity.

Such a sketchy summary of the material as that given in Chapter X

* Dunbar et al.[152, 153]

may be confusing because it may give a vague idea of conflict with authority, conflict over sexual role, as entering in various ways, into all the groups of patients mentioned, and the reader will remember stern parents cropping up in several groups and lax parents in others. Nevertheless, the problem here in so far as it is descriptive follows very much the pattern of Martin Hewitt's formula for the detective:

If I were in search of a man (Martin Hewitt would say) of whom I knew nothing but that he squinted, bore a birthmark on his right hand, and limped, and I observed a man who answered to the first peculiarity, so far the clue would be trivial, because thousands of men squint. Now, if that man presently moved and exhibited a birthmark on his right hand, the value of that squint and that mark would increase at once a hundred or a thousand fold. Apart they are little; together much. The weight of evidence is not doubled merely; it would be only doubled if half the men who squinted had right-hand birthmarks; whereas the proportion, if it could be ascertained, would be, perhaps, more like one in ten thousand. The two trivialities, pointing in the same direction, become very strong evidence. And, when the man is seen to walk with a limp, that limp (another triviality), re-enforcing the others, brings the matter to the rank of a practical certainty. The Bertillon system of identification—what is it but a summary of trivialities? Thousands of men are of the same height, thousands of the same length of foot, thousands of the same girth of head—thousands correspond in any separate measurement you may name. It is when the measurements are taken *together* that you have your man identified forever.[342]

If the point is kept clearly in mind that the general pattern of the patient's difficulties and his reaction to them must be evaluated for psychosomatic diagnosis, confusion need not result from the discovery of minor variations. In this field physicians are just reaching a stage corresponding with that in general medicine when Osler and others were giving us a nomenclature together with description of various disease syndromes. Every experienced physician knows that it is the fundamental pattern that is important, not the presence or absence of this or that minor symptom.

THERAPY

When thorough treatment is possible, the results are favorable except in cases where the disease process has advanced too far and has resulted in serious organic damage before the therapy is applied. The conclusion from this is that common to all medicine, that prevention or early diagnosis and treatment is of supreme importance.

The illnesses here discussed are essentially chronic illnesses. Even in the fracture group a majority suffered from accident-proneness or the accident habit. Furthermore, the fact should be recalled that even in a hospital that specializes in quick turnover of patients and does not keep patients needing chronic care, it was found that more than four-fifths of the patients were chronic cases in the sense that they were not suffering from the first attack of the illness in question, or were suffering from an illness which had incapacitated them for more than a year: of the patients with cardiovascular disease, 77 per cent; of the patients with diabetes, 86 per cent; of the patients with fracture, 80 per cent. The psychic factor was of particular importance in the chronic patients in the groups studied, and a large percentage of them were being kept ill unnecessarily by this component of their illness.

Thorough-going changes may be indicated in the management of chronic illnesses:

(1) The best care for the chronically ill, as for example, the cardiac invalid who has suffered repeated breaks, is not always provision for special care, relief from responsibility, restricted regime, and so on. These may instead help to keep him in an invalid and dependent condition.

(2) Although the psychic factor is more regularly overlooked in the case of severe somatic damage (where, as a matter of fact, its detection may make the difference between life and death), and in the handling of convalescence and chronic illness, it is no less important in our failures—patients who wander from physician to physician and clinic to clinic. If a patient has received treatment from a dozen or two private physicians and half a dozen clinics, and has submitted to elaborate and expensive laboratory procedures in each place, one may be justified in suspecting that his physicians have in some way failed to find out what was the matter. Usually when this happens it is because a prominent psychic factor is present. Such patients are a real drain on hospital and clinic time and funds. They can be effectively treated only if equal attention is given to the psychic and somatic aspects of their illness.

(3) There is need of an adequate basis for the inclusion of attention to the psychic component in illness in our public health program. Its inclusion is exigent, both because of the facts just stated, and in view of the problems of health insurance and socialized medicine with which we are confronted. A major weakness of such systems as are in operation results from a lack of knowledge concerning emotions and physiological changes. This is the more serious in that some of the most significant advances, that is, control of epidemics, prolongation of life expectancy in general and particularly with certain diseases, such for example as diabetes, have actually increased the bulk of chronic illness. And it is chronic illness as well as those illnesses which have the greatest tendency to become chronic in which the psychic component is of the greatest significance to therapy.

The clinical evidence presented demonstrates that even at the present stage of knowledge a more widespread use of the techniques herein described might save the nation an immense amount of expense in care for the chronically ill, and at the same time raise the average of the national health. As Galdston [197a] pointed out,

> To the extent that medicine fails directly and indirectly to ameliorate the interrelationships of man and his life's realm, it can succeed only in deferring mortality but not in decreasing morbidity, and it may be taken as a corollary that to the extent that mortality is deferred, and life prolonged, to that extent is morbidity multiplied and increased.

It is to be hoped also that by these methods the problems, in solving which the general practitioner has had the least help from medical science, may be somewhat advanced to a solution.

It is well known that the types of diseases here described account for by far the greatest number of hospital days and hours of incapacity in the nation. If at least 80 per cent of such diseases have significant emotional complications, and if adequate attention to these personality factors, in conjunction with somatic treatment which is up to the standard of present knowledge, can remove the symptoms in nearly all but those who have already suffered severe and irreversible structural damage, the gains to be realized from this type of psychosomatic treatment are almost incalculable. The physician should remember that the illness is a dispute between the patient and his disease and that therefore in many cases results will be discouraging unless equal attention is paid to both participants in this dispute.

BIBLIOGRAPHY

Except where special reference has been made in this volume to pioneer contributions, no relevant titles prior to 1935 are listed here. The reader interested in earlier material on a given topic should refer to Dunbar.[149] Even for
the period since 1935 this bibliography is not complete because of the rapidly
increasing interest during recent years in the subject matter here presented.

1. Accident facts. Chicago, National Safety Council, 1940.
2. Accident facts. Chicago, National Safety Council, 1942.
3. Accident, Motor drivers' proneness to. From Report No. 84, Industrial Health Research Board. *Brit. M. J.*, 1:307, 1940.
4. Accidents, The personal factor in. Emergency Report No. 3, Medical
   Research Council, Industrial Health Research Board. London, H. M.
   Stationery Office, 1942.
5. ACKERMAN, N. W., and CHIDESTER, L. "Accidental" self-injury in
   children. *Arch. Pediat.*, 53:711, 1936.
6. ADLER, A. Beitrag zum Problem der Unfallshäufung. *Wien. med.
   Wchnschr.*, 84:293, 1934.
7. ADLER, A. The psychology of repeated accidents in industry. *Am. J.
   Psychiat.*, 98:99, 1941.
8. Age, race, and sex distribution of rheumatic fever. See No. 232.
9. ALEXANDER, F. The relation of structural and instinctual conflicts.
   Psychoanalyt. Quart., 2:207, 1933.
10. ALEXANDER, F. Addenda to "The medical value of psychoanalysis."
    Psychoanalyt. Quart., 5:548, 1936.
11. ALEXANDER, F. The Medical Value of Psychoanalysis. New York,
    Norton, 1938.
12. ALEXANDER, F. Emotional factors in essential hypertension. *Psychosom.
    Med.*, 1:173, 1939.
13. ALEXANDER, F. Psychoanalytic study of a case of essential hyperten-
    sion. *Psychosom. Med.*, 1:139, 1939.
14. ALEXANDER, F., BACON, C., WILSON, G. W., LEVY, H. B., and LEVINE,
    M. The influence of psychological factors upon gastrointestinal dis-
    turbances; a symposium. *Psychoanalyt. Quart.*, 3:501, 1934.
15. ALEXANDER, F., and HEALY, W. Roots of Crime—Psychoanalytic Stud-
    ies. New York, Knopf, 1935.
16. ALEXANDER, F., and SAUL, L. J. Psychic influences on respiration. In:
    Institute for Psychoanalysis, Chicago, Review for the year, 1933–
    1934, p. 31.

17. ALEXANDER, F., and SAUL, L. J. Three criminal types as seen by the psychoanalyst; symposium presentation for expert opinion given to a German court (jury) about a case of a nineteen year old murderer; case presentation of a young sexual delinquent. *Psychoanalyt. Rev.*, 24:113, 1937.

18. ALEXANDER, F., and WILSON, G. Quantitative dream studies: a methodological attempt at a quantitative evaluation of psychoanalytical material. *Psychoanalyt. Quart.*, 4:371, 1935.

19. ALEXANDER, G. H. Anorexia nervosa (with emphasis on psychotherapy). *Rhode Island M. J.*, 22:189, 1939.

20. ALKAN, L. Anatomische Organkrankheiten aus seelischer Ursache. Stuttgart, Hippokrates-Verlag, 1930.

21. ALLEN, E. V., and ADSON, A. W. Physiological effects of extensive sympathectomy for essential hypertension. *Am. Heart J.*, 14:415, 1937.

22. Analysis of 5,116 deaths reported as due to acute coronary occlusion in Philadelphia, 1933–1937. See No. 229.

23. ANDERSON, O. D., and LIDDELL, H. S. Observations on experimental neurosis in sheep. *Arch. Neurol. & Psychiat.*, 34:330, 1935.

24. ANDERSON, O. D., and PARMENTER, R. A long-term study of the experimental neurosis in the sheep and dog. *Psychosom. Med. Monographs*, 2: nos. 3 and 4, 1941.

25. ANDERSON, O. D., PARMENTER, R., and LIDDELL, H. S. Some cardiovascular manifestations of the experimental neurosis in sheep. *Psychosom. Med.*, 1:93, 1939.

26. ANDERSON, V. V. Psychiatry in Industry. New York, Harper, 1934.

27. ATWATER, R. M. Studies in the epidemiology of acute rheumatic fever and related diseases in the United States, based on mortality statistics. *Am. J. Hyg.*, 7:343, 1927.

28. Automobiles kill fewer children. *Statist. Bull., Metropolitan Life Ins. Co.*, 14:no. 3, 11, 1933.

29. BAKER, Z., FAZEKAS, J. F., and HIMWICH, H. E. Carbohydrate oxidation in normal and diabetic cerebral tissues. *J. Biol. Chem.*, 125:545, 1938.

30. BARD, P. A diencephalic mechanism for the expression of rage, with special reference to the sympathetic nervous system. *Am. J. Physiol.*, 84:490, 1928.

31. BAUCH, M. Beeinflussung des Diabetes mellitus durch psychophysische Entspannungsübungen. *Deutsches Arch. f. klin. Med.*, 178:149, 1935–36.

32. BENNETT, A. E., and SEMRAD, E. V. Common errors in diagnosis and treatment of the psychoneurotic patient: study of one hundred case histories. *Nebraska State M. J.*, 21:90, 1936.

33. BERGMANN, G. VON. Klinische funktionelle Pathologie des vegetativen Nervensystems. In: *Handb. d. norm. u. path. Physiol.* (Bethe *et al.*). Berlin, Springer, 1930, v. 16, pt. 1, pp. 1019–1070.

34. BERGMANN, G. VON. Funktionelle Pathologie. Eine klinische Sammlung von Ergebnissen und Anschauungen einer Arbeitsrichtung. Berlin, Springer, 1932.

35. BERLINER, B. The psychogenesis of a fatal organic disease. *Psychoanalyt. Quart.*, 7:368, 1938.

36. BILLINGS, E. G. The general hospital; its psychiatric needs and the opportunities it offers for psychiatric teaching. *Am. J. M. Sc.*, 194:234, 1937.

37. BILLINGS, E. G., McNARY, W. S., and REES, M. H. Financial importance of general hospital psychiatry to hospital administrator. *Hospitals*, 11:40, 1937.

38. BINGHAM, W. V. Individual difference in industrial personnel. A study of accident-prone workmen. *Eugenical News*, 15:19, 1930.

39. BLAND, E. F., JONES, T. D., and WHITE, P. D. Disappearance of physical signs of rheumatic heart disease. *J.A.M.A.*, 107:569, 1936.

40. BLEULER, E. Physisch und psychisch in der Pathologie. *Ztschr. f. d. ges. Neurol. u. Psychiat.*, 30:426, 1916.

41. BLEULER, M., and BLEULER, R. Rorschach's inkblot test and racial psychology. *Character and Personality*, 1:286, 1933.

42. BLUMENTHAL, B., and REISINGER, J. A. Predromal pain in coronary occlusion. *Am. Heart J.*, 20:141, 1940.

43. BOAS, E. P. Angina pectoris and cardiac infarct from trauma or unusual effort. *J.A.M.A.*, 112:1887, 1939.

44. BOAS, E. P. The Unseen Plague—Chronic Disease. New York, Augustin, 1940.

45. BORTZ, E. L. Diabetes. Practical Suggestions for Doctor and Patient. Ed. 2. Philadelphia, Davis, 1940.

46. BOURNE, G. Angina of effort as the only symptom of coronary thrombosis. *Lancet*, 1:1155, 1939.

47. BOURNE, G., and WITTKOWER, E. Psychological treatment of cases with cardiac pain. *Brit. Heart J.*, 2:25, 1940.

48. BRAY, G. W. Recent Advances in Allergy. Ed. 2. London, Blakiston, 1934.

49. BREYFOGLE, H. S. Frequency of coexisting gallbladder and coronary artery disease; statistical analysis and biometric evaluation of 1,493 necropsies. *J.A.M.A.*, 114:1434, 1940.

50. BRIDGMAN, P. W. The Nature of Thermodynamics. Cambridge, Harvard Univ. Press, 1941.

51. BRINTON, H. P. Nonindustrial injuries among male and female industrial employees. *Pub. Health Rep.*, 54:6, 1939.

52. BRINTON, H. P., SEIFERT, H. E., and FRAZIER, E. S. Disabling morbidity among employees in the slaughter and meat packing industry, 1930–1934, inclusive. *Pub. Health Rep.*, 54:2196, 1939.

53. BRITTEN, R. H. Important causes of sickness and death. *Pub. Health Rep.*, 51:947, 1936.

54. BRUCH, H. Obesity in childhood. IV. Energy expenditure of obese children. *Am. J. Dis. Child.*, 60:1082, 1940.

55. BRUCH, H. Obesity in childhood; physiologic and psychologic aspects of food intake of obese children. *Am. J. Dis. Child.*, 59:739, 1940.

56. BRUCH, H. Obesity in childhood and personality development. *Am. J. Orthopsychiat.*, 11:467, 1941.

57. BRUNDAGE, D. K. Trend of disabling sickness among employees of a public utility. *Pub. Health Rep.*, 43:1957, 1928.

58. BRUNDAGE, D. K. Sickness among industrial employees during the first three months of 1929. *Pub. Health Rep.*, 44:2204, 1929.

59. BRUNDAGE, D. K. Sickness among industrial employees in the second and third quarters of 1929. *Pub. Health Rep.*, 45:321, 1930.

60. BRUNDAGE, D. K. Sickness among industrial employees during the last three months of 1929. *Pub. Health Rep.*, 45:1203, 1930.

61. BRUNDAGE, D. K. Sickness among industrial employees in the first half of 1930. *Pub. Health Rep.*, 45:2611, 1930.

62. BRUNDAGE, D. K. Sickness among male industrial employees in the first quarter of 1931. *Pub. Health Rep.*, 46:1799, 1931.

63. BRUNDAGE, D. K. Sickness among male industrial employees in the second quarter of 1931. *Pub. Health Rep.*, 46:2499, 1931.

64. BRUNDAGE, D. K. Sickness among male industrial employees during the second quarter and first half of 1934. *Pub. Health Rep.*, 49:1229, 1934.

65. BRUNDAGE, D. K. Sickness among male industrial employees during the final quarter of 1934 and the entire year. *Pub. Health Rep.*, 50:557, 1935.

66. BRUNDAGE, D. K. Disabling illness among industrial employees in 1934 as compared with earlier years. *Pub. Health Rep.*, 50:1527, 1935.

67. BRUNDAGE, D. K. Sickness among male industrial employees during the final quarter of 1935 and the entire year. *Pub. Health Rep.*, 51:643, 1936.

68. BRUNDAGE, D. K. Sickness among the male industrial employees during the final quarter of 1936 and the year as a whole. *Pub. Health Rep.*, 52:537, 1937.

69. BYRNE, H. A., and HILLYER, C. Unattached women on relief in Chicago, 1937. U. S. Women's Bureau, Bull. No. 158. Washington, Govt. Printing Office, 1938.

70. CADY, L. D. The physician's care of emotional health. *Ment. Health Observ.*, 8:3, 1941.

71. CALVER, G. W. Coronary accidents. Remarks on anticipation and prevention. *U. S. Nav. M. Bull.*, 37:385, 1939.

72. CAMPBELL, C. M. The field of clinical psychiatry. Address given at the annual meeting of the New York Society for Clinical Psychiatry, Jan. 11, 1934.

73. CANNON, W. B. Significance of the emotional level. *Scient. Monthly*, 38:101, 1934.

74. CANNON, W. B. Bodily Changes in Pain, Hunger, Fear and Rage. Ed. 2. New York, Appleton, 1929.

75. CANNON, W. B. The Wisdom of the Body. New York, Norton, 1932.

76. CAUGHEY, J. L., JR. Cardiovascular neurosis—a review. *Psychosom. Med.*, 1:311, 1939.

77. CAUTERMAN, F. Considérations cliniques sur l'allergie dans les affections rhumatismales. *Acta rheumatol.*, 8:5, Aug. 1936.

78. CECIL, R. L. A Text-Book of Medicine by American Authors. Philadelphia, Saunders, 1930.

79. Changing mortality trends and their therapeutic implications. *Therap. Rev.* 30:1, 1941.

80. CHASSELL, J. Limitations of suggestive psychotherapy. *Psychiatry*, 1:309, 1938.

81. CHATTOCK, A. P., and GRINDLEY, G. C. The effect of delayed reward on the maze performance of chickens. *Brit. J. Psychol.*, 23:382, 1933.

82. CHRISTIAN, H. A. The Principles and Practice of Medicine (Osler). Ed. 14. New York, Appleton-Century, 1942.

83. CIOCCO, A. On the mortality in husbands and wives. *Proc. Nat. Acad. Sc.*, 26:610, 1940.

84. Classified (A) list of diagnoses for hospital morbidity reporting. New York, Welfare Council of New York City. Welfare Council Publications, 1939—IX.

85. COBB, P. W. The limit of usefulness of accident rate as a measure of accident proneness. *J. Applied Psychol.*, 24:154, 1940.

86. COBB, S., WHITING, I., and BAUER, W. Environmental factors in rheumatoid arthritis. *J.A.M.A.*, 109:1157, 1937.

87. COBURN, A. F. The Factor of Infection in the Rheumatic State. Baltimore, Williams & Wilkins, 1931.

88. COGHILL, G. E. Corollaries of the anatomical and physiological study of Amblystoma from the age of the earliest movement to swimming. *J. Comp. Neurol.*, 53:157, 1931.

89. COHEN, E. The social component in heart disease. *Am. Heart J.*, 16:422, 1938.

90. COHN, A. E. Heart disease from the point of view of public health. *Am. Heart J.*, 2:275; 386, 1927.

91. COHN, A. E., and LINGG, C. The natural history of the rheumatic cardiac disease: a statistical study. II. Manifestations of rheumatic activity: recurrence, severity of infection and prognosis. *J.A.M.A.*, 121:113, 1943.

92. COLLINS, S. D. Causes of illness in 9,000 families, based on nation-wide periodic canvasses, 1928–1931. *Pub. Health Rep.*, 48:283, 1933.

93. COLLINS, S. D. Age incidence of illness and death considered in broad disease groups, based on records for 9,000 families in 18 states visited periodically for 12 months, 1928–1931. *Pub. Health Rep.*, 50:507, 1935.

94. COLLINS, S. D. Age incidence of specific causes of illness, based on records for 9,000 families in 18 states visited periodically for 12 months, 1928–1931. *Pub. Health Rep.*, 50:1404, 1935.

95. COLLINS, S. D. A general view of the causes of illness and death at specific ages, based on records for 9,000 families in 18 states visited periodically for 12 months, 1928–1931. *Pub. Health Rep.*, 50:237, 1935.

96. COLLINS, S. D. Frequency of surgical procedures among 9,000 families, based on nation-wide periodic canvasses, 1928–1931. *Pub. Health Rep.*, 53:587, 1938.

97. COLLINS, S. D. Percentage of illnesses treated surgically among 9,000 families, based on nation-wide periodic canvasses, 1928–1931. *Pub. Health Rep.*, 53:1593, 1938.

98. COLLINS, S. D. Cases and days of illness among males and females with special reference to confinement in bed, based on 9,000 families visited periodically for 12 months, 1928–1931. *Pub. Health Rep.*, 55:47, 1940.

99. Columbia University Text-book of Psychiatry. Chapter by F. Dunbar on: Psychiatric-medical problems. (To be published.)

100. CONNER, L. A. Cardiac diagnosis in the light of experiences with army physical examinations. *Am. J. M. Sc.*, 158:773, 1919.

101. CONNER, L. A. Comments upon certain aspects of rheumatic fever and rheumatic heart disease. *New England J. Med.*, 217:503, 1937.

102. Consumer incomes in the United States; their distribution in 1935–1936. National Resources Committee. Washington, Govt. Print. Office, 1938.

103. CORNWALL, E. E. Benign angina pectoris. *M. Times, New York*, 67:69, 1939.

104. CROOKSHANK, F. G. Organ-jargon. *Brit. J. M. Psychol.*, 10:295, 1930.

105. CULPIN, M. Psychological disorders in industry. *Practitioner*, 137:324, 1936.

106. Current prevalence of communicable diseases in the United States, January 28–February 24, 1934. *Pub. Health Rep.*, 49:357, 1934.

107. DANIELS, G. E. Analysis of a case of neurosis with diabetes mellitus. *Psychonalyt. Quart.*, 5:513, 1936.

108. DANIELS, G. E. Present trends in the evaluation of psychic factors in diabetes mellitus. *Psychosom. Med.*, 1:527, 1939.

109. DARROW, C. W. Continuous records of systolic and diastolic blood pressure. *Arch. Neurol. & Psychiat.*, 38:365, 1937.

110. DAVIS, D., and KLAINER, M. J. Studies in hypertensive heart disease. Factors in the production of angina pectoris. *Am. Heart J.*, 19:198, 1940.

111. DAVIS, D., and KLAINER, M. J. Development of concept of hypertensive heart disease. *New England J. Med.*, 224:679, 1941.

112. DAVIS, D., and WEISS, S. Rheumatic heart disease; life history of severe form of disease. *Am. Heart J.*, 10:486, 1935.

113. DAVIS, H. Electroencephalography. *J.A.M.A.*, 117:983, 1941.

114. DAVIS, H., and WALLACE, W. M. Factors affecting changes produced in electroencephalogram by standardized hyperventilation. *Arch. Neurol. & Psychiat.*, 47:606, 1942.

115. Deaths, number of (exclusive of stillbirths) from all causes and death rates per 1,000 estimated population: 1920–1935. U. S. Bureau of the Census. Vital Statistics. Special reports, 3:No. 7, 1937.

116. Deaths, number of (exclusive of stillbirths) in continental United States from selected causes, by age and sex: 1935. U. S. Bureau of the Census. Special Reports, 8:No. 8, 1937.

117. Deaths, number of (exclusive of stillbirths) from each cause and death rates in the United States: 1930–1935. U. S. Bureau of the Census, Special Reports, 3:No. 10, 1937.

118. DeGRAFF, A. C., and LINGG, C. The course of rheumatic heart disease in adults. *Am. Heart J.*, 10:459; 478, 1935.

119. Department of Health, City of New York, Bureau of Records, Statistical Division. Summary of vital statistics. Population, births, marriages, deaths and infant mortality, 1898–1936.

120. DERSHIMER, F. W. The prevention of traumatic neuroses. *J. Indust. Hyg.*, 16:40, 1934.

121. DEUTSCH, F. Der Einfluss von Gemutsbewegungen auf den Energiestoffwechsel. Hypnotische Experimente. *Wien. klin. Wchnschr.*, 38:1127, 1925.

122. DEUTSCH, F. Associative anamnesis. *Psychoanalyt. Quart.*, 8:354, 1939.

123. DEUTSCH, F. The choice of organ in organ neuroses. *Internat. J. Psychoanalyt.*, 20:252, 1939.

124. DEUTSCH, F. Capillary studies in Raynaud's disease. *J. Lab. & Clin. Med.*, 26:1729, 1941.

125. DEUTSCH, F., and NADELL, R. Autonomic skin test with electrophoresis. *J. Invest. Dermat.*, 5:87, 1942.

126. Differential tables. *New York City. Health Department. Quart. Bull.*, 5:57, 1937.

127. DONZELOT, E. Les "éclipses cérébrales" au cours des poussées hypertensives. *Presse méd.*, 49:4, 1941.

128. DRAPER, G., DUPERTUIS, C. W., and CAUGHEY, J. L. Differentiation by constitutional methods between pancreatic diabetes and diabetes of pituitary origin. *Tr. A. Am. Physicians*, 55:146, 1940.

129. DREWRY, P. H., and WALL, J. H. Mental reactions and their management in patients with cardiac disease. *Am. J. Psychiat.*, 94:561, 1937.

130. DUBLIN, L. I. Mortality from cardiovascular-renal diseases. New York, Metropolitan Life Ins. Co., 1936.

131. DUBLIN, L. I. Statistical aspects of the problem of organic heart disease. *New York State J. Med.*, 25:986, 1925.

132. DUBLIN, L. I., and ARMSTRONG, D. B. Favorable aspects of heart disease, with special reference to the health officer. New York, Metropolitan Life Ins. Co., 1933.

133. DUBLIN, L. I., and LOTKA, A. J. Length of Life. A Study of the Life Table. New York, Ronald Press, 1936.

134. DUBLIN, L. I., and LOTKA, A. J. Twenty-Five Years of Health Progress. New York, Metropolitan Life Ins. Co., 1937.

135. DUBLIN, L. I., and LOTKA, A. J. The mortality from the principal cardiovascular disease. A study of the experience among the industrial policyholders of the Metropolitan Life Insurance Company, 1911 to 1935. Reprinted from No. 134.

136. DUBLIN, L. I., KARSNER, H. T., PEPPER, O. H. P., and BROOKS, B. Medical Problems of Old Age. Philadelphia, Univ. of Penn. Press, 1941.

137. DuBOIS, C., and OBERHOLZER, E. Rorschach test and native personality in Alor, Dutch East Indies. N. Y. Acad. Sci. Transactions, Series 2, 5:168, 1942.

138. DUNBAR, F.* The bearing of emotional factors on social health programs for dealing with economic disability. Am. A. Advancement Sc., Publ. No. 9, 1939, pp. 199–210.

139. DUNBAR, F. Character and symptom formation. Some preliminary notes with special reference to patients with hypertensive, rheumatic and coronary disease. Psychonalyt. Quart., 8:18, 1939.

140. DUNBAR, F. Psychosomatic history and techniques of examination. Am. J. Psychiat., 95:1277, 1939.

141. DUNBAR, F. Emotions and bodily changes; a report of some recent psychosomatic studies. Ann. Int. Med., 14:839, 1940.

142. DUNBAR, F. The relationship between anxiety states and organic disease. Clinics, 1:879, 1942.

143. DUNBAR, F. Medical aspects of accidents and mistakes; in the industrial army and in the armed forces. War Med., 3:7, 1943.

144. DUNBAR, H. F. Physical mental relationships in illness. Trends in modern medicine and research as related to psychiatry. Am. J. Psychiat., 91:541, 1934.

145. DUNBAR, H. F. Problems of convalescence and chronic illness. A preliminary discussion. Am. J. Psychiat., 92:1095, 1936.

146. DUNBAR, H. F. Psychic factors in cardiovascular disease. New York State J. Med., 36:423, 1936.

147. DUNBAR, H. F. The psychic component in disease, from the point of view of the medical social worker's responsibility. Bull. Am. A. Med. Social Workers, 10:69, 1937.

148. DUNBAR, H. F. The refractory patient with diabetes. Abstr. J. Nerv. & Ment. Dis., 86:712, 1937.

149. DUNBAR, H. F. Emotions and Bodily Changes. Ed. 2, with supplementary introduction and additional bibliography. New York, Columbia Univ. Press, 1938.

* Dunbar, F. For earlier references by this author, see Dunbar, H. F.

150. DUNBAR, H. F. Psychoanalytic notes relating to syndromes of asthma and hay fever. *Psychoanalyt. Quart.*, 7:25, 1938.

151. DUNBAR, H. F. Psychoanalysis and the general hospital. *Psychiatry*, 2:167, 1939.

152. DUNBAR, H. F., WOLFE, T. P., and RIOCH, J. M. The psychic component of the disease process (including convalescence) in cardiac, diabetic, and fracture patients. *Am. J. Psychiat.*, 93:649, 1936.

153. DUNBAR, H. F., WOLFE, T. P., *et al*. The psychic component of the disease process (including convalescence) in cardiac, diabetic, and fracture patients. *Am. J. Psychiat.*, 95:1319, 1939.

154. DUNN, H. L. Instruction manual—part II. Instructions for coding causes of death. Ed. 6. Washington, U. S. Bureau of the Census, 1940.

155. EATON, E. R. Chronic arthritis. A study of the symptomatology; systemic manifestations. *J. Am. Inst. Homeop.*, 25:612, 1932.

156. EATON, E. R., and LOVE, J. Chronic arthritis; a study of the dietary of five hundred patients, with results of an experimental course of insulin treatment in twenty-two cases of malnutrition. *J. Am. Inst. Homeop.*, 26:404, 1933.

157. EATON, E. R. Chronic arthritis; a study of the habits of five hundred patients. *J. Am. Inst. Homeop.*, 26:568, 1933.

158. EATON, E. R. Chronic arthritis; a study of the symptomatology—local joint manifestations. *J. Am. Inst. Homeop.*, 26:321, 1933.

159. EDDINGTON, SIR A. The Philosophy of Physical Science. Cambridge, Univ. Press, 1939.

160. Editorial. *Science*, 93:2424, 1941.

161. EDWARDS, A. M. Alphabetical index of occupations by industries and social-economic group (1937). Washington, Govt. Print. Office, 1937.

162. EDWARDS, A. M. Social-economic grouping of the gainful workers of the United States. Washington, Govt. Print. Office, 1938.

163. ELDBLOM, E. A method for making a graphical, intermittent-continuous registration of the arterial blood pressure (pletonography). *Acta med. Scandinav.*, 88:45, 1936.

164. Eleven, the safest age. *Statist. Bull. Metropolitan Life Ins. Co.*, 17:11, 1936.

165. ELMORE, E. Psychic heart disease; a study of three generations. *Psychoanalyt. Rev.*, 23:286, 1936.

166. EMERSON, C. P. The emotional element in the production of organic diseases. *Tr. A. Am. Physicians*, 42:346, 1927.

167. Emotions and the educative process; a report to the American Council on Education, edited by D. A. Prescott. New York, Am. Council on Education, 1938.

168. Establishing a national health program. U. S. Congress, Senate, 1st Session, 76th Congress. Report No. 1139, 1939.

169. Estimate (An) of the amount of disabling illness in the country as a whole. National Health Survey, 1935–36. Preliminary Reports. Washington, 1938.

170. FAHR, G. Hypertension hearts. *Am. J. M. Sci.*, 175:453, 1928.

171. FAHRENKAMP, K. Die psycho-physischen Wechselwirkungen bei den Hypertonieerkrankungen. Eine klinische Studie über die praktische Bedeutung der Blutdruckkurve. Stuttgart, Hippokrates-Verlag, 1926.

172. FALK, I. S., and HIRSCH, N. D. M. Social security measures as factors in mental health programs. *Am. A. Advancement Sc., Publ.*, No. 9, 1939.

173. FARMER, E., and CHAMBERS, E. G. A study of personal qualities in accident proneness and efficiency. London, H. M. Stat. Office, 1939.

174. Fatal accidents most frequent under age five. *Statist. Bull. Metropolitan Life Ins. Co.*, 15:11, 1934.

175. Fatal rheumatic heart disease in Philadelphia hospitals. *See* No. 233.

176. FEDERN, P. Hysterie und Zwang in der Neurosenwahl. *Internat. Ztschr. f. Psychoanal. u. Imago*, 25:245, 1940.

177. FENICHEL, O. Perversionen, Psychosen, Charakterstörungen. Wien, Internat. Psychoanalyt. Verlag, 1931.

178. FENICHEL, O. Outline of Clinical Psychoanalysis. New York, Psychoanalyt. Quart. Press, 1934.

179. FERENCZI, S. Further Contributions to the Theory and Technique of Psycho-analysis. Compiled by J. Rickman. Trans. by J. I. Suttie and others. London, Hogarth Press, 1926.

180. FERENCZI, S., *et al.* Psychoanalysis and the War Neuroses. London, Internat. Psychonalyt. Press, 1921.

181. FERRIS, E. B., JR., and MYERS, W. K. Initial attacks of rheumatic fever in patients over 60 years of age. *Arch. Int. Med.*, 55:809, 1935.

182. FLEMING. *See* Marsh, Fleming, and Blackler, No. 290.

183. FORSTER, W. K. Mental attitudes, their relationship to industrial accidents. *Indust. Med.*, 6:93, 1937.

184. FRANK, L. K. Structure, function and growth. *Philos. Sc.*, 2:210, 1935.

185. FRANK, L. K. Family planning and cultural change. *J. Heredity*, 30:273, 1939.

186. FRANK, L. K. Projective methods for a study of personality. *J. Psychol.*, 8:389, 1939.

187. FRANK, L. K. Freud's influence on Western thinking and culture. *Am. J. Orthopsychiat.*, 10:880, 1940.

188. FRANKEL, L. K., and DUBLIN, L. I. A sickness survey of North Carolina. *Pub. Health Rep.*, 31:2820, 1916.

189. FREEMAN, W., and WATTS, J. W. Prefrontal lobotomy in treatment of mental disorders. *South. M. J.*, 30:23, 1937.

190. FREMONT-SMITH, F. The physiological basis of aggression. *Child Study*, 15, 1938.

191. FREMONT-SMITH, F. The influence of emotional factors upon physiological and pathological processes. *Bull. New York Acad. Med.*, 15:560, 1939.

192. FRENCH, T. Physiology of behavior and choice of neurosis. *Psychoanalyt. Quart.*, 10:561, 1941.

193. FRENCH, T. M., and ALEXANDER, F. Psychogenic factors in bronchial asthma. Psychosom. Med. Monographs 1:No. 4, 1941, Part I; 2:No. 1 and 2, 1941, Part II.

194. FREUD, S. Gesammelte Schriften, Bd. I–XII. Leipzig, Internat. Psychoanalyt. Verlag, 1925.

195. FREUD, S. Psychogenic Visual Disturbances According to Psychoanalytical Conceptions. Trans. by E. C. Mayne. Collected Papers, 4 vols. London, Hogarth Press, 1924. (Die psychogene Sehstörungen in psychoanalitischer Auffassung. Gesammelte Schriften, V.)

196. FREUD, S. Autobiography. Trans. by J. Strachey. New York, Norton, 1935.

197. FROMM, E. Escape from Freedom. New York, Farrar & Rinehart, 1941.

197a. GALDSTON, I. The epidemic constitution in historical perspective. *Bull N. Y. Acad. Med.*, 18:606, 1942.

198. GALLAVARDIN, L. Les Angines de Poitrine. Paris, Masson, 1925.

199. GEIGER, J. C. The 1940 Year Book of Public Health. Chicago, Year Book Pub., 1940.

200. GELLHORN, E., ALLEN, A., and FELDMAN, J. Influence of emotional excitement on insulin content of the blood in normals and psychotic patients. *Proc. Soc. Exper. Biol. & Med.*, 46:572, 1941.

201. GELLHORN, E., CORTELL, R., and FELDMAN, J. Autonomic basis of emotion. *Science*, 92:288, 1940.

202. General Medicine, The 1940 Year Book of. Ed. by G. F. Dick, and others. Chicago, Year Book Pub., 1940.

202a. General Medicine, The 1942 Year Book of. Ed. by G. F. Dick, and others. Chicago, Year Book Pub., 1942.

203. GLOVER, E. Psycho-analysis. London, Bale, 1939.

204. GLOVER, E., and BRIERLEY, M. An Investigation of the Technique of Psychoanalysis. Baltimore, Williams & Wilkins, 1940.

205. GODDARD, J. C. Comparison of occupational class and physicians' estimate of economic status. *Pub. Health Rep.*, 54:2159, 1939.

206. GORDON, R. G. Psychological factors in chronic rheumatism. *Brit. M. J.*, 1:1165, 1939.

207. GORDON, W. H., BLAND, E. F., and WHITE, P. D. Coronary artery disease analyzed post mortem. *Am. Heart J.*, 17:10, 1939.

208. GORHAM, L. W., and MARTIN, S. J. Coronary occlusion with and without pain; analysis of one hundred cases in which autopsy was done with reference to the tension factor in cardiac pain. *Arch. Int. Med.*, 62:821, 1938.

209. GREEN, H. D., and GREGG, D. E. Changes in coronary circulation following increased aortic pressure, augmented cardiac output, ischemia and valve lesions. *Am. J. Physiol.*, 130:126, 1940.

210. GREENACRE, P. Surgical addiction—case illustration. *Psychosom. Med.*, 1:325, 1939.

211. GRINDLEY, G. C. The variation of sensory thresholds with the rate of application of the stimulus. I. The differential threshold for pressure. *Brit. J. Psychol.*, 27:86, 1936. II. Touch and pain. *Ibid.*, 189.

212. GRINKER, R. R. Hypothalamic functions in psychosomatic interrelations. *Psychosom. Med.*, 1:19, 1939.

213. GROLLMAN, A., HARRISON, T. R., and WILLIAMS, J. R., JR. Therapeutics of experimental hypertension. *J. Pharmacol. & Exper. Therap.*, 69:76, 1940.

214. HALLIDAY, J. L. Psychoneurosis as cause of incapacity among insured persons; preliminary inquiry. *Brit. M. J.* (suppl.), p. 85, March 9, 1935; p. 99, March 16, 1935.

215. HALLIDAY, J. L. Psychological factors in rheumatism; preliminary study. *Brit. M. J.*, 1:213; 264, 1937.

216. HALLIDAY, J. L. Psychological approach to rheumatism. *Proc. Roy. Soc. Med.*, 31:167, 1938.

217. HALLIDAY, J. L. The rising incidence of psychosomatic illness. *Brit. M. J.*, 2:11, 1938.

218. HALLIDAY, J. L. Social pathology. *Brit. M. J.*, 2:1012, 1938.

219. HALLIDAY, J. L. The concept of psychosomatic rheumatism. *Ann. Int. Med.*, 15:666, 1941.

220. HALLIDAY, J. L. Psychological aspects of rheumatoid arthritis. *Proc. Roy. Soc. Med.*, 25:455, 1942.

221. HALLOWELL, A. I. The Rorschach method as an aid in the study of personalities in primitive societies. *Character & Personality*, 9:235, 1941.

222. HALLOWELL, A. I. The Rorschach test as a tool for investigating cultural variables and individual differences in the study of personality in primitive societies. *Rorschach Research Exch.*, 5:31, 1941.

223. HAMBURGER, W. W. The treatment of hypertension. *M. Clin. North America*, 25:129, 1941.

224. HARRIS, M. M. Metabolic consideration regarding diabetic psychosis. *Arch. Neurol. & Psychiat.*, 31:881, 1934.

225. HEDLEY, O. F. A critical analysis of heart disease mortality. *J.A.M.A.*, 105:1405, 1935.

226. HEDLEY, O. F. An etiological study of 450 fatal cases of heart disease. *Pub. Health Rep.*, 50:1127, 1935.

227. HEDLEY, O. F. Mortality from rheumatic heart disease in Philadelphia. *Pub. Health Rep.*, 52:1907, 1937.

228. HEDLEY, O. F. Incidence of rheumatic heart disease among college students in the United States. *Pub. Health Rep.*, 53:1635, 1938.

229. HEDLEY, O. F. Analysis of 5,116 deaths reported as due to acute coronary occlusion in Philadelphia, 1933–1937. *Pub. Health Rep.*, 54:972, 1939.

230. HEDLEY, O. F. Trends, geographical and racial distribution of mortality from heart disease among persons 5–24 years of age in the United States during recent years (1922–1936). *Pub. Health Rep.*, 54:2271, 1939.

231. HEDLEY, O. F. Rheumatic heart disease in Philadelphia hospitals. *Pub. Health Rep.*, 55:1599, 1940.

232. HEDLEY, O. F. Rheumatic heart disease in Philadelphia hospitals. II. Age, race, and sex distribution and interrelation of rheumatic fever, Sydenham's chorea, rheumatic heart disease, and subacute bacterial endocarditis. *Pub. Health Rep.*, 55:1647, 1940.

233. HEDLEY, O. F. Rheumatic heart disease in Philadelphia hospitals. III. Fatal rheumatic heart disease and subacute bacterial endocarditis. *Pub. Health Rep.*, 55:1707, 1940.

234. HEDLEY, O. F. Rheumatic heart disease in Philadelphia hospitals. IV. Influence of season and certain meteorological conditions. *Pub. Health Rep.*, 55:1809, 1940.

235. HEDLEY, O. F. Rheumatic heart disease in Philadelphia hospitals. V. Distribution by locality of rheumatic conditions in Philadelphia. *Pub. Health Rep.*, 55:1845, 1940.

236. HEINRICH, H. W. The foundation of a major injury. *Travelers Standard*, Jan. 1929.

237. HENCH, P. S., *et al.* The present status of rheumatism and arthritis; review of American and English literature for 1936. *Ann. Int. Med.*, 11:1089, 1938.

238. HENRY, G. W. Sex Variants. A Study of Homosexual Patterns. New York, Hoeber, 1941, v. 1, p. 546; v. 2, p. 1179.

239. HEYER, G. R. Psychische Faktoren bei organischen Krankheiten. *München. med. Wchnschr.*, 69:1241, 1922.

240. HILL, L. B., Psychoanalytic observations on essential hypertension. *Psychoanalyt. Rev.*, 22:60, 1935.

241. HOUSTON, W. R. The spasmogenic aptitude. *M. Clin. North America*, 12:1285, 1929.

242. How many are we? *Statist. Bull. Metropolitan Life Ins. Co.*, 15:No. 5, 1934.

243. HUDDLESON, J. H. Accidents, Neuroses and Compensation. Baltimore, Williams & Wilkins, 1932.

244. HUTTON, J. H. Endocrine progress and its relation to essential hypertension and diabetes mellitus. *Illinois M. J.*, 71:469, 1937.

245. HUTTON, J. H., *et al.* Endocrine aspects of essential hypertension and diabetes mellitus. *Endocrinology*, 26:418, 1940.

246. Illness and medical care in relation to economic status. National Health Survey, 1933–1936. Preliminary reports. National Health Survey Sickness and Medical Care Series, Bull. No. 2. Washington, 1939.

247. INGRAM, W. R. The hypothalamus; a review of the experimental data. *Psychosom. Med.*, 1:48, 1939.

248. ISELIN, H. Rheuma und Sympathikus. *Schweiz. med. Wchnschr.*, 68:709; 758; 884, 1938.

249. JACOBSON, E. Progressive Relaxation. A Physiological and Clinical Investigation of Muscular States and their Significance in Psychology and Medical Practice. Chicago, Univ. Chicago Press, 1929.

250. JAFFÉ, R., and BROSS, K. Befunde bei Herzrupturen (Zugleich ein Beitrag zur Frage der Angina pectoris). *Ztschr. f. klin. Med.*, 123:63, 1933.

251. JELLIFFE, S. E. What price healing? *J.A.M.A.*, 94:1393, 1930.

252. JOHNSON, H. M. Born to crash. *Collier's*, July 25, 1936.

253. JONES, E. Papers on Psycho-analysis. Ed. 3. New York, Wood, 1923.

254. JONES, H. E. An experimental cabinet for physiological studies of emotions. *Child Development*, 7:183, 1938.

255. JOSLIN, E. P. Treatment of Diabetes Mellitus. Philadelphia, Lea & Febiger, 1937.

256. JOSLIN, E. P., ROOT, H. F., and MARBLE, A. Trauma and Diabetes Mellitus. Philadelphia, Lea & Febiger, 1937.

257. KAHN, J., and INGRAHAM, E. Cardiac hypertrophy and coronary arteriosclerosis in hypertension. *Arch. Path.*, 31:373, 1941.

258. KARDINER, A. The bio-analysis of the epileptic reaction. *Psychoanalyt. Quart.*, 1:375, 1932.

259. KARDINER, A. The Individual and his Society. The Psychodynamics of Primitive Social Organization. New York, Columbia Univ. Press, 1939.

260. KARDINER, A. The Traumatic Neuroses of War. *Psychosom. Med. Monographs*, 1:Nos. 2 and 3, 1941.

261. KARN, H. W. The experimental study of neurotic behavior in infrahuman animals. *J. Gen. Psychol.*, 22:431, 1940.

262. KATZ, S. E. A catatonic syndrome associated with diabetes mellitus. *Arch. Neurol. & Psychiat.*, 31:880, 1934.

263. KEMPF, E. J. The integrative functions of the nervous system applied to some reactions in human behavior, and their attending psychic functions. *Proc. Am. Med.-Psychol. A.*, 70:449, 1914.

264. KEMPF, E. J. Some studies in the psychopathology of acute dissociation of the personality. *Psychoanalyt. Rev.*, 2:361, 1915.

265. KEMPF, E. J. The Autonomic Functions and the Personality. *Nerv. & Ment. Dis. Monogr. Ser.*, No. 28. New York, Nerv. & Ment. Dis. Pub. Co., 1921.

266. KEMPF, E. J. Affective-respiratory factors in catatonis. *M. J. & Rec.*, 131:181, 1930.

267. KEMPF, E. J. Physiology of attitude—emergence of ego-organization. *M. Rec.*, 141:136, 254, 478, 512, 560; 142:15, 115, 173, 220, 264, 336, 356, 403, 446, 1935.

268. KEMPF, E. J. Fundamental factors in the psychopathology and psychotherapy of malignant disorganization neuroses. *M. Rec.*, 146:341, 1937.

269. KENNEY, J. S. Inaugural address. *J. M. Soc. County of New York*, 11: No. 7, pt. 2, p. 3, Feb. 13, 1943.

270. KERR, W. J., GLIEBE, P. A., SOLEY, M. H., and SHOCK, N. W. Treatment of the anxiety states, with special attention to certain physiologic manifestations. *J.A.M.A.*, 113:637, 1939.

271. KLEMPERER, G. Gemutsbewegungen und Herzkrankheit. *Therap. d. Gegenw.*, 70:1, 1929.

272. KLOPFER, B. The Rorschach Technique. A Manual for a Projective Method of Personality Diagnosis, with Clinical Contributions by D. M. Kelley. New York, World Book Co., 1942.

273. KOELSCHE, G. A. How to elicit and evaluate the patient's complaint. *J.A.M.A.*, 113:2359, 1939.

274. KOFFKA, K. The ego in his world. *Advanc. Sc.*, 1:444, 1940.

275. KORTH, C. The production of extrasystoles by means of the central nervous system. *Ann. Int. Med.*, 11:492, 1937.

276. KRAINES, J. H., and SHERMAN, I. C. Neurotic symptoms and changes in blood pressure and pulse following injection of epinephrine. *J.A.M.A.*, 114:843, 1940.

277. KUBIE, L. S. Critical analysis of concept of a repetition compulsion. *Internat. J. Psychoanal.*, 20:390, 1939.

278. See No. 285.

279. LEVY, D. M. Studies in sibling rivalry. *Am. Orthopsychiat. A., Research Monogr.*, No. 2, 1937.

280. LEVY, R. L., BRUENN, H. G., and KURTZ, D. Facts on disease of the coronary arteries based on a survey of clinical and pathological records of 762 cases. *Am. J. M. Sc.*, 187:376, 1934.

281. LEWIS, A., and SLATER, E. Neurosis in soldiers. *Lancet*, 1:496, 1942.

282. LIDDELL, H. S., JAMES, W. T., and ANDERSON, O. D. The comparative physiology of the conditioned motor reflex (based on experiments with the pig, dog, sheep, goat and rabbit). *Comp. Psychol. Monogr.*, 11, 1934.

283. LINDBERG, B. J., Diabetic psychosis. *Acta psychiat. et neurol.*, 11:267, 1936–37.

284. LONG, C. N. H. Diabetes mellitus in the light of our present knowledge of metabolism. *Tr. & Stud. Coll. Physicians, Phila.*, 7:21, 1936.

285. Longevity of the American people increasing. *Statist. Bull. Metropolitan Life Ins. Co.*, 20:No. 8, 1939.

286. Magnitude (The) of the chronic disease problem in the United States. National Health Survey. Preliminary Reports, Sickness and Medical Care Series, Bull. 6, 1938 (rev. 1939).

287. MAINZER, F., and KRAUSE, M. Changes in electrocardiogram brought about by fear. *Cardiologia*, 3:286, 1939.

288. MAINZER, F., and KRAUSE, M. The influence of fear on the electro-cardiograph. *Brit. Heart J.*, 2:221, 1940.

289. MARBE, K. Praktische Psychologie der Unfälle und Betriebsschäden. München, 1926.

290. MARSH, L. C., FLEMING, A. G., and BLACKLER, C. F. Health and Un-employment; Some Studies of their Relationships. Toronto, Oxford Univ. Press, 1938.

291. MARTIN, S. J., and GORHAM, L. W. An experimental study with reference to the tension factor. *Arch. Int. Med.*, 62:840, 1938.

292. MASTER, A. M., GUBNER, R., DACK, S., and JAFFE, H. L. Angina pectoris of psychogenic origin. *Arch. Int. Med.*, 67:647, 1941.

293. MCCARTHY, D. J. Physical factors of the psychoneurosis. *Atlantic M. J.*, 29:446, 1925–26.

294. MCGREGOR, H. G. Psychological factor in rheumatic disease. *Practitioner*, 143:627, 1939.

295. MCKENDREE, C. A. The insignificance of local disturbances in the production of constitutional nervous symptoms. *Neurol. Bull.*, 2:253, 1929.

296. MEISELS, H. B. A follow-up study of psychoneurotic patients. *Smith College Studies Soc. Work*, 11:175, 1940.

297. MENNINGER, K. A. Purposive accidents as an expression of self-destruction tendencies. *Internat. J. Psychoanalyt.*, 17:6, 1936.

298. MENNINGER, K. A. Emotional factors in hypertension. *Bull. New York Acad. Med.*, 14:198, 1938.

299. MENNINGER, K. A., and MENNINGER, W. C. Psychoanalytic observations in cardiac disorders. *Am. Heart J.*, 11:10, 1936.

300. MENNINGER, W. C. The inter-relation of mental disorders and diabetes mellitus. *J. Ment. Sc.*, 81:332, 1935.

301. MENNINGER, W. C. Psychological factors in the etiology of diabetes mellitus. *J. Nerv. & Ment. Dis.*, 81:1, 1935.

302. MENNINGER, W. C. Psychiatric hospital therapy designed to meet unconscious needs. *Am. J. Psychiat.*, 93:347, 1936.

303 Mental hygiene and adjustment (Literature reviewed to approximately Jan. 1, 1936). Prepared by Comm. on Ment. Hyg. *Rev. Educ. Research*, 6:No. 5, Dec. 1936.

304. MERTON, R. K. Bureaucratic structure and personality. *Social Forces*, 18:560, 1940.

305. MEYER, A. Misconceptions at the bottom of "Hopelessness of all psychology." *Psychol. Bull.*, 4:170, 1907.

306. MILLER, M. L. Blood pressure findings in relation to inhibited aggressions in psychotics. *Psychosom. Med.*, 1:162, 1939.

307. MITTELMANN, B., and WOLFF, H. G. Emotions and gastroduodenal function; experimental studies on patients with gastritis, duodenitis and peptic ulcer. *Psychosom. Med.*, 4:5, 1942.

308. MOHR, F. Die Wechselwirkung körperlicher und seelischer Faktoren in Krankheitsgeschehen. *Klin. Wchnschr.*, 6:772, 1927.

309. MORRISON, L. M., and SWALM, W. A. Role of gastrointestinal tract in production of cardiac symptoms; experimental and clinical observations. *J.A.M.A.*, 114:217, 1940.

310. Mortality from certain causes during the first 9 months of 1936. *Pub. Health Rep.*, 52:157, 1937.

311. MORGAN, J. J. B. Shock as a preparation for readjustment. *J. Psychol.*, 10:313, 1940.

312. Motor-vehicle traffic conditions in the United States. Part 6. The accident-prone driver. U. S. House Doc. No. 462. Washington, Govt. Print. Office, 1938.

313. MUHL, A. M. Behavior problems in general medicine. *M. J. Australia*, 1:651, 1940.

314. NEUSTATTER, W. L. Nature and relationship of functional nervous disorders to rheumatism in childhood. *Guy's Hosp. Rep.*, 87:8, 1937.

315. NEUSTATTER, W. L. The effect of poor social conditions in the production of neuroses. *Lancet*, 1:1436, 1938.

316. NICHOL, E. S. Geographic distribution of rheumatic fever and rheumatic heart disease in the United States. *J. Lab. & Clin. Med.*, 21:588, 1936.

317. Notifiable diseases—prevalence in states, 1935. Suppl. 19 to Pub. Health Rep.

318. Notifiable diseases—prevalence in states, 1936. Suppl. 134 to Pub. Health Rep.

319. Notifiable diseases—prevalence in states, 1938. Suppl. 160 to Pub. Health Rep.

320. OLDSFIELD, R. C. Some recent experiments bearing on "internal inhibition." *Brit. J. Psychol.*, 28:28, 1937.

321. OSLER. *See* Christian, No. 82.

322. PARKER, G. H. Types of animal reflexes. *Science*, 91:216, 1940.

323. Patients in Hospitals for Mental Disease, 1937. Washington, Govt. Print. Office, 1939.

324. PAUL, J. B. Rheumatic fever. *Milbank Mem. Fund Quarterly*, 18:156, 1940.

325. PENNEL, E. H., MOUNTIN, J. W., and PEARSON, K. Business census of hospitals, 1935. General Report. Suppl. 154 to Pub. Health Rep.

326. PERROTT, G. S. The state of the nation's health. *Ann. Am. Acad. Polit. & Soc. Science*, Nov. 1936.

327. PERROTT, G. S. Chronic illness in New York City; a report by its citizens. Address, May 5, 1938.

328. PERROTT, G. S., and COLLINS, S. D. Relation of sickness to income and income change in 10 surveyed communities. *Pub. Health Rep.*, 50:595, 1935.

329. PERROTT, G. S., and GRIFFIN, H. C. An inventory of the serious disabilities of the urban relief population. *Milbank Mem. Fund Quarterly*, 14:213, 1936.

330. PERROTT, G. S., and HOLLAND, D. F. Chronic disease and gross impairments in a northern industrial community. *J.A.M.A.*, 108:1876, 1937.

331. PERROTT, G. S., and HOLLAND, D. F. Disabling illness among negroes and low-income white families in New York City; a report of a sickness survey in the spring of 1933. Part I. *Milbank Mem. Fund Quarterly*, 16:No. 1, 1938.

332. PERROTT, G. D., and HOLLAND, D. F. Health as an element in social security. *Ann. Am. Acad. Polit. & Soc. Sc.*, March 1939.

333. PETERSON, P. A method of continuous registration of the pulse rate; preliminary communication. *Sc. Communic., Balneol. Inst. Univ. Giessen*, Bad-Nauheim, No. 4, 1937.

PINCUS and WHITE. *See* Joslin, No. 255.

334. PIOTROWSKI, Z. A. On the Rorschach method and its application in organic disturbances of the central nervous system. *Rorschach Research Exchange*, 1:23, 1936–37.

335. PIOTROWSKI, Z. A. Blind analysis of a case of compulsion neurosis. *Rorschach Research Exchange*, 2:89, 1937–38.

336. PIOTROWSKI, Z. A. On Rorschach method of personality analysis. *Psychiat. Quart.*, 16:480, 1942.

337. Preliminary analysis of audiometric data in relation to clinical history of impaired hearing. National Health Survey, 1935–36. Preliminary Reports. Hearing Study Series Bull., No. 2. Washington, 1938.

338. PRESTON, M. I. Physical complaints without organic basis. *J. Pediat.*, 17:279, 1940.

339. Prevalence of aural pathology and clinical history of impaired hearing among males and females of various ages. National Health Survey, 1935–36. Preliminary Reports. Hearing Study Series Bull., No. 3. Washington, 1938.

340. Prevalence and causes of orthopedic impairments. National Health Survey. Preliminary Reports. Sickness and Medical Care Series Bull., No. 4. Washington, 1938.

341. Progress in venereal disease control during the fiscal year 1939. *Ven. Dis. Inform.*, 20:376, 1939.

342. QUEEN, ELLERY. Challenge to the Reader; an Anthology. New York, Blue Ribbon Books, 1940. (The case of Mr. Foggatt, by Arthur Morrison.)

343. RANKIN, F. W. The responsibilities of medicine in wartime. *Science*, 95:611, 1942.

344. REICH, W. Die triebhafte Charakter. Leipzig, Internat. Psychoan. Verlag, 1925. (Neue Arb. z. ärztl. Psychoanalyse, No. 4.)

345. REICH, W. Orgasmusreflex, Muskelhaltung und Körperausdruck. In: Abhandl. z. personellen Sexualökonomie, No. 5. Oslo-Kopenhagen, Sexpol-Verlag, 1937.

346. REISS, M. The role of the sex hormones in psychiatry. *J. Ment. Sc.*, 86:767, 1940.

347. RENNIE, T. A. C. Relation of psychiatry to internal medicine. *Bull. Johns Hopkins Hosp.*, 65:265, 1939.

348. RENNIE, T. A. C. The role of personality in certain hypertensive states. *New England J. Med.*, 221:448, 1939.

349. Report of the British health services; a survey of the existing health services in Great Britain with proposals for future development. London, 1937.

350. Report of the hospital survey for New York . . . presented to the Survey Committee by the Study Committee. New York, United Hospital Fund, 1937. 3 vols. *See esp.* Vol. 2.

351. Report (3rd) of the Miners' Nystagmus Committee, Medical Research Council. London, H. M. Stationery Office, 1932.

352. Rheumatic heart disease as a problem in Philadelphia. *See* No. 231.

353. RIPLEY, H. S. Psychiatric consultation service in medical in-patient department; function in diagnosis, treatment and teaching. *Am. J. M. Sc.*, 199:261, 1940.

354. RITTER, W. E. The Unity of the Organism, or the Organismal Conception of Life. Boston, Badger, 1919. 2 vols.

355. ROBINSON, G. C. Relation of emotional strain to illness. *Ann. Int. Med.*, 11:345, 1937.

356. ROBERTSON, S., and KATZ, L. N. Observations on referred pain of cardiac origin. *Am. J. M. Sc.*, 196:199, 1938.

357. ROBINSON, S. C., and BRUCER, M. Range of normal blood pressure. *Arch. Int. Med.*, 64:409, 1939.

358. ROBINSON, S. K. Comparison of medical and surgical treatment in hypertension, with special reference to importance of psychic factors in evaluation results. *J. Nerv. & Ment. Dis.*, 91:157, 1940.

359. ROESLER, H. The relation of the endocrines to the circulation. *Modern Concepts of Cardiovascular Dis.*, 10:No. 9, 1941.

360. ROREM, C. R. Mental health and medical economics. *Am. A. Advance. Sc.*, Publ. No. 9, 1939.

361. RORSCHACH, H. Psychodiagnostics; a Diagnostic Text Based on Perception. Trans. by P. Lemkau and B. Kronenberg; editor, W. Morgenthaler. Berne, Huber, 1942.

362. ROSENZWEIG, S., MOWRER, O. H., QUIN, F., and BARKER, C. and R. G. Frustration as an experimental problem. *Character & Personality*, 1938.

363. RUPP, F., and BATTEY. Hurt at home. Works Progress Admin., Project No. 2950, sponsored by the Cook County Bureau of Public Welfare, and supervised by the National Safety Council, Part II, p. 7.

364. RYTAND, D. A., and HOLMAN, E. Arterial hypertension and section of aplanchnic nerves. *Arch. Int. Med.*, 67:1, 1941.

365. Safety first. Advertisement. *Time*, Aug. 4, 1941, p. 59.

366. SAUL, L. J. Hostility in cases of essential hypertension. *Psychosom. Med.*, 1:153, 1939.

367. SAUL, L. J., and BERNSTEIN, C., JR. The emotional settings of some attacks of urticaria. *Psychosom. Med.*, 3:349, 1941.

368. SCHILDER, P. Social organization and psychotherapy. *Am. J. Orthopsychiat.*, 10:911, 1940.

369. SCHLESINGER, B. Cause and prevention of acute rheumatism in childhood. *Quart. Bull. Health Organ. League of Nations*, 5:239, 1936.

370. SCHLESINGER, M. J. Relation of anatomic pattern to pathologic conditions of coronary arteries. *Arch. Path.*, 30:403, 1940.

371. SCHNUR, S. Cardiac neurosis associated with organic heart disease. *Am. Heart J.*, 18:153, 1939.

372. SCHULTZ, J. H. Das autogene Training (Konzentrative Selbstentspannung). Leipzig, Thieme, 1932.

373. SCHUR, M. Zur Frage der traumatischen Genese innerer Erkrankungen. *Ztschr. f. klin. Med.*, 123:800, 1933.

374. SCHWAB, S. I. The heart in emotional conflicts. *Tr. Sect. Nerv. & Ment. Dis., A. M. A.*, 1926, p. 67.

375. SCUPHAM, G. W., DE TAKATS, G., VAN DELLEN, T. R., and BECK, W. C. Vascular diseases. A review of some of the recent literature, with a critical review of the surgical treatment. *Arch. Int. Med.*, 62:482, 1938.

376. Seasonal variation in rheumatic infection in Philadelphia. *See* No. 234.

377. SELINSKY, H. Psychological study of the migrainous syndrome. *Bull. New York Acad. Med.*, 15:757, 1939.

378. SHEEHAN, H. L., and SUTHERLAND, A. M. Sex and age factors in acute and chronic valvular disease. *Brit. Heart J.*, 1:303, 1939.

379. SHERRINGTON, C. The Brain and Its Mechanism. Cambridge, Macmillan, 1933.

380. Shifting (The) battle line in the health campaign. *Statist. Bull Metropolitan Life Ins. Co.*, 19:No. 2, 1938.

381. SHRYOCK, R. H. The Development of Modern Medicine; an Interpretation of the Social and Scientific Factors Involved. Philadelphia, Univ. Penn. Press, 1936.

382. SHOCK, N. W. A continuous recorder for obtaining synchronous curves of physiological responses to stimuli in human subjects. *Child Development*, 7:169, 1936.

383. Significance, scope and method of a clinical investigation of hearing in the general population. National Health Survey, 1935–36. Preliminary Reports. Hearing Study Series, Bull. No. 1. Washington, 1938.

384. Significance, scope and method of a nationwide family canvass of sickness in relation to its social and economic setting. National Health Survey, 1935–36. Division of Public Health Methods. Washington, 1938.

385. SILVER, H. B. Emotional and social development of girls with heart disease. *J. Pediat.*, 12:218, 1938.

386. SIMONINI, A. Sopra le turbe della psiche e del carattere nelle sindromi coreiche; nota clinica. *Clin. pediat.*, 18:242, 1936.

387. SLOCOMBE, C. S. It's a habit. *Personnel Serv. Bull.*, 10:1, 1934.

388. SLOCOMBE, C. S., and BRAKEMAN, E. E. Psychological tests and accident proneness. *Brit. J. Psychol.* (gen. sect.), 21:29, 1930.

389. SMITH, G. Plague On Us. New York, Commonwealth Fund, 1941.

390. SMITH, M., and LEIPER, M. A. Sickness Absence and Labour Wastage. London, H. M. Stationery Office, 1936. (Industrial Health Research Board, Report No. 75.)

391. SOLOMON, A. P., DARROW, C. W., and BLAUROCK, M. Blood pressure and palmar sweat (galvanic) response of psychotic patients before and after insulin and metrazol therapy. *Psychosom. Med.*, 1:118, 1939.

392. SOULE, G. The Strength of Nations; a Study in Social Theory. New York, Macmillan, 1942, esp. pp. 91–97.

393. Statistical abstract of the United States, 1939, 61st number. Washington, Govt. Print. Office, 1940.

394. STEAD, E. A., JR., and KINKEL, P. Nature of peripheral resistance in arterial hypertension. *J. Clin. Investigation*, 19:25, 1940.

395. STEWART, D. A. Medical histories and history writing, with special reference to tuberculosis. *Wisconsin M. J.*, 30:257, 1931.

396. STOKVIS, B. Hypnose, Psyche und Blutdruck (Blutdruckregistrierung als Methode der psychologischen Untersuchung). Lochem, "De Tijdstroom," 1937.

397. STONE, L. Concerning the psychogenesis of somatic disease: physiological and neurological correlations with the psychological theory. *Internat. J. Psychoanal.*, 19:63, 1938.

398. STRECKER, E. A., BRILL, A. A., LEWIS, N. D. C., and RUGGLES, A. H. Therapeutic Advances in Psychiatry. Philadelphia, Univ. Penn. Press, 1941.

399. Summary of natality and mortality data for each state: 1936. U. S. Bureau of the Census. Vital Statistics. Special Report, 5:No. 11, 1938.

400. SWIFT, H. F. Factors favoring the onset and continuation of rheumatic fever. *Am. Heart J.*, 6:625, 1931.

401. SWIFT, H. F. Nature of rheumatic fever. *J. Lab. & Clin. Med.*, 21:551, 1936.

402. SYDENSTRICKER, E. The incidence of disease according to age: Hagerstown morbidity studies no. 3. *Pub. Health Rep.*, 43:1124, 1928.

403. Symposium on hypertension. *Psychosom. Med.*, 1:93, 1939.

404. SYZ, H. Burrow's differentiation of tensional patterns in relation to behavior disorders. *J. Psychol*, 9:153, 1940.

405. TAKAORI, S. Comparison of the frequency of disease and wound in a certain railway company at the commencement of the Chinese affair. *J. Sc. Labour*, 16:721, 1939.

406. TAUBER, E. S. Notes on identification and oral traits in relation to character. *Psychiatry*, 2:55, 1939.

407. TIDY, H. L. A synopsis of medicine. Ed. 7. Baltimore, Wood, 1939.

408. TODD, T. W., The alimentary canals of the medical student; radiographic studies. *Ann. Int. Med.*, 1:420, 1927.

409. *U. S. Naval Medical Bulletin, See* No. 71.

410. Vital statistics summary for New York: 1935. U. S. Bureau of the Census. Vital Statistics—Special Reports, 2:No. 38, 1937.

411. Vital statistics summary for the U. S. registration area: 1935. U. S. Bureau of the Census. Vital Statistics—Special Reports, 2:No. 54. 1937.

412. WARREN, B. S., and SYDENSTRICKER, E. Statistics of disability; a compilation of some of the data available in the United States. *Pub. Health Rep.*, 31:989, 1916.

413. WASSON, V. P. Management of children with subacute rheumatic fever. *Arch. Pediat.*, 56:553, 1939.

414. WEISS, E. Recent advances in the pathogenesis and treatment of hypertension: a review. *Psychosom. Med.*, 1:180, 1939.

415. WEISS, E., and ENGLISH, O. S. Psychosomatic Medicine: the Clinical Application of Psychopathology to General Medical Problems. Philadelphia, Saunders, 1943.

416. WHITE, B. V., COBB, S., and JONES, C. M. Mucous colitis; a psychological medical study of sixty cases. *Psychosom. Med. Monogr. Ser.*, 1:No. 1, 1939.

417. WHITE, W. A. Medical psychology: the mental factor in disease. *Nerv. & Ment. Dis. Monogr. Ser.*, no. 54, 1931.

418. WILSON, G. W. Report of a case of acute laryngitis occurring as a conversion symptom during analysis. *Psychoanalyt. Rev.*, 21:408, 1934.

419. WILSON, G. W. The transition from organ neurosis to conversion hysteria. *Internat. J. Psycho-Anal.*, 19:23, 1938.

420. WILSON, M. G. Natural history of rheumatic fever in first three decades. *J. Pediat.*, 10:456, 1937.

421. WILSON, M. G. Diagnosis of heart disease in children. *J.A.M.A.*, 110:501, 1938.

422. WILSON, M. G. Rheumatic Fever: Studies of the Epidemiology, Manifestations, Diagnosis and Treatment of the Disease During the First Three Decades. New York, Commonwealth Fund, 1940.

423. WIRTH, W. R. Angina pectoris and coronary thrombosis. *New Orleans M. & S. J.*, 92:671, 1940.

424. WITTKOWER, E. Studies on the influence of emotions on the functions of the organs (including observations in normals and neurotics). *J. Ment. Sc.*, 81:533, 1935.

425. WOLFE, T. P. Dynamic aspects of cardiovascular symptomatology. *Am. J. Psychiat.*, 91:563, 1934.

426. WOLFE, T. P. Emotions and organic heart disease. *Am. J. Psychiat.*,
     93:681, 1936.
427. WOLFE, T. P. Psychotherapy and the general hospital. *Am. J. Psychiat.*,
     95:1307, 1939.
428. World's fairs as milestones of American longevity. *Statist. Bull. Metro-
     politan Life Ins. Co.*, 20:No. 3, March 1939.

INDEX

Accident habit, existence of, 175, 188
  in various disease groups, 599
  versus accident-proneness, 559
Accident proneness. *See* Accident habit.
Accident statistics:
  group, of accident habit, 599
    of age, 549, 550
    of cardiac pattern, 300, 555, 556
    of childhood incidence, 548, 550
    of circumstantial nature of accident,
      552
    incidence of one, two, three or more,
      160, 548
    incidence of two or more, 546, 547
    of physical nature of accident, 551
  national, 168, 172, 550
Accidents. *See also* Accident statistics *and*
    Fractures.
  in anginal syndrome, **345,** 641
    case report of, 610
    in profile, 356, 583
  in cardiac arrhythmia, **438,** 444, 641
    case reports of, 635, 637
    in profile, 446, 585
  cardiac type of, 186, 551
    in anginal syndrome, 345
    in coronary occlusion, 300, 309, 312,
      550, 582
    percentage of, in various disease
      groups, 555, 556
  in coronary occlusion, **299,** 312, 641
    in profile, 309, 582
  in diabetes, **486,** 540, 642
    case reports of, 612, 615, 617
    in profile, 502, 585
  in fractures, **185**
    in profile, 213, 582
  in hypertensive cardiovascular disease,
    256, 292, 641
    case reports of, 600, 617, 637
    in profile, 265, 583

Accidents— *(Continued)*
  industrial, in nation, 165, 169
    studies of, 172, 174
    in total group, 165, 552
  innocent, 169, 186, 256, 553
  prevalence of, 168, 172
  in rheumatic fever and rheumatoid
    arthritis, **376,** 642
    case report of, 600
    in profile, 394, 584
  in rheumatic heart disease, **417,** 642
    case reports of, 600, 605
    in profile, 424, 584
  studies of, 168, 174
Acting out, 53, 219, 225. *See also* Tension,
    in thought, speech, action.
Action. *See* Tension, in thought, speech,
    action; *and under individual*
    diseases—activity.
"Action syndrome," 140, 647, 655
Adjustment, spheres of, 32, 84. *See also*
    under individual diseases—edu-
    cation, marriage and children,
    occupation, parents, sexual ad-
    justment, social adjustment.
Age, of patients, 127, 131, 143
  with anginal syndrome, 343
  with cardiac arrhythmia, 436
  with coronary occlusion, 298
  with diabetes, 485
  with fractures, 182, 187
  with hypertensive cardiovascular dis-
    ease, 253
  with rheumatic fever and rheuma-
    toid arthritis, 374
  with rheumatic heart disease, 416
Aggression and resentment, 53. *See also*
    under individual diseases.
  in anginal syndrome, 362
  in cardiac arrhythmia, 456
  in coronary occlusion, 310

PAUL B. HOEBER, INC., Medical Book Department of Harper & Brothers, 49 East 33rd Street, New York, N. Y.